STATISTICAL THEORY

A mathematics text under the editorship of
Carl B. Allendoerfer

STATISTICAL THEORY

Second Edition

B. W. LINDGREN

University of Minnesota

THE MACMILLAN COMPANY

COLLIER-MACMILLAN LIMITED, LONDON

Earlier edition © 1960, 1961, and 1962
by Bernard W. Lindgren.

Library of Congress catalog card number: 68–10631

THE MACMILLAN COMPANY
866 THIRD AVENUE, NEW YORK, NEW YORK 10022
Collier-Macmillan Canada, Ltd., Toronto, Ontario

Printed in the United States of America

PREFACE

Like the first edition, this is a textbook for a one-year course in the mathematical theory of statistical inference assuming a knowledge of differential and integral calculus. No prior knowledge of statistics is assumed. Mathematically, the level, spirit, and degree of completeness are comparable to those of the traditional course in advanced calculus.

The first three chapters present the mathematics of probability distributions, random variables, and independence, introducing the mathematical models about which inferences are made and the mathematical framework in which inferential statements are given meaning. Chapters 4 through 6 introduce the basic problems and procedures of statistical inference in a setting of decision theory. The remaining chapters treat more special models and methods of classical and modern inference.

The principal motivation in the revision has been to make the material more readable and more teachable—by expanding and clarifying some of the exposition, by adding a number of problems, and by altering somewhat the order of presentation. The need for such changes was felt in my own experience with the first edition and in the comments of other users—which have been greatly appreciated (as will be comments on the present edition).

Specific changes of some substance have been the complete revision of the material on expected value and the deferring of the treatment of the multivariate normal distribution to a point where it is actually used. The lesser changes are too numerous to list completely and will be appreciated only by one who has used the first edition. Just a few of these are the amplification of the notions of Borel field and measurability, the more unified discussion of the distributions related to the Poisson process, a greater emphasis on the notion of a partition, the use of the generating function in the calculation of probabilities, the discussion of the finiteness of the moments of the sample size in a sequential test, the unification of the treatment of the various sign tests and also of the treatment of contingency tables, and the presentation of some basic ideas of testing hypotheses before the detailed theory. The few sections dropped from the first edition were ones I found myself regularly omitting in teaching from the book.

One comment on the first edition not consciously taken into account in the revision is the preference of some instructors for problems taken from "real" life. Because of the loss of realism in pulling a problem from its context and trimming it down to usable proportions, and the possible obfuscation of ideas by the mass of computations, I am not convinced that this tradition is of value for a course on theory. But, perhaps in a third edition . . . .

The material included has been found to be ample for a course meeting three hours per week; it can only be completely covered by pushing the students unreasonably. Thus, there appears to be no need to be apologetic about topics that might have been included but were not. In particular, I have not taken pains to include purely methodological schemes or devices, since although many students do learn such methodology in other courses, the course based on this book would be the last exposure to theory for most of these students.

Problems for the student are given at intervals of a size corresponding approximately to what might be covered in a single lecture. There has been no effort to pad the list of problems so that, say, every other one would give the student adequate exercise. Yet, only the very industrious student will be likely to solve them all.

The list of references (page 475) includes books that are referred to in the text, as well as books that have influenced the writing of this one and books that might be considered for further study. One's debt to such literature is difficult to enumerate. Surely the influence of books by Lehman [13] and by Chernoff and Moses [3] can be seen in this one.

I acknowledge again my debt to Richard Savage, Herman Chernoff, Andrew Sterrett, Donald Richter, and Patrick Ahern for their various contributions to the preparation of the first edition. I am grateful for critical comments on the first edition by those who taught from it (in particular J. H. Curtiss and Edward Thorp) and by the numerous students at the University of Minnesota who struggled with it. Of the latter group, Maya Weil was especially helpful; she also read critically portions of this revision. Patricia Pesci did a particularly fine job of typing, cutting, and pasting.

I am indebted to the editors of *Biometrika*, *The Annals of Mathematical Statistics*, and the *Journal of the American Statistical Association* for permission to adapt tables for use in this book, and to the late Professor Sir Ronald A. Fisher, Cambridge, to Dr. Frank Yates, Rothamsted, and to Messrs. Oliver and Boyd, Ltd., Edinburgh, for permission to reprint a portion of Table 2 from their book *Statistical Tables for Biological, Agricultural, and Medical Research*.

B. W. L.

CONTENTS

STATISTICAL THEORY

1

PROBABILITY MODELS

The term *experiment* will denote doing something or observing something happen under certain conditions, resulting in some final state of affairs or "outcome." The experiment may be physical, chemical, social, industrial, or medical; it may be conducted in the laboratory or in real-life surroundings—in the factory, in the economy, in the hospital, etc. Occasionally, an experiment is of such a nature that the outcome of the experiment is uniquely defined by a specification of the conditions under which it is performed; indeed, a determinist would insist that this would always be the case if the conditions were completely specified. In practice one finds that experiments are not precisely repeatable, even under supposedly identical conditions. This is the case when there are factors affecting the outcome that the experimenter is not aware of or that he cannot control, and also when factors supposedly under control are really not. The outcome cannot then be predicted from a knowledge of the "conditions" (those taken into account) under which the experiment is performed. One speaks of the experiment as an "experiment involving chance," or simply, as an "experiment of chance." Because of the unpredictability or the element of chance in the experiment, the usual kind of mathematical model involving equations of motion or equations of state (that express physical, chemical, social laws) is inadequate, and a rather new kind of mathematical structure is needed to represent what takes place.

Because the outcome of the experiment is not predictable—is one of many possible outcomes—the model for the experiment should include some kind of list of these possible outcomes. This set of possible outcomes is the "sample space" of the experiment, to be discussed in the first section. The second main ingredient of the mathematical model for an experiment of chance is the notion of probability, which formalizes the common concept that some sets of outcomes may be more or less likely than others. This is taken up in the second section.

Later chapters will then consider the basic problem of statistics—making inferences about certain unknown aspects of the correct model, on the basis of results of one or more trials of the experiment under consideration.

1.1 Sample Spaces

The collection of possible outcomes of an experiment is called a *space*, whose individual points are then the individual outcomes. The word "space" here is used in the mathematical sense of a set of points or objects, rather than in the commonly encountered meaning of "three-dimensional space." The *sample space* of an experiment of chance is simply the set of possible outcomes of the experiment. This is a mathematical concept; operations, relations, and functions will be defined on the points and subsets of this space.

Describing the outcome of an experiment is something that can be done in more than one way. For example, an individual selected by lot from a large group of individuals can be described as white, or as male, or as weighing 147 lb, etc., depending upon what is of interest. Thus, the sample space used by one person in constructing a model for an experiment of chance may be different from that used by another. So there is need at the outset for an agreement as to what will be defined and considered as the sample space.

1.1.1 Elementary Outcomes

The term elementary outcome will be used to denote one of the various ways in which an experiment can terminate. It is assumed that these "ways" are defined according to some scheme that is sufficiently detailed as to permit describing in terms of them any event likely to be of interest. Because of this dependence on one's interest, the list of outcomes in one case might be different from the list of outcomes in another case—even though the same physical process is being carried out. When the lists of elementary outcomes are different, the sample spaces are different, and the experiments are thought of as different experiments.

EXAMPLE 1–1.   A coin is tossed. If the coin is an ordinary coin, its two faces are different and are referred to as "Heads" and "Tails" (even though in many instances the "Tails" side actually pictures an eagle). Although it is conceivable that when the coin falls, it may land on edge or roll into a sewer beyond reach, the natural and useful list of outcomes contains just these two: Heads up, or Tails up. These two elementary outcomes make up the sample space, and in this simple experiment there is not much occasion to invent a more complicated model. (One could imagine, however, being interested in the *orientation* of the fallen coin in some reference frame, in which case a more involved model would indeed be required.)

EXAMPLE 1–2.   A cube whose six faces are marked with one, two, three, four, five, and six dots, respectively, is called a *die*. When tossed, it falls (on a horizontal surface) with one of the six faces turned up. The up-turned face is usually the outcome of interest, and the six faces (each of which can turn up) are the elementary outcomes. Whether the elementary outcomes are thought of as the faces or as the dot patterns identifying the faces—or indeed as the numbers (1, 2, 3, 4, 5, 6) of dots involved—is a matter of indifference.

EXAMPLE 1–3.   Three coins are tossed. The most detailed classification of results would involve knowing what happens with each of the coins. But if one is interested in knowing only the number of Heads that show among the three coins, a sample space with the outcomes 0, 1, 2, 3 is adequate.

EXAMPLE 1–4.   When a missile is fired at a target on the earth's surface, the result cannot be predicted in terms of known or measurable quantities, because of uncertainties in the propellant, in atmospheric conditions, and in the direction of aiming. The experiment is then best thought of as an experiment of chance. The outcome of the experiment is the landing point of the missile, and the set of all points on the earth's surface (perhaps restricted to those lying within some reasonable distance of the target) would make up the sample space. If a plane surface is assumed, and a rectangular grid is placed over the target area, the landing point's coordinate representation in this grid can be used to identify the outcome. The sample space is then essentially the collection of ordered pairs of numbers—that is, of sets of coordinates (x, y).

EXAMPLE 1–5.   Four chips marked, respectively, A, B, C, and D, are placed in a container and mixed. If two chips are selected blindly, the outcome cannot be predicted, and a chance model is again appropriate. The elementary outcomes can be thought of as the possible pairs of chips, which can easily be listed: *AB, AC, AD, BC, BD, CD*. (In writing these down, it is unfortunately necessary—or at least, convenient—to impose an apparent order. That is, in *AB*, the *A* is written first and the *B* second. However, this is nothing more than a quirk of writing things down, and there is no significance in the order. The only question that need be answered in identifying an outcome is this: Which two chips were drawn?)

A related experiment is that in which two chips are drawn *one at a time*, the first not being replaced for the second drawing. In this case the order *can* be observed and may be significant; to take it into account, a sample space is required in which the elementary outcome *AB* is distinct from *BA*. The complete list would be as follows: *AB, AC, AD, BC, BD, CD, BA, CA, DA, CB, DB, DC*. If the order is not significant, even though the chips are drawn in succession, this twelve-point sample space is unnecessarily complicated, but there is no harm in using it.

EXAMPLE 1–6. A certain material is thought of as being composed of tubes or fibers, each assumed to be oriented in a certain direction with respect to some given reference frame. A fiber selected "at random" will have an orientation that can be any of infinitely many possible orientations of a line in space. These orientations make up the sample space. However, the sample space can be identified with the set of points on a hemisphere of unit radius by identifying a given point on the sphere—or its coordinate representation in some system—with the orientation of the vector from the center of the sphere out to that point. It is immaterial whether the sample space is taken as the set of orientations, the set of points on the hemisphere, or the set of possible coordinate representations of these points.

1.1.2 Composition of Experiments

In many instances it is easier to analyze a complex experiment by treating it as a combination of two or more simpler experiments, and so it is natural to consider two or more experiments jointly. Suppose, then, that performing an experiment $\mathscr{E}$ is equivalent to first performing an experiment $\mathscr{E}_1$ and then performing an experiment $\mathscr{E}_2$. There is a natural (but not unique) way of itemizing the outcomes of the composite experiment $\mathscr{E}$ in terms of the outcomes of $\mathscr{E}_1$ and of $\mathscr{E}_2$. This way is to associate each elementary outcome of $\mathscr{E}_1$ in turn with each elementary outcome of $\mathscr{E}_2$ to obtain what are then the elementary outcomes of the experiment $\mathscr{E}$. Clearly, if the number of elementary outcomes of $\mathscr{E}_1$ is n_1, and the number of elementary outcomes of $\mathscr{E}_2$ is n_2, then the number of elementary outcomes in the composite experiment, counted according to the convention just described, is the product: $n_1 n_2$. (Of course, if either n_1 or n_2 is infinite, there will be infinitely many outcomes in the composite sample space.)

The elementary outcomes of a composite experiment, when specified in this fashion, may turn out to be more "elementary" than needed for some purpose. On the other hand, they will certainly be elementary enough, and it is convenient to have such a standard method of defining a sample space for a composite experiment.

EXAMPLE 1–7.   If a coin and a die are tossed together, it does not usually matter whether the coin or die lands first, but the same possible outcomes can be achieved by tossing the coin and then the die. And so the experiment can be thought of as a composite of these simpler experiments (first tossing the coin and then tossing the die). Each of the two elementary outcomes in the toss of the coin can be associated with each of the six elementary outcomes of the toss of the die to form the following twelve elementary outcomes of the composite experiment:

$$H\text{-}1, \quad H\text{-}2, \quad H\text{-}3, \quad H\text{-}4, \quad H\text{-}5, \quad H\text{-}6; \quad T\text{-}1, \quad T\text{-}2, \quad T\text{-}3, \quad T\text{-}4, \quad T\text{-}5, \quad T\text{-}6.$$

EXAMPLE 1–8.   Consider again (as in Example 1–5) the drawing of two chips from a container in which there are four chips marked A, B, C, and D, respectively. The experiment can be performed in two steps: First, one chip is drawn, and then from the remaining chips a second chip is drawn. In the first subexperiment, there are four elementary outcomes; namely, A, B, C, D. In the second subexperiment, the elementary outcomes depend on what was drawn first; but *no matter what is drawn first*, the number of chips available for the second draw is three. Thus, there are $4 \cdot 3 = 12$ elementary outcomes in the composite experiment—just those listed at the end of Example 1–5.

EXAMPLE 1–9.   An experiment consists of arranging three objects in a sequence. If the objects are identified as A, B, and C, respectively, the *six* possible arrangements are the elementary outcomes:

$$ABC, \quad ACB, \quad BAC, \quad BCA, \quad CAB, \quad CBA.$$

This count can be obtained without writing out the list by considering the experiment as a composite of three subexperiments. First, select one of the three objects (three outcomes) for the first position of the sequence; second, select one of the remaining two objects (two outcomes) for the second position of the sequence; and third, put the remaining object in the last position (one outcome). The product of the numbers of outcomes in these subexperiments is the desired number of arrangements: $3 \cdot 2 \cdot 1 = 6$.

An obvious generalization of the argument in the last example shows that the number of arrangements of n objects in a sequence is $n! = n(n-1)(n-2) \cdots 3 \cdot 2 \cdot 1$.

It is also useful to be able to count arrangements (without actually making a list), in cases in which some objects are *alike*. This is not to say that the objects lose their identities; it is just that the identities of "like" objects will be ignored in distinguishing arrangements. The following example will illustrate what is meant.

EXAMPLE 1–10.   Four blocks are painted, two red, one blue, and the other yellow. These four blocks can be arranged in 24 ways which are really distinct; but if one chooses to consider one red block as *not* distinguishable from the other, the possible arrangements are:

$$RRYB, \quad RYRB, \quad RYBR, \quad YRRB, \quad YRBR, \quad YBRR,$$
$$RRBY, \quad RBRY, \quad RBYR, \quad BRRY, \quad BRYR, \quad BYRR.$$

The number of these—twelve—is easily seen to be 24/2, since what has been done is to count R_1R_2YB and R_2R_1YB as the same arrangement—the same color pattern (the subscripts simply serve to point out that the two red blocks are not the same block). That is, putting subscripts on the R's to distinguish them would permit two arrangements for each one listed above, thereby yielding the 4! or 24 arrangements of four distinct objects.

Again the generalization is almost obvious. For example, if one has r red objects, b blue objects, and y yellow objects among n objects, and if the remaining objects (if any) are distinct from these and from each other, the number of *color patterns* (which is what is now meant by distinct arrangements) is $n!/(r!b!y!)$.

A particular instance of some importance is that in which there are just two colors, so that among n objects, k are of one color (or kind) and the remaining $n - k$ are of another color (or kind). The number of distinct arrangements or patterns is

$$\frac{n!}{k!(n-k)!}.$$

The importance of this calculation lies in the fact that this count of arrangements is also a count of the number of selections (without regard to order) of k objects from n distinct objects. For, to arrange the k and $n - k$ objects in a sequence, one can proceed by *selecting* k of the n sequence positions in which to place the objects of one kind, the remaining $n - k$ positions being given to the objects of the other kind. The symbol[1] for the number of distinct combinations or selections of k out of n objects is $\binom{n}{k}$. It is computed as follows:

$$\binom{n}{k} = \frac{n!}{k!(n-k)!} = \frac{n(n-1)(n-2)\cdots(n-k+1)}{k(k-1)(k-2)\cdots 3\cdot 2\cdot 1}.$$

This is called a *binomial coefficient*, for reasons that become clear in Problem 1–9. The formula given remains valid for $k = 0$ and $k = n$ if it is understood (as is customary) that 0! means 1.

EXAMPLE 1–11. From a container with four chips marked 1, 2, 3, and 4, respectively, two chips are selected. The number of such selections is $\binom{4}{2}$ or 6, which can easily be listed:

$$1\,2, \quad 1\,3, \quad 1\,4, \quad 2\,3, \quad 2\,4, \quad 3\,4.$$

---

[1] Other symbols are sometimes used: $_nC_k$, C_k^n.

Each of these selections corresponds to an arrangement of two *A*'s and two *B*'s:

$$AABB, \quad ABAB, \quad ABBA, \quad BAAB, \quad BABA, \quad BBAA,$$

the numbers 1 3 indicating, for instance, that *A*'s will appear in the 1st and 3rd positions of the sequence and *B*'s in the other positions: *ABAB*.

Problems

1–1. In how many ways can four plus signs and six minus signs be arranged in a row?

1–2. Write out and compare the expressions, in terms of factorials, for $\binom{n}{k}$ and $\binom{n}{n-k}$. Then compute $\binom{100}{97}$.

1–3. A *function* assigns a value, one of a set of possible values called the *range* of the function, to each point in a set called the *domain* (or domain of definition) of the function. If a domain has exactly *m* points and the range exactly *k* values, how many distinct functions can be defined?

1–4. A bowl contains black, white, and red chips. An experiment consists of drawing four chips from the bowl, one at a time, and the outcome is a recorded sequence of observed colors of the chips drawn. How many outcomes are in the sample space of this experiment, assuming that each chip drawn is replaced prior to the next drawing? (Ask yourself: Would it make any difference if the chips drawn were not replaced? For example, consider the cases in which (a) there are only two red chips to begin with, and (b) there are at least four chips of each color.)

1–5. Each symbol in a sequence of ten symbols is a $(+)$ or a $(-)$.
(a) How many distinct sequences are possible?
(b) How may of these have at least eight $+$'s in them?
(c) How many sequences contain exactly five $+$'s and exactly five $-$'s?
(d) Of the sequences in (c), how many have at least four $+$'s in a row?

1–6. How many outcomes are there in the sample space of each of the following experiments, using the most detailed classification?
(a) The toss of three ordinary dice.
(b) The toss of *n* coins.
(c) The selection of four persons from a group of ten, without regard to order.
(d) The selection of four persons from ten, to serve as President, Vice-president, Secretary, and Treasurer.

1–7. A *standard bridge deck* contains 52 distinct cards, namely, thirteen cards of these denominations: 2, 3, . . ., 10, Jack, Queen, King, Ace, in each of four suits: Spades, Hearts, Diamonds, Clubs. How many elementary outcomes are in the sample space for each of the following experiments?
(a) One card is drawn from the deck.
(b) A "hand" of five cards is dealt from the deck.
(c) A card is drawn from the deck, and only the color and denomination of the card are noted. (Spades and Clubs are black, and Hearts and Diamonds are red.)

1–8. Show that for any positive integer *n* and any positive integer $j \leq n$

$$\binom{n}{j-1} + \binom{n}{j} = \binom{n+1}{j}.$$

1–9. Prove the *binomial theorem*:

$$(x + y)^n = \sum_0^n \binom{n}{k} x^k y^{n-k}, \qquad n = 1, 2, \dots .$$

[*Hint*: First verify the result for $n = 1$. Then, assuming it to be true as written for some given n, show by multiplying through both sides by $(x + y)$ that it remains valid for the next integer $n + 1$.]

1–10. Show the following by expressing each side in terms of factorials:

$$\binom{n}{m}\binom{n-m}{r}\binom{n-m-r}{k-m} = \binom{n}{k+r}\binom{k+r}{k}\binom{k}{m}.$$

Also, interpret each side of the equation as the number of ways of performing a sequence of selections and deduce the equality from this reasoning.

1–11. (a) Show that

$$\sum_0^n \binom{n}{k} = 2^n, \qquad \text{for } n = 1, 2, \dots .$$

[*Hint*: Set $x = y = 1$ in the result of Problem 1–9.]

(b) Determine the total number of distinct subsets of a set containing n elements (two ways).

1.1.3 Events

An *event* is any set or collection of elementary outcomes in the sample space of an experiment of chance. Such a collection may be defined by listing the elementary outcomes that make it up or by giving some property that characterizes or determines that list of outcomes. Events will ordinarily be referred to by names such as $E, F, \dots$. In specifying an event by making a list of its points, braces will be used, for example: $\{a, e, q, \dots\}$. In specifying an event by means of a characterizing condition, the notation will also employ braces, as follows:

$$E = \{x \mid x \text{ satisfies condition } E\},$$

which is read "the set of points x such that x satisfies condition E" (whatever condition that may be).

The set of *all* outcomes in a sample space Ω is a particular subset of a sample space and will therefore be an event. It is also convenient to define as an event the *empty set*, or set containing no outcomes, denoted by $\varnothing$. This event is defined by any condition that is not satisfied by any of the points in the sample space.

EXAMPLE 1–12. Consider again the drawing of two chips from a container with four chips marked A, B, C, and D, respectively; and take as the sample space the twelve elementary outcomes in which order is taken into account:

$$\Omega = \{AB, AC, AD, BC, BD, CD, BA, CA, DA, CB, DB, DC\}.$$

(The first letter denotes the first and the second letter the second chip drawn.) The condition that the *first chip is A* defines the event

$$E = \{AB, AC, AD\}.$$

The condition that the first chip is A or B and the second is B or D defines the event

$$F: \{AB, AD, BD\}.$$

The condition that one of the chips is A defines the event

$$G = \{AB, AC, AD, BA, CA, DA\}.$$

The condition that both chips be A defines the empty set since no outcome has this property.

EXAMPLE 1–13.   The number of phone calls coming into a certain exchange during a given five-minute period is counted. The possible outcomes of this experiment can be taken to be the nonnegative integers:

$$\Omega = \{0, 1, 2, 3, \ldots\}.$$

An event is then any set of these integers. For instance, the condition that *at least four calls* come in defines the event

$$E = \{4, 5, 6, \ldots\},$$

and the condition that *at most two calls* come in defines the event

$$F = \{0, 1, 2\}.$$

EXAMPLE 1–14.   Consider the sample space of Example 1–6, consisting of the possible orientations of the fibers of a material. These orientations can be identified by pairs of colatitude and longitude angles (θ, ϕ), where $0 \leq \theta \leq \pi/2$ and $0 \leq \phi < 2\pi$. Events can then be described by conditions imposed on these coordinate pairs. For instance, the conditions

$$E: \theta = 3\pi/8, \phi = 0; \qquad F: \theta \leq \pi/4; \qquad G: 0 \leq \phi < \pi$$

define sets of orientations that are examples of events. If the orientation of a fiber selected at random is determined to be $\theta = \pi/8$, $\phi = \pi/2$, the conditions defining F and G are satisfied, and one says that F has "happened"—and also that G has happened.

When all of the points in one event E are included in another event F, the one is said to be a subset of the other, and one writes $E \subset F$. This would mean that the condition defining F is necessarily true of the outcomes in E, but it may be that some further condition not satisfied by all of the outcomes of F is required to pick out those in the subset E. That is, the statement $E \subset F$ is equivalent to

condition E implies   condition F.

Notice that for any event E, $\emptyset \subset E \subset \Omega$.

When the *same* set of outcomes is defined by two superficially different conditions, the events defined by these conditions are really the same event and are said to be equal. That is, $E = F$ means that every outcome in E is also contained in F and conversely, or that both $E \subset F$ and $F \subset E$. To show that $E = F$, then, it suffices to show that any element of E is also in F and that any element of F is also in E.

In case the number of elementary outcomes in a sample space is finite, there are only finitely many distinct events that can be defined. In particular, if the sample space contains N outcomes, there are exactly 2^N subsets or events. For, each of the outcomes either is or is not included in a given subset, so in making up an event one has these two choices for each of the N outcomes: multiplication of the N 2's yields 2^N. (Observe that the events Ω and $\varnothing$ are included in this count—one may use all of the outcomes to make up an event, or he may use none of them.) That the number of possible events is 2^N also follows from Problem 1–11(a).

1.1.4   Complements, Intersections, Unions

Events can be combined or operated on in many ways to form new events. One such operation is that of set *union* or *addition*. A point is in the union of E and F if and only if it lies either in E or in F (or possibly in both). The symbol $+$ and the symbol $\cup$ are both used to denote this operation:

$$E \cup F = E + F = \{E \text{ or } F\} = \{\omega \mid \omega \text{ is in } E \text{ or in } F\}.$$

This operation is both commutative:

$$E + F = F + E$$

and associative:

$$[E + F] + G = E + [F + G],$$

as may readily be established.

The *intersection* or *product* of two events is defined to be that event whose outcomes are those lying in *both* of the events. An intersection is indicated either by ordinary product notation or by the symbol $\cap$:

$$E \cap F = EF = \{E \text{ and } F\} = \{\omega \mid \omega \text{ is in both } E \text{ and } F\}.$$

This operation is also commutative ($EF = FE$) and associative ($[EF]G = E[FG]$). One reason for thinking of set intersection as "multiplication" is that it combines with set union or addition in a distributive law:

$$E(F + G) = EF + EG.$$

However, another distributive law, obtained formally from the above by inter-changing indicated unions and intersections, is also valid:

$$E + FG = (E + F)(E + G).$$

Two events are said to be *disjoint* or *mutually exclusive* when their inter-section is empty: $EF = \varnothing$. The *difference* $E - F$ of two events is the event consisting of those outcomes lying in E but not in F, that is, outcomes satisfy-ing the condition E but not the condition F. [Notice, however, that $(E - F) + F$ is not necessarily the event E. See Problem 1–13(j).]

The *complement* of an event E, to be denoted here by E^c (elsewhere by $\bar{E}$ or by CE), is defined to be $E^c = \Omega - E$, or the set of all outcomes in the sample space that are not in E. Observe that $E + E^c = \Omega$, and that $EE^c = \varnothing$. Ob-serve also that a difference can be expressed in terms of the complement: $E - F = EF^c$.

EXAMPLE 1–15.   A card is drawn from a standard deck of cards (defined in Problem 1–7). The sample space Ω consists of the 52 cards in the deck, any one of which might be drawn. (These are perhaps the most "elementary" outcomes one can define here, and again there might be instances in which a coarser classification of results would be adequate.) Consider the following events:

  E: The card drawn is a Spade;
  F: The card drawn is a Jack;
  G: The card drawn is a face card.

(The Jacks, Queens, and Kings picture faces and are called "face cards.") Then $E + F$, for example, is the set of cards consisting of all of the Spades plus the other three Jacks. The event $E - F$ is the set consisting of all of the Spades except the Jack. The event FG is identical with F. The event $\Omega - E$ is the set consisting of all Hearts, Diamonds, and Clubs. The event $(E + G) - F$ is the set of all Spades, except the Jack, together with the remaining three Queens and three Kings.

EXAMPLE 1–16.   A pointer is spun about a pivot, in a horizontal plane, and a scale from 0 to 1 is marked around the circle traced by the tip of the pointer. (The 0 and 1 fall at the same point.) The pointer is spun once and allowed to come to rest. The sample space may be taken to be the set of possible stopping points—essentially, the set of real numbers on the interval from 0 to 1. Consider the follow-ing events:

$$E = \{x \mid .5 < x < .8\},$$
$$F = \{x \mid x > .6\},$$
$$G = \{x \mid x < .4\}.$$

The event $E + F$ is the set $\{x \mid .5 < x < 1\}$. The intersection EF is the set $\{x \mid .6 < x < .8\}$. The event G^c is $\{x \mid x \geq .4\}$. The difference $E - F$ is $\{x \mid .5 < x \leq .6\}$.

It is helpful to have the schematic picture of these various concepts provided by the "Venn diagram." In such a diagram, the sample space is symbolized by a region in the plane, and its events by subsets of that region. For instance, events E, F, and G might be represented by the points within the circle, rectangle, and triangle, respectively, in Figure 1–1. (The sample space is represented by the points in the larger rectangle.) Figure 1–2 exhibits the events EF, $E + F$, $E - F$, and E^c.

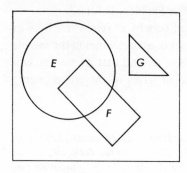

Figure 1–1.   A Venn diagram.

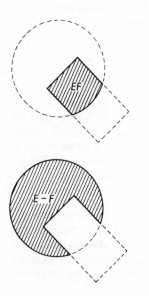

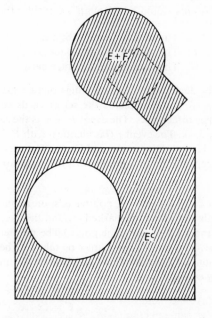

Figure 1–2.   Set operations.

Unions and intersections of infinitely many events are easier to define than are sums and products of infinitely many numbers. Even if the number of events is uncountably infinite, the union is the set of all points that are contained in at least one of the sets of the collection. The intersection is the set of points such that each is contained in every set of the collection. (These definitions apply also if the collection is countable or finite.) The union and intersection of a collection of sets E_α, where the subscript α indexes the sets of the collection, will be denoted, respectively, by $\bigcup E_\alpha$ and $\bigcap E_\alpha$.

EXAMPLE 1–17.   Let Ω be the set of all real numbers $(-\infty, \infty)$, and let E_n denote the interval $(a - 1/n, a + 1/n)$, for $n = 1, 2, \ldots$. Since the only number in all of these intervals (that is, for each n) is the number a, the intersection of the intervals E_n is the set whose only element is that number:

$$\bigcap E_n = \{a\}.$$

Problems

1–12.   The sample space for the experiment of tossing two dice and recording the number of points showing on each die contains the 36 elementary outcomes obtained by associating each number of points on one die with each number on the other. In each case, make a list of the outcomes in the event defined by the given condition:

(a) The sum is divisible by 4.
(b) Both numbers are even.
(c) The numbers on the dice are equal.
(d) The numbers differ by at least 4.
(e) The total number of points showing is 10.

1–13.   Show the following, for any events E, F, G in a sample space Ω. (Make a Venn diagram in each case, but establish each set equality by showing that each side is contained in the other.)

(a) $E = EF + EF^c$
(b) $E = E\Omega, \quad \varnothing = \varnothing E$
(c) $(EF)^c = E^c + F^c$
(d) $(E + F)^c = E^c F^c$
(e) $G(F - E) = GF - GE$
(f) $E(F + G) = EF + EG$
(g) $EF = E \quad$ if $\quad E \subset F$
(h) $E + F = E \quad$ if $\quad F \subset E$
(i) $E + FG = (E + F)(E + G)$
(j) $(E - F) + F = E + F$

1–14.   Show that for any collection of events $\{E_\alpha\}$,

$$\left(\bigcup E_\alpha\right)^c = \bigcap E_\alpha^c, \quad \text{and} \quad \left(\bigcap E_\alpha\right)^c = \bigcup E_\alpha^c.$$

1–15.   Five cards are selected from a standard bridge deck (Problem 1–7). Let the elementary outcomes of this experiment be all possible selections of 5 cards from the 52. Determine the number of elementary outcomes in each of the following events:

(a) The hand contains exactly one "pair." (A pair consists of two cards of the same denomination; for example, two Kings. The other three cards in the hand are to be of three different denominations.)
(b) The hand contains two pairs of different denominations and a fifth card of still a different denomination.
(c) The hand contains two cards of one denomination and three of another.

(d) The hand contains three cards of one denomination, but the other two do not form a pair.

(e) The hand consists of five cards, all of the same suit.

1–16.   The outcomes of a certain experiment are points in a plane, each identified by its rectangular coordinates in a given reference system; that is, ω is (x, y). Sketch the events defined by each of the following conditions:

(a) $x^2 + y^2 = 1$ (d) $x - y \leq 2$ (g) (b) $\cap$ (c)
(b) $x^2 + y^2 \leq 4$ (e) $2x \leq y$ (h) (e) $\cup$ (f)
(c) $x + y > 3$ (f) $x - 3y \leq 6$ (i) (a) $-$ (e).

1–17.   A sample space contains just three outcomes, a, b, and c. Determine the eight possible events (specifying each by making a list of its outcomes).

1–18.   Consider an *increasing* sequence of events: $E_1 \subset E_2 \subset E_3 \subset \ldots$. Show that (with $E_0 \equiv \varnothing$):

$$\bigcup E_i = \bigcup (E_i - E_{i-1}).$$

[*Hint*: If ω is in the union $\bigcup E_i$, there is a *first* event in the sequence $E_1, E_2, \ldots$, which includes it.]

1.1.5   Borel Fields

A *Borel field* of events or sets (also called a σ-field or σ-algebra) is a collection $\mathscr{B}$ of events so constituted as to include along with any event its complement, and also to include the union of any countable number of sets in the collection. Because it includes the union and intersection of any of its sets E with the complement E^c, a Borel field always includes Ω and $\varnothing$. Moreover, because

$$\bigcap E_n = (\bigcup E_n{}^c)^c,$$

it follows that countable intersections of events in a Borel field $\mathscr{B}$ are also contained in $\mathscr{B}$. In particular, the difference $E - F$ or EF^c of two sets E and F in $\mathscr{B}$ is also in $\mathscr{B}$. A rather trivial example of a Borel field is the collection consisting of just $\varnothing$ and Ω, since complements and unions of these are included in the list $\{\varnothing, \Omega\}$.

A somewhat less trivial example of a Borel field is the collection of *all* subsets of a sample space. In the case of a finite sample space this Borel field of all subsets contains 2^N subsets, where N is the number of points in the sample space (see Problem 1–11). A sample space having as many points, say, as the interval of real numbers [0, 1] has altogether too many subsets for this Borel field to be useful in the construction of probability models. In such cases one works with the "smallest" Borel field containing some simple collection $\mathscr{C}$ of events that are useful—such as the collection of subintervals. By "smallest" Borel field is meant one big enough to contain the given collection but which does not contain a smaller Borel field (that is, one with fewer members) that also contains the sets of the collection $\mathscr{C}$. The following example illustrates this idea.

EXAMPLE 1–18.   A sample space Ω contains four points $\{a, b, c, d\}$. Consider the collection $\mathscr{C}$ consisting of two events: $\{a\}$, $\{c, d\}$. If it is desired to expand this collection to a Borel field, the complements of each event must be included, so $\{b, c, d\}$ and $\{a, b\}$ must be added to the collection. Because unions and inter-sections must be included, the events $\{a, c, d\}$, $\varnothing$, Ω, and $\{b\}$ must also be added. In summary, then, a Borel field of sets or events that includes the events $\{a\}$ and $\{c, d\}$ consists of the following eight events:

$$\varnothing, \quad \{a\}, \quad \{c, d\}, \quad \{b, c, d\}, \quad \{a, b\}, \quad \{a, c, d\}, \quad \{b\}, \quad \Omega.$$

(The reader should verify that operations of union, intersection, and comple-mentation do not require leaving this collection.) Moreover, each of these is needed, so there is no smaller Borel field that includes the two given events. This smallest one is called the Borel field *generated* by $\{a\}$ and $\{c, d\}$. Observe, though, that the collection of all of the $2^4 = 16$ events that can be defined on a sample space with four points is also a Borel field; but it includes the one defined above, and is not then the smallest Borel field containing $\{a\}$ and $\{c, d\}$.

EXAMPLE 1–19.   Let Ω denote the sample space of the spinning pointer experi-ment, that is, the interval $0 \leq x < 1$. The collection of events needed to discuss and analyze situations that arise in practice must surely include intervals—sets of the form $(a, b) = \{x \mid a < x < b\}$. The collection of such intervals may seem to be a large collection of sets, but it does not include, for instance, sets containing a single point, or sets consisting of two disjoint intervals. The Borel field generated by the collection of all intervals of the form (a, b) would, however, necessarily in-clude single points (as the intersection of intervals of the form $a - 1/n < x < a + 1/n$ for $n = 1, 2, 3, \ldots$), along with other unions and intersections of in-tervals. It includes, in particular, closed intervals:

$$\{x \mid a \leq x \leq b\} = \{x \mid a < x < b\} + \{a\} + \{b\},$$

and, similarly, half-open intervals (that is, including one endpoint but not the other). On the other hand—and this is perhaps the point of concentrating on a Borel field—the Borel field generated by the open subintervals does *not* include *all*[2] subsets; and while it is possible to define probabilities consistently (in a way to be seen in the next section) for the Borel field generated by the open intervals, it happens to be impossible to do so for the set of all subsets of $[0, 1]$.

1.1.6   Functions on a Sample Space

A given outcome ω, the result of performing an experiment of chance, may have associated with it one or more numerical characteristics. For example, if

---

[2] To construct a counter example and show that it is not included in the Borel field generated by open intervals is nontrivial. See P. Halmos, *Measure Theory* (Van Nostrand), Princeton, New Jersey, 1950, p. 69.

the experiment is the drawing of one person from a given group of people (called a *population*), one may be interested in that person's height, his age, his weight, or in all three. Since the person chosen can be any of the outcomes ω, these numerical characteristics of interest are dependent variables—functions of ω:

$$X(\omega) = \text{Age of } \omega, \qquad Y(\omega) = \text{Weight of } \omega, \quad \text{etc.}$$

If one has reason to consider simultaneously the age and weight, say, for each ω, the pair $[X(\omega), Y(\omega)]$ defines a vector-valued function on Ω.

A function provides and can be thought of as a *mapping* from the space on which it is defined to the space of its values (from its "domain" to its "range," in mathematical terminology). Each *point* in the sample space Ω has then an *image point* in the set $\mathscr{X}$ of values of the function; and a *set E* of points in Ω has an *image set* of values in this space $\mathscr{X}$ of values of the function. Conversely, given any value x in the value space $\mathscr{X}$ of a function $\mathscr{X}(\omega)$, there are certain points in Ω that are assigned that value; these make up what is called the *pre-image* of x. Similarly, a set F of values of a function $\mathscr{X}(\omega)$ defines a pre-image set of outcomes ω, namely, the set of all ω's that are assigned values in F by $\mathscr{X}(\omega)$.

EXAMPLE 1–20.   Let ω denote the six faces of a die, one of which turns up when the die is tossed onto a flat surface. When these faces are marked with dots, as is customary, the function

$$X(\omega) = \text{number of dots on the face } \omega$$

assigns a number to each face. The set ω of values of this function is (for an ordinary die) $\{1, 2, 3, 4, 5, 6\}$. The pre-image of the set $\{x \mid x \leq 4\} = \{1, 2, 3, 4\}$ is the set of faces marked with these numbers of dots: $\{\omega \mid X(\omega) = 1, 2, 3, \text{ or } 4\}$. If instead one calls the number of dots on the upturned face the outcome ω, that is, if one takes the sample space to be the set $\{1, 2, 3, 4, 5, 6\}$, then the function $X(\omega) = \omega$ is an example of a function on the sample space. Another function on this sample space might be

$$Y(\omega) = \begin{cases} 1, & \text{if } \omega = 1, 3, \text{ or } 5 \\ 0, & \text{if } \omega = 2, 4, \text{ or } 6. \end{cases}$$

This is an example of an *indicator function* of a set—a function that is defined to have the value 1 for each point of the set and the value 0 for each point not in the set; this particular function "indicates" the set $\{1, 3, 5\}$.

EXAMPLE 1–21.   When an e.m.f. (voltage) is applied to a known, fixed load, the power consumed is proportional to the square of the voltage. If to determine the power one places a volt-meter across the load, the measured voltage ω can be treated as an outcome of an experiment of chance with sample space $(-\infty, \infty)$, owing to the random inaccuracies introduced in the measurement process. The power W is a function of the outcome ω: $W = k\omega^2$, with values in the interval $[0, \infty)$. Then the set $\{W < k\}$, for instance, has as its pre-image the set $\{-1 < \omega < 1\}$.

EXAMPLE 1–22. Let ω denote the landing point of a projectile aimed at a target point in a plane. The rectangular coordinates $X(\omega)$ and $Y(\omega)$ in a set of perpendicular axes centered at the target point, that is, the coordinate functions in this reference system, can be taken either as single functions of ω or as defining a vector function $[X(\omega), Y(\omega)]$. The value spaces (or range spaces) of the functions $X(\omega)$, $Y(\omega)$ can each be taken to be the whole real line $(-\infty, \infty)$; the value space of the vector $[X(\omega), Y(\omega)]$ is then the whole xy-plane. The set of coordinate pairs

$$E = \{(x, y) \mid x^2 + y^2 \leq 1\}$$

has as its pre-image the set of all landing points within one unit of the target point. The event in $\mathscr{X}$: $\{x \mid x < 0\}$ has as its pre-image the set of landing points to the left of the reference axis from which x is measured: $\{\omega \mid X(\omega) < 0\}$.

It is common to find, having expressed interest in one function $X(\omega)$ on a sample space Ω, that one is also interested in a certain function, say, $g(x)$ of the computed value x of $X(\omega)$. This defines a function of ω as a function of a function:

$$Z(\omega) = g(X(\omega)).$$

Values of this composite function $Z(\omega)$ can be thought of as coming either directly from ω via the function $Z(\omega)$, or indirectly as a value $g(x)$ where x comes from ω as $X(\omega)$. That is, ω is mapped by $X(\omega)$ into a point x, and x is then mapped by $g(x)$ into z:

$$\omega \xrightarrow{\ X(\omega)\ } x \xrightarrow{\ g(x)\ } z,$$

and this is equivalent to the mapping from ω directly to $g(X(\omega))$:

$$\omega \xrightarrow{\ Z(\omega)\ } z.$$

An event E or set of values on the value space of $Z(\omega)$ has a pre-image in the set of values $\mathscr{X}$ of $X(\omega)$, and this in turn has a pre-image set in Ω, which would be the same as the pre-image of E under $Z(\omega)$.

In the case of a vector function $[X_1(\omega), \ldots, X_n(\omega)]$, one might define another vector function $[Y_1(\omega), \ldots, Y_m(\omega)]$ by introducing functions $g_i(x_1, \ldots, x_n)$ of the values of $[X_1(\omega), \ldots, X_n(\omega)]$:

$$Y_1(\omega) = g_1[X_1(\omega), \ldots, X_n(\omega)]$$
$$\vdots \qquad\qquad \vdots$$
$$Y_m(\omega) = g_m[X_1(\omega), \ldots, X_n(\omega)].$$

EXAMPLE 1–23. In Examples 1–6 and 1–14, a sample space was taken to be the set of possible orientations of a fiber. For each orientation ω the colatitude and longitude define a vector function of the orientation: $[\theta(\omega), \phi(\omega)]$. The same model might apply in the case of a force of given magnitude K whose direction of application is random, although it would be then more suitable to take the set of *directed* orientations as the sample space. In this case the coordinate function $\theta(\omega)$ would have values on the interval $[0, \pi]$. (In the identification of orientations with points on a unit sphere, the whole sphere would be used rather than just the upper hemisphere.) The components of force along the direction $\theta = 0$, along the direction $\theta = \pi/2$, $\phi = 0$, and along the direction $\theta = \pi/2$, $\phi = \pi/2$ would be as follows:

$$F_1 = K \cos \theta$$
$$F_2 = K \sin \theta \cos \phi$$
$$F_3 = K \sin \theta \sin \phi$$

thereby defining a vector function $[F_1(\omega), F_2(\omega), F_3(\omega)]$ of the sample point ω as a function of a function.

A function $X(\omega)$ on a sample space Ω provides what is called a "partition" of the sample space. A *partition* of a space is a collection of disjoint events (sets) $\{E_\alpha\}$ having the property that their union is the whole space:

(i) $\bigcup E_\alpha = \Omega$
(ii) $E_\alpha \cap E_\beta = \varnothing$,   for all α, β such that $\alpha \neq \beta$.

The partition provided in a natural way by a function $X(\omega)$ consists of the sets on which $X(\omega)$ is constant:

$$\{\omega \mid X(\omega) = x\},$$

for all values x in the value space of $X(\omega)$. These partition sets are "level curves" or "level surfaces" of the function. One common example of such curves is that of the "contour curves" on a map, indicating sets of points at which the altitude (a function of position) is a given constant.

EXAMPLE 1–24. Suppose a sample space consists of points in a three-dimensional space, and let $R(\omega)$ denote the distance between the point and a reference origin. Then the condition $R(\omega) = 3$ defines the surface of a sphere of radius 3, and the collection of all sets of the form $\{\omega \mid R(\omega) = \lambda\}$, for λ a nonnegative real number, constitutes a partition of the space. Every point in the sample space lies on one of these spherical surfaces, the surfaces are disjoint, and the union of all such surfaces is the whole space.

A partition determined by a function may also be determined by a different function, if that function is also constant on each set of the partition and has a distinct value on each of these sets. For instance, in Example 1–24 above, the function $X^2(\omega) + Y^2(\omega)$, where $X(\omega)$ is the horizontal distance and $Y(\omega)$ is the vertical distance to a given set of rectangular coordinate axes, determines the same partition as the function $R(\omega)$, because there is a one to one correspondence between values of these two functions.

Problems

1–19. Show that for any event E, in a sample space Ω, the collection consisting of the events E, E^c, $\varnothing$, and Ω is a Borel field.

1–20. Determine the Borel field generated by the set $\{a, b\}$ in the sample space consisting of the four outcomes a, b, c, d.

1–21. A sample space contains just the five points, a, b, c, d, e. Consider the function whose values are $X(a) = X(b) = 0$, $X(c) = X(d) = 1$, and $X(e) = 2$. Show that the Borel field generated by $\{a, b\}$ and $\{e\}$ includes all events of the form $\{\omega \mid X(\omega) \leq \lambda\}$ for various λ.

1–22. Determine the partition of the sample space defined by the function $X(\omega)$ in the preceding problem.

1–23. A sample space consists of points in a plane, specified by means of rectangular coordinates relative to a given axis system: $\omega = (x, y)$. Determine the partition defined by the function

$$f(\omega) = |x - y|.$$

1–24. Let $X(\omega)$ denote the function of Problem 1–21 and let $Y(\omega) = X^2(\omega)$. Does this function determine the same partition? Would the same be true for an arbitrary function on a sample space?

1–25. A sample space consists of the set of points in three dimensions, identified by rectangular coordinates $(x, y, z) = \omega$ in a given reference system. Let $U_1(\omega)$ denote the smallest, $U_2(\omega)$ the second smallest, and $U_3(\omega)$ the largest of the three coordinates of ω. (Ignore the fact that some points ω have coordinates that are not all different.) What is the range space of this vector function $[U_1(\omega), U_2(\omega), U_3(\omega)]$? What are the partition sets of Ω determined by this vector function?

1–26. A cube has its six sides colored red, white, blue, green, yellow, and violet, respectively. Consider the function $X(\omega)$ defined as follows:

$$\begin{aligned} X(R) &= X(W) = 1, \\ X(G) &= X(B) = 2, \\ X(Y) &= X(V) = 3. \end{aligned}$$

Determine the partition sets of the sample space defined by the function $Y(\omega)$, where Y has values obtained as $y = (x - 2)^2$, for a given value x of $X(\omega)$.

1–27. Let Ω denote the sample space which is the set of real numbers $(-\infty, \infty)$. Determine the pre-image of the set $\{y \mid y < 1\}$ in the space of values of $Y(\omega) = \omega^2$. If for each y one computes z as

$$z = \frac{y}{1 + y}.$$

what is the range space of the composite function $Z(\omega)$ defined by this relation?

1–28. Determine the smallest Borel field generated by the partition of the sample space in Problem 1–21 induced by the function $Y(\omega)$ whose values y are obtained from values x of $X(\omega)$ by the relation $y = (x - 1)^2$.

1-29. Show that if $E_1 \subset E_2 \subset \ldots$, the events $E_1, E_2 - E_1, E_3 - E_2, \ldots$ constitute a partition of the union $\bigcup E_i$ (see Problem 1–18).

1.2   Probability

To complete the construction of a model for an experiment of chance there remains the specification of "probabilities." A *probability space* (the name for the completed model) consists of a sample space, a Borel field that includes all events of possible interest, and an assignment of a number called *probability* to each event of the Borel field. A probability space is often denoted $(\Omega, \mathscr{F}, P)$, where Ω is the sample space, $\mathscr{F}$ is the Borel field, and P is short for $P(E)$, the probability measure assigned to each set E in $\mathscr{F}$.

For a given event E the probability of E, written $P(E)$, is a number that is intended to embody what is commonly thought of as E's "chance of occurring." This notion seems to be bound up in the following fact of observation: When an experiment is performed repeatedly, the proportion of trials in which a given event E occurs is found to stabilize—approach a limiting value as the number of trials increases without limit. The probability $P(E)$ in the mathematical model is something that is assumed to exist as a property of the experiment, intended to represent the limiting proportion of trials in which E occurs—whether or not a long sequence of trials is actually carried out.

In constructing a probability model it would of course be desirable to know the correct probabilities for each event, but since correctness is only judged on the basis of infinitely many trials of the experiment, one will never really "know" whether a given probability space faithfully represents the experiment. In a sense this is true of all mathematical models for physical or "real" experiments, and yet mathematical models for such experiments are certainly useful. One obtains evidence as to the adequacy of a model, or about certain of its unknown characteristics, by performing the experiment—and it is inferences about probability models, based on experimental data, that are the central problems of statistics.

It is claimed by some that probability models only make sense for experiments that could be repeated indefinitely. Others feel that a probability model can be useful in other experiments with unpredictable outcomes. Probabilities in the latter sense are usually subjective (not objective—not an intrinsic property of the experiment, independent of the observer), and so are personal but sometimes useful in guiding behavior.

EXAMPLE 1–25.   A thumbtack tossed on a table will land in one of two positions, with point up or with point down. Repeated tossings of a thumbtack will reveal a tendency of the proportion of points up toward a limiting value. At any rate, it is assumed that a probability for the event "point up" exists, even though it would be quite hard to guess the correct value of this probability without some experimentation. And even *with* experimentation one has at best an estimate or approximation of the correct value; different series of trials of the experiment would generally yield different estimates. The complete probability space for this experiment would consist of the two outcomes, "point up" and "point down," and the Borel field that comprises the four events Ω, $\varnothing$, U, and D is certainly adequate (where U and D denote the events containing the single points, respectively, point up and point down). The probabilities for these events are

$$P(\Omega) = 1, \qquad P(\varnothing) = 0, \qquad P(U) = p, \qquad P(D) = 1 - p,$$

where p is a number representing the proportion of U's in an infinitely long series of tosses. Observe that the specification of the value of p would completely define the model.

EXAMPLE 1–26.   A man is told by his physician that he has a certain disease. Upon inquiry he learns that according to past records, some 85 per cent of patients having this disease have recovered. As viewed by the clinic's statistician, this patient (considered as a trial of an experiment) has a certain chance of recovery which seems to be near 85 per cent. But there is a real question as to whether the patient himself should adopt this as his model—indeed, whether he should consider the whole thing as experiment of chance. Certainly the statistician's estimate of the chances of recovery ignores many factors peculiar to the patient, some of which might be known to the patient and so influence his personal probability of recovery. This experiment, as viewed by the patient, would never be repeated, for some aspects of the situation are bound to be different even if he recovers and contracts the disease again. Nevertheless, an assessment (appropriate or not) of his chances of recovery might motivate him to certain action—such as making a will.

EXAMPLE 1–27.   An experiment that is difficult to imagine as being repeatable is the observation of some aspect of the weather at a given time. Yet it is becoming common to find weather forecasts given in terms of "chances"—for instance, it might be stated that there is one chance in ten that it will rain the following day. This is equivalent to stating that the probabilty of the event "rain" for the following day is .1, an item of information that can be quite useful for people making plans dependent on the weather. Different meteorologists might well view the same data and yet announce different rain probabilities. It might be argued that the experiment is repeatable in the sense that the meteorologist has seen the same patterns before, and found them to result in rain one time in ten. But ordinarily he will not have seen *exactly* the same pattern.

1.2.1   *Probability Axioms*

Whether one adopts the personal or the more traditional, objective attitude in applying probabilities, the mathematical structure of a probability model is the same—the assignment of probabilities to all of the events of interest in the sample space for the experiment in question. Of course, not just any numbers will do. Naturally, the "correct" probabilities for a given experiment will automatically have the properties of a proportion and will be consistent. But in constructing a model which is hoped will represent a given experiment, it is necessary to impose restrictions on the assigned probabilities.

Probabilities must satisfy many conditions, but it has been found that if the following three conditions, called *axioms*, are satisfied, the other conditions that one would want to require are also satisfied:

(1) $P(\Omega) = 1$,

(2) $0 \le P(E) \le 1$,   for every event E,

(3) $P(\bigcup E_i) = P(E_1) + P(E_2) + \cdots$,   for every sequence of disjoint events $E_1, E_2, \ldots$.

[Axiom (1) reflects the fact that Ω occurs whenever the experiment is performed, and Axiom (2) the fact that a proportion is a number between 0 and 1. Axiom (3) is certainly reasonable for a finite sequence; for instance, if E and F are disjoint, then the proportion of times E occurs plus the proportion of times F occurs equals the proportion of times their union $E + F$ occurs.]

One easy consequence of the above axioms is an expression relating the probabilities of an event and of its complement. An event and its complement constitute a partition of the sample space:

$$E + E^c = \Omega, \quad \text{and} \quad EE^c = \varnothing .$$

Hence, by Axiom (3),

$$P(E + E^c) = P(E) + P(E^c),$$

and by Axiom (1) this probability is 1. Therefore,

$$P(E^c) = 1 - P(E).$$

The significance of this is that it is often more convenient to calculate $P(E^c)$ when one really wants $P(E)$. As an important special case, the probability of the empty set is zero:

$$P(\varnothing) = 1 - P(\Omega) = 0.$$

Another property that can be derived from the axioms is the following. Let $E_1, E_2, \ldots$ be an *ascending* sequence—that is,

$$E_1 \subset E_2 \subset E_3 \subset \cdots .$$

Then

$$P(\bigcup_1^\infty E_n) = \lim_{n \to \infty} P(E_n), \quad \text{(ascending sequence)}.$$

For, according to the result of Problem 1-18 (setting $E_0 = \varnothing$),

$$P(\bigcup E_i) = P[\bigcup(E_i - E_{i-1})]$$

$$= \sum_1^\infty P(E_i - E_{i-1})$$

[by Problem 1–29 and Axiom (3)]

$$= \lim_{n\to\infty} \sum_{i=1}^n P(E_i - E_{i-1}) = \lim_{n\to\infty} P(E_n),$$

the last step following from an application of Axiom (3) to the relation $E_n = E_1 + (E_2 - E_1) + \cdots + (E_n - E_{n-1})$. A similar property deals with *descending* sequences:

$$F_1 \supset F_2 \supset F_3 \supset \cdots,$$

namely,

$$P(\bigcap_1^\infty F_n) = \lim_{n\to\infty} P(F_n), \qquad \text{(descending sequence)}.$$

This follows from an application to the above result for ascending sequences to the sequence $F_1^c, F_2^c, \ldots$, as follows:

$$P(\bigcap F_n) = 1 - P(\bigcup F_n^c) = 1 - \lim_{n\to\infty} P(F_n^c) = \lim_{n\to\infty} P(F_n).$$

EXAMPLE 1–28.   Let the sample space for the toss of a die consist of the six numbers 1, 2, 3, 4, 5, 6. The collection of all possible events (of which there are $2^6 = 64$) is a Borel field. One possible specification of a probability for each event is defined by assigning to a given event the number which is the proportion of the total number of outcomes that it includes. For instance,

$$P(\{2, 4, 6\}) = 3/6, \qquad P(\{5\}) = 1/6, \qquad \text{etc.}$$

This assignment clearly satisfies Axioms (1) and (2), and just a little more thought shows that (3) is also satisfied. Notice that the individual outcomes, each considered as an event whose only element is that outcome, are equally likely.

EXAMPLE 1–29.   The sample space for the experiment of a spinning pointer (Example 1–16) is taken to be the numbers on the unit interval [0, 1]. The number of possible events is of course very infinite.[3] The kinds of events that one is usually interested in are intervals, points, and combinations (at most countable) of these. Thus, the Borel field generated by the collection of all intervals contained in [0, 1] is big enough for practical purposes, and yet is not so big as the set of *all* subsets. This latter collection turns out to be too big to permit a consistent definition of a probability measure of its sets. One useful model for this experiment assigns to an interval a probability equal to its width. That is, for $0 \le a < b \le 1$,

$$P[\text{pointer stops in } (a, b)] = b - a.$$

[3] That is, it is of even higher cardinality than the set of real numbers.

From this assignment of probability to intervals, probabilities for events that are the results of countable operations on intervals follow from the axioms. (Indeed, the significance of the Borel field generated by a class of sets is that from an assignment of probability to the sets of this class the axioms imply a definite extension of probabilities to the whole field of sets.) For example, the probability that the pointer stops precisely at .2 is (in this model) computed as follows:

$$
\begin{aligned}
P(.2) &= P[\bigcap_{n=1}^{\infty} (.2 - 1/n, \ .2 + 1/n)] \\
&= \lim_{n \to \infty} P(.2 - 1/n, \ .2 + 1/n) \\
&= \lim_{n \to \infty} (2/n) = 0.
\end{aligned}
$$

1.2.2 The Addition Law

A general rule for determining the probability of a union of two events in terms of the probabilities of these events is as follows:

$$
P(E + F) = P(E) + P(F) - P(EF).
$$

This is reasonable from the point of view that interprets probability as a limiting proportion, since in adding the proportions of a sequence of trials in which E and F occur, respectively, one counts twice those trials in which both occur; and since one does want to count them *once*, the subtraction of $P(EF)$ is appropriate.

The preceding general addition law is a consequence of Axiom (3), which is a special addition law for disjoint events, as follows. The set $E + F$ can be decomposed into three disjoint parts:

$$
E + F = EF + EF^c + E^cF,
$$

and then according to Axiom (3),

$$
\begin{aligned}
P(E + F) &= P(EF) + P(EF^c) + P(E^cF) \\
&= [P(EF) + P(EF^c)] + [P(EF) + P(E^cF)] - P(EF) \\
&= P(E) + P(F) - P(EF),
\end{aligned}
$$

where the bracketed terms have reduced to $P(E)$ and $P(F)$ by still another application of Axiom (3) and the distributive law.

EXAMPLE 1–30. Let E denote the event that the spinning pointer of the preceding example falls in the interval $(0, .5)$, and F the event that it falls in the interval $(.4, .6)$. According to the probabilities assigned in that example,

$$
P(E) = .5, \qquad P(F) = .2, \qquad \text{and} \qquad P(EF) = .1,
$$

and then

$$
P(E + F) = .5 + .2 - .1 = .6,
$$

which is indeed the probability of the union $E + F = (0, .6)$.

1.2.3   The Discrete Case

To construct a probability model in which the sample space has only a finite or countably infinite number of outcomes, it suffices to define a probability as a nonnegative number for each individual outcome in such a way that the total of the assigned probabilities is 1. The probability of a given event then must be, according to Axiom (3), simply the sum of the probabilities assigned to the outcomes that make up the event:

$$P(E) = \sum_{\omega \text{ in } E} P(\omega).$$

(The Borel field of events is here the collection of all possible events.) It is clear, moreover, that $P(\Omega) = 1$ and that since the total of the assigned probabilities is 1, any sum of less than all of the assigned probabilities will not exceed 1: $0 \leq P(E) \leq 1$. That is, Axioms (1) and (2) are also satisfied.

EXAMPLE 1–31.   One useful model for the experiment of drawing a card from a standard deck is that in which each card has the same chance of being drawn as any other, that is, in which the probability assigned to each card is 1/52. Since the event "the card is an Ace" includes four of the fifty-two cards, its probability is

$$P(\text{Ace}) = 4 \cdot \frac{1}{52} = \frac{1}{13}.$$

EXAMPLE 1–32.   A coin is tossed until Heads first appears. The elementary outcomes of this experiment are sequences each of whose last element is Heads, preceded by nothing but Tails:

$$H, \quad TH, \quad TTH, \quad TTTH, \quad TTTTH, \quad \text{etc.}$$

One way (seen later to be a natural way) to assign probabilities to these outcomes is according to the formula

$$P(T, T, \ldots, T, H) = 1/2^k,$$

where k = number of tosses, for $k = 1, 2, 3, \ldots$. According to the formula for the sum of a geometric series, these probabilities total 1:

$$\frac{1}{2} + \frac{1}{4} + \frac{1}{8} + \cdots = \frac{1/2}{1 - 1/2} = 1.$$

The probability that the first Heads occurs in three or fewer tosses is

$$P(1, 2, \text{ or } 3 \text{ tosses required}) = P(H) + P(TH) + P(TTH)$$

$$= \frac{1}{2} + \frac{1}{4} + \frac{1}{8} = \frac{7}{8}.$$

The probability that an even number of tosses is required is

$$P(2 \text{ or } 4 \text{ or } 6 \text{ or } \ldots \text{ tosses required}) = \frac{1}{4} + \frac{1}{16} + \frac{1}{64} + \cdots$$

$$= \frac{1/4}{1 - 1/4} = \frac{1}{3}.$$

And so on.

Problems

1–30. Let each of the 52 cards, the elementary outcomes in the sample space for drawing a card from a standard deck, be assigned probability 1/52 (as in Example 1–31 above). In this model, determine the probability of each of the following events:

(a) The card is a Spade.
(b) The card is a face card.
(c) The card is a Spade or a face card.
(d) The card is an Ace or a Heart.
(e) The card is not an Ace or a Heart.
(f) The card is black or is an Ace.
(g) The card is red or a face card.

1–31. The outcomes of an experiment are the nine pairs (x, y) where x and y are each one of the integers 1, 2, 3. Let probability 1/6 be assigned to each of the pairs in which $x = y$ and the probability 1/12 to each of the other outcomes. Determine the probabilities of each of the following events:

(a) $x = 2$ (c) $x = 2$ or $y = 1$ (e) $y > 1$
(b) $y = 1$ (d) $x + y \leq 4$ (f) $|x - y| = 1$.

1–32. (a) Show that if $A \subset B$, then $P(A) \leq P(B)$.
(b) Show that $P(E) = P(EF) + P(EF^c)$.
(c) Show that $P(A) = \sum P(AE_n)$, where the E_n's constitute a partition of the sample space.
(d) Show: $P(EF) \leq P(E) \leq P(E + F) \leq P(E) + P(F)$.

1.2.4 A Priori Models in Finite Discrete Cases

In certain kinds of experiments with finitely many outcomes the appropriate probability model is strongly suggested by intuition. These are called *a priori* models, being constructed without actual experimentation, although experience would bear out the usefulness of the model. In these experiments there are reasons, usually geometrical, to believe that all outcomes should be equally likely—have the same chance of occurring. The model that represents this belief assigns equal probabilities to the outcomes; so if there are n outcomes, each is assigned probability $1/n$.

One kind of experiment of this category is that in which a symmetrical object is tossed—a coin, a cube, or some other regular polyhedron. It comes to rest on one of its sides, and this side—or, if more convenient, the side on top (if there is one)—is the outcome. The geometrical symmetry suggests that no one side ought to be weighted more than any other, and one would be greatly surprised to find one side predominating in a long sequence of trials; hence, the outcomes are taken to be equally likely, and each assigned probability $1/n$ where n is the number of sides. The spinning of a roulette wheel and the spinning of the cylinder of a revolver are other experiments of this kind. Incidentally, there is no regular polyhedron having five sides, for example; but an experiment with five equally likely outcomes can be devised. A cylinder, sufficiently long, whose cross section is a regular pentagon, will come to rest (when rolled) with one of its five sides down, and *a priori* reasoning suggests assigning probability $1/5$ to each of the sides.

Another class of *a priori* models is that in which the experiment consists of blindly drawing from a finite collection of objects a certain number of them, and noting which objects are selected but not taking any order into account. There are $\binom{N}{n}$ distinct selections of n from N objects, and the model suggested by *a priori* considerations for blind selections assigns equal probabilities to the possible selections, that is, the probability $1/\binom{N}{n}$ to each one. The statement that the selection is made "at random" will be taken to *mean* that the appropriate model is that in which all possible selections are equally likely. Sometimes the phrase "random selection" is used, but the question "is this a random selection?" really means "was the process by which this selection was made one to which the model of equally likely selections applies?"

This last question cannot be answered, strictly speaking. One can mix or shuffle the objects prior to the selection and do the selection in a truly "blind" manner, but aside from exercising precautions such as these, one can never know whether the ideal model is really applicable. Similarly, whether a die and a mechanism by which it is tossed are really represented by the ideal model (in which all sides are equally likely) is something one would never know—although again one could take certain precautions such as using a homogeneous die and giving it a vigorous toss with a substantial spin.

In any model in which the outcomes are equally probable the probability of an event E is simply the ratio of the number of outcomes in E to the total number of outcomes in the experiment. The problem of computing the probability of an event is then reduced to a problem of counting the number of outcomes for which the condition defining the event is satisfied.

It is to be understood that when questions are asked about probabilities of

events in the kinds of experiments discussed here, the *ideal* model is assumed
or decreed to be the one that governs.

EXAMPLE 1–33.   Two chips are selected at random from a container that holds
four white and three black chips. What is the probability that both chips are white?
   The phrasing of the description of the experiment, that is, "selected at random"
means that the $\binom{7}{2}$ possible selections of two chips from seven are to be assigned
equal probabilities, $1/\binom{7}{2}$. The desired probability is then the number of selections
in which both chips are white, $\binom{4}{2}$, times the probability $1/\binom{7}{2}$:

$$P(\text{both white}) = \frac{\text{Number of selections of two white}}{\text{Number of selections of two chips}} = \frac{6}{21} = \frac{2}{7}.$$

EXAMPLE 1–34.   The twelve faces of a die in the shape of a regular duodecahe-
dron are numbered 1, 2, . . ., 12. What is the probability that an even number turns
up when the die is tossed on a table?
   Because there are as many even-numbered as odd-numbered faces, and all are
equally likely, the probability that an even number turns up is 1/2:

$$P(\text{even number}) = \frac{\text{Number of even faces}}{\text{Number of faces}} = 1/2.$$

1.2.5   Nondiscrete Cases

   Assigning probabilities to individual elementary outcomes, as in the discrete cases discussed above, does not work in the case of a sample space
which is uncountably infinite. In most such cases the probabilities assigned to
individual outcomes ought to be zero, and it would not be possible to calculate probabilities for events with nonzero probabilities from the zeros
assigned to the outcomes. To construct a probability model in such cases it is
necessary to assign probabilities to events rather than to individual points.
   When a sample space is nondiscrete, it is usually: (1) a set of ordinary real
numbers such as the interval [0, 1] or the whole real line $(-\infty, \infty)$; (2) a set of
points in a plane, either a two-dimensional set such as the points within a
circle, or some set of points constituting a curve in the plane; (3) a set of
points in a three-dimensional space, either a three-dimensional set such as the
set of points in a cube, or a two-dimensional set such as a portion of a given
surface, or a one-dimensional set of points on a curve; or (4) a set of points in
a Euclidean space of dimension higher than three. In such sample spaces it is
helpful to have in mind an analogy with distributions of mass.
   A distribution of mass implies a function defined on the sets of our three-
dimensional space of visualization—for any given region one can define the

amount of mass in that region, a nonnegative quantity. Moreover, the amount of mass in a region consisting of two disjoint parts is the sum of the amounts in those parts. The same would be true then for a region composed of a finite number of disjoint parts, and could be assumed true for a countable number without offending the intuition. Thus, a given distribution of mass defines a set function having properties like those of probability; that is, the axioms for a probability measure are satisfied, except that the "measure" assigned to the whole space is the total mass, which may not even be finite. If it *is* finite, then the *relative* mass in a region—the fraction of the whole—is a quantity that does satisfy all of the probability axioms. At any rate, a probability distribution can be thought of as having an analog in a distribution of a finite amount of mass, probability corresponding to relative mass. Regions of high probability correspond to regions with a large mass concentration, that is, high density. Lumps or point masses in the distribution correspond to positive probability assigned to those points where the lumps occur. (A distribution with lumps only is then a discrete distribution, and is concentrated at most at a countable number of such points.)

Mass distributions (and thus probability) over a sample space of only two dimensions—a surface—would be something like a coat of paint on that surface, spread with variable density, but imagined somehow to be infinitely thin. Distributions on a one-dimensional sample space would be like a coat of paint on a thin wire.

If there is no lumpiness or discreteness, a distribution of mass or probability can be described in terms of a *density* of the distribution. The density at a point is the limiting ratio of the amount of material (mass or probability, as the case may be) contained in a tiny region including the point to the content of that region, as the region approaches 0 in all dimensions. (If the distribution is three-dimensional, the region is a solid region and its content is its volume; if two-dimensional, it is a region on a surface and its content is its area; if one-dimensional, it is a portion of a curve and its content is its length.) A density function has the property that its integral over any region gives the amount of mass or probability in that region:

$$\text{Mass in region } E = \int_E (\text{Mass density function}) \, dR,$$

where E and dR represent a region and element of content (for example, surface region and element of surface area) on the sample space over which the density is defined.

A mass distribution that has constant density over a certain region E (and is zero outside that region) is said to be *uniform* over E. In such a case, the amount of mass in a subregion is proportional to the content (volume, area, or length) of that subregion, since the constant density factors out of the integral. If a distribution of *probability* is uniform over a region E (and confined to that region), then E must have at most finite content; for the constant value of the density on E would have to be the reciprocal of the content of E, inasmuch as the total probability assigned to Ω is 1:

$$1 = \int_\Omega (\text{prob. density}) \, dR$$

$$= \int_E (\text{prob. density}) \, dR = \int_E k \, dR = k \, (\text{content of } E).$$

Notice, too, that if one started by assuming that the probability of sets E is proportional to the content of E, then the density (the limiting ratio as defined above) would turn out to be constant—equal to the constant of proportionality.

In summary then, when a sample space is a portion of the "space" of our experience, a probability measure for sets in the space is a quantity that resembles the geometrical content of sets (in the property of additivity over disjoint sets, and in its nonnegativenss), but which allows for a variable weighting of different portions of the sample space—and even permits weighting individual points with nonzero values (although the geometrical content of individual points is zero).

EXAMPLE 1–35. A consequence of Maxwell's law in physics states that the speed of a molecule of an ideal gas can be thought of as the outcome of an experiment of chance having as its sample space the set of nonnegative real numbers $(0, \infty)$, and having a distribution of probability defined by the density

$$f(v) = (\text{const.})v^2 \exp(-hmv^2), \qquad (v > 0),$$

where h and m are physical constants. The "constant" is determined so that the integral of the point density $f(v)$ over the sample space $(0, \infty)$ is unity. The probability that the speed of a molecule falls in a set E (of nonnegative real numbers) is then

$$P(E) = \int_E f(v) \, dv.$$

EXAMPLE 1–36. The probability space postulated for the spinning pointer in Example 1–29 assigned probabilities to intervals proportional to the width of the intervals, in fact, equal to the width. Extending this to more complicated sets, made up from intervals by countable operations, results in a probability measure for sets that is the same as its geometrical measure; the distribution is therefore *uniform* on the sample space [0, 1].

EXAMPLE 1–37. The sample space for random orientations (of a fiber in a material, for instance, such as in Example 1–6, 1–14, and 1–23) is essentially the set of points on a unit hemisphere. An event is a set of points on that hemisphere (identified with a corresponding solid angle of orientations), and the ideal model for perfectly random orientations assigns probability to such sets proportional to their areas on the surface of the unit hemisphere. Since the area of the entire hemisphere is 2π, the probability of an event E is

$$P(E) = \frac{1}{2\pi} \text{ (area of } E \text{ on hemisphere)}.$$

For example, the event $0 \le \phi \le \pi/4$ (where ϕ is the longitude coordinate of the orientation) consists of points on one-eighth of the hemisphere; it is therefore assigned probability $\frac{1}{8}$.

Problems

1–33.   A committe of three is chosen at random from a group of five men and five women. What is the probability that

(a) the committee will consist of all men or all women?
(b) at least one man and at least one woman are on the committee?
(c) at least one man is on the committee?

1–34.   The order on a ballot of the names of six candidates for three municipal judgeships is determined in such a way that all orders are equally likely. What is the probability that the names of the three already in office (the incumbents, who are running for reelection) will appear at the head of the list?

1–35.   A lot of 20 articles is to be accepted or rejected on the basis of an inspection of four drawn at random from the lot. If it is decided to accept the lot when at most one of the four articles inspected is defective, but otherwise to reject the lot, what is the probability that following this decision rule results in rejecting a lot that is only 10 per cent defective?

1–36.   The 36 elementary outcomes in the sample space for the experiment of tossing two dice are assigned equal probabilities. Determine the probabilities of the following events (see Problem 1–12):

(a) The sum is divisible by 4.
(b) Both numbers are even.
(c) The numbers on the dice are equal.
(d) The numbers on the dice differ by at least 4.
(e) The total number of points showing is 10.

1–37.   Five cards are selected at random from a standard deck of cards. Determine the probabilities of the following events (see Problem 1–15):

(a) The hand contains exactly one "pair."
(b) The hand contains two pairs (and an odd card).
(c) The hand contains two cards of one denomination and three of another.
(d) The hand contains three of one denomination, but the other two do not form a pair.
(e) The hand consists of five cards all of the same suit.

1–38.   Consider an experiment whose outcomes are positive numbers. Given that the distribution of probability is described by a density function which at any positive number x is e^{-x}, compute the probability that

(a) the outcome exceeds 2;
(b) the outcome is at most 1;
(c) the outcome lies between 1 and 2.

1–39. Consider an experiment whose outcomes are the points in the square bounded by $x = 0$, $y = 0$, $x = 2$, and $y = 2$ in the xy-plane. If probability is distributed uniformly over this sample space, determine probabilities of each of the following events:

(a) $x + y < 2$ (d) $x^2 + y^2 > 1$ (g) $|x - y| < 1$
(b) $x + y < 1$ (e) $x > 1$ and $y < \frac{3}{2}$ (h) $x - y < 1$
(c) $x > \frac{1}{2}$ (f) $x > 1$ or $y > 1$ (i) $x - y > 2$.

1–40. Let the sample space of an experiment consist of the points within the unit cube defined by $0 \le x \le 1, 0 \le y \le 1, 0 \le z \le 1$. Assuming probability to be uniformly spread throughout the cube, determine the probability of the event consisting of those points (x, y, z) such that $x + y + z \le 1$.

1–41. Referring to the probability space representing random orientations in Example 1–37, determine the probability of the event $0 \le \theta \le \pi/4$, where θ is the colatitude angle (that is, angular distance from the pole of the hemisphere).

1.3 Dependence and Independence

An aspect of probability theory that perhaps most distinguishes it from measure theory, and from the study of mass distributions, is the concept of independence. Although the concept can be translated into measure theoretic terms, it seems to have no particular significance in any other application of measure theory. It will be helpful, in appreciating the meaning of independence, to introduce it in terms of the notion of conditional probability.

1.3.1 Conditional Probability

It often happens that the sample space for an experiment must be altered to take into account the availability of certain limited information about the outcome of the experiment. Such information may well eliminate certain outcomes as impossible which were otherwise (without the information) possible, and in such a case either the appropriate sample space would omit these impossible outcomes or the probabilities assigned to them would be zero. In the revised model, the probabilities are said to be *conditional* on the occurrence of the event defined by the information. This new model is again a probability space, and the term "conditional" refers only to its origin in a larger probability space.

EXAMPLE 1–38.   A standard die is tossed, and before seeing the outcome, one is told by a bystander who does see the result that an even number of points is showing. How should he then bet?

Certainly one would be foolish to place any money on the outcomes 1, 3, or 5—the information that the outcome is an *even* number eliminates these from consideration. The sample space now is effectively just the set of even outcomes {2, 4, 6}, whose occurrence constitutes the information. But, in addition to betting nothing on the odd outcomes, one would find that his probabilities for the even outcomes are increased over what they are in the standard model for the toss of a die (with no information). For, *a priori* considerations would again suggest that there is no reason for any one of the outcomes 2, 4, or 6 to predominate, and each would be assigned probability $\frac{1}{3}$. The same conclusion would be reached in considering a long sequence of tosses of the die; in such a sequence the proportions of 1's, 2's, . . ., and 6's would be about equal, and the information that the outcome is even would simply eliminate from the sequence those trials that resulted in an odd number of points—leaving a sequence with equal proportions of 2's, 4's, and 6's.

Conditional probabilities, given an event F (or given that F has occurred), are obtained from the unconditional ones in the original sample space by taking F as a new sample space, and distributing a total probability of 1 over this smaller sample space in such a way that the new probabilities are in the same proportions as the old within F. That is, for any event E contained in an event F of positive probability the conditional probability of E given F, written $P(E \mid F)$, is defined to be

$$P(E \mid F) = \frac{P(E)}{P(F)}, \qquad (\text{when } E \subset F).$$

Notice that with this definition (for events in F), conditional probabilities are indeed proportional to the unconditional ones, and further, that the assignment of these conditional probabilities to events satisfies the probability axioms. That is, $P(F \mid F) = 1$, $P(E \mid F) \geq 0$, and the additivity axiom holds because it held in the original space.

Thus, conditioning with the information that F has occurred simply introduces a smaller probability space—and yet it is usually desirable to stay in the framework of the original probability space; thus, the adjective "conditional" is used, to refer to the reduced model. Events in the original sample space define events in the smaller space—for instance, the event G in Ω can be interpreted as a condition that characterizes its outcomes, and imposing this condition in the reduced model amounts to imposing *both* conditions G and F. Thus the conditional probability of G given F (again assume $P(F) > 0$) is taken to be

$$P(G \mid F) = P(GF \mid F) = \frac{P(GF)}{P(F)}.$$

This definition includes the earlier one, but it can be used without having to check whether or not G is contained in F. The definition is often useful in the form of a *multiplication law*:

$$P(EF) = P(E \mid F)P(F).$$

[With this one can compute the probability of EF from what is sometimes an easier determination of the factors $P(E \mid F)$ and $P(F)$.]

EXAMPLE 1–39.   A card is drawn at random from a standard deck of cards. (This wording implies that each card is assigned probability 1/52.) Given that the card drawn is a face card, the probability that it is a Jack would be computed as follows, since a Jack is a face card:

$$P(\text{Jack} \mid \text{face card}) = \frac{P(\text{Jack})}{P(\text{face card})} = \frac{4/52}{12/52} = \frac{1}{3}.$$

But not all Hearts are face cards, so

$$P(\text{Heart} \mid \text{face card}) = \frac{P(\text{Heart and face card})}{P(\text{face card})} = \frac{3/52}{12/52} = \frac{1}{4}.$$

That is, one-third of the face cards are Jacks, and one-quarter of the face cards are Hearts.

EXAMPLE 1–40.   A card is drawn at random from a standard deck, and then a second card is drawn at random from the remaining cards. What is the probability that the first is a Queen and the second is a face card?

Here, although the experiment consists of a sequence of two selections, the wording of the problem implies an assignment of probabilities for the individual draws, namely, on the first draw each of the 52 cards has probability 1/52 and on the second draw each of the 51 remaining cards has probability 1/51. Clearly, the probability of a Queen on the first draw is 4/52; and *given* that a Queen is obtained on the first draw, there are 11 remaining face cards among the 51 remaining cards. Hence,

$P(\text{Queen on 1st, face card on 2nd})$

$\qquad = P(\text{face card on 2nd} \mid \text{Queen on 1st}) \, P(\text{Queen on 1st})$

$\qquad = \dfrac{11}{51} \cdot \dfrac{4}{52} = \dfrac{11}{663}.$

In similar fashion one could determine probabilities for other events in the composite experiment from the assumption of random selection in the subexperiments.

The technique of the last example can be used to derive a useful result about composite experiments. Suppose that the experiment $\mathscr{E}$ consists of performing an experiment $\mathscr{E}_1$ and then performing an experiment $\mathscr{E}_2$. Suppose further that $\mathscr{E}_1$ has m equally likely elementary outcomes, $u_1, \ldots, u_m$, and that $\mathscr{E}_2$ has

n equally likely elementary outcomes $v_1, \ldots, v_n$. (These outcomes of $\mathscr{E}_2$ may depend on the result of $\mathscr{E}_1$; but it is assumed that the *number* of available outcomes in $\mathscr{E}_2$ is the same no matter how $\mathscr{E}_1$ turns out, and that these are equally probable.) The elementary outcomes of the composite experiment are the mn distinct pairs (u_j, v_k). The multiplication law is then used to determine probabilities in $\mathscr{E}$:

$$P(u_j, v_k) = P(v_k \mid u_j)P(u_j) = \frac{1}{m} \cdot \frac{1}{n} = \frac{1}{mn}.$$

That is, the elementary outcomes of the composite experiment are equally likely.

EXAMPLE 1–41.   A coin is tossed three times. Given that the two elementary outcomes for each toss are equally likely, the eight elementary outcomes

$$HHH, \quad HHT, \quad HTH, \quad THH, \quad TTH, \quad THT, \quad HTT, \quad TTT$$

are equally likely, each having probability $\tfrac{1}{8}$.

EXAMPLE 1–42.   The experiment of selecting one card and then a second card from a standard deck and recording the results so as to keep track of the order has $52 \cdot 51$ elementary outcomes, according to the principle explained in Section 1.1.2. If the 52 outcomes of the first draw are assumed equally likely, and the 51 outcomes of the second draw are also assumed equally likely, then the $52 \cdot 51$ elementary outcomes of the composite experiment are equally likely. Thus, the probability of each elementary outcome or particular sequence of two different cards, such as: Queen of Hearts, 3 of Spades, is $1/2652$. The probability of any other event can then be computed from these; for instance, the probability that both cards are Spades is $1/2652$ times the *number* of sequences of two distinct cards of which both are Spades:

$$P(\text{both cards Spades}) = \frac{13 \cdot 12}{2652} = \frac{13}{52} \cdot \frac{12}{51}.$$

Writing it in the last form shows that this probability can also be computed as

$$P(\text{both cards Spades}) = P(\text{2nd Spade} \mid \text{1st Spade}) \, P(\text{1st Spade}).$$

An extension of the multiplication rule follows from successive applications of the one given, for two events. For instance,

$$P(EFG) = P(E \mid FG) \, P(FG)$$

$$= P(E \mid FG) \, P(F \mid G) \, P(G).$$

Similarly,

$$P(EFGH) = P(E \mid FGH) \, P(F \mid GH) \, P(G \mid H) \, P(H).$$

EXAMPLE 1–43. Five chips are drawn, one at a time, from a bowl containing 8 white and 12 black chips. At each drawing the selection is done blindly—at random—from the remaining chips, and none is put back after having been drawn. The colors of the chips drawn are recorded in the sequence in which they are drawn; so the elementary outcomes are sequences of five colors, each being black or white. The probability of a given sequence can be computed using the extended multiplication law, together with the assumption of random selections. For instance, the probability of the sequence (W, B, B, W, B) is computed as follows:

$$P(WBBWB) = P(W)P(B \mid W)P(B \mid WB)P(W \mid WBB)P(B \mid WBBW)$$

$$= \frac{8}{20} \cdot \frac{12}{19} \cdot \frac{11}{18} \cdot \frac{7}{17} \cdot \frac{10}{16}.$$

(The factor $P(W \mid WBB)$, for example, means the conditional probability of white on the fourth draw, given that the first was white and the second and third were black.)

The above product can also be obtained in terms of combination symbols as follows:

$$\frac{\binom{8}{2}\binom{12}{3}}{\binom{20}{5}\binom{5}{3}}.$$

Upon noting the origins of these numbers the "scheme" used to write this down becomes apparent—the 8 and 12 are the numbers of white and black chips available, the 2 and 3 are the numbers of white and black chips drawn; and in the denominator $20 = 8 + 12$ and $5 = 2 + 3$ are the number of chips available and the number drawn, respectively. That this is not simply a happenstance can be demonstrated by showing (by induction) that the scheme works generally. A special case of this demonstration will perhaps suffice, and suggest the general technique. Assuming that the scheme works for sequences of four, one has

$$P(WBBW) = \frac{\binom{8}{2}\binom{12}{2}}{\binom{20}{4}\binom{4}{2}},$$

and then

$$P(WBBWB) = P(WBBW)P(B \mid WBBW) = \frac{\binom{8}{2}\binom{12}{2}}{\binom{20}{4}\binom{4}{2}} \cdot \frac{10}{16} = \frac{\binom{8}{2}\binom{12}{3}}{\binom{20}{5}\binom{5}{3}}.$$

From this it follows, incidentally, that the probability of a given number of whites among the five draws (disregarding order) can be found by a formula that has another interpretation; for there are precisely $\binom{5}{3}$ sequences in which two are black and three are white, and *each* has the above probability:

$$P(2 \text{ whites and } 3 \text{ blacks}) = \binom{5}{3} \cdot \frac{\binom{8}{2}\binom{12}{3}}{\binom{20}{5}\binom{5}{3}} = \frac{\binom{8}{2}\binom{12}{3}}{\binom{20}{5}}.$$

This last expression is the probability that if five beads are *selected at random* from the container with the 8 whites and 12 blacks, there are exactly 2 whites and 3 blacks in the selection—the assumption of a "random" selection implying that all $\binom{20}{5}$ selections are equally likely. What has been shown in this instance, then, is that if one keeps track only of the numbers of whites and blacks in a selection, performing the selection one at a time at random is equivalent to making a random selection of five. This is actually a general rule.

1.3.2 Bayes' Theorem

The multiplication rule can be used in two ways to express the probability of an intersection as a product:

$$P(EF) = P(E \mid F)P(F) = P(F \mid E)P(E),$$

assuming that neither $P(E)$ nor $P(F)$ is zero. Solving the last equality for $P(F \mid E)$ yields

$$P(F \mid E) = \frac{P(E \mid F)P(F)}{P(E)},$$

and provides a means of effectively interchanging the roles of event and condition.

A version of the above relation known as *Bayes' Theorem* is obtained when the denominator is expressed in terms of conditional probabilities, with the aid of the result in Problem 1–32(b):

$$P(E) = P(EF) + P(EF^c) = P(E \mid F)P(F) + P(E \mid F^c)P(F^c).$$

Substituting this one obtains

$$P(F \mid E) = \frac{P(E \mid F)P(F)}{P(E \mid F)P(F) + P(E \mid F^c)P(F^c)}.$$

Similarly, if the sets A_1, A_2, ... constitute a partition of Ω, one has the following form of Bayes' Theorem:

$$P(A_i \mid E) = \frac{P(E \mid A_i)P(A_i)}{P(E \mid A_1)P(A_1) + P(E \mid A_2)P(A_2) + \cdots}.$$

(Notice that the sum of these conditional probabilities of the partition sets, given E, is 1.)

EXAMPLE 1–44.   A certain disease is present in about 1 out of 1,000 persons in a given population, and a program of testing is to be carried out using a detection device which gives a positive reading with probability .99 for a diseased person and with probability .05 for a healthy person. It is desired to determine the probability that a person who has a positive reading actually does have the disease.

With obvious notations for diseased, healthy, positive, and negative, the given quantities are as follows:

$$P(D) = .001, \qquad P(+ \mid D) = .99, \qquad P(+ \mid H) = .05.$$

Bayes' theorem permits the computation of $P(D \mid +)$ from these:

$$P(D \mid +) = \frac{P(+ \mid D)P(D)}{P(+)}.$$

The denominator is computed as in the text above:

$$P(+) = P(+ \mid D)P(D) + P(+ \mid H)P(H) = .99 \times .001 + .05 \times .999$$

$$= .05094.$$

Then the desired conditional probability is the ratio of the first term to the sum:

$$P(D \mid +) = \frac{.00099}{.05094} = 0.0194,$$

or about one chance in 50. This result may seem a bit odd at first, since the characteristics of the detector as given seem rather good; the explanation is that when a positive reading is obtained, it is much more frequently a machine malfunction than a diseased person which gives the reading. For, even with a perfect detection device, only one in 1,000 readings would be positive; whereas with the given device and a completely healthy population, five out of every 100 readings would be positive.

Problems

1–42. (a) Determine the probability that a tossed die shows 4, given that the outcome is an even number.

(b) Determine the probability that it shows 6, given that the outcome is divisible by 3.

1–43. A sample space consists of exactly five outcomes, a, b, c, d, and e. Given that $P(\{a, b, c\}) = 1/2$ and $P(\{a\}) = 1/4$,

(a) determine the probabilities of all events whose probabilities can be computed from those given;

(b) compute $P(\{b, c, d\} \mid \{a, b, c\})$;

(c) compute $P(\{a\} \mid \{a, b, c\})$.

1–44. Each person among six married couples gathered for bridge draws a slip at random from twelve slips of paper (no replacement). Two slips are marked "Table 1, Couple 1," two are marked "Table 2, Couple 1," and so on:

(a) What is the probability that Table 1 has all men?

(b) What is the probability that Table 1 has four people who form two married couples?

(c) What is the probability that a certain man draws his own wife as a partner?

(d) What is the probability that a certain man draws his wife as a partner, given that they draw the same table number?

1–45. Two cards are drawn at random from a standard deck. Determine the probability that

(a) they are both face cards, given that they are of the same suit;
(b) they are both face cards;
(c) both are Hearts, given that both are red.

1–46. The outcomes of an experiment are real numbers, and the distribution of probability is continuous, having a density function given by $[\pi(1 + \omega^2)]^{-1}$ at the point ω. Determine the probability that the outcome

(a) exceeds 1, given that it is positive;
(b) is positive, given that it is on the interval $(-1, 1)$.

1–47. Show the following:

(a) If $P(F) = 0$, then $P(EF) = 0$.
(b) $P(AC \mid B) = P(A \mid BC)P(C \mid B)$.
(c) $P(EFGH) = P(E \mid FGH)P(F \mid GH)P(G \mid H)P(H)$.

1–48. Machines A and B turn out, respectively, 10 and 90 per cent of the total production of a certain type of article. Suppose the probability that machine A turns out a defective article is .01 and that machine B turns out a defective article is .05. What is the probability that an article taken at random from a day's production was made by machine A, given that it is found to be defective?

1–49. Of a large group of college students containing equal numbers of freshmen, sophomores, juniors, and seniors, it is found that 35 per cent of the freshmen, 25 per cent of the sophomores, 20 per cent of the juniors, and 15 per cent of the seniors are girls. What is the probability that a girl picked at random from the group is a freshman?

1–50. Students are classed as either "resident" or "commuter." Of a group of 50 students, 14 are male residents, 20 are female commuters, and 24 are males. What is the probability that a name drawn at random from a list of these students is that of

(a) a female resident?
(b) a resident?
(c) a female, given that the student is a resident?

1–51. A bowl contains M black and $N - M$ white chips; n chips are drawn one at a time at random (without replacing any). Let $\mathscr{P}_n$ denote the proposition that the probability of each sequence of n chip colors consisting of k blacks and $n - k$ whites is given by the formula

$$\frac{\binom{M}{k}\binom{N-M}{n-k}}{\binom{N}{n}\binom{n}{k}}, \qquad \text{for } k = 0, 1, \ldots, n.$$

Show (a) that $\mathscr{P}_1$ is true, and (b) that $\mathscr{P}_n$ implies $\mathscr{P}_{n+1}$, using the multiplication rule as illustrated in Example 1–43.

1.3.3   *Independent Events*

It can happen that a condition does not alter the probability assigned to an event:

$$P(E \mid F) = P(E).$$

That is, the probability that E will occur is the same with as without the information that F has occurred. If this is so and if $P(E) \neq 0$, then (according to Bayes' theorem):

$$P(F \mid E) = \frac{P(F)P(E \mid F)}{P(E)} = P(F),$$

which says that the probability assigned F is the same with as without the information that E has occurred. The multiplication rule in this case assumes the form

$$P(EF) = P(E)P(F),$$

which happens to be true even if E or F has zero probability, since EF is contained both in E and in F. Moreover, if this multiplication relation is true and $P(E) \neq 0$, then

$$P(F \mid E) = \frac{P(EF)}{P(E)} = \frac{P(E)P(F)}{P(E)} = P(F).$$

That is, for events of positive probability, the multiplication rule in the above form is equivalent to the equality of conditional and unconditional probabilities, and either can then be taken to be the definition of *independence* of E and F. Thus, events E and F are said to be *independent* if and only if $P(EF) = P(E)P(F)$. (According to this formulation, an event of zero probability is independent of any other event.)

EXAMPLE 1–45.   A card is drawn at random from a standard bridge deck. In Example 1–39 the conditional probability that the card drawn is a Heart given that it is a face card was computed to be

$$P(\text{Heart} \mid \text{face card}) = \frac{3/52}{12/52} = \frac{1}{4}.$$

This is also the probability that the card drawn is a Heart, without the information as to whether or not it is a face card. (One-quarter of all the cards are Hearts, and one-quarter of all the face cards are Hearts.) That is, the events "Heart" and "face card" are independent events. Notice that the multiplication law defining independence holds:

$$P(\text{Heart and face card}) = \frac{3}{52} = \frac{13}{52} \cdot \frac{12}{52}$$

$$= P(\text{Heart})P(\text{face card}),$$

and also that

$$P(\text{face card} \mid \text{Heart}) = \frac{3/52}{13/52} = \frac{3}{13}.$$

(Three-thirteenths of all of the cards are face cards, and three-thirteenths of the Hearts are face cards.)

It should be emphasized that independence is a concept associated with the assignment of probabilities; it is not, therefore, represented in a Venn diagram, which pictures only sets or events. In particular, a student sometimes gets the notion that independence and disjointness are somehow the same thing, whereas disjointness is not defined in terms of probabilities—it is a property that *can* be represented in a Venn diagram. Indeed, disjointness and independence are almost incompatible, as seen in Problem 1–57(c).

The notion of independence can be extended to the case of three events. Events E, F, and G are said to be independent if and only if

   (i) they are pairwise independent, and
   (ii) $P(EFG) = P(E)P(F)P(G)$.

(Pairwise independent, or independent in pairs, means that each combination of two of the three events is a set of independent events, in the sense defined earlier for two events.)

Lest this definition seem unnecessarily complicated it should be pointed out that (i) does not imply (ii), nor does (ii) imply (i). Example 1–46 below shows that pairwise independence does not imply that $P(EFG)$ factors as in (ii); and Problem 1–55 gives an instance in which $P(EFG)$ factors properly, but E, F, and G are not pairwise independent. Neither (i) nor (ii) would then adequately characterize the intuitive notion of independence. For, if only the factorization (ii) were assumed, one might not have pairwise independence; and if only pairwise independence were taken as defining independence of E, F, and G, one could not guarantee (for instance) that EF and G are independent. Thus, both (i) and (ii) are needed to define in the model what intuition and practice require for the notion of independence of three events.

Independence of four events could be defined in terms of a factorization of $P(EFGH)$ and a requirement that any three of them are independent, and so on. But the notion can be defined once and for all, for the case of the n events $E_1, E_2, \ldots, E_n$, as follows. The n events $E_1, E_2, \ldots, E_n$ are *independent* if and only if for every subset of k events $E_{i_1}, E_{i_2}, \ldots, E_{i_k}$ the factorization holds:

$$P(E_{i_1} E_{i_2} \cdots E_{i_k}) = P(E_{i_1})P(E_{i_2}) \cdots P(E_{i_k}).$$

The implications of this definition seem to include all of what is thought of intuitively as independence.

EXAMPLE 1–46. The probability space for a certain experiment of chance consists of the four equally probable outcomes $(1, 0, 0)$, $(0, 1, 0)$, $(0, 0, 1)$ and $(1, 1, 1)$. Consider the events

    E: The first coordinate is 1;
    F: The second coordinate is 1;
    G: The third coordinate is 1.

Each of these events has probability $1/2$, so

$$P(E)P(F)P(G) = (1/2)^3 = 1/8.$$

However, only one of the four outcomes has all three coordinates equal to 1:

$$P(EFG) = P(\{(1, 1, 1)\}) = 1/4.$$

Thus the three events E, F, and G are *not* independent. But they are pairwise independent; for example,

$$P(EF) = P(\{(1, 1, 1)\}) = 1/4 = P(E)P(F),$$

and similarly,

$$P(FG) = P(F)P(G) \quad \text{and} \quad P(EG) = P(E)P(G).$$

To see why one would not want to call E, F, and G independent in this instance, notice that the probability of the event EF depends on whether or not G is known to have occurred:

$$P(EF \mid G) = \frac{P(EFG)}{P(G)} = 1/2, \qquad P(EF) = 1/4.$$

1.3.4 Independent Experiments

An experiment $\mathscr{E}$, represented by a given probability space, consists of performing first experiment $\mathscr{E}_1$ and then experiment $\mathscr{E}_2$. Outcomes of $\mathscr{E}$ are pairs of outcomes—an outcome of $\mathscr{E}_1$ paired with an outcome of $\mathscr{E}_2$. An event in $\mathscr{E}$ is defined by a condition E_1 on the first element of the pair, and another event in $\mathscr{E}$ is defined by a condition E_2 on the second element of the pair. Experiments $\mathscr{E}_1$ and $\mathscr{E}_2$ are said to be *independent experiments* if each event E_1 relating to $\mathscr{E}_1$ is independent of each event E_2 relating to $\mathscr{E}_2$.

This definition can be used, as its statement implies, to check whether a given probability structure for a composite experiment has the property that the component experiments are independent. But it is more common that the definition is used the other way—to *construct* a probability space for the composite experiment so as to achieve independence of the component experiments, by using the multiplication rule for independent events to assign probabilities to events of the type E_1E_2, where E_1 and E_2 are conditions only on $\mathscr{E}_1$ and $\mathscr{E}_2$, respectively. This class of events is not usually large enough to include all events relating to the composite experiment that might be of interest; but on the other hand the Borel field generated by this class usually is adequate, and probabilities are extended to this Borel field in the usual manner.

EXAMPLE 1–47.   From a bowl containing four chips numbered 1, 2, 3, 4, a first chip is drawn and then a second, without replacement of the first. The twelve outcomes are as follows:

$$1, 2 \quad 2, 1 \quad 3, 1 \quad 4, 1$$
$$1, 3 \quad 2, 3 \quad 3, 2 \quad 4, 2$$
$$1, 4 \quad 2, 4 \quad 3, 4 \quad 4, 3.$$

Consider the events

   E: The first chip drawn is 1 or 3.
   F: The second chip drawn is 1 or 2.

In the model for the composite experiment that assigns equal probabilities (1/12) to each outcome, these events have probabilities $P(E) = 1/2$ and $P(F) = 1/2$, since there are six outcomes satisfying condition E and six satisfying F. The intersection EF consists of the pairs (1, 2), (3, 1), and (3, 2), so that

$$P(EF) = 1/4 = P(E)P(F).$$

Thus, E and F are independent events. However,

$$P(\text{2nd chip is } 3 \mid \text{1st is } 3) = 0 \neq P(\text{2nd chip is } 3),$$

and so the component experiments (drawing the first chip and then drawing the second chip) are *not* independent in this model. All it takes for this conclusion is a *single* instance of a pair of events, one relating to the first experiment and one to the second, that are not independent.

EXAMPLE 1–48.   Consider the composite experiment made up of two tosses of a coin (or a toss of two coins). Let the outcomes of the first toss be denoted H and T, and the outcomes of the second h and t. The elementary outcomes of the composite experiment are then the four pairs Hh, Ht, Th, Tt. For an ideal, balanced, or "fair" coin one decrees $P(H) = P(T) = 1/2$, and $P(h) = P(t) = 1/2$. But these probabilities for the component experiment say nothing about probabilities in the composite experiment, without some further assumption about the relationship of the two experiments. One would ordinarily assume that probabilities relating to one coin should not be influenced by information as to how the other one has fallen, and so would assume independence of the tosses. From this assumption and the probabilities for the component experiments, one can construct a model for the composite experiment:

$$P(Hh) = P(H)P(h) = 1/4, \qquad P(Th) = P(T)P(h) = 1/4,$$
$$P(Ht) = P(H)P(t) = 1/4, \qquad P(Tt) = P(T)P(t) = 1/4.$$

And from these one can compute probabilities of events that are not of the type which are the intersections of events in one subexperiment with events in the other. For example,

$$P(\{Ht, Th\}) = 1/4 + 1/4 = 1/2.$$

Although stated above for only two experiments, the notion of independence for any finite number of experiments is similarly defined. It might be noticed that the model has nothing in it that requires that the subexperiments be actually carried out in any particular order, which is as it should be if they are truly independent in the intuitive sense. That is, tossing ten coins simultaneously is equivalent to tossing them in any given sequence, so long as information about the result for one or more of the coins would not alter how one would bet on the remaining coins.

Problems

1–52. A coin and a die are tossed. Assuming the twelve elementary outcomes of the composite experiment to be equally likely, show that the component experiments (the toss of the coin and the toss of the die) are independent.

1–53. A card is drawn at random from a standard deck. Show that

(a) the events "Heart" and "black" are not independent;
(b) the events "black" and "Ace" are independent;
(c) "under 10" and "red" are independent;
(d) the three events "red," "face card," and "Heart or Spade," are independent.

1–54. Two chips are drawn at random from four chips numbered 1, 2, 3, 4. List the six (equally likely) possible selections of two. For each outcome let R denote the magnitude of the difference and S the sum of the numbers on the two chips drawn.

(a) Determine probabilities for the events defined by the condition $R = 2$ and by the condition $S = 5$. Are these independent events?
(b) Are the events $R = 1$ and $S = 5$ independent?

1–55. An experiment can result in one of five outcomes, assigned probabilities as follows: ω_1 with probability $\frac{1}{8}$, ω_2, ω_3, and ω_4 each with probabilities $\frac{3}{16}$, and ω_5 with probability $\frac{5}{16}$. Define E, F, and G as follows:

$$E = \{\omega_1, \omega_2, \omega_3\}, \qquad F = \{\omega_1, \omega_2, \omega_4\}, \qquad G = \{\omega_1, \omega_3, \omega_4\},$$

and show that they are not pairwise independent, but that

$$P(EFG) = P(E)P(F)P(G).$$

1–56. Show that when the eight elementary outcomes for the composite experiment of tossing a coin three times are assigned equal probabilities, the three tosses are independent.

1–57. Show the following:

(a) If A and B are independent events, then A and B^c are independent.
(b) If A, B, and C are independent events, then A, B, and C^c are independent.
(c) Disjoint events are not independent unless at least one of them has probability zero.

1–58.   A die is tossed eight times in succession, and after each toss it is noted whether the result is a six (6) or is not a six (*N*). Determine the probability

(a) of this sequence of results: *N*, 6, *N*, 6, *N*, *N*, *N*, 6;
(b) of this sequence: 6, 6, *N*, *N*, *N*, *N*, 6, *N*;
(c) of any particular sequence in which there are 2 *N*'s and the rest 6's.

1–59.   A certain type of device is used to shut off a flow when a container is filled to a certain depth; its "reliability" (probability that it works when it should) is assumed to be .9. A second type of shutoff device is placed "in parallel," that is, so that the flow is shut off if either device works; the reliability of this second device is assumed to be .7. What is the reliability of the combination? What is the probability that when the depth is reached, just one of the devices will work? (Assume that the devices operate independently.)

1–60.   A certain device consists of four parts so connected that the device works only if all four parts work, where "works" means operates successfully in a certain mission. If the probability that each part individually works is .9, what is the probability that the device works? (Assume independence.)

1–61.   Two teams are to play a series of games for the best four out of seven games; as soon as one team wins four games, the series ends. The probability that team *A* wins over team *B* is assumed to be .5 if the game is played on team *B*'s field, and .7 if the game is played on team *A*'s field. The first two games are to be played on team *B*'s field, the next three on team *A*'s field, and the last two (if the series runs that long) on team *B*'s field. What is the probability that team *A* wins the series on four games? In five games? What is the probability that the series does not run to six games?

CHAPTER 2

RANDOM VARIABLES AND THEIR DISTRIBUTIONS

The term "random variable" is an apt one, being used to denote a variable that is random, that is, a numerical quantity whose value is determined by an experiment of chance. Other names for the concept are "chance variable" and "stochastic variable." Because its value is dependent, a random variable is an example of the mathematical idea of "function"; and so the formal definition given below is in terms of this, although the domain of the function is somewhat more general than it is in the usual use of the term.

The adjective "random" in this context does *not* mean, as it does in the case of "random selection," that the appropriate model involves outcomes that are necessarily equally likely. It refers only to the fact that the value of the numerical quantity under consideration cannot be predicted from a knowledge of the experimental conditions. What is different, then, from the general concept of an experiment of chance, is that one is concerned with an experiment whose outcomes either are numerical themselves, or have numbers assigned to them. The sample space or the induced sample space (in the latter case) is then a space of numbers or a space of vectors of numbers, and the structure of such spaces permits analyses and descriptions that are not possible in the general case.

2.1   Random Variables and Vectors

Consider a probability space $(\Omega, \mathscr{F}, P)$, that is, a sample space Ω, a Borel field $\mathscr{F}$ of events, and a probability $P(E)$ for each event E in this field. A function $X(\omega)$ defined on Ω is said to be *measurable* with respect to the given Borel field $\mathscr{F}$ if the event defined by the condition $X(\omega) \leq \lambda$ is included in $\mathscr{F}$ for every real number λ.

Definition.   A *random variable* is a measurable function defined on a probability space.

The condition of measurability is almost always satisfied; indeed, the construction of a *non*measurable function takes considerable ingenuity in continuous cases and some artificiality in discrete cases. Yet it is a condition that seems necessary to make the definition mathematically workable. With this acknowledgment of what is actually needed, it will be assumed in what follows (with impunity, it turns out) that all functions encountered are in fact measurable—without taking the trouble to verify this claim in any case. When the sample space is discrete, however, there would seldom be any reason to use a Borel field smaller than the field of all subsets of the sample space; and in such a case *every* function on the sample space is automatically measurable! In the following example a nonmeasurable function is constructed on a discrete sample space by using a Borel field smaller than the field of all subsets.

EXAMPLE 2–1.   Consider a sample space containing the five elements a, b, c, d, e, and the Borel field generated by the partition of the sample space given by the function $X(\omega)$ defined as follows:

$$X(a) = X(b) = 0, \qquad X(c) = X(d) = 1, \qquad X(e) = 2.$$

Let the probabilities of the events $\{a, b\}$ and $\{e\}$ be 1/3 and 1/6, respectively; from these one can easily compute the probabilities of the remaining events of the Borel field:

$$P(\{c, d, e\}) = 2/3 \qquad\qquad P(\{c, d\}) = 1/2 \qquad P(\{a, b, e\}) = 1/2,$$
$$P(\{a, b, c, d\}) = 5/6, \qquad P(\{a, b, c, d, e\}) = 1, \qquad\quad P(\varnothing) = 0.$$

With this probability structure on the sample space Ω, the function $X(\omega)$ given above defined a random variable, because $X(\omega)$ is measurable with respect to the given Borel field, as can be readily verified. (For instance, for any λ on the range $0 < \lambda < 1$, the event defined by $X(\omega) \leq \lambda$ is just the event $\{a, b\}$, which is a member of the Borel field.) On the other hand, the function $Y(\omega)$, defined as follows:

$$Y(\omega) = \begin{cases} 0, & \text{for} \quad \omega = a, \\ 1, & \text{for} \quad \omega = b, c, d, \text{ or } e, \end{cases}$$

is *not* measurable. It is the "indicator function" of a set that is not a member of the given Borel field; and the event $Y(\omega) \leq \frac{1}{2}$ (to give one instance, which is enough) is simply $\{a\}$, not a member of the Borel field. As mentioned above, however, if one were to use as the basic Borel field the set of all subsets of $\{a, b, c, d, e\}$, then every function on this probability space would be a random variable, including in particular the function $Y(\omega)$ just defined.

To say that a certain physical, biological, or social quantity "is a random variable" means, usually, that the measure of this quantity is numerical and dependent on the outcome of an experiment of chance; but it also carries the implication that the quantity can be represented by the mathematical model of a function defined on an appropriate probability space (although the precise characteristics of this model may be unknown or only partly known).

EXAMPLE 2–2. The resistance of a certain electrical resistor is measured. Because of variations introduced in the process of measurement, repeated measurements of resistance will vary, and the measured resistance is a numerical quantity depending on an experiment of chance—a random variable. Further variation would be introduced if the resistor were taken from a supply of "100-ohm" resistors, whose resistances are in fact not all equal to this nominal value nor even all alike, owing to uncontrolled variables in the process of their manufacture. The "outcome" of the experiment of drawing a resistor and measuring its resistance is perhaps most expediently identified by the reading of the ohm-meter, that is, ω is itself a real number. The simple random variable $X(\omega) = \omega$ is then surely of interest, as is possibly the deviation about the nominal resistance, $Y(\omega) = \omega - 100$.

EXAMPLE 2–3.   An individual tosses a coin infinitely often. The sample points or outcomes are then infinite sequences of Heads and Tails. Some of the random variables that might be of interest are

   $X(\omega) =$ number of tosses required to equalize the number of Heads and the number of Tails for the first time;

   $Y(\omega) =$ proportion of the tosses in which the number of Heads exceeds the number of Tails;

   $Z(\omega) =$ 1 or 0, depending whether the third toss is Heads or Tails.

Thus, suppose the outcome of the experiment is the sequence

$$H, H, T, H, T, T, T, H, T, \ldots$$

For this sequence, $X(\omega) = 6$, $Z(\omega) = 0$, and $Y(\omega)$ cannot be determined from only the finite portion of the sequence given.

Although a random variable is a function, it has become common practice to drop the reference to the independent variable ω, and to write just X in place of $X(\omega)$, Y in place of $Y(\omega)$, etc. This is especially appropriate when ω is a real number and $X(\omega) = \omega$, but it is also generally convenient since it turns out that the main interest is in the value space of a random variable, and in the induced probability distribution in that space, discussed in the next section.

A vector-valued function $[X_1(\omega), \ldots, X_n(\omega)]$ defined on a sample space Ω is said to be measurable with respect to the Borel field $\mathscr{F}$ if and only if $\mathscr{F}$ includes all events of the type defined by the condition

$$X_1(\omega) \le \lambda_1, \quad X_2(\omega) \le \lambda_2, \quad \ldots, \quad X_n(\omega) \le \lambda_n,$$

(that is, for every choice of $\lambda_1, \ldots, \lambda_n$). A *random vector* is a vector-valued function defined on a probability space $(\Omega, \mathscr{F}, P)$ that is measurable with respect to $\mathscr{F}$. But again the verification that a given vector function is actually measurable will always be *assumed* possible, and omitted. As in the case of a single random variable, the simpler notation $(X_1, \ldots, X_n)$ will often be used in place of $[X_1(\omega), \ldots, X_n(\omega)]$.

EXAMPLE 2–4.   A person is picked at random from a large population, and his height H, weight W, and age A are determined. Thinking of the people in the population as constituting the sample space and the person picked as an elementary outcome ω, the triple of measured quantities is a random vector: $[H(\omega), W(\omega), A(\omega)]$, or (H, W, A). Since the population is finite, the collection of all subsets will serve as the Borel field of a probability space, and the phrase "picked at random" calls for the assignment of a probability to each event that is proportional to the number of people in it.

2.1.1   The Distribution in the Value Space

It was seen in Section 1.1.6 that a function on a probability space maps the events of Ω into sets of values in the value space of the function, and conversely, that it determines for each given set of values an event in the sample space—the pre-image of that set. A random variable, being a function on a sample space, does these things; but the sample space has a probability structure, and so the function also provides a natural transfer of probability from Ω to the space of values $\mathscr{X}$.

Because the value space of a random variable $X(\omega)$ is always a set of real numbers, and so is imbedded in the set of *all* real numbers, it will be convenient in the general discussion to take $\mathscr{X}$ to be this set $\mathscr{R}$ of all real numbers,.

$(-\infty, \infty)$, even though some numbers may not be actually assumed as values of $X(\omega)$. An arbitrary set A in $\mathscr{X}$ does define a pre-image set E_A in Ω, namely

$$E_A = \{\omega \mid X(\omega) \text{ in } A\}.$$

A particular kind of set A of special interest is the semi-infinite interval $(-\infty, \lambda]$, and the assumption that $X(\omega)$ is measurable with respect to the given Borel field $\mathscr{F}$ ensures that the pre-images of such semi-infinite intervals are contained in $\mathscr{F}$. Moreover, every set in the Borel field generated by the class of all such semi-infinite intervals has a pre-image which is also in $\mathscr{F}$. For, pre-images of the complements and unions of sets in $\mathscr{R}$ are the complements and unions (respectively) of the pre-images of these sets:

$$E_{A^c} = \{\omega \mid X(\omega) \text{ in } A^c\} = \{\omega \mid X(\omega) \text{ in } A\}^c = (E_A)^c,$$

and

$$E_{\cup A_i} = \{\omega \mid X(\omega) \text{ in } \bigcup A_i\} = \bigcup\{\omega \mid X(\omega) \text{ in } A_i\} = \bigcup E_{A_i}.$$

Therefore, the construction of a set B in $\mathscr{R}$ by using countable operations of union and complementation has a parallel construction (using these same operations on pre-images) that results in the pre-image of B.

Probability is defined in $\mathscr{R}$, on the events of the Borel field generated by intervals of the form $(-\infty, \lambda]$, as follows:

$$P^{\mathscr{R}}(A) = P^{\Omega}(E_A) = P^{\Omega}(\{\omega \mid X(\omega) \text{ in } A\}),$$

and this probability will usually be denoted simply by $P(X \text{ in } A)$ or $P(A)$. In particular, then,

$$P(X \leq \lambda) = P^{\Omega}(\{\omega \mid X(\omega) \leq \lambda\}).$$

Moreover, if $\mathscr{B}$ denotes the Borel field of sets in $\mathscr{R}$ generated by the semi-infinite intervals as described above, then $(\mathscr{R}, \mathscr{B}, P^{\mathscr{R}})$ constitutes a probability space. That is, $P^{\mathscr{R}}(A)$ defines a probability measure in the set of real numbers—it is an assignment of probability that satisfies the axioms for a probability space. For, surely,

$$P(X \text{ in } \mathscr{R}) = P(-\infty < X(\omega) < \infty) = P(\Omega) = 1,$$

and if $A_1, A_2, \ldots$ is a sequence of disjoint events in $\mathscr{R}$, then their pre-images are disjoint and

$$P(\bigcup A_i) = P(E_{\cup A_i}) = P(\bigcup E_{A_i}) = \sum P(E_{A_i}) = \sum P(A_i).$$

This probability distribution in $\mathscr{R}$ is said to be *induced* by the random variable $X(\omega)$ from the distribution in the sample space Ω. Observe, however, that in the special case that sometimes arises, when Ω is itself a set of real numbers and $X(\omega) = \omega$, the induced distribution is essentially the same as the original one.

It should be mentioned that the same distribution in $\mathscr{R}$ can be induced from different sample spaces by correspondingly different functions. For instance, the random variable

$$X(\omega) = \begin{cases} 1, & \text{if a coin falls Heads,} \\ 0, & \text{if the coin falls Tails,} \end{cases}$$

has precisely the same distribution as the random variable

$$Y(\omega) = \begin{cases} 1, & \text{if a die shows an even number of points,} \\ 0, & \text{if it shows an odd number,} \end{cases}$$

provided the usual unbiased or fair coin and die are used (that is, equally likely outcomes). Indeed, it may be said that a feature of probability theory that distinguishes it from the theory of measurable functions on measure spaces is that the main interest in probability is only in the distribution in the value space, and not in the sample space.

Problems

2–1. Four coins are tossed. List the 16 outcomes in the sample space that keeps track of the individual coins. For each outcome ω compute $X(\omega)$, the number of Heads. Determine the probability assigned to each value of $X(\omega)$ by the assumption that the 16 outcomes are equally likely.

2–2. A dart is thrown at a circular target of radius one foot in such a way that the probability of hitting a certain portion of the target is proportional to the area of that region. The dart misses completely one-half of the time. Let a score be assigned equal to the number of inches from the circumference of the target, except that the score 0 is assigned if the dart misses entirely.

Denoting the point where the dart hits by ω and the score by $X(\omega)$, determine

(a) $P(X = 0)$
(b) $P(X > 9)$
(c) $P(X = 2)$
(d) $P(X < 5)$
(e) $P(3 < X < 9)$

2–3. For an infinite sequence of coin tosses let

$U(\omega)$ = number of trials needed to get the first Heads;
$V(\omega)$ = number of trials needed to get two Heads.

Determine the following:

(a) $P(U = 2)$
(b) $P(V = 3)$
(c) $P(U = 4 \text{ and } V = 6)$
(d) $P(U \leq 3 \text{ and } V = 5)$

2-4. Consider a sample space with four outcomes: a, b, c, d.

(a) Show that the function $X(\omega)$ defined by

$$X(a) = X(b) = 0, \qquad X(c) = X(d) = 1$$

is measurable with respect to the Borel field generated by the events $\{a, b\}$ and $\{c\}$.

(b) Construct a function $Y(\omega)$ *not* measurable with respect to the Borel field in (a).

2.1.2   *The Distribution Function*

Because the Borel field of sets of real numbers that is generated by the class of semi-infinite intervals is sufficiently large as to include all sets of real numbers of practical interest, these semi-infinite intervals play a special role. The probability assigned to the interval $(-\infty, \lambda]$, in the probability distribution on $\mathscr{R}$ induced by $X(\omega)$ from the distribution in Ω, depends of course on λ as well as on the random variable X, and so it is expressed by the following notation:

$$F_X(\lambda) = P(X \leq \lambda).$$

(This can be thought of either as a probability in Ω of the set $\{\omega \mid X(\omega) \leq \lambda\}$ or as the probability in $\mathscr{R}$ of the interval $(-\infty, \lambda]$, since they are the same.) This function of λ is called[1] the *distribution function* of the random variable X or of its distribution in $\mathscr{R}$. If X is the only random variable in view, the subscript may be dropped: $F(\lambda)$.

The significance of the distribution function is that from it one can compute the probabilities of the large class of sets comprising the Borel field generated by the intervals $(-\infty, \lambda]$, whose probabilities define the distribution function.

One of the inadequacies of traditional functional notation is that the same notation is used for a whole function, $f(x)$, as is used for the specific value of the function corresponding to x. When referring to a whole function (that is, to the *rule* for associating values of one variable with those of another), the particular letter employed within the parentheses is not significant: $f(y)$ denotes the same functional relationship as $f(x)$. Perhaps a better notation would be $f(\cdot)$. The x or y used is a "dummy" variable, in that $f(x)$ means that a certain operation is to be performed on *whatever* number x is "plugged" in. Thus, if $F(\lambda)$ is the distribution function of X, then

$$F(\lambda) = P(X \leq \lambda), \qquad F(x) = P(X \leq x), \qquad F(q) = P(X \leq q), \quad \text{etc.}$$

---

[1] It is also called the *cumulative* distribution function, for reasons that will emerge subsequently, and abbreviated to c.d.f.

But the *function* $F(\cdot)$ is the same in each case. A different distribution function results from using a different random variable; if more than one random
variable is involved in a problem, the subscript will help to identify the various
distribution functions:

$$F_X(\lambda) = P(X \le \lambda), \quad F_Y(\lambda) = P(Y \le \lambda), \quad \text{etc.}$$

Here the function $F_X(\cdot)$ defines a relationship different from that defined by
$F_Y(\cdot)$ and it makes no difference that the same dummy variable was used in
defining both.

EXAMPLE 2–5.   In the model proposed in Examples 1–29 and 1–36 for the stopping position of a spinning pointer, the probability that it stops in a given angle
was assumed proportional to the size of the angle. Marking the circle traced by
the pointer's tip with a uniform scale from 0 to 1 introduces a random variable
$X(\omega)$, which maps the stopping positions ω into the real numbers on the interval
[0, 1]. The distribution function of this random variable is

$$F(\lambda) = P(X \le \lambda) = P(0 \le X \le \lambda) = \begin{cases} 0, & \text{if } \lambda < 0, \\ \lambda, & \text{if } 0 \le \lambda \le 1, \\ 1, & \text{if } \lambda > 1. \end{cases}$$

The graph of this function is shown in Figure 2–1. Notice that if the pointer's
position is identified by the number that marks where it stops on the superim-
posed scale, then in effect $X(\omega) = \omega$.

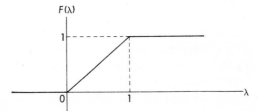

Figure 2–1.   Distribution
function for the spinning pointer.

EXAMPLE 2–6.   Consider again the spinning pointer of the preceding example,
and define the following random variable:

$$Y(\omega) = \begin{cases} 0, & \text{if } \omega \text{ is in the left half circle,} \\ 1, & \text{if } \omega \text{ is in the right half circle,} \end{cases}$$

where "left" and "right" are measured with respect to some given reference
diameter. For this random variable, any interval containing just 0 (and not 1) has
probability 1/2, and any interval containing both 0 and 1 has probability 1. That
is,

$$F_Y(\lambda) = P(Y \le \lambda) = \begin{cases} 0, & \text{if } \lambda < 0, \\ 1/2, & \text{if } 0 \le \lambda < 1, \\ 1, & \text{if } \lambda \ge 1. \end{cases}$$

The graph of this function is shown in Figure 2–2. (This distribution in $\mathcal{R}$ is precisely the same as that of the variable defined to be 1 or 0, according as a fair coin falls Heads or Tails.)

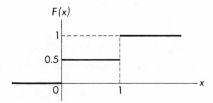

Figure 2–2.

As mentioned above, probabilities of sets in the Borel field generated by the semi-infinite intervals can be computed from the probabilities assigned to these semi-infinite intervals, that is, from the distribution function $F(\lambda)$. Thus, the probability of the half-open interval $a < x \leq b$ or $(a, b]$ can be computed in terms of $F(\lambda)$ by first applying the addition law to the decomposition

$$(-\infty, b] = (-\infty, a] + (a, b],$$

to obtain

$$F(b) = F(a) + P(a, b],$$

and then transposing for the desired result:

$$P(a < X \leq b) = F(b) - F(a).$$

That is, the probability of an interval open on the left and closed on the right is the difference in the values of $F(\lambda)$ at the two endpoints; or in other words, it is the amount of increase in the function $F(\lambda)$ over the interval.

The probability of a single value, $X = a$, is obtained by expressing the set consisting of that single value as the intersection of a decreasing family $I_1, I_2, \ldots$, where $I_n = \{x \mid a - 1/n < x \leq a + 1/n\}$. For then

$$P(X = a) = P(\bigcap I_n) = \lim_{n \to \infty} P(I_n)$$

$$= \lim_{n \to \infty} [F(a + 1/n) - F(a - 1/n)].$$

$$= F(a+) - F(a-),$$

the difference between the limits from the right and left of $F(\lambda)$ at the point $\lambda = a$. This difference is called the *jump* in the function $F(\lambda)$ at $\lambda = a$; if the function $F(\lambda)$ happens to be continuous at $\lambda = a$, the amount of the jump and hence the probability that $X = a$ is zero.

Intervals that are closed, or open, or open on the right and closed on the left can be expressed in terms of single points and intervals that are closed on the right and open on the left:

$$(a, b) + \{a\} = [a, b),$$
$$[a, b] \qquad = \{a\} + (a, b],$$
$$[a, b) + \{b\} = [a, b],$$

from which

$$P(a < X < b) = F(b) - F(a) - P(X = b),$$
$$P(a \le X \le b) = F(b) - F(a) + P(X = a),$$
$$P(a \le X < b) = F(b) - F(a) + P(X = a) - P(X = b).$$

Sets of numbers more complicated than finite combinations of semi-infinite intervals and single points are seldom encountered in practice.

To use the distribution function in such computations it is necessary to be able to determine its value at a given point. Sometimes a distribution function can be expressed using simple algebraic or other "elementary" functions, but in many instances it is not so expressible and cannot be evaluated using the familiar tables of logarithms, exponential functions, trigonometric functions, or powers and roots. New tables are then required and have been constructed for many useful distribution functions of "nonelementary" type.

A tabulation of values of a function is often given in terms of a set of conveniently spaced (usually, evenly spaced) values of the independent variable, interpolation being required if a value is needed between tabulated entries. The values of the independent variable used for tabulation are ordinarily taken sufficiently close together such that a linear interpolation is adequate, even though the graph of the tabulated function is not linear.

Another method of tabulation commonly employed for distribution functions is to give values of the independent variable corresponding to equally spaced values of the function. The range of values of a distribution function is [0, 1], and it is this interval that is divided into equal parts. If a distribution function rises steadily from 0 to 1, with no jumps or intervals of constancy, there is a unique number x_p for each p on the interval [0, 1] such that

$$F(x_p) = P(X \le x_p) = p.$$

The number x_p, a number on the set of values of the random variable X, is that value such that the fraction p of the total probability 1 is assigned to the interval $(-\infty, x_p)$. The number x_p is called a *fractile* or a *quantile* of the distribution. If p is such that $100p = k$, then x_p is called the kth *percentile* of the distribution. Thus, for instance, the probability that X assumes a value less than its 70th percentile is .70. This is illustrated in Figure 2–3. Values x_p are called *deciles* if $10p$ is an integer, and quartiles if $4p$ is an integer. Thus, the first quartile is the same as the 25th percentile, and the third decile is the 30th percentile.

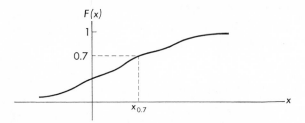

Figure 2–3. Determination of the 70th percentile.

If a distribution function does not increase steadily, but has horizontal sections or jumps in its graph, the above definition of a percentile is inadequate. But it can be patched in a way that is illustrated for the case of the 50th percentile (or 5th decile or 2nd quartile), called the *median m* of the distribution, as follows:

$$P(X \le m) \ge 1/2, \quad \text{and} \quad P(X \ge m) \ge 1/2.$$

That is, the median is any number m satisfying both of these conditions—it is not necessarily unique. Three possible situations are illustrated in Figure 2–4.

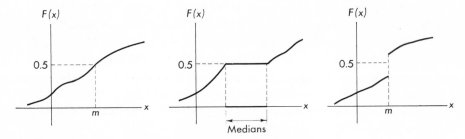

Figure 2–4. Determination of medians in three cases.

Problems

2–5. Table I in the Appendix gives values of a certain distribution function, $\Phi(z)$. Plot a sufficient number of points to obtain a smooth graph, and estimate the deciles of the distribution from the graph. (These can be checked with the entries in Table Ia.)

2–6. Given that a random variable Z has the distribution given in Table I (see Appendix), compute the following:

(a) $\Phi(1.4)$ (e) $P(Z > 2)$
(b) $\Phi(-2.33)$ (f) $P(|Z| > 3)$
(c) $\Phi(-.436)$ (g) $P(|Z - 1| < 2)$
(d) $P(-.3 < Z < 1.4)$ (h) $P(Z^2 < 2)$

2-7. A random variable X has the distribution function shown in Figure 2-5. Determine the following:

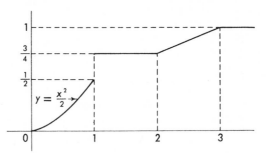

Figure 2-5. Distribution function for Problem 2-7.

(a) $P(X = 1/2)$ (d) $P(X \leq 1)$
(b) $P(X = 1)$ (e) $P(X > 2)$
(c) $P(X < 1)$ (f) $P(1/2 < X < 5/2)$

2-8. A random variable X has the following distribution function:

$$F(\lambda) = \begin{cases} 1 - .75e^{-\lambda}, & \text{if } \lambda \geq 0, \\ 0, & \text{if } \lambda < 0. \end{cases}$$

Determine the following:

(a) $P(X > 2)$
(b) $P(X \leq 0)$
(c) $P(X = 0)$

2-9. Determine the distribution function for the random variable X defined in Example 2-1, namely, $X(a) = X(b) = 0$, $X(c) = X(d) = 1$, $X(e) = 2$, where $P(\{a, b\}) = \frac{1}{3}$ and $P(\{e\}) = \frac{1}{6}$. (The sample space consists of just a, b, c, d, and e.)

2-10. Consider the random variables $\theta(\omega)$ and $\phi(\omega)$, as defined in Example 1-37 and earlier examples, the colatitude and longitude angles of a point on the upper hemisphere, with a uniform distribution of probability over this sample space. Determine the distribution functions $F_\theta(\lambda)$ and $F_\phi(\lambda)$.

2-11. Each horizontal line in Table II (Appendix) gives percentiles of a member of a certain class of distribution functions. Plot the distribution function for "five degrees of freedom" (that is, using the fifth line in the table). From the graph, estimate the following (in which X denotes a random variable with this distribution):

(a) the 40th percentile   (c) $P(|X - 5| < 2)$
(b) $P(X > 8)$ (d) $P(X < 3)$.

2-12. Each horizontal line in Table III (Appendix) gives certain percentiles of a random variable. Let T have the distribution given opposite 10 "degrees of freedom," where the earlier percentiles are obtained using the fact that this distribution is symmetric about the value 0. [That is, the probability assigned to an interval of negative numbers, $(-a, -b)$ is the same as that assigned to the interval (b, a).] Sketch the distribution function of T and determine the following:

(a) the median of the distribution.
(b) $P(|T| > 3)$
(c) the 98th percentile of T.
(d) $P(|T - 1| < 1.7)$

2.1.3   Discrete Random Variables

Let $x_1, x_2, x_3, \ldots$ be a sequence of distinct numbers such that there are only finitely many in any finite interval. A random variable X whose distribution function jumps at these values $x_1, x_2, \ldots$, and is constant between adjacent jump points is called *discrete*. As seen in the preceding section the amount of a jump in a distribution function is the probability assigned to the value x_i at which it occurs. That is,

$$p_i = [\text{jump at } x_i] = P(X = x_i).$$

And then

$$p_1 + p_2 + \cdots = 1.$$

Thus, the distribution of probability in the space of values of X defines a discrete probability space.

The distribution of a discrete random variable is characterized by the function (or sequence) p_i, sometimes denoted by $p(x_i)$ or $f(x_i)$ and called the probability function of the random variable. In some cases it can be given by a "formula," algebraic or otherwise, but sometimes it is simplest just to make a list of the values and corresponding probabilities in a table:

Values	x_1	x_2	$\ldots$
Probabilities	p_1	p_2	$\ldots$

, etc.

If the original probability space Ω on which $X(\omega)$ is defined is discrete, then any function $X(\omega)$ defines a *discrete* distribution in the value space, since $X(\omega)$ cannot assume more values than there are ω's. On the other hand, a continuous distribution of probability in Ω can lead to a discrete distribution in the value space of $X(\omega)$, as will be evident in some of the examples to follow.

EXAMPLE 2–7.   Three chips are drawn together at random from a bowl containing five chips numbered 1, 2, 3, 4, and 5. There are ten possible outcomes in this experiment:

123,   124,   125,   134,   135,   145,   234,   235,   245,   345, each having probability 1/10. Let $X(\omega)$ denote the *sum* of the numbers on the chips in outcome ω. The values of X corresponding to the above list of outcomes are, respectively,

$$6, \quad 7, \quad 8, \quad 8, \quad 9, \quad 10, \quad 9, \quad 10, \quad 11, \quad 12.$$

The possible values of $X(\omega)$ and the corresponding probabilities for those values are then as follows:

x_i	6	7	8	9	10	11	12
p_i	.1	.1	.2	.2	.2	.1	.1

The distribution function is that shown in Figure 2–6.

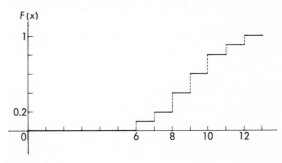

Figure 2–6.

EXAMPLE 2–8. In packaging a certain product it is desirable that at least 8 oz. be included in each package. For certain purposes, then, one might be interested only in whether a package contained less than 8 oz. or at least 8 oz. Thinking of the possible weights of packages as the points ω in the sample space, introduce the random variable

$$X(\omega) = \begin{cases} 1, & \text{if } \omega < 8 \text{ oz.,} \\ 0, & \text{if } \omega \geq 8 \text{ oz.,} \end{cases}$$

that is, 1 corresponds to a "defective" package and 0 to a "nondefective" one. The random variable X can take on just the values 0 and 1, and the corresponding probabilities are determined by the distribution of probability in the sample space:

$$P(X = 0) = P^{\Omega}(\omega \geq 8) = P(\text{package weighs 8 oz. or more}),$$
$$P(X = 1) = P^{\Omega}(\omega < 8) = P(\text{package weighs less than 8 oz.}).$$

EXAMPLE 2–9. The lengths of "10-foot" sections of pipe are measured in inches to the nearest inch. Here, even though the length might be thought of as assuming any of a continuum of possible values, the round-off process introduces discreteness into the set of values. The only possible values of the *measured* lengths are

$$\ldots, 118, \quad 119, \quad 120, \quad 121, \quad 122, \ldots,$$

and each value in this list has a corresponding probability—the probability that, in measuring, a length is rounded off to that value. More precise measurements of length would lead to possible values that are more numerous but nonetheless discrete (even should the precision be carried to, say, ten decimal places). Of course, a discrete model involving lengths to ten decimal places would be more complicated to deal with than the idealization to a continuous model. In any case, however, the data must be recorded discretely.

2.1.4 Continuous Random Variables

A distribution function that is *continuous*, having no jumps, will define a distribution in the value space of $X(\omega)$ that asigns probability zero to any single value:

$$P(X = b) = \lim_{n \to \infty} [F(b + 1/n) - F(b - 1/n)] = 0.$$

However, the class of continuous distribution functions includes many that are not useful in probability theory, being nondifferentiable over a large set of points. Models involving a limited number of points of nondifferentiability are useful, as for example the distribution of Example 2–5 (and Figure 2–1). Distribution functions that provide useful models are those which are differentiable everywhere with the possible exception of at most a finite number of points in any finite interval. In such a case[2] $X(\omega)$ is said to be a *continuous random variable*.

The distribution function of a continuous random variable will then have a derivative except at isolated points, and this derivative is usually denoted by $f(\lambda)$:

$$f(\lambda) = F'(\lambda).$$

Again notice that the dummy variable λ, used here in defining the function $f(\cdot)$, is completely immaterial. That is, $f(x), f(\lambda), f(R)$, etc., define the same function. It is common to find that in referring to a random variable X, the corresponding lower case x is used as a dummy variable (and y for Y, etc.). Indeed, some use the same name for both the random variable and the dummy denoting possible values, a practice that can be convenient when understood, but which leads to such strange statements as this: $P(x \le x) =$

---

[2] The class of distributions included under the heading *continuous* can be (and often is) defined to be just a bit wider than the one given here, namely, as the class of distributions defined by distribution functions that have the property of being recoverable from their derivatives by integration:

$$\int_{-\infty}^{x} F'(\lambda) \, d\lambda = F(x).$$

The functions satisfying the differentiability condition given above do satisfy this condition, but constitute a proper subclass.

$F(x)$. This latter practice will be avoided here, but the capital and lower case convention will be used when convenient.

The derivative function $f(\lambda)$ is called the *density function* of the distribution or of the random variable defining the distribution. If more than one random variable is under consideration, a subscript will be used to distinguish between their density functions, for example, $f_X(\lambda)$. The term "density" is appropriate in accordance with the discussion in Section 1.2.5, as applied to the sample space $\mathcal{R}$, the set of real numbers. That is, at a point x_0 where the derivative of the distribution function exists,

$$F'(x_0) = f(x_0) = \lim_{h \to 0} \frac{1}{h} [F(x_0 + h/2) - F(x_0 - h/2)]$$

$$= \lim_{h \to 0} \frac{1}{h} P(x_0 - h/2 < X \leq x_0 + h/2).$$

This is the limiting value of the ratio of the probability in a small interval about x_0 to the length of the interval, that is, the density of probability at that point.

A function satisfying the continuity and differentiability conditions imposed here on a distribution function is the integral of its derivative:

$$F(x) = \int_{-\infty}^{x} f(\lambda) \, d\lambda,$$

the lower limit being chosen to satisfy the obvious condition

$$F(-\infty) = P(X \leq -\infty) = 0.$$

From this it follows that

$$P(a < X < b) = F(b) - F(a) = \int_{a}^{b} f(\lambda) \, d\lambda.$$

These relations are shown in Figures 2–7 and 2–8. Notice that whether one or the other endpoint is included is immaterial, since the probability assigned to these individual points is zero in this continuous case.

A particular case of the calculation of the probability of an interval is the following:

$$1 = P(\mathcal{R}) = P(-\infty < X < \infty) = F(\infty) = \int_{-\infty}^{\infty} f(x) \, dx.$$

That is, the total area under the graph of the density function (and above the x-axis) is 1.

A derivative is a "differential coefficient" corresponding to a small change in the independent variable, in the sense that the differential

$$dF(\lambda) = f(\lambda)\, d\lambda$$

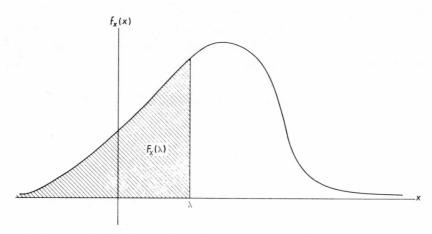

Figure 2–7.   Distribution function value as area.

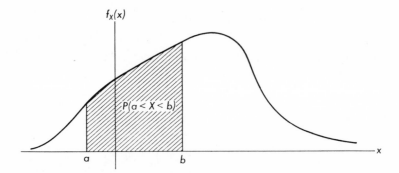

Figure 2–8.   Probability of an interval as area.

is used as an approximation of the change in the value of $F(\lambda)$ corresponding to a change in the independent variable from λ to $\lambda + d\lambda$. And this change in $F(\lambda)$ is a probability:

$$P(\lambda < X \le \lambda + d\lambda) = F(\lambda + d\lambda) - F(\lambda) \doteq f(\lambda)\, d\lambda.$$

This approximation, based on approximating $F(\lambda)$ by the tangent to its graph at λ, can be interpreted in terms of area and the density function graph as seen in Figure 2–9.

It is of interest to note the anology between certain relations in the discrete case and those in the continuous case:

Discrete	Continuous
$f(x_i) = P(X = x_i)$	$f(x)\,dx \doteq P(x < X < x + dx)$
$F(x) = \displaystyle\sum_{x_i \le x} f(x_i)$	$F(x) = \displaystyle\int_{-\infty}^{x} f(\lambda)\,d\lambda$
$P(A) = \displaystyle\sum_{x_i \text{ in } A} f(x_i)$	$P(A) = \displaystyle\int_{A} f(\lambda)\,d\lambda$
$\displaystyle\sum_{\text{all } i} f(x_i) = 1$	$\displaystyle\int_{-\infty}^{\infty} f(x)\,dx = 1$
$f(x_i) = F(x_i) - F(x_{i-1})$	$f(x) = F'(x)$

(In the last relation for the discrete case, it is assumed that the x_i's are arranged in numerical order—that x_{i-1} and x_i are adjacent values of X.)

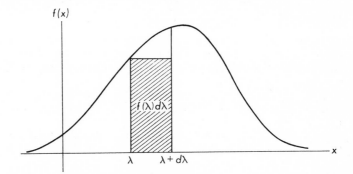

Figure 2–9.   The probability element.

EXAMPLE 2–10.   In Problem 2–10 the distribution functions of the colatitude angle $\theta(\omega)$ and the longitude angle $\phi(\omega)$ of the random orientation ω were found to be as follows:

$$F_\theta(\lambda) = \begin{cases} 0, & \text{for } \lambda < 0, \\ 1 - \cos \lambda, & \text{for } 0 \le \lambda \le \pi/2, \\ 1, & \text{for } \lambda > \pi/2. \end{cases}$$

and

$$F_\phi(\lambda) = \begin{cases} 0, & \text{for } \lambda < 0, \\ \lambda/2\pi, & \text{for } 0 \le \lambda \le 2\pi, \\ 1, & \text{for } \lambda > 2\pi. \end{cases}$$

The corresponding density functions are then the derivatives of these:

$$f_\theta(\lambda) = \frac{d}{d\lambda}(1 - \cos \lambda) = \sin \lambda, \qquad \text{for } 0 < \lambda < \pi/2,$$

$$f_\phi(\lambda) = \frac{d}{d\lambda}(\lambda/2\pi) = 1/2\pi \qquad \text{for } 0 < \lambda < 2\pi.$$

(Outside the given λ-intervals the densities are zero.) The graphs of these density functions are shown in Figure 2–10.

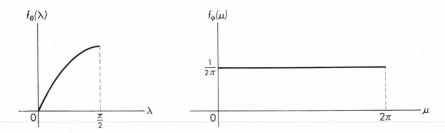

Figure 2–10. Density functions for θ and ϕ in Example 2–10.

So as not to leave the impression that random variables must be either discrete or continuous, the following example is given to illustrate a useful distribution model in which there is a discrete component and a continuous component.

EXAMPLE 2–11.   A model used in describing the life of an electron tube in a certain type of use involves the following distribution function for this life:

$$F(x) = \begin{cases} 1 - R_0 e^{-kx}, & \text{for } x \geq 0, \\ 0, & \text{for } x < 0. \end{cases}$$

This is shown in Figure 2–11. It is seen here that there is a jump in the amount $1 - R_0$ at $x = 0$, indicating a probability $1 - R_0$ that a tube taken from the shelf

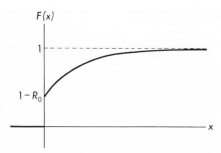

Figure 2–11.   Distribution function for tube life in Example 2–11.

is bad to begin with, or a probability R_0 (possibly less than 1) that the tube is good. The quantity

$$R(x) = P(\text{tube life exceeds } x) = 1 - F(x) = R_0 e^{-kx}$$

is called the *reliability* of the tube in a mission of x time units, and R_0 might then be termed the *initial reliability*.

Problems

2–13. Two articles among ten articles in a lot are defective. Determine the possible values and the corresponding probabilities for the random variables X, the number of defectives in a random slection of one article from the lot, and Y, the number of defective articles in a random selection of four.

2–14. Five electron tubes in a box are to be tested one at a time until the one defective tube among the five is located. Determine the possible values and the corresponding probabilities for the random variable defined to be the number of tests required. (The answer will depend on whether it is assumed that the tester knows that exactly one defective is present and can omit the fifth test, or is required to carry out the fifth test before he is considered to have "located" the defective.)

2–15. A tester is to identify three cigarettes of three different brands and is told to assign the brand name A to one, the name B to another, and the name C to the third. Suppose that he cannot really tell the difference by smoking the cigarettes and assigns the three names at random. Determine the possible values and corresponding probabilities for the random variable defined to be the number of correct identifications.

2–16. Let X denote the number of "points" assigned to a card drawn at random from a standard bridge deck of cards, when points are assigned as follows to the individual cards: Ace, 4 points; King, 3 points; Queen, 2 points; Jack, 1 point; Ten or Lower, no points. Determine the probabilities for the possible values of X.

2–17. Two dice are thrown repeatedly until a "seven" is thrown. Let X denote the number of throws necessary, and determine the probability distribution for X.

2–18. As in Example 2–7, three chips are drawn together at random from a bowl containing five chips numbered 1, 2, 3, 4, and 5. Let Y denote the smallest of the three numbers drawn and R the largest number drawn minus the smallest. Determine the distributions of probability for Y and R. Compute also $P(Y \leq 2)$ and $P(R > 2)$.

2–19. Determine the probability function $f(x_i)$ for the random variable X defined to be the sum of the numbers of points showing in the toss of two dice.

2–20. The distribution function for the value X on the scale [0, 1] at which the spinning pointer stops, when probability is assumed proportional to the angle subtended by a given event, was seen in Example 2–5 to be $F(x) = x$ for $0 < x < 1$, 0 for $x < 0$, and 1 for $x > 1$. Determine the density function of X. Determine also the density function of Y, the value at which the pointer stops when the scale from 0 to 2π is used.

2–21. A random variable X has the distribution function $F(x) = x^2$ for x on [0, 1], 0 for x on $(-\infty, 0)$, and 1 for $x \geq 1$. First observe that this distribution is of the continuous type and then determine the density function of the distribution.

2–22. A random variable X has the distribution function

$$F(x) = \frac{1}{\pi}\left(\frac{\pi}{2} + \text{Arctan } x\right),$$

where the value of Arctan x is taken to be that on the range from $-\pi/2$ to $\pi/2$. Determine the density function, the third quartile of the distribution, and the probability that $|X| < 1$.

2–23. A random variable X has the density function

$$f(x) = \begin{cases} 1 - |x|, & \text{for } |x| < 1, \\ 0, & \text{elsewhere.} \end{cases}$$

Determine and sketch the distribution function of X. Compute also $P(X > 0)$ and $P(|X| > 1/2)$. Interpret these with respect to both the graph of the density function and the graph of the distribution function.

2–24. As in Example 2–2, let ω denote the measured resistance (in ohms) in a resistor taken from a certain production line. Suppose that the random variable $Z(\omega) = (\omega - 100)/2$ has the distribution function $\Phi(z)$ given in Table I (see Appendix).

(a) Use your sketch from Problem 2–5 to plot some points on the graph of the density $\Phi'(z)$, and sketch this curve.
(b) Determine the probability that the measured resistance is within 4 ohms on either side of the nominal resistance of 100 ohms, and indicate the area representing this probability on your sketch of the density function.

2–25. Show that if $f(a - x) = f(a + x)$, so that the graph of $f(x)$ is symmetrical about the ordinate $x = a$, then the median of the distribution with density function $f(x)$ is a.

2.1.5 Specification of a Distribution

The distribution function of a random variable is of course determined by the function defining that random variable and by the probability space $(\Omega, \mathscr{F}, P^{\Omega})$ on which the function is defined. However, because the main interest usually lies in the induced distribution in the value-space $\mathscr{R}$, it is often convenient and desirable to construct a probability model by specifying the distribution in $\mathscr{R}$ directly—by specifying a distribution function. That is, the probabilities of the semi-infinite intervals $(-\infty, \lambda]$ given by a distribution function $F(\lambda)$ will determine probabilities for the Borel field $\mathscr{B}$ generated by the class of such intervals and so determine the probability space $(\mathscr{R}, \mathscr{B}, P^{\mathscr{R}})$, on which $X(x) = x$ defines a random variable with distribution function $F(x)$.

In specifying a distribution function, not just any function will serve. Some indication as to what restrictions should be imposed can be seen upon examining certain properties of distribution functions that are defined from the distribution on Ω by the relation $F(x) = P[X(\omega) \leq x]$. Notice first that since $F(x)$ is a probability, its values lie on the range $[0, 1]$. Clearly, $F(\infty) = P(\mathscr{R}) = 1$ and $F(-\infty) = P(\varnothing) = 0$. Further, since for $a < b$ the difference $F(b) - F(a)$ is a probability—the probability of the interval $(a, b]$—it follows that $F(x)$ must be a nondecreasing function:

$$F(b) - F(a) \geq 0 \qquad \text{if } b > a.$$

Another property is that $F(x)$ is continuous from the right:

$$\lim_{y \to x+} F(y) = F(x).$$

This follows from the fact that for every decreasing sequence $y_1, y_2, \ldots$ whose limit is x, the corresponding intervals $(-\infty, y_n]$ constitute a descending sequence whose intersection is $(-\infty, x]$; for then

$$\lim_{n \to \infty} P(-\infty, y_n] = P(\bigcap(-\infty, y_n)] = P(-\infty, x].$$

To be sure, a distribution function satisfies other conditions, but these, summarizing the above, are the essential ones:

(i) $F(-\infty) = 0$,
(ii) $F(\infty) = 1$,
(iii) $F(x)$ is nondecreasing,
(iv) $F(x)$ is continuous from the right at each x.

That is, it can be shown (see Cramer [4], pp. 53–54) that given a function satisfying conditions (i)–(iv) it is possible to construct a probability measure for the Borel field generated by the semi-infinite intervals $(-\infty, x]$, starting with the assignment of $F(x)$ as the probability of $(-\infty, x]$. Thus, any function $F(x)$ subject to conditions (i)–(iv) will define a distribution on $\mathscr{R}$, and the construction of a probability model can begin with a specification of such a function $F(x)$.

EXAMPLE 2–12.   The function $F(x)$ defined as follows:

$$F(x) = \begin{cases} 0, & \text{for } x < 0, \\ 1 - e^{-x}, & \text{for } x \geq 0 \end{cases}$$

is a nondecreasing function, everywhere continuous (and therefore certainly continuous from the right at each x), satisfying the conditions that $F(-\infty) = 0$ and $F(\infty) = 1$. It can therefore be used as the basis of a probability model, and defines a random variable X having the property that $P(X \leq x) = F(x)$.

The probability model for a continuous distribution can be defined by specifying a density function. When obtained as the derivative of a distribution function defined by a given distribution in $\mathscr{R}$, the density function has the properties:

(a) $f(x) \geq 0$,
(b) $\int_{-\infty}^{\infty} f(x)\, dx = 1$.

The first of these follows from the fact that the derivative of a nondecreasing function, when it exists, is nonnegative. On the other hand, any function satisfying these conditions and whose integral over the arbitrary interval $(-\infty, x]$ exists can be used to construct a distribution function $F(x)$ as follows:

$$F(x) = \int_{-\infty}^{x} f(u) \, du.$$

Because this satisfies conditions (i)–(iv) given earlier for distribution functions, it can then be used to construct the distribution in $\mathscr{R}$.

EXAMPLE 2–13. The function $(1+x^2)^{-1}$ is continuous, nonnegative, and integrable over any interval. The total area under its graph is

$$\int_{-\infty}^{\infty} \frac{dx}{1 + x^2} = \text{Arctan } \infty - \text{Arctan } (-\infty) = \pi.$$

Hence, the function

$$f(x) = \frac{1/\pi}{1 + x^2}$$

can be used as the density of a probability distribution on $(-\infty, \infty)$, the area under its graph being 1. The corresponding distribution function is

$$F(x) = \int_{-\infty}^{x} \frac{1/\pi}{1 + u^2} \, du = \frac{1}{\pi} [\text{Arctan } x + \pi/2],$$

which, of course, increases steadily from 0 at $-\infty$ to 1 at ∞.

A *discrete* distribution in $\mathscr{R}$ can be specified by a sequence of possible values $x_1, x_2, \ldots$ and an assignment of probabilities $p_i = P(\{x_i\})$ having the properties

(1) $p_i \geq 0$ for all i,

(2) $\sum_i p_i = 1.$

The function $F(x)$ defined from these p_i's as the cumulative sum:

$$F(x) = \sum_{x_i \leq x} p_i,$$

again satisfies the conditions for a distribution function. It is constant between successive values in the list of possible values, and jumps an amount p_i at x_i.

EXAMPLE 2–14. The formula

$$1/2 + 1/2^2 + 1/2^3 + \cdots = 1$$

follows from the general formula for the sum of a geometric series. Because each term in the sum is nonnegative and their sum is 1, the individual terms can be used as the basis of a probability distribution on any sequence of real numbers.

2.1.6 Functions of Random Variables

Since $(\mathscr{R}, \mathscr{B}, P^{\mathscr{R}})$ as induced by a random variable $X(\omega)$ on the probability space $(\Omega, \mathscr{F}, P^{\Omega})$ is itself a probability space, then any function $g(x)$ on $\mathscr{R}$ that is measurable with respect to $\mathscr{B}$ defines a random variable: $Y = g(X)$. This defines a composite function on Ω,

$$Y(\omega) = g(x), \quad \text{where } x = X(\omega),$$

providing a mapping from ω to $Y(\omega)$, either directly, or through the mapping of ω into $X(\omega) = x$ and then the mapping from x to $g(x)$, as discussed in Section 1.1.6. A probability distribution for Y is induced in the value space of $g(x)$, which is again the set of reals $\mathscr{R}$, either from the distribution of X in $\mathscr{R}$ by means of $g(x)$, or directly from Ω by the composite function $g(X(\omega))$. Thus, the distribution function of Y can be expressed as

$$P(Y \le y) = P^{\mathscr{R}}(g(x) \le y) = P^{\Omega}[g(X(\omega)) \le y]$$

and computed either from the distribution of X in $\mathscr{R}$ or from the initial distribution in Ω.

Of course, if the probability model is constructed directly in $\mathscr{R}$ for the random variable X by specification of a distribution function $F_X(x)$, then there is no Ω and corresponding distribution—or Ω can be thought of as $\mathscr{R}$. At any rate, $g(x)$ simply defines a random variable $Y = g(X)$ on $\mathscr{R}$.

EXAMPLE 2–15. A discrete random variable X has values and probabilities as given in the following table:

x_i	-1	0	1
p_i	.3	.4	.3

The function $g(x) = x^2 - 1$ defines a random variable $Y = X^2 - 1$ whose values are 0 and -1. The value 0 comes from $X = 1$ and also from $X = -1$, and the value -1 from $X = 0$. The probability table for the distribution of Y is then:

y_j	-1	0
$P(Y = y_j)$	.4	.6

EXAMPLE 2–16. Let X have the probability distribution defined by

$$F_X(x) = \begin{cases} 1 - e^{-x}, & \text{for } x \ge 0, \\ 0, & \text{for } x < 0, \end{cases}$$

as in Example 2–12. The function $g(x) = \sqrt{x}$ defines a random variable $Y = \sqrt{X}$, since X is nonnegative with probability 1. (This $g(x)$ does not map negative x's into $\mathscr{R}$, but would only be applied to nonnegative x's. It could be defined arbitrarily for negative x's; and because $P(X < 0) = 0$, this would in no way affect the distribution of Y.) The distribution function of Y is computed as follows:

$$F_Y(y) = P(Y \le y) = P(\sqrt{X} \le y) = P(X \le y^2) = F_X(y^2) = 1 - \exp(-y^2),$$

a computation that is valid for any nonnegative y. If y is a negative number, then $P(Y \le y) = 0$. The density function of Y can be obtained by differentiation:

$$f_Y(y) = \begin{cases} 2y \exp(-y^2), & \text{for } y > 0, \\ 0, & \text{for } y < 0. \end{cases}$$

EXAMPLE 2–17.   Consider the *linear* function $Y = aX + b$, where X is any random variable, and a and b are any constants with $a \ne 0$. Assume first that $a > 0$. Then

$$F_Y(y) = P(aX + b \le y) = P(X \le (y - b)/a) = F_X\left(\frac{y - b}{a}\right).$$

If X is a continuous random variable, that is, if its distribution function is continuous at every point and differentiable except perhaps for at most a finite number of points in any finite interval, then the function $F_Y(y)$ has these properties also, and Y is continuous. Its density function is obtained by differentiation:

$$f_Y(y) = \frac{d}{dy} F_Y(y) = \frac{d}{dy} F_X\left(\frac{y - b}{a}\right) = \frac{1}{a} f_X\left(\frac{y - b}{a}\right).$$

If a had been assumed negative, the division by a in the early stages would have reversed the direction of the inequality; the result would be the same as for $a > 0$, except that the multiplier would be $-1/a$ in place of $1/a$. The two cases can be summarized in one formula:

$$f_{aX+b}(y) = \frac{1}{|a|} f_X\left(\frac{y - b}{a}\right).$$

The technique employed in this last example can be used more generally. The simplest case is that in which, as in the example, the function $g(x)$ is strictly monotonic, either increasing or decreasing. For definiteness, suppose that $g(x) < g(x')$ whenever $x < x'$, which is what is meant by saying that $g(x)$ is (strictly) monotonically increasing. Suppose further that $g(x)$ is differentiable (and hence continuous). Then there is a unique inverse $x = g^{-1}(y)$ for each y, having the property that $g(g^{-1}(y)) = y$ and $g^{-1}(g(x)) = x$, and

$$P(Y \le y) = P(g(X) \le y) = P(X \le g^{-1}(y)) = F_X(g^{-1}(y)).$$

If X is a continuous random variable, then this distribution function of Y has the properties that make Y a continuous random variable, with density

$$f_Y(y) = \frac{d}{dy} P(Y \le y) = \frac{d}{dy} F_X(g^{-1}(y)) = f_X(g^{-1}(y)) \frac{d}{dy} g^{-1}(y).$$

Of course, the derivative $(d/dy)g^{-1}(y)$ or dx/dy can be computed as the reciprocal of dy/dx, so that

$$f_{g(X)}(y) = f_X(g^{-1}(y))/g'(x).$$

The derivative $g'(x)$ may be zero even if $g(x)$ is strictly monotonic, but at such a point the density of Y is infinite unless $f_X(x)$ is zero there—in which case the above formula becomes an indeterminate form at that point (see Problem 2–34).

The above relation can be interpreted—or derived—in terms of "probability elements." If $y = g(x)$ and the differential dy is calculated corresponding to a differential dx:

$$dy = g'(x)\,dx \qquad \text{or} \qquad dx = \frac{1}{g'(x)}\,dy,$$

then all of the probability assigned to dx in the value space of X is assigned by the function $g(x)$ to the differential element dy in the value space of Y. (Actually, it is assigned to the increment Δy for which dy is a linear approximation, as in Figure 2–12.) It follows that

$$P^{\mathscr{Y}}(dy) = P^{\mathscr{X}}(dx) = f_X(x)\,dx = f_X(x)\,\frac{1}{g'(x)}\,dy,$$

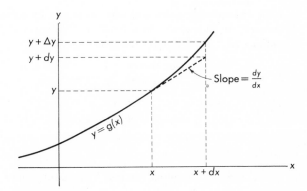

Figure 2–12.

and the coefficient of the differential dy is then the density of Y, which agrees with the earlier result. Notice that where $g(x)$ is steep, a given amount of probability on the x-axis is spread over a wider region on the y-axis, and so the density there is smaller—the distribution is "thinner"—by a factor $1/g'(x)$. And where $g(x)$ is only slowly increasing, a given region on the x-axis corresponds to a smaller region on the y-axis; transferring the probability from the x-region to the corresponding y-region yields a "thicker" distribution—the density on the y-axis is increased by the factor $1/g'(x)$, which is now large (since $g'(x)$ is small).

It should be noticed that the monotonic character of $g(x)$ is used in assuming that the only probability assigned to dy comes from dx; but if the inverse of $g(x)$ is not single valued, there would be more than one probability element on the x-axis corresponding to a given dy. This kind of situation can be handled by taking into account these various possible inverses, as in the following example.

EXAMPLE 2–18. Suppose that X has the density $[\pi(1 + x^2)]^{-1}$, and let $Y = X^2$. The function x^2 has two inverses, and so to each element dy on the positive y-axis there correspond two elements dx, one on the positive and one on the negative x-axis, both of which contribute to the density on the y-axis. If y is negative, $P(Y \le y) = 0$, but for $y \ge 0$,

$$F_Y(y) = P(Y \le y) = P(X^2 \le y) = P(-\sqrt{y} \le X \le \sqrt{y})$$
$$= F_X(\sqrt{y}) - F_X(-\sqrt{y}).$$

Differentiation yields

$$f_Y(y) = \frac{d}{dy} P(Y \le y) = f_X(\sqrt{y}) \frac{1}{2\sqrt{y}} - f_X(\sqrt{y}) \frac{-1}{2\sqrt{y}} = \frac{1/\sqrt{y}}{\pi(1 + y)}, \quad \text{for } y \ge 0.$$

Problems

2–26. In each case determine whether or not, for a suitable choice of constant k, the given function can serve as a density function. For those that can determine the value that k must have for the given function to be a density:

(a) $f(x) = \begin{cases} kx, & \text{for } 0 < x < 2 \\ 0, & \text{for } x < 0 \quad \text{or} \quad x > 2. \end{cases}$

(b) $f(x) = \begin{cases} kx(1 - x), & \text{for } 0 < x < 1, \\ 0, & \text{for } x < 0 \quad \text{or} \quad x > 1. \end{cases}$

(c) ke^{-x}.
(d) $ke^{-|x|}$.

2–27. A discrete random variable X can assume only the values 0, 1, 2, 3, $\ldots$

(a) Can equal probabilities be assigned these values?
(b) Determine k such that $P(X = j) = kp^j$ is a proper assignment of probability, where $0 < p < 1$.

2–28. A random variable assumes only values in the list 0, 1, $\ldots$, n. Show that $f(j) = \binom{n}{j} p^j(1 - p)^{n-j}$, where $0 < p < 1$ is a proper assignment of probability.

2–29. Show that the function $F(x) = (1/\pi)(\text{Arctan } x + \pi/2)$ has the characteristics of a distribution function and so can serve to define a probability model. (Here "Arctan" denotes the principal value, a number on the range from $-\pi/2$ to $\pi/2$.) Determine also the density of this distribution.

2–30. Given $A > 0$, show that the function

$$F(x) = \begin{cases} 0, 1, & \text{for } x < -A, \quad x > A, \text{ resp.}, \\ \dfrac{1}{2A}(x + A), & \text{for } |x| < A \end{cases}$$

can serve as the distribution function of a random variable X. Determine also the density of X.

2–31. Let X have a zero density outside the interval $[-1, 1]$ and a constant density inside that interval. Determine the density function of the random variable $Z = |X|$.

2–32. Determine the density function of $Y = X^2$, where X has the distribution defined as in Problem 2–31.

2–33. Determine the distribution of $Y = X^2 - 7X + 10$, where X denotes the number of points thrown in a toss of a die whose faces are equally likely.

2–34. Let X have the distribution function

$$F(x) = \begin{cases} 0, & x < 0, \\ x^2, & 0 \le x \le 1, \\ 1, & x > 1. \end{cases}$$

Determine the distribution function of $Y = X^2$. (Does this function have a single-valued inverse—and does it make any difference?)

2–35. Let X have a strictly monotonic, continuous distribution function $F(x)$ and define the random variable Y by the relation $Y = F(X)$. (That is, for "g" use the particular function which is the distribution function of X.) Determine the distribution of Y.

2–36. Let X have a strictly monotonic, continuous distribution function $F(x)$ and let $G(x)$ be strictly monotonic, continuous distribution function. Show that $G^{-1}(F(X))$ has (Gx) as its distribution function. (G^{-1} denotes the inverse of G.)

2.1.7 Bivariate Distributions

A two-dimensional random vector is a measurable function $(X(\omega), Y(\omega))$ defined on a probability space $(\Omega, \mathscr{F}, P)$. Here the term "measurable" means that all events of the form

$$\{\omega \mid X(\omega) \le \alpha, \text{ and } Y(\omega) \le \beta\}$$

are contained in the Borel field $\mathscr{F}$, but again it will be assumed that vector functions to be encountered are measurable without explicit verification.

The random vector $(X(\omega), Y(\omega))$ induces a probability distribution in the plane; given any plane set S in the Borel field $\mathscr{B}$ generated by the semi-infinite rectangles of the above type, the probability assigned to S is simply the probability of its pre-image, which is in $\mathscr{F}$:

$$P(S) = P^{\Omega}\{(X(\omega), Y(\omega)) \text{ lies in } S\}.$$

Thus, $(\mathscr{R}_2, \mathscr{B}, P)$ is a probability space. And it is the distribution in this space that is of interest, as in the case of a single random variable, and the reference to Ω is often dropped: (X, Y). This distribution in $\mathcal{R}_2$ is characterized by the *distribution function* (also called the *joint* distribution function):

$$F(x, y) = P(X \leq x \text{ and } Y \leq y)$$
$$= P(\{\omega \mid X(\omega) \leq x \text{ and } Y(\omega) \leq y\}).$$

The probability of any event E in the Borel field $\mathcal{B}$ generated by the quadrants whose probabilities define $F(x, y)$ can be calculated in principle from $F(x, y)$.

EXAMPLE 2–19.   Consider again the probability space for random orientations (as in Example 2–10, Problem 2–10, and earlier examples), in which the probability of a region on the surface of the unit hemisphere is proportional to the area of that region. The spherical coordinate functions $\theta(\omega)$ and $\phi(\omega)$, representing colatitude and longitude, respectively, of the point ω, define together a random vector—mapping points on the hemisphere into $\mathcal{R}_2$, the Cartesian plane with coordinates (θ, ϕ). The distribution function of the distribution in this plane is

$$F_{\theta, \phi}(u, v) = P(\theta \leq u, \phi \leq v).$$

This is the relative area of the portion of the hemisphere bounded by the curves $\phi = 0$, $\phi = v$, and $\theta = u$, as shown in Figure 2–13. Since the area of the entire

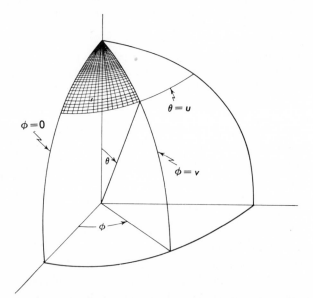

Figure 2–13.   Area defining the joint distribution function for (θ, ϕ).

polar cap bounded by $\theta = u$ is $2\pi(1 - \cos u)$, the portion of it subtended by the angle from $\phi = 0$ to $\phi = v$ has the area $v(1 - \cos u)$. Hence,

$$F_{\theta, \phi}(u, v) = \frac{v}{2\pi}(1 - \cos u), \qquad \text{for } 0 \leq v < 2\pi, \ 0 \leq u \leq \pi/2.$$

Although this formula gives the distribution function in the portion of the value space of most interest, similar (but simpler) computations will yield the correct formulas for other portions of the plane.

Again two useful types of distribution stand out: the *discrete* type, with probability concentrated in lumps at isolated points, and the *continuous* type, in which probability is spread over a region, no single points or curves having any positive probability. Again, however, these two types do not include all useful models. For instance, a bivariate distribution might be continuous in one variable and discrete in the other, or be otherwise concentrated along lines or curves in the plane. Also a distribution can include discrete lumps at isolated points, concentrations along curves, and smears over regions of the plane.

In the case of a discrete distribution it is again convenient to work in terms of a *probability function*:

$$f(x, y) = P(X = x \text{ and } Y = y).$$

This may be specified directly, or it may be defined indirectly by a distribution of probability on an underlying space Ω. The possible outcomes (x, y) are sometimes presented in a rectangular tabulation, all possible values of X along the top margin, say, and all possible values of Y along the left margin; the probability for each pair (x, y) is entered under the x and across from the y. The probabilities must, of course, total 1.

EXAMPLE 2–20.   Three balls numbered from 1 to 3 are placed in a container. Two balls are drawn, one at a time, at random, without replacement. Let

$$X = \text{number of the first ball drawn,}$$

$$Y = \text{number of the second ball drawn.}$$

The outcomes are pairs of numbers (x, y). The possible values of X as well as the possible values of Y are 1, 2, and 3. The probabilities for the various possible combinations are easily computed to be those given in the following table:

Y \ X	1	2	3
1	0	$\frac{1}{6}$	$\frac{1}{6}$
2	$\frac{1}{6}$	0	$\frac{1}{6}$
3	$\frac{1}{6}$	$\frac{1}{6}$	0

The probability of any event concerning (X, Y) can be computed from this table. For instance,

P(number drawn first is smaller than number drawn second)

$$= P(X < Y) = P[(1, 2), (1, 3), \text{ or } (2, 3)] = \tfrac{1}{6} + \tfrac{1}{6} + \tfrac{1}{6} = \tfrac{1}{2}.$$

A distribution having a distribution function $F(x, y)$ that is continuous is called a *continuous* distribution if in addition the second mixed partial derivative of $F(x, y)$ exists, except possibly along a finite set of curves. This second derivative is called the *density function* of the distribution of (X, Y):

$$f_{X,Y}(x, y) = \frac{\partial^2}{\partial x \, \partial y} F_{X,Y}(x, y),$$

having the property that the distribution function is recoverable from it as follows:

$$F_{X,Y}(x, y) = \int_{-\infty}^{x} \int_{-\infty}^{y} f_{X,Y}(u, v) \, du \, dv.$$

This calculation of the probability of the event $\{X \leq x$ and $Y \leq y\}$ as the double integral of the density over the portion of the plane in which these inequalities hold is a special case of the more general computation:

$$P(S) = \int \int_{S} f_{X,Y}(u, v) \, du \, dv = P[(X, Y) \text{ lies in } S].$$

(If this event S is a curve or a discrete set of points, the integral, and hence the probability assigned to S, is zero.)

The above relation follows from the fact that the second difference of F:

$$\Delta^2 F = F(x + h, y + k) - F(x + h, y) - F(x, y + k) + F(x, y)$$

represents the probability in a rectangle (Figure 2–14) of sides h and k

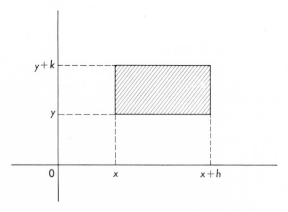

Figure 2–14. Region whose probability is $\Delta^2 F$.

bounded by vertical lines at x and $x + h$ and by horizontal lines through y and $y + k$, and that

$$\Delta^2 F \doteq f(x, y) \, hk.$$

Subdividing a region S into rectangular pieces by coordinate nets in a familiar fashion, one has

$$P(S) = \sum \Delta^2 F \doteq \sum f(x, y)hk,$$

a quantity that tends to the double integral over S as the net dimensions h and k tend to zero (which also improves the indicated approximation).

EXAMPLE 2–21.   The distribution function $F_{\theta,\phi}(u, v)$ of the coordinate variables on the probability space for random orientations (Example 2–19 above) was found to be

$$F_{\theta,\phi}(u, v) = \begin{cases} 0, & \text{for } v \le 0 \quad \text{or} \quad u \le 0, \\[2mm] \dfrac{v}{2\pi}(1 - \cos u), & \text{for } 0 < v < 2\pi, \quad 0 < u < \pi/2, \\[2mm] \dfrac{v}{2\pi}, & \text{for } 0 < v < 2\pi, \quad u \ge \pi/2, \\[2mm] 1 - \cos u, & \text{for } 0 < u < \pi/2, \quad v \ge 2\pi, \\[1mm] 1, & \text{for } u \ge \pi/2, \quad v \ge 2\pi. \end{cases}$$

This is differentiable except at some points along the curves $v = 0$, $u = \pi/2$, and $v = 2\pi$. The derivative is then the density:

$$f_{\theta,\phi}(u, v) = \begin{cases} \dfrac{1}{2\pi} \sin u, & \text{for } 0 < v < 2\pi, \quad 0 < u < \pi/2, \\[2mm] 0, & \text{elsewhere.} \end{cases}$$

From this one can calculate such things as

$$P(\theta > \pi/4, \ \pi/2 < \phi < \pi) = \frac{1}{2\pi} \int_{\pi/2}^{\pi} \int_{\pi/4}^{\pi/2} (\sin u) \, du \, dv$$

$$= \frac{1}{4}\left(\cos \frac{\pi}{4} - \cos \frac{\pi}{2}\right) = \frac{1}{4\sqrt{2}}.$$

(This particular probability could also be computed as

$$F(\pi/2, \pi) - F(\pi/2, \pi/2) - F(\pi/4, \pi) + F(\pi/4, \pi/2),$$

since the event happens to be a rectangle with sides parallel to the axes in the $\theta\phi$-plane.)

A bivariate distribution function $F(x, y)$ is easily seen to have the following properties (see Problem 2–45):

(i) $F(x, \infty)$ and $F(\infty, y)$ are distribution functions in $\mathcal{R}_1$ as functions of x and y, respectively;

(ii) $F(-\infty, y) = F(x, -\infty) = 0$;

(iii) $\Delta^2 F \ge 0$,

where $\Delta^2 F$ refers to the second difference defined earlier. The significance of these properties is that any function satisfying them can be used as a bivariate distribution function, if one chooses to construct the probability space $(\mathscr{R}_2, \mathscr{B}, P)$ directly. This is done by specifying F and by defining the probability of an event S in $\mathscr{R}_2$ as the integral over S of the corresponding density in the continuous case, or as a summation of probabilities of outcomes in S in the discrete case.

A bivariate density function $f(x, y)$ satisfies the conditions

(a) $f(x, y) \geq 0$,

(b) $\displaystyle\iint\limits_{\mathscr{R}_2} f(x, y)\, dx\, dy = 1$.

A function (assumed integrable) that satisfies these conditions can be used to define a bivariate distribution by defining

$$F(x, y) = \int_{-\infty}^{y} \int_{-\infty}^{x} f(u, v)\, du\, dv.$$

In particular, a *uniform* bivariate distribution over a region R in $\mathscr{R}_2$ is defined by $f(x, y) = (\text{area of } R)^{-1}$, since the double integral of this function is 1. In such a case the *probability* of a subregion is just proportional to the area of the subregion.

A function $g(x, y)$ defines a random variable as a function of the random vector (X, Y):

$$Z(\omega) = g(X(\omega), Y(\omega)).$$

This can be thought of either as the function $Z(\omega)$ on Ω, or if probability is assigned initially in the value space of (X, Y), as a function or random variable on the probability space $(\mathscr{R}_2, \mathscr{B}, P)$. In either case, there is an induced distribution in the space of values of Z, which can be taken to be the set of real numbers $\mathscr{R}$. And this distribution has a distribution function defined in the usual way as $F_Z(z) = P(Z \leq z)$.

EXAMPLE 2–22.   Let (X, Y) have the joint density function

$$f_{X,Y}(x, y) = \frac{1}{2\pi} \exp\left[-\tfrac{1}{2}(x^2 + y^2)\right].$$

(It will be verified below that the constant multiplier is chosen so that the total volume under the surface representing this function is 1.) Consider the random variable Z which is the distance from $(0, 0)$ out to the point (X, Y); that is, $Z^2 = X^2 + Y^2$. The distribution function of Z is computed as follows, for $z > 0$:

$$P(Z \leq z) = P(Z^2 \leq z^2) = P(X^2 + Y^2 \leq z^2)$$

$$= \iint\limits_{x^2 + y^2 < z^2} \left\{ \frac{1}{2\pi} \exp\left[-\tfrac{1}{2}(x^2 + y^2)\right] \right\} dx\, dy$$

$$= \int_{0}^{2\pi} \int_{0}^{z} \frac{1}{2\pi} \exp\left[-\tfrac{1}{2}r^2\right] r\, dr\, d\theta = 1 - \exp\left[-\tfrac{1}{2}z^2\right].$$

(Polar coordinates, $x = r \cos \theta$ and $y = r \sin \theta$, were used in evaluating the double integral.) The density function of Z is $z \exp\left(-\frac{1}{2}z^2\right)$ for $z > 0$. Observe that since $P(Z < \infty) = P(X \leq \infty,\ Y \leq \infty) = 1$, the choice of constant multiplier in the given density of (X, Y) has been justified.

The functions $F(x, \infty)$ and $F(\infty, y)$, claimed in Property (i) above to be univariate distribute functions, define distributions in $\mathscr{R}_1$ which are in fact the distributions of X and Y considered separately as single random variables:

$$F(x, \infty) = P(X \leq x \text{ and } Y \leq \infty) = P(X \leq x),$$
$$F(\infty, y) = P(X \leq \infty \text{ and } Y \leq y) = P(Y \leq y).$$

These distributions are called the *marginal distributions* of X and Y, the adjective "marginal" referring only to their origin and not altering the fact that they are indeed probability distributions in $\mathscr{R}_1$.

In the discrete case, with $p_{ij} = P(X = x_i,\ Y = y_j)$, the probability that $X = x_i$ is obtained by summing these joint probabilities over all pairs (x_i, y_j) in which the first element is x_i, that is, over all y_j's for fixed x_i:

$$P(X = x_i) = \sum_j P(X = x_i,\ Y = y_j) = \sum_j p_{ij}.$$

Similarly,

$$P(Y = y_j) = \sum_i p_{ij}.$$

These probabilities are the row and column sums in the rectangular tabulation of the values of p_{ij} described earlier. The writing of these sums in the margins of such an array is the source of the term "marginal" distribution.

EXAMPLE 2–23. As in Example 2–20, let (X, Y) denote the numbers on the first and second balls drawn from a container in which are three balls numbered 1, 2, 3. The drawing is random, without replacement. The table of probabilities given in that example is reproduced below with the marginal totals also shown:

x_i $\diagdown$ y_j	1	2	3	$f_Y(y_j)$
1	0	$\frac{1}{6}$	$\frac{1}{6}$	$\frac{1}{3}$
2	$\frac{1}{6}$	0	$\frac{1}{6}$	$\frac{1}{3}$
3	$\frac{1}{6}$	$\frac{1}{6}$	0	$\frac{1}{3}$
$f_X(x_i)$	$\frac{1}{3}$	$\frac{1}{3}$	$\frac{1}{3}$	1

(The marginal distributions here are identical, representing the fact that each ball drawn can be 1, 2, or 3, and in each case these results are equally likely. Observe that the probabilities for the second ball drawn are *un*conditional—nothing is assumed known about the result of the first selection.)

In the continuous case, the marginal density function (that is, the density of the marginal distribution) is obtained by differentiating the marginal distribution function,

$$F_X(x) = F_{X,Y}(x, \infty) = \int_{-\infty}^{x} \int_{-\infty}^{\infty} f(u, y) \, dy \, du,$$

to obtain

$$f_X(x) = F_X'(x) = \int_{-\infty}^{\infty} f_{X,Y}(x, y) \, dy.$$

That is, to obtain a marginal density one "integrates out" the unwanted variable from the joint density. Interpreted geometrically, the marginal density of X at $x = x_0$ is the area of the cross-section at $x = x_0$ of the solid region under the surface that represents the joint density $f_{X,Y}(x, y)$.

EXAMPLE 2–24.   Suppose that (X, Y) has a distribution which is uniform over a unit circle centered at $(0, 0)$; that is, the density of the distribution is constant over that circle. The constant must be the reciprocal of the area of the circle in order for the volume of the region under the density surface to be 1:

$$f_{X,Y}(x, y) = \begin{cases} 1/\pi, & \text{for } x^2 + y^2 \leq 1 \\ 0, & \text{elsewhere.} \end{cases}$$

The marginal density of Y at $y = y_0$ can be expressed as an integral:

$$f_Y(y_0) = \int_{-\infty}^{\infty} f_{X,\cdot}(x, y_0) \, dx = \int_{-a}^{a} \frac{1}{\pi} \, dx$$

or computed as the area of the cross section—a rectangle of height $1/\pi$ and base a,

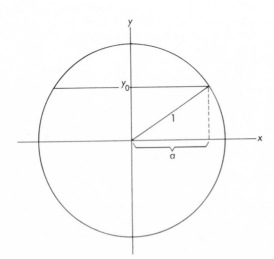

Figure 2–15. Figure for Example 2–24.

where a is determined (see Figure 2–15) by $a^2 + y_0^2 = 1^2$. Hence, the desired density is

$$f_Y(y_0) = \frac{2}{\pi}(1 - y_0^2)^{1/2}, \qquad \text{for } -1 < y_0 < 1.$$

It is zero outside the interval $[-1, 1]$, and one can easily check to see that the integral of this density function is, as it should be, 1.

Problems

2–37. A random point (X, Y) is distributed uniformly (that is, with constant density function) on the square whose vertices are $(1, 1)$, $(-1, 1)$, $(1, -1)$, and $(-1, -1)$. Determine the probabilities of these events:

(a) $X^2 + Y^2 < 1$
(b) $2X - Y > 0$
(c) $|X + Y| < 2$
(d) $|X - Y| < \frac{1}{2}$.

2–38. Show that the following is not a distribution function:

$$F(x, y) = \begin{cases} 1 - e^{-x-y}, & \text{if } x > 0 \text{ and } y > 0, \\ 0, & \text{otherwise.} \end{cases}$$

2–39. Show that

$$F(x, y) = \begin{cases} (1 - e^{-x})(1 - e^{-y}), & \text{if } x > 0 \text{ and } y > 0, \\ 0, & \text{otherwise,} \end{cases}$$

does have the properties of a distribution function, and compute

(a) the corresponding density function,
(b) $P(X < 1)$,
(c) $P(X + Y \leq 2)$,
(d) $P(X > Y)$.

2–40. Let X be the number of 5's and Y the number of 6's that turn up in a toss of two standard dice. Construct the table of bivariate probabilities p_{ij} for the distribution of (X, Y); from this table compute the following:

(a) $P(X + Y \geq 1)$,
(b) The probability functions $P(X = x_i)$ and $P(Y = y_j)$.

2–41. Let (X, Y) have the distribution defined by the following table of probabilities:

Y \ X	1	2	3
2	1/12	1/6	1/12
3	1/6	0	1/6
4	0	1/3	0

Determine the following:

(a) The marginal probability distributions.
(b) $P(X = Y)$.
(c) $P(X = 2 \text{ or } Y = 4)$.
(d) $P(X + Y \leq 4)$.

2–42. Let (X, Y) have a uniform density over the circle $x^2 + y^2 \leq 4$. Determine the following:

(a) $P(Y > kX)$.
(b) $f_X(x)$.
(c) $P(X^2 + Y^2 > 1)$.
(d) The distribution function of $X^2 + Y^2$.
(e) The distribution function of $(X^2 + Y^2)^{1/2}$.

2–43. Let (X, Y) have the distribution defined in Problem 2–39.

(a) Determine the marginal densities of X and Y.
(b) Determine the distribution function of $Z = X + Y$.

2–44. Let (X, Y) have the distribution defined in Problem 2–37.

(a) Determine the marginal distributions of X and Y.
(b) Determine the distribution function of the random variable $W = \max (X, Y)$, the larger of X and Y. [*Hint:* $W \leq w$ if and only if both X and Y are no larger than w.]

2–45. Show that a joint distribution function $F(x, y)$ has the properties indicated as (i)–(iii) on page 77.

2.1.8 *Conditional Distributions*

The information that a given event E of positive probability has occurred alters an initial probability structure—the appropriate probabilities are now *conditional* probabilities. In particular, the probability structure in the value space of a random variable is altered, and the new distribution is called a *conditional distribution*, characterized by a conditional distribution function:

$$F(x \mid E) = P(X \leq x \mid E) = \frac{P(X \leq x \text{ and } E)}{P(E)}, \quad \text{if} \quad P(E) \neq 0.$$

This has the properties of a distribution function and so defines a distribution in the space of values of X. If this distribution is discrete, it can also be characterized by a conditional probability function:

$$f(x \mid E) = P(X = x \mid E) = \frac{P(X = x \text{ and } E)}{P(E)}.$$

If the distribution is continuous, it can be defined by a density function, the derivative of the above conditional distribution function:

$$f(x \mid E) = \frac{d}{dx} P(X \leq x \mid E).$$

EXAMPLE 2–25.   Let Ω consist of the 52 cards in a standard deck, one of which is drawn at random. Let $X(\omega)$ denote the number of points assigned to the card ω as follows:

$$\text{Ace—4,   King—3,   Queen—2,   Jack—1,   other—0.}$$

Let E denote the event that the card drawn is a *Heart or a face card*. Of the 22 equally likely cards in E, one is an Ace, four are Kings, four are Queens, four are Jacks, and nine are other cards. Hence,

$$P(X = 4 \mid E) = 1/22$$
$$P(X = 3 \mid E) = 4/22$$
$$P(X = 2 \mid E) = 4/22$$
$$P(X = 1 \mid E) = 4/22$$
$$P(X = 0 \mid E) = 9/22.$$

These total 1, and define a distribution of probability on the values 0, 1, 2, 3, 4 somewhat different than the unconditional probabilities (which are 9/13, 1/13, 1/13, 1/13, 1/13, respectively).

EXAMPLE 2–26.   Let Ω denote the unit square bounded by (0, 0), (1, 1), (0, 1), and (1, 0) in a given Cartesian coordinate system and assume that the probability of an event in this sample space is proportional to its area. Let $X(\omega)$ be defined to be the x-coordinate of the point ω, and E the event that the x-coordinate exceeds the y-coordinate. Then

$$P(X \le \lambda \mid E) = \frac{P(\{(x, y) \mid x \le \lambda \text{ and } x > y\})}{P(\{(x, y) \mid x > y\})}$$

$$= \frac{\lambda^2/2}{1/2} = \lambda^2, \qquad \text{for } 0 \le \lambda \le 1.$$

The pertinent areas may be determined geometrically from Figure 2–16.

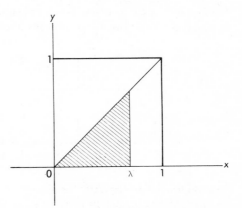

Figure 2–16. Areas for computing the conditional c.d.f. in Example 2–26.

The most commonly used conditional distributions have to do with one of the two variables comprising a random vector, the condition then being a condition on the value of the other variable. That is, given a random vector $[X(\omega),\ Y(\omega)]$ one is interested in the conditional distribution of X given that Y takes on a value in some set. Moreover, that set is usually just a single value. Thus, if $(X,\ Y)$ has a discrete distribution in the xy-plane, with values (x_i, y_j) for $i = 1, \ldots, m$ and $j = 1, \ldots, n$, the conditional probabilities for X given $Y = y_j$ are denoted and computed as follows:

$$f(x_i \mid y_j) = P(X = x_i \mid Y = y_j) = \frac{P(X = x_i \text{ and } Y = y_j)}{P(Y = y_j)}.$$

This formula, of course, assumes that $P(Y = y_j) \neq 0$.

(The notation here is not the best, since $f(x_i \mid y_j)$ is really a different function than $f(y_j \mid x_i)$ which would be used for the conditional probability that $Y = y_j$ given that $X = x_i$. To exhibit this difference, some such notation as this might be better:

$$f_{X \mid Y = y_j}(x_i) = P(X = x_i \mid Y = y_j).$$

Because this is cumbersome, the notation $f(y_j \mid x_i)$ will usually be used—when it is clear from the context what is meant.)

The conditional probability $f(x_i \mid y_j)$ is a probability function (for a given, fixed y_j) being nonnegative and summing to 1 on i:

$$\sum_i f(x_i \mid y_j) = \frac{1}{P(Y = y_j)} \sum_i P(X = x_i \text{ and } Y = y_j) = 1.$$

It is *proportional* to the joint probability function, the constant of proportionality being what is needed to make the above sum 1.

EXAMPLE 2–27. Let $(X,\ Y)$ have the distribution defined by the table of probabilites $p_{ij} = P(X = x_i \text{ and } Y = y_j)$ as shown below. (This is the distribution of Example 2–23, and the marginal probabilities obtained there are also shown.)

x_i $\diagdown$ y_j	1	2	3	
1	0	$\frac{1}{6}$	$\frac{1}{6}$	$\frac{1}{3}$
2	$\frac{1}{6}$	0	$\frac{1}{6}$	$\frac{1}{3}$
3	$\frac{1}{6}$	$\frac{1}{6}$	0	$\frac{1}{3}$
	$\frac{1}{3}$	$\frac{1}{3}$	$\frac{1}{3}$	

The conditional probabilities for X given $Y = 1$ are proportional to those in the first row, being obtained by dividing those entries by their sum:

x_i	1	2	3
$f(x_i \mid 1)$	0	$\frac{1}{2}$	$\frac{1}{2}$

Similarly, the conditional probabilities for Y given $X = 2$ are proportional to those in the second column:

y_j	$f(y_j \mid 2)$
1	$\frac{1}{2}$
2	0
3	$\frac{1}{2}$

Denoting the joint probability function by $f(x_i, y_j)$, one has

$$f(x_i, y_j) = f(x_i \mid y_j)f_Y(y_j).$$

If A is a set of X-values and B a set of Y-values, the probability of the intersection is

$$P(X \text{ in } A \text{ and } Y \text{ in } B) = \sum_B \sum_A f(x_i, y_j)$$

$$= \sum_B \left\{ \sum_A f(x_i \mid y_j) \right\} f_Y(y_j)$$

$$= \sum_B P(X \text{ in } A \mid Y \text{ in } y_j)f_Y(y_j).$$

(The sum written as extending over B really extends over all subscripts j such that y_j is in B, with a similar meaning for the sum over A.) In particular, taking B to be the set of all Y-values, one finds

$$P(X \text{ in } A) = \sum_j P(X \text{ in } A \mid Y = y_j)f_Y(y_j).$$

That is, the probability of an event A in the space of X-values can be computed as a weighted average of conditional probabilities, given particular Y-values, where the weights are the corresponding Y-probabilities.

If Y is continuous, the probability that Y takes on a particular value is zero; an attempt at defining conditional probability as it was defined above in the discrete case yields

$$P(X \leq x \mid Y = y) = \frac{P(X \leq x \text{ and } Y = y)}{P(Y = y)} = \frac{0}{0},$$

which leads nowhere. And yet, since one *can* observe a single value $Y = y$, it is certainly desirable to have a model with conditional probabilities of events given $Y = y$, and to be able to derive these from the model for the random vector (X, Y).

In the case of a continuous bivariate distribution for (X, Y) with density function $f(x, y)$, the conditional density of X given $Y = y$ is denoted and defined as follows:

$$f(x \mid y) = \frac{f(x, y)}{f_Y(y)}.$$

From this one defines the conditional probability of a set A of possible X-values as

$$P(A \mid Y = y) = \int_A f(x \mid y) \, dx.$$

In particular, if A is the interval $(-\infty, x)$, this integration will yield the conditional distribution function:

$$F(x \mid Y = y) = P(X \le x \mid Y = y) = \int_{-\infty}^{x} \frac{f(u, y)}{f_Y(y)} \, du.$$

The above definition of conditional density has the following property:

$$\int_{-\infty}^{\infty} P(A \mid Y = y) f_Y(y) \, dy = \int_{-\infty}^{\infty} \left\{ \int_A f(x \mid y) \, dx \right\} f_Y(y) \, dy$$

$$= \int_{-\infty}^{\infty} \int_A f(x, y) \, dx \, dy = P(X \text{ in } A),$$

and similarly:

$$\int_B P(A \mid Y = y) f_Y(y) \, dy = P(X \text{ in } A \text{ and } Y \text{ in } B).$$

This is analogous to a property enjoyed by the corresponding conditional probability (with sums instead of integrals) in the discrete case, and is a result that would certainly be required of a reasonable definition of conditional density. Because it can be shown[3] that the definition of conditional density given here is essentially the only one that would yield the above properties, the definition is justified. (The qualification "essentially" is inserted just to recognize that a density can be altered at a limited number of points without changing the values of integrals in which it enters.)

The definition of conditional density as the joint density divided by the marginal density of the conditioning variable at the given value is intuitively appealing. The geometrical representation of the joint density function is a surface, and the function $f(x \mid y)$—for a given y—varies with x according to the variation along the surface $z = f(x, y)$ in the cross section at the given Y-value. The division by $f_Y(y)$ has the effect of adjusting the heights of this cross section curve by a constant factor so that the total area under the cross section is 1:

$$\int_{-\infty}^{\infty} f(x \mid y) \, dx = \frac{\int_{-\infty}^{\infty} f(x, y) \, dx}{f_Y(y)} = 1.$$

That is, $F(\infty \mid y) = 1$, where $F(x \mid y)$ is the conditional c.d.f.:

$$F(x \mid y) = \int_{-\infty}^{x} f(u \mid y) \, du.$$

---

[3] See Lehmann, E. [13], p. 39 ff.

This situation is quite analogous to that in the discrete case, in which the conditional probabilities for X given $Y = y_j$ are proportional to the joint probabilities $f(x_i, y_j)$ in the row for $Y = y_j$, each being divided by the row sum, $f_Y(y_j)$, so that the sum of the conditional probabilities given $Y = y_j$ is equal to 1.

EXAMPLE 2–28. A random vector (X, Y) has a density that is zero outside the triangle with vertices $(0, 0)$, $(0, 1)$, and $(1, 0)$ and is constant within that triangle:

$$f(x, y) = \begin{cases} 2, & \text{if } x + y \le 1, \quad x \ge 0, \quad \text{and} \quad y \ge 0, \\ 0, & \text{otherwise.} \end{cases}$$

The marginal density for X is the area under the cross section at $X = x$ as a function of x:

$$f_X(x) = \int_{-\infty}^{\infty} f(x, y)\, dy = \int_0^{1-x} 2\, dy = 2(1 - x), \qquad \text{for } 0 \le x \le 1.$$

The conditional density for Y given $X = x$ is then

$$f(y \mid x) = \frac{f(x, y)}{f_X(x)} = \frac{2}{2(1 - x)} = \frac{1}{1 - x}, \qquad 0 < y \le 1 - x.$$

(Its value is 0 outside the indicated range.) That is, the density of Y given $X = x$ is constant on the interval $[0, 1 - x]$. This reflects the fact that the cross section of $f(x, y)$ at $X = x$ is of constant height (namely, 2) on this interval. Division by the

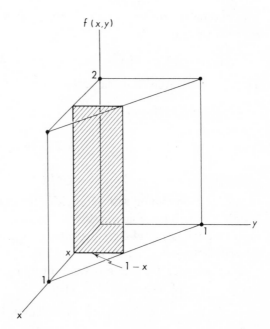

Figure 2–17.

area of the cross section, namely, by $2(1 - x)$, yields a function whose graph encloses with the horizontal a rectangle of area of 1 (see Figure 2–17).

EXAMPLE 2–29.   Let (X, Y) have the distribution defined by the density function of Problem 2–39, namely

$$f_{X,Y}(x, y) = e^{-x-y}, \quad \text{for } x > 0, \quad y > 0.$$

The marginal distribution for Y is the integral of this on x:

$$f_Y(y) = \int_{-\infty}^{\infty} e^{-x-y} \, dx = e^{-y}, \quad \text{for } y > 0.$$

The conditional density of X given $Y = y$ is then

$$f(x \mid y) = \frac{e^{-x-y}}{e^{-y}} = e^{-x}, \quad \text{for } x > 0.$$

It will be seen in the next section that the fact that this conditional density of x is independent of y and is indeed equal to the marginal density of X is of particular significance.

2.1.9   Independence

It can happen, as in Example 2–29, that the conditional distribution of one variable in the pair (X, Y) is independent of any condition imposed on the other. The random variables X and Y are then said to be *independent random variables*.

In particular, suppose that for every event A in the value space of X, and for each value y of Y,

$$P(X \text{ in } A \mid Y = y) = P(X \text{ in } A).$$

Then for every event B in the value space of Y,

$$P(X \text{ in } A \text{ and } Y \text{ in } B) = \int_B P(X \text{ in } A \mid Y = y) f_Y(y) \, dy$$

$$= P(X \text{ in } A) \int_B f_Y(y) \, dy$$

$$= P(X \text{ in } A) P(Y \text{ in } B).$$

(A similar computation with sums yields the same result in the discrete case.) Then the experiment that consists of observing a value of X and the experiment that consists of observing a value of Y are independent experiments, in the terminology of Chapter 1.

If the above factorization is valid for all events A and B, it must hold in particular for $\{X \leq x\}$ and $\{Y \leq y\}$:

$$F_{X,Y}(x, y) = F_X(x)F_Y(y).$$

In the discrete case it also holds for the events $\{X = x_i\}$ and $\{Y = y_j\}$:

$$f_{X,Y}(x_i, y_j) = f_X(x_i)f_Y(y_j).$$

In the continuous case, differentiation of the above relation for cumulative distribution functions yields the following relation for densities:

$$f_{X,Y}(x, y) = f_X(x)f_Y(y).$$

But then whether f denotes density or probability,

$$f(x \mid y) = \frac{f(x, y)}{f_Y(y)} = \frac{f_X(x)f_Y(y)}{f_Y(y)} = f_X(x),$$

which means that the conditional distribution of X given $Y = y$ is independent of y—the criterion used at the outset to define independence. Therefore, this defining criterion for independence and the various factorization conditions—for probabilities, cumulative distribution functions, and density or probability functions—are *equivalent*. It does not matter which is taken as defining independence of X and Y.

EXAMPLE 2–30.   Let (X, Y) have the joint density e^{-x-y}, for positive x and y, as in Example 2–29. It was seen in that example that

$$f(x \mid y) = e^{-x}, \qquad \text{for} \quad x > 0,$$

which is exactly the marginal density of X. Moreover, the marginal density of Y is e^{-y}, for $y > 0$, so that

$$f(x, y) = e^{-x-y} = e^{-x}e^{-y} = f_X(x)f_Y(y).$$

The component variables X and Y are independent.

EXAMPLE 2–31.   Consider the distribution which has a constant density in the triangle bounded by the coordinate axes and by $x + y = 1$ in the plane of values of the random vector (X, Y). This does *not* have the factorization property defining independence of X and Y. The marginal densities are (see Example 2–28)

$$f_X(x) = 2(1 - x), \qquad f_Y(y) = 2(1 - y)$$

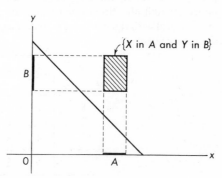

Figure 2–18. Nonfactorization of the support set in Example 2–31.

for $0 < x < 1$ and $0 < y < 1$, respectively, whereas the joint density is 2 on the given triangle and 0 outside. In this instance, the dependence of X and Y can be deduced without any calculation, if it is noticed that there are events A and B in the interval [0, 1], with positive probabilities, whose intersection is a region in the plane entirely outside the triangle that carries all of the probability. Figure 2–18 illustrates this situation; the shaded region has zero probability, but this zero is not the product of the probabilities of A and B, which are positive.

The reasoning in the last example shows that in general the region in the plane where the joint density or joint probability is not zero must "factor." That is, it must be the intersection of "cylinder sets" with bases on the coordinate axes. (A cylinder set here is a set in the plane defined by a condition on only one coordinate; its base is the set on the axis of that coordinate defined by the condition. Thus, the events $\{X \text{ in } A\}$ and $\{Y \text{ in } B\}$, when considered as sets in the plane, are cylinder sets with bases A and B, respectively.) If the bases are intervals, the product is an ordinary rectangle with sides parallel to the coordinate axes.

EXAMPLE 2–32.　The probability table for (X, Y) given in Example 2–27 and repeated below is another illustration of a situation in which the dependence of X and Y can be seen at a glance.

Y \ X	1	2	3	
1	0	$\frac{1}{6}$	$\frac{1}{6}$	$\frac{1}{3}$
2	$\frac{1}{6}$	0	$\frac{1}{6}$	$\frac{1}{3}$
3	$\frac{1}{6}$	$\frac{1}{6}$	0	$\frac{1}{3}$
	$\frac{1}{3}$	$\frac{1}{3}$	$\frac{1}{3}$	

There are zeros in this table corresponding to combinations of X- and Y-values that have nonzero probabilities, whereas for independence, each entry in the table must be the product of corresponding marginal entries. The following table of probabilities for random variables X' and Y' is one in which the entries are obtained by multiplication of marginal probabilities. The distributions of X' and Y' are identical with the marginal distributions of X and Y above, but here X' and Y' are independent.

Y' \ X'	1	2	3	
1	$\frac{1}{9}$	$\frac{1}{9}$	$\frac{1}{9}$	$\frac{1}{3}$
2	$\frac{1}{9}$	$\frac{1}{9}$	$\frac{1}{9}$	$\frac{1}{3}$
3	$\frac{1}{9}$	$\frac{1}{9}$	$\frac{1}{9}$	$\frac{1}{3}$
	$\frac{1}{3}$	$\frac{1}{3}$	$\frac{1}{3}$	

(It should not be concluded from this example that independence implies equal likelihood of the pairs (x_i, y_j); the pairs are equally likely simply because the marginal values are equally likely.)

Although not generally the case, it is true for *independent* random variables that the marginal distributions uniquely define a joint distribution. To construct a joint density for a model with independence, it is only necessary to multiply together the marginal densities (or to multiply the marginal c.d.f.'s to obtain the joint c.d.f.). Example 2–32 above gives two bivariate distributions having the same marginal distributions; but only one of them has independent marginals.

An important consequence of the independence of two random variables, to be exploited later, is that any functions of the individual variables are independent; that is, if $Z = g(X)$ and $W = h(Y)$ and X and Y are independent, then so also are Z and W independent. For, if A' denotes the set of X-values such that $g(X)$ is in A, and B' denotes the set of Y-values such that $h(Y)$ is in B, then

$$P[g(X) \text{ in } A \text{ and } h(Y) \text{ in } B] = P(X \text{ in } A' \text{ and } Y \text{ in } B')$$

$$= P(X \text{ in } A')P(Y \text{ in } B')$$

$$= P[g(X) \text{ in } A]P[h(Y) \text{ in } B].$$

Problems

2–46. The random vector (X, Y) has a discrete distribution, defined by the accompanying table of probabilities. Determine the following:

(a) $P(X = 1 \mid X + Y \leq 5)$
(b) $P(X = 2 \mid Y = 2)$
(c) $P(Y = 2 \mid X > 1)$
(d) $f(y \mid X = 2)$

Y \ X	1	2	3
2	$\frac{1}{12}$	$\frac{1}{6}$	$\frac{1}{12}$
3	$\frac{1}{6}$	0	$\frac{1}{6}$
4	0	$\frac{1}{3}$	0

2–47. Let (X, Y) have a joint density function that is constant over the circle $x^2 + y^2 \leq 4$, and zero outside that region. Compute the following:

(a) $f(x \mid y)$ for $y = 1$
(b) $P(|X| < 1 \mid Y = .5)$
(c) $f(y \mid x)$.

2–48. Given the joint density function of (X, Y):

$$f(x, y) = \begin{cases} 6(1 - x - y), & \text{for } 0 < y < 1 - x, \quad x > 0, \\ 0, & \text{elsewhere.} \end{cases}$$

Determine the conditional density functions, for X given $Y = y$, and for Y given $X = x$.

2–49. Show, without any computations, that the random variables (X, Y) in each of the Problems 2–46, 2–47, and 2–48 are not independent.

2–50. Show that the random variables (θ, ϕ) in Example 2–21 are independent. Show also that the random variables $X = \sin \theta \cos \phi$ and $Y = \sin \theta \sin \phi$ are *not* independent.

2–51. Determine the joint density function of (X, Y) where X and Y are independent and each has a constant density on the interval $[0, 1]$ (and zero outside).

2–52. Show that if X is discrete with values $x_1, \ldots, x_m$ and Y is discrete with values $y_1, \ldots, y_n$, if the X-values are equally likely and the Y-values are equally likely, and if X and Y are independent, then the mn possible pairs (x_i, y_j) are equally likely.

2–53. Show that the random variables U and V in Problem 2–3 are not independent. (U is the number of trials needed to get the first Heads, and V the number needed to get two Heads, in repeated tosses of a coin.)

2.1.10   Multivariate Distributions

A random vector with more than two components defines a distribution in the space of its "values" (ordered triples of real numbers for three, ordered n-tuples of real numbers for n components). This distribution can be discussed in much the same manner as that in which the bivariate distribution of a random vector with two components was given in the preceding sections. The distribution can be characterized by its joint or multivariate *distribution function*:

$$F_{X_1, \ldots, X_n}(x_1, \ldots, x_n) = P(X_1 \leq x_1, \ldots, \text{ and } X_n \leq x_n)$$

$$= P^{\Omega}(X_1(\omega) \leq x_1, \ldots, \text{ and } X_n(\omega) \leq x_n).$$

[As is customary by now, probability is assigned to any set in the space of n-tuples as the probability of the image set in Ω under the vector function defining $(X_1, \ldots, X_n)$.] Marginal distributions of various types are obtained by setting the arguments corresponding to unwanted variables equal to ∞. For instance, the bivariate marginal distribution function of X_1 and X_2 is

$$F_{X_1, X_2}(x_1, x_2) = F_{X_1, \ldots, X_n}(x_1, x_2, \infty, \ldots, \infty).$$

Clearly, then, if one wishes to take n-dimensional Euclidean space itself as the sample space Ω, with $\omega = (x_1, \ldots, x_n)$, and to define probabilities of events by specifying as a distribution function some function $F(x_1, \ldots, x_n)$, then this function must have the property that an $n - k$ dimensional distribution function is obtained upon setting k of the arguments x_i equal to ∞. It must also have the property that it is zero if $x_i = -\infty$ for any i; and to make sure that the probability of every "rectangle" (rectangular parallelepiped) is nonnegative, its nth order mixed difference must be nonnegative.

(This is the quantity that appears in the numerator of the quantity whose limit defines the nth order, mixed partial derivative, when this exists.)

Again there are two special classes of distributions of importance—continuous and discrete. The continuous distributions are defined by distribution functions that are continuous and have an nth order, mixed partial derivative:

$$f(x_1, \ldots, x_n) = \frac{\partial^n}{\partial x_1 \cdots \partial x_n} F(x_1, \ldots, x_n),$$

called the density function of the distribution, sufficiently smooth as to permit recovery of the distribution function by integration:

$$F(x_1, \ldots, x_n) = \int_{-\infty}^{x_1} \cdots \int_{-\infty}^{x_n} f(u_1, \ldots, u_n) \, du_n \cdots du_1.$$

Moreover, the probability of any event S is the multiple integral over S of the joint density function:

$$P[(X_1, \ldots, X_n) \text{ in } S] = \int \cdots \int_S f(x_1, \ldots, x_n) \, dx_1 \cdots dx_n,$$

and of course the probability of the whole space, $F(\infty, \ldots, \infty)$, is the integral of the density over the whole space and is 1. A distribution can be specified by defining its density to be a particular nonnegative function $f(x_1, \ldots, x_n)$ having the property that its integral over the whole space is 1.

It is helpful to consider the marginal distribution of a subset of variables as the *projection* of the probability or "mass" in a joint distribution of all the variables onto the subspace of values of the subset. For example, given (X, Y, Z), the joint distribution of (X, Y) is the projection onto the xy-plane of the joint distribution of (X, Y, Z) in space. All of the probability in a right cylinder of base A in the xy-plane is collapsed down onto the plane and is the probability of A.

EXAMPLE 2–33.   Consider the distribution for (X, Y, Z) defined by the density

$$f(x, y, z) = \begin{cases} 3/(4\pi), & \text{if } x^2 + y^2 + z^2 \leq 1, \\ 0, & \text{otherwise.} \end{cases}$$

That is, the density is constant inside a unit sphere, and the value of that constant is the reciprocal of the volume of the sphere (so that the integral of $f(x, y, z)$ over the sphere is 1). The probability of a subset of this sphere is then proportional to its volume. The distribution of Z is obtained by projecting the probability in the (X, Y, Z)-space onto the Z-axis. Thus, for $|\lambda| < 1$,

$$P(Z \leq \lambda) = \frac{\text{volume of portion of sphere below } Z = \lambda}{\text{volume of sphere}}$$

$$= \frac{3}{4\pi} \int_{-1}^{\lambda} \pi(1 - z^2) \, dz = \tfrac{1}{4}(2 + 3\lambda - \lambda^3)$$

and the density of Z is therefore

$$f_Z(\lambda) = \tfrac{3}{4}(1 - \lambda^2), \qquad \text{for } -1 < \lambda < 1.$$

Notice that the density is large near $z = 0$ and smallest at $z = 1$ and -1, as is to be expected. (It vanishes outside $|\lambda| < 1$.)

Conditional distributions are defined just as in the bivariate case. If the given condition is that certain components of a random vector have specified values, the conditional density (speaking in terms of the continuous case) is the joint density of all the components divided by the joint marginal density of those components whose values are given—with those particular values used wherever the corresponding dummy variables appear.

EXAMPLE 2–34. Consider the uniform distribution in the unit sphere, as introduced in the preceding example. The joint conditional density of X and Y given $Z = k$ would be

$$f(x, y \mid Z = k) = \frac{f(x, y, k)}{f_Z(k)} = \frac{3/(4\pi)}{3(1 - k^2)/4} = \frac{1}{\pi(1 - k^2)},$$

for $x^2 + y^2 \le 1 - k^2$. That is, the conditional distribution given $Z = k$ is uniform within the circle of radius $1 - k^2$. The density of this distribution in the plane $Z = k$ varies just as does the joint density of (X, Y, Z) in that plane, and the division by $f_Z(k)$ furnishes precisely the right normalization to make the integral of the conditional density over the cross section equal to 1.

As in the bivariate case, independence can be defined in any of several ways, according to one of the following criteria:

(1) $f(x_1, \ldots, x_n) = f_{X_1}(x_1)f_{X_2}(x_2) \cdots f_{X_n}(x_n)$,

(2) $F(x_1, \ldots, x_n) = F_{X_1}(x_1)F_{X_2}(x_2) \cdots F_{X_n}(x_n)$,

(3) $P(X_1 \text{ in } A_1, \ldots, \text{ and } X_n \text{ in } A_n) = P(X_1 \text{ in } A_1) \cdots P(X_n \text{ in } A_n)$, for every choice of the n events $A_1, \ldots, A_n$.

(The f in (1) denotes the density function in continuous cases or the probability function in discrete cases.) These conditions are equivalent. Notice that independence automatically obtains in the marginal distribution of any subset of $(X_1, \ldots, X_n)$, since it follows from (2) upon replacing the dummy variables corresponding to the remaining variables by ∞, or from (3) by taking the A's corresponding to those remaining variables to be the interval $(-\infty, \infty)$.

Again any functions of the individual variables, $g_1(X_1), \ldots, g_n(X_n)$ are independent if $X_1, \ldots, X_n$ are. Moreover, any functions of nonoverlapping subsets of the independent random variables $X_1, \ldots, X_n$ define independent random variables. Thus, for example, if $X_1, X_2, X_3,$ and X_4 are independent, so are $Y = g(X_1, X_4)$ and $Z = h(X_2, X_3)$. For, if A and B denote sets in the value space of Y and of Z, and A' and B' denote their respective pre-images under the functions g and h, then

$$P(Y \text{ in } A \text{ and } Z \text{ in } B) = P[(X_1, X_4) \text{ in } A' \text{ and } (X_2, X_3) \text{ in } B']$$

$$= \int\!\!\int_{A'} \int\!\!\int_{B'} f(x_1, x_2, x_3, x_4) \, dx_2 \, dx_3 \, dx_1 \, dx_4$$

$$= \int\!\!\int_{A'} f_{X_1, X_4}(x_1, x_4) \, dx_1 \, dx_4 \cdot \int\!\!\int_{B'} f_{X_2, X_3}(x_2, x_3) dx_2 \, dx_3$$

$$= P[(X_1, X_4) \text{ in } A'] P[(X_2, X_3) \text{ in } B']$$

$$= P[Y \text{ in } A] P[Z \text{ in } B].$$

A similar argument would establish the more general assertion.

The factorization condition for independence can be used to check a given multivariate distribution for independence of the components; but it is more often used to *construct* a multivariate model that is to incorporate an observed or postulated independence by multiplying marginal densities or c.d.f.'s to form the multivariate density or c.d.f.

EXAMPLE 2–35.   The model for an experiment of chance is defined by the density function $f(x)$ for the random variable X. Suppose that the experiment is repeated n times in such a way that no performance is influenced by the result of any others. One would then like a model for the results of the successive trials of the experiment. These make up the random vector $(X_1, X_2, \ldots, X_n)$ in which X_i denotes the result of the ith trial of the experiment. The joint density function of the n observations is defined to be the *product* of the marginal distributions; and because each X_i is a replica (in distribution) of the basic experiment, these marginal distributions are identical and defined by the density $f(x)$. Thus,

$$f_{X_1, \ldots, X_n}(x_1, \ldots, x_n) = f_{X_1}(x_1) \cdots f_{X_n}(x_n) = f(x_1)f(x_2) \cdots f(x_n).$$

Problems

2–54. A discrete distribution for (X, Y, Z) is defined by assigning equal probabilities to the following six points: $(0, 0, 0)$, $(0, 0, 1)$, $(2, 0, 1)$, $(2, 1, 0)$, $(1, 2, 1)$, $(0, 2, 0)$.

(a) Determine the marginal distributions of X, Y, and Z.
(b) Determine the probability table for the joint marginal distribution of (X, Y).
(c) Determine the probability table for the joint conditional distribution of (X, Y) given $Z = 1$.

2–55. Let (X, Y, Z) have a continuous joint distribution that is given by a constant density in the portion of the first octant ($x \geq 0$, $y \geq 0$, $z \geq 0$) that is bounded by the plane $x + y + z = 1$ (with zero density outside this region).

(a) Determine the constant value of the density.
(b) Determine the density of the marginal distribution of (X, Y).
(c) Determine the density of the marginal distribution of X.
(d) Determine the conditional density of (X, Y) given $Z = 1/2$.

2–56. Write out the density or probability function for the joint distribution of $(X_1, \ldots, X_n)$, where X_i denotes the outcome of the ith in a sequence of independent trials of an experiment whose result

(a) has the density function e^{-x}, for $x > 0$,
(b) has the probability function $p^x (1 - p)^{1-x}$, for $x = 0, 1$, where p is a given number on $(0, 1)$.

2–57. Show that the density function

$$f(x_1, \ldots, x_n) = \begin{cases} 1, & \text{for } 0 < x_i < 1, \quad i = 1, \ldots, n, \\ 0, & \text{elsewhere,} \end{cases}$$

defines a distribution for the random vector $(X_1, \ldots, X_n)$ in which the marginal variables are independent.

2–58. Show that the density function

$$f(x_1, \ldots, x_n) = \begin{cases} K, & \text{for } x_i > 0, \quad x_1 + \cdots + x_n \leq 1, \\ 0, & \text{elsewhere} \end{cases}$$

defines a distribution in which the marginal variables are not independent.

2.2 Expectation

The terms *expectation*, *expected value*, *average value*, and *mean value* are all used for the same concept. They refer in the case of a probability distribution in the value space of a random variable to what is the analog of the center of gravity of a mass distribution along a line. The term *expected value* will be used most frequently here, even though it is slightly misleading—the expected value of a given random variable may not even be a possible value, let alone an "expected" one.

Like the center of gravity of a mass distribution, the expected value is used as a measure of centering or location of a probability distribution. The term *average* can be motivated in the context of a long series of plays of a game of chance, as the reward per trial when the total winnings are distributed equally among the trials to determine an entry fee.

EXAMPLE 2–36. Suppose a reward is offered, a number of dollars equal to the number of points showing when a die is tossed. If the game is to be fair, an entry fee should be charged for the privilege of playing the game. In a long series of plays, say N of them, the total amount of fees collected would be Nx dollars, if x is the fee for a single play. In this series of plays, the numbers 1, 2, 3, 4, 5, 6 would turn up approximately equally often as the number of points showing. Assuming exactly $N/6$ of each, the total reward would be a number of dollars equal to

$$1 \cdot \frac{N}{6} + 2 \cdot \frac{N}{6} + \cdots + 6 \cdot \frac{N}{6}.$$

If the game is to be fair, this total should equal the total of the entry fees; setting it equal to Nx one finds the equitable entry fee to be

$$x = 1 \cdot \frac{1}{6} + 2 \cdot \frac{1}{6} + \cdots + 6 \cdot \frac{1}{6} = \frac{7}{2}.$$

or \$3.50. This is sometimes called the "mathematical expectation" of a single play of the game, but of course the actual amount won in a single play will never equal \$3.50—it will be either \$1, \$2, ..., or \$6. The expectation or entry fee is in a sense an idealization, since in an actual sequence of N plays, the proportions will not be exactly equal to $N/6$, although close to it. The \$3.50 is then obtained only upon distributing the winnings in an *infinite* sequence of plays, which of course constitutes an idealization, and accounts for the qualifier "mathematical."

The number of dollars won in the above example is a random variable, and the same computation—multiplying values by proportions and summing —will be used in defining the expected value of more general random variables. In continuous cases it will be necessary to integrate instead of sum— the appropriate definition of expectation in general is given as an integral. And so after a definition in the discrete case to set the stage, it will be necessary to define some new kinds of integrals.

2.2.1 Simple Random Variables

A random variable is said to be *simple* which assumes one of a set of values that is at most finite. That is, there is a list of possible values $x_1, x_2, \ldots, x_k$ and corresponding probabilities $p_1, p_2, \ldots, p_k$ such that $p_1 + \cdots + p_k = 1$. The *expected value* of a simple random variable having these values and corresponding probabilities is defined to be

$$EX = x_1 p_1 + x_2 p_2 + \cdots + x_k p_k = \sum_{i=1}^{k} x_i p_i.$$

(This will also be written as $E(X)$, especially when the name of the random variable is more complicated than just X.) The symbol μ or the more specific μ_X will also be used for this quantity, referring to the alternative terminology of *mean* value.

The above "weighted sum" that defines expected value (the weights for the various values are the corresponding probabilities) is precisely the kind of weighted sum that defines center of gravity. If a mass m_1 is located on the x-axis at x_1, the mass m_2 at $x_2, \ldots$, and the mass m_k at x_k, the center of gravity of this system of masses is computed as follows:

$$\text{c.g.} = \frac{\sum x_i m_i}{\sum m_i} = \sum x_i \left(\frac{m_i}{m}\right),$$

where m is the total mass and each sum extends from $i = 1$ to $i = k$. Notice that the relative mass—the proportion of the total mass at x_i—is the weight attached to x_i and is therefore the analog of the probability that $X = x_i$. Notice also that the sum of the relative masses equals 1, as does the sum of the probabilities.

The formula for EX can be rewritten in terms of probabilities in Ω, if this sample space has a finite number of points. For, the probability p_i can be expressed as a sum of the probabilities of all points ω such that $X(\omega) = x_i$; and therefore

$$EX = \sum_i x_i p_i = \sum_{\omega \text{ in } \Omega} X(\omega) P(\omega).$$

EXAMPLE 2–37. The model for three independent tosses of a fair coin assigns equal probabilities (each 1/8) to the eight distinct sequences making up the sample space. Let $X(\omega)$ denote the number of Heads in the sequence ω (for example, $X(H, H, T) = 2$). The mean value of the random variable X can be computed either as a sum over the sample space or as a sum over the value space. The sample points are: $HHH, HHT, HTH, THH, TTH, THT, HTT, TTT$, and the values of X are 3, 2, 2, 2, 1, 1, 1, 0, respectively. Thus, $p(3) = p(0) = 1/8$ and $p(1) = p(2) = 3/8$, so that

$$EX = 0 \cdot \frac{1}{8} + 1 \cdot \frac{3}{8} + 2 \cdot \frac{3}{8} + 3 \cdot \frac{1}{8} = \frac{3}{2}.$$

The calculation using the sample space is as follows:

$$EX = 0 \cdot \frac{1}{8} + 1 \cdot \frac{1}{8} + 1 \cdot \frac{1}{8} + 1 \cdot \frac{1}{8} + 2 \cdot \frac{1}{8} + 2 \cdot \frac{1}{8} + 2 \cdot \frac{1}{8} + 3 \cdot \frac{1}{8}.$$

The equivalence of these two computations of EX is at once apparent—the 3/8 multiplying 1 corresponding to three terms in the second sum in which 1/8 multiplies 1, etc.

As discussed in Section 2.1.6, a function $g(x)$ defines with $X(\omega)$ a new random variable $Y = g(X(\omega))$, written usually as $Y = g(X)$. Whether or not Ω is discrete, the space of X-values is a discrete probability space if X is a simple random variable, and Y can be thought of as a random variable on this probability space. But then, interpreting the X-space as Ω and the function $g(x)$ as the $X(\omega)$ in the formula preceding Example 2–37, one obtains:

$$EY = Eg(X) = \sum_j y_j P(Y = y_j) = \sum_i g(X_i) P(X = x_i).$$

Of course if Ω is discrete, there is a third level at which the computation can be performed:

$$EY = E[g(X(\omega))] = \sum_{\omega \text{ in } \Omega} g(X(\omega))P(\omega).$$

The formula involving the probabilities $P(X = x_i)$ is ordinarily the simplest, since these probabilities are given, whereas the probabilities $P(Y = y_j)$ would have to be computed.

EXAMPLE 2–38.   A cube has its six sides colored red, white, blue, green, yellow, and violet. It is assumed that these six sides are equally likely to show, when the cube is tossed. That is, we consider a probability space with elementary outcomes R, W, B, G, Y, V and probabilities 1/6 for each of these outcomes; this space is Ω.

Consider now the random variable that assigns the number 1 to R and W, the number 2 to G and B, and the number 3 to Y and V:

$$X(R) = X(W) = 1;$$
$$X(G) = X(B) = 2;$$
$$X(Y) = X(V) = 3.$$

The space $\mathscr{X}$ of values of $X(\omega)$ can be thought of as consisting of the numbers 1, 2, and 3, each with probability 1/3, the distribution induced by $X(\omega)$ from that on Ω.

Next let $Y = (X - 2)^2$. The values $X = 1$ and $X = 3$ give rise to $Y = 1$; the value $X = 2$, to $Y = 0$. Thus $\mathscr{Y}$ consists of the values 1 and 0 with probabilities 2/3 and 1/3, respectively. There are then three possible computations of

$$E(Y) = E[(X - 2)^2] = E[(X(\omega) - 2)^2].$$

One uses the distribution on Ω:

$$\tfrac{1}{6}[X(R) - 2]^2 + \cdots + \tfrac{1}{6}[X(V) - 2]^2 = \tfrac{2}{3};$$

another uses the distribution on $\mathscr{X}$:

$$\tfrac{1}{3}(1 - 2)^2 + \tfrac{1}{3}(2 - 2)^2 + \tfrac{1}{3}(3 - 2)^2 = \tfrac{2}{3};$$

and the third uses the distribution on $\mathscr{Y}$:

$$1 \cdot \tfrac{2}{3} + 0 \cdot \tfrac{1}{3} = \tfrac{2}{3}.$$

Following the mappings and transfers of probability makes it clear in this example that the computations are equivalent.

A special case of a simple random variable is that in which only one value is assumed: $P(X = k) = 1$. In such a case the expected value computation reduces to a single term and yields $EX = k$.

A special case of a function of a random variable is $Y = kX$. The mean value of Y can be computed from X-probabilities:

$$EY = \sum_i kx_ip_i = k \sum_i x_ip_i = kEX.$$

That is, the averaging operation is *homogeneous*—multiplying a random variable by a constant multiplies the mean value by that constant.

A frequently encountered type of random variable is one which is a sum of random variables. Given the random vector $(X(\omega), Y(\omega))$, then, consider the random variable $Z(\omega) = X(\omega) + Y(\omega)$. The mean value of Z can be computed in terms of the mean values of X and Y as follows:

$$EZ = E[X(\omega) + Y(\omega)] = \sum [X(\omega) + Y(\omega)]P(\omega)$$

$$= \sum X(\omega)P(\omega) + \sum Y(\omega)P(\omega)$$

$$= EX + EY.$$

This is readily extended by induction to the proposition that the average of any finite sum of random variables is the sum of the averages. Combining this *additivity* property of $E(\omega)$ with the homogeneity property derived above, one obtains the condition of *linearity* of the averaging operation:

$$E(aX + bY) = aEX + bEY.$$

(The above derivation would seem to depend on the existence of an Ω on which both X and Y are defined. However, this sample space can be taken to be the space of points (x, y), with $X(x, y) = x$ and $Y(x, y) = y$. Moreover, the joint probabilities in this space can be taken to be anything at all with the given marginal probabilities for X and for Y, since the computation only involves those marginal probabilities.)

Problems

2–59. Determine the expected number of defectives in a random selection of four articles from a lot of ten of which two are defective (see Problem 2–13). The distribution is given in the following table:

x_i	0	1	2
p_i	$\frac{1}{3}$	$\frac{8}{15}$	$\frac{2}{15}$

2–60. Determine the expected number of tests required to locate one defective tube among five tubes (see Problem 2–14). The probabilities (assuming at most four tests are required) are $1/5$ for $X = 1, 2, 3$, and $2/5$ for $X = 4$.

2–61. Determine the expected number of correct identifications in the random assignment of three brand names to three cigarettes (see Problem 2–15). The probabilities are

x_i	0	1	3
p_i	$\frac{1}{3}$	$\frac{1}{2}$	$\frac{1}{6}$

2–62. Determine the expected number of points assigned (as in Problem 2–16)

to a card drawn at random from a standard deck. The distribution is as follows:

x_i	0	1	2	3	4
p_i	$\frac{9}{13}$	$\frac{1}{13}$	$\frac{1}{13}$	$\frac{1}{13}$	$\frac{1}{13}$

2–63.   Determine the expected value of the smallest of the numbers on three chips drawn at random from five chips numbered 1 through 5, respectively (see Problem 2–18). The distribution is as follows:

y_j	1	2	3
p_j	.6	.3	.1

2–64.   Referring to the situation of Problems 2–63 and 2–18, compute the expected value of Z, the largest of the three numbers drawn, and also of $R = Z - Y$. Verify that $ER = EZ - EY$.

2–65.   Show that $E(X - EX) = 0$, for any simple random variable X.

2–66.   Write out the proof by induction that the expected sum of finitely many random variables is the sum of the expectations.

2–67.   Thirteen cards are drawn at random from a standard deck of cards. Given that the number of points on each card is a random variable distributed as in Problem 2–62, determine the expected total number of points in the hand of thirteen cards. If all 52 cards are dealt out to form four hands of thirteen cards, determine the expected number in each hand and the total expected number of points in all four hands.

2–68.   Determine the expected total number of points showing in a toss of two dice.

2.2.2   *Riemann–Stieltjes integrals*

Consider a continuous function $g(x)$ defined on $a \leq x \leq b$, and another function $h(x)$, this one bounded and monotonically increasing (but not necessarily strictly so):

$$x < x' \quad \text{implies} \quad h(x) \leq h(x').$$

Let the interval $[a, b]$ be partitioned by points x_i:

$$a = x_0 < x_1 < \cdots < x_n = b,$$

and let M_i and m_i denote the least upper bound of $g(x)$ and the greatest lower bound of $g(x)$, respectively, on the ith subinterval of the partition, $x_{i-1} \leq x \leq x_i$.

The ordinary integral of elementary calculus is then defined for the function $g(x)$ as the common value of the following, when they are equal:

$$\underline{I} = \sup \sum m_i(x_i - x_{i-1})$$
$$\bar{I} = \inf \sum M_i(x_i - x_{i-1}),$$

where "sup" and "inf" mean, respectively, the least upper bound and greatest lower bound over all possible partitions of $[a, b]$. It can be shown, indeed, that $\underline{I} = \bar{I}$ whenever $g(x)$ is continuous, as assumed here. The integral defined in this way:

$$\int_a^b g(x)\, dx = \underline{I} = \bar{I},$$

is called a *Riemann integral*.

If in the defining expressions for $\underline{I}$ and $\bar{I}$ the interval length $x_i - x_{i-1}$ is replaced by the amount of change of the function $h(x)$ on that interval, namely by $h(x_i) - h(x_{i-1})$, the quantities $\bar{I}$ and $\underline{I}$ are again equal, and define the *Riemann–Stieltjes integral* of $g(x)$ with respect to $h(x)$:

$$\int_a^b g(x)\, dh(x).$$

If the value $g(\xi_i)$ is used in place of the m_i or M_i, where ξ_i is some point on the interval $[x_{i-1}, x_i]$, then the resulting sums and their limits over any sequence of successively finer partitions are squeezed between $\bar{I}$ and $\underline{I}$ and may be used to evaluate the integral when (as can be shown when h is monotonic and bounded as it is here) $\bar{I} = \underline{I}$. (This situation is analogous to that of the ordinary Riemann case.) For example, one could take the partition points to be equally spaced, of width $(b - a)/n$, and evaluate the function $g(x)$ at the right-hand endpoint of each subinterval to obtain:

$$\int_a^b g(x)\, dh(x) = \lim_{n \to \infty} \sum_{k=1}^n g(x_k)[h(x_k) - h(x_{k-1})].$$

If $h(x)$ is differentiable on $[a, b]$, the difference in its values at the endpoints of the interval $[x_{i-1}, x_i]$ can be expressed as the product of its derivative at some intermediate point ξ_i and the width of the interval (according to the mean value theorem):

$$h(x_i) - h(x_{i-1}) = h'(\xi_i)(x_i - x_{i-1}).$$

With this inserted into the above limit, the result looks much like an ordinary Riemann integral of $g(x)h'(x)$:

$$\lim_{n \to \infty} \sum_{k=1}^n g(x_k)h'(\xi_k)(x_k - x_{k-1}),$$

and so one would expect that

$$\int_a^b g(x)\, dh(x) = \int_a^b g(x)h'(x)\, dx.$$

That this is valid is a result of Duhamel's theorem.[4] Thus, the Riemann–

----

[4] See Widder, D. V., *Advanced Calculus*, 2nd ed. (New York: Prentice-Hall, 1961), p. 173.

Stieltjes integral not only contains the Riemann integral as a special case (that is, when $h(x) = x$), it also can be evaluated as a Riemann integral when the integrator function $h(x)$ is differentiable; the notation itself suggests the method: $dh(x)$ is replaced by $h'(x)\,dx$.

EXAMPLE 2–39.   The function $g(x) = e^x$ is continuous, and the function $h(x) = x^2$ is differentiable on the interval $[0, 1]$. Hence

$$\int_0^1 e^x\, d(x^2) = \int_0^1 2xe^x\, dx = 2.$$

If the integrator function $h(x)$ is constant on some subinterval of the interval of integration, the terms in the defining sum coming from that subinterval are all zero, since the differences in values of $h(x)$ would be zero. A special case of considerable importance is that in which $h(x)$ is a *step function*, that is, a function that increases only in jumps, and is constant between jumps. Suppose that $h(x)$ jumps an amount j_k at the point η_k, for $k = 1, \ldots, m$, and is constant between these points. (The amount j_k of the "jump" in $h(x)$ is simply the difference between the limit from the left and the limit from the right.) (See Figure 2–19.) The only terms in the approximating sums that con-

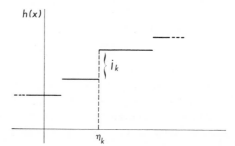

Figure 2–19.

tribute something are those coming from partition subintervals containing the jump points—the other terms will all be zero because $h(x)$ does not change over those subintervals. Thus,

$$\int_a^b g(x)\, dh(x) = \lim_{n \to \infty} \sum_{k=1}^m g(x_{i_k}) j_k = \sum_{k=1}^m g(\eta_k) j_k,$$

where x_{i_k} is the partition point just to the right of η_k, and approaches η_k as n becomes infinite. So the Riemann–Stieltjes integral reduces to an ordinary sum of values of $g(x)$ at the jump points, each weighted with the corresponding amount of the jump in $h(x)$.

EXAMPLE 2–40.   Let $F(x)$ denote the cumulative distribution function for the random variable which is the number of points showing in the toss of a die. This function jumps an amount $\frac{1}{6}$ at each of the values $x = 1, 2, 3, 4, 5, 6$, and is constant between these jump points. Hence,

$$\int_0^7 x \, dF(x) = 1(1/6) + 2(1/6) + \cdots + 6(1/6) = EX = 7/2.$$

(The interval of integration could, of course, have been any interval containing the points $1, \ldots, 6$, without altering the result.)

Suppose next that the integrator function $h(x)$ is continuous except for jumps j_i at x_i, $i = 1, \ldots, m$, and is differentiable between these jumps. Then $h(x)$ can be written as a sum of two functions, $h_1(x)$ a pure step function with the same jumps as $h(x)$, and $h_2(x)$, a continuous function that is differentiable except possibly at the finitely many points where $h(x)$ has jumps. It is not hard to show in terms of the definition of the integral that when the integrator function is a sum, the integral can be expressed as the sum of integrals in which the integrator functions are the summands of the original integrator. Thus,

$$\int_a^b g(x) \, dh(x) = \int_a^b g(x) \, dh_1(x) + \int_a^b g(x) \, dh_2(x)$$

$$= \sum_{i=1}^m g(x_i) j_i + \int_a^b g(x) h_2'(x) \, dx.$$

EXAMPLE 2–41.   Let $g(x) = x$ and consider the following integrator function:

$$F(x) = \begin{cases} 0, & \text{for } x < 0, \\ 1 - .8e^{-x} & \text{for } x \geq 0. \end{cases}$$

This is the distribution function for a model for the operating life of a certain type of equipment, introduced in Example 2–11 (page 64) and sketched in Figure 2–11. This function $F(x)$ can be expressed as the sum of a step function with a single jump of height .2 at $x = 0$ and a function which is differentiable. Therefore, the integral over, say $(-1, 1)$ is

$$\int_{-1}^1 x \, dF(x) = 0 \times .2 + \int_0^1 .8xe^{-x} \, dx.$$

The case of an infinite interval of integration can be handled in the same fashion as it is for Riemann integrals, namely, by evaluating the integral over a truncated interval and passing to the limit as the right-hand and left-hand truncation points move independently to ∞ and $-\infty$, respectively:

$$\int_{-\infty}^\infty g(x) \, dh(x) = \lim_{\substack{A \to -\infty \\ B \to \infty}} \int_A^B g(x) \, dh(x).$$

EXAMPLE 2–42.   Let X denote the number of Tails preceding the first Heads thrown in an infinite sequence of tosses of a fair coin. Then

$$p_k = P(X = k) = 1/2^{k+1}, \qquad k = 0, 1, 2, \ldots,$$

and the c.d.f. is a step function with jump p_k at the nonnegative integer k. And then

$$\int_{-\infty}^{\infty} x \, dF(x) = \lim_{\substack{A \to -\infty \\ B \to \infty}} \int_{A}^{B} x \, dF(x)$$

$$= \lim_{N \to \infty} (0 \cdot p_0 + 1 \cdot p_1 + \cdots + N \cdot p_N)$$

$$= \lim_{N \to \infty} \sum_{k=0}^{N} k/2^{k+1} = 1.$$

Problems

2–69. Evaluate the following:

(a) $\int_0^1 x^2 \, d(x^3)$

(b) $\int_1^2 x^2 \, d(\log x)$

(c) $\int_0^{\infty} x \, d(1 - e^{-x})$

2–70. Evaluate the following, in which $F(x)$ denotes the c.d.f. of the number of points in the toss of a die, as in Example 2–40:

(a) $\int_{-\infty}^{\infty} x \, dF(x)$

(b) $\int_{-\infty}^{\infty} x^2 \, dF(x)$

(c) $\int_{-\infty}^{\infty} (x - 3/2) \, dF(x)$

2–71. Evaluate the following, in which $F(x)$ denotes the c.d.f. in Example 2–41:

(a) $\int_{-\infty}^{\infty} x \, dF(x)$

(b) $\int_{-\infty}^{\infty} x^2 \, dF(x)$

(c) $\int_{-\infty}^{\infty} e^{tx} \, dF(x)$, $t < 1$.

2–72. Compare the values of the integrals of $g(x)$ over the range $[0, \infty)$ with respect to these two integrator functions:

$$h_1(x) = \begin{cases} 0, & x < 0 \\ 1, & x \geq 0, \end{cases} \qquad h_2(x) = \begin{cases} 0, & x \leq 0 \\ 1, & x > 0. \end{cases}$$

2–73. Compute the value of the integral

$$\int_0^1 x \, d(x^2)$$

as a limit of approximating sums, using partitions with n equal subdivisions and evaluating the integrand at the right-hand endpoints of the subintervals, as n becomes infinite.

2.2.3   General Definition of Expectation

Let the random variable $X(\omega)$ be defined on the probability space $(\Omega, \mathscr{F}, P)$, and let $A_1, \ldots, A_m$ constitute a partition of Ω (that is, these are mutually disjoint and exhaust Ω). Let M_i denote the least upper bound, and m_i the greatest lower bound of $X(\omega)$ on A_i, and define

$$\bar{E} = \inf \sum_i M_i P(A_i)$$

and

$$\underline{E} = \sup \sum_i m_i P(A_i),$$

where the inf and sup are taken over *all partitions* of Ω. The motivation for these definitions lies in the earlier definition for the case of a simple random variable. A general random variable rounded off to M_i in the set A_i would become a simple random variable with mean $\sum M_i P(A_i)$; and similarly, $\sum m_i P(A_i)$ is the mean of a simple random variable obtained by rounding off $X(\omega)$ to m_i on A_i. If the partition is a fine one, it would appear that these rounded-off variables could be thought of as approximations to $X(\omega)$, one on the high and one on the low side. Clearly $\underline{E} \leq \bar{E}$; and if ever $\underline{E} = \bar{E}$, this common value is said to be the *expected value* (or mean, or average value) of X:

$$EX \equiv \underline{E} = \bar{E} \quad \text{(when these are equal).}$$

One of the immediate consequences of this definition is that if $X(\omega)$ is nonnegative with probability 1, then its mean is nonnegative:

$$P(X(\omega) \geq 0) = 1 \qquad \text{implies} \qquad EX \geq 0,$$

for the partition of Ω into the sets B and B' where $X \geq 0$ and $X < 0$, respectively, yields the nonnegative sum

$$m_1 P(B) + m_2 P(B') \geq 0,$$

since $P(B') = 0$ and the first term is nonnegative. This sum, on the other hand, does not exceed $\underline{E}$, so the desired result is established. This result in turn implies that if $X(\omega) \leq Y(\omega)$ with probability 1, then $EX \leq EY$. (For, the function $Y(\omega) - X(\omega)$ is then nonnegative, and has a nonnegative mean.) Moreover, since $-X \leq |X|$ and $X \leq |X|$, it follows that both $-EX$ and EX will not exceed $E|X|$, or in other words,

$$|EX| \leq E|X|.$$

(To conclude that $E(-X) = -EX$ and that $E(Y - X) = EY - EX$ the linearity of $E(\cdot)$, as discussed on page 108, must be assumed.)

Of course, the evaluation of an expected value according to the above definition would be difficult, in general. But it can be carried out using ordinary integrals or sums in most cases of interest. To see this, consider a partition of Ω as defined by a partition of the value space, in the case in which the entire distribution is contained on the interior of a finite interval $[a, b]$. That is, for $a = x_0 < x_1 < \cdots < x_n = b$, let

$$A_i = \{\omega \mid x_{i-1} < X(\omega) \leq x_i\}, \qquad i = 1, \ldots, n,$$

and let A_0 denote all points of Ω not in one of these sets. Then the sets $A_0, A_1, \ldots, A_n$ constitute a partition of Ω, and on the ith set, the inf and sup of the function $X(\omega)$ are, respectively, $m_i = x_{i-1}$ and $M_i = x_i$. The sums

$$\sum_{i=1}^{n} m_i P(A_i) = \sum_{i=1}^{n} x_{i-1}[F(x_i) - F(x_{i-1})]$$

and

$$\sum_{i=1}^{n} M_i P(A_i) = \sum_{i=1}^{n} x_i[F(x_i) - F(x_{i-1})]$$

are particular instances of sums whose sup and inf, respectively, define $\underline{E}$ and $\bar{E}$. Taking the sup and inf over all partitions of the present type, that is, generated by partitions of the interval $[a, b]$, yields numbers $\underline{I}$ and $\bar{I}$ which are ordered as follows:

$$\underline{I} \leq \underline{E} \leq \bar{E} \leq \bar{I}.$$

But $\underline{I} = \bar{I}$, and the Riemann-Stieltjes integral of x with respect to $F(X)$ is defined to be this common value; and, therefore, the quantities $\underline{E}$ and $\bar{E}$ must also be equal to each other and to this integral:

$$EX = \int_a^b x \, dF(x).$$

The case in which the distribution of X is not contained in a finite interval can be handled by introducing a truncated variable:

$$X_{A, B}(\omega) = \begin{cases} A, & \text{if } X(\omega) \leq A, \\ X(\omega), & \text{if } A < X(\omega) < B, \\ B, & \text{if } X(\omega) \geq B, \end{cases}$$

and passing[5] to the limit:

$$EX = \lim_{\substack{A \to -\infty \\ B \to \infty}} E(X_{A, B}) = \lim_{\substack{A \to -\infty \\ B \to \infty}} \int_A^B x \, dF(x) = \int_{-\infty}^{\infty} x \, dF(x).$$

In summary, then, it is seen that if the Riemann–Stieltjes integral of x with respect to $F(x)$ exists, then so does the expected value of X, and these are

---

[5] To do this it would be necessary to know that the expected value of the limit is the same as the limit of the expected value, a point that will not be considered here.

equal. The integral may fail to exist, but only if one or both of the integrals over $[0, \infty)$ and $(-\infty, 0]$ fail to exist (in the sense of not being finite).

The particular cases of discrete and continuous distributions can now be given in terms of a sum and an integral, since the Riemann–Stieltjes integral reduces to these:

Discrete: $EX = \sum_i x_i f(x_i),$

Continuous: $EX = \int_{-\infty}^{\infty} xf(x)\,dx,$

where $f(x)$ denotes the probability function or density function, as appropriate. It is to be observed that the mean value of a simple random variable turns out to be the same sum as that given earlier.

An important property of expectations, seen to hold when X is a simple random variable, is that of linearity:

$$E(aX + bY) = aEX + bEY.$$

This can be proved to hold generally. The method exploits the fact that an arbitrary random variable can be expressed as the limit of a sequence of simple random variables. Thus, if X_n is simple and tends to X, and Y_n is simple and tends to Y,

$$E(X + Y) = E(\lim X_n + \lim Y_n) = \lim E(X_n + Y_n)$$

$$= \lim [E(X_n) + E(Y_n)] = EX + EY.$$

For this to work, it is again necessary to interchange limiting and expectation operations, as discussed in a footnote earlier in this section.

EXAMPLE 2–43.   Consider a random variable with density

$$f(x) = K e^{-x^2/2},$$

where K is determined so that the area under the graph of $f(x)$ is 1. Since

$$\int_0^{\infty} x e^{-x^2/2}\,dx = \lim_{B \to \infty} (-e^{-x^2/2}) \Big|_0^B = 1,$$

and

$$\int_{-\infty}^0 x e^{-x^2/2}\,dx = \lim_{A \to -\infty} (-e^{-x^2/2}) \Big|_A^0 = -1,$$

it follows that the improper integral defining EX exists and is 0:

$$EX = \int_{-\infty}^{\infty} Kx\, e^{-x^2/2}\,dx = 0.$$

That is, the center (as measured by the mean) of this symmetrical distribution is 0, the center of symmetry.

EXAMPLE 2–44.   If X denotes the number of Tails preceding the first Heads in a sequence of independent tosses of a fair coin, with probability function

$$f(x) = P(X = x) = 1/2^{x+1}, \qquad x = 0, 1, \ldots,$$

the mean value of X is

$$EX = \sum_{i=0}^{\infty} i/2^{i+1} = 1,$$

as computed in an earlier example (2–42).

EXAMPLE 2–45.   Let X have the distribution defined by the c.d.f.

$$F(x) = \begin{cases} 0, & \text{if } x < 0, \\ 1 - .8e^{-x}, & \text{if } x \geq 0. \end{cases}$$

This is neither of the discrete nor of the continuous type. However, the appropriate Stieltjes integral was discussed in Example 2–41:

$$EX = \int_{-\infty}^{\infty} x \, dF(x) = 0 \times .2 + \int_{0}^{\infty} .8xe^{-x} \, dx = 0 + .8 = .8.$$

EXAMPLE 2–46.   Consider the density function

$$f(x) = \frac{1/\pi}{1 + x^2}.$$

Although this function goes down to zero fast enough (for large x) for the area to be finite, multiplication by x yields a function which goes to zero like $1/x$, and does not have a finite integral:

$$\int_{0}^{\infty} \frac{x \, dx/\pi}{1 + x^2} = \lim_{B \to \infty} \frac{1}{2\pi} \log (1 + x^2) \Big|_{0}^{B} = \infty.$$

The integral over $(-\infty, 0)$ would also be divergent, and divergence at either end is sufficient for EX not to exist.

Since a conditional distribution, say of X given $Y = y$ as obtained from a given joint distribution of (X, Y), is again a distribution, the concept of expected value applies to conditional distributions. The mean value of a conditional distribution of a random variable is called the *conditional mean*, just to refer to the origin of the distribution as obtained by imposing a condition on one of two variables in a bivariate distribution, but the computation of a conditional mean is no different.

EXAMPLE 2–47.   Let (X, Y) have the discrete distribution defined in the accompanying table (as in Problem 2–46).

Y \ X	1	2	3
2	$\frac{1}{12}$	$\frac{1}{6}$	$\frac{1}{12}$
3	$\frac{1}{6}$	0	$\frac{1}{6}$
4	0	$\frac{1}{3}$	0
	$\frac{1}{4}$	$\frac{1}{2}$	$\frac{1}{4}$

The conditional probabilities for $X = 1, 2, 3$ given $Y = 3$ are $\frac{1}{2}, 0, \frac{1}{2}$, respectively, so the conditional mean is

$$E(X \mid Y = 3) = 1 \cdot \tfrac{1}{2} + 2 \cdot 0 + 3 \cdot \tfrac{1}{2} = 2.$$

It can be seen, similarly, that the conditional mean given $Y = 2$ and the conditional mean given $Y = 4$ are also 2, and moreover, that the "unconditional" mean, or the mean of the marginal distribution of X, is also 2:

$$E(X) = 1 \cdot \tfrac{1}{4} + 2 \cdot \tfrac{1}{2} + 3 \cdot \tfrac{1}{4} = 2.$$

Observe, then, that the conditional mean *can* be independent of the condition and equal to the unconditional mean, even though the random variables are *not* independent.

EXAMPLE 2–48.   Given $f(x, y) = 6(1 - x - y)$ for $0 < y < 1 - x$, $x > 0$, and $f(x, y) = 0$ elsewhere, the conditional density (see Problem 2–48) is $f(x \mid y) = 2(1 - x - y)/(1 - y)^2$, for $0 < x < 1 - y$. The conditional mean, given $Y = y$, is then the integral of x with respect to this conditional density:

$$E(X \mid Y = y) = \int_{-\infty}^{\infty} x f(x \mid y) \, dx$$

$$= \int_{0}^{1-y} \frac{2(1 - x - y)x}{(1 - y)^2} \, dx = \frac{1}{3}(1 - y).$$

Problems

2–74.   Compute the expected value of a random variable X whose c.d.f. is $F(x) = x$, for $0 \le x \le 1$.

2–75.   Compute the expected value of a random variable Y whose density function is $f(y) = \frac{1}{2} \exp(-|y|)$

2–76.   Compute the expected value of the random variable Z whose density is $f(z) = 1 - |z|$, for $|z| < 1$, and $f(z) = 0$ outside that interval.

2–77.   Determine the mean value of the random variable X with density $6x(1 - x)$ for $0 < x < 1$ and 0 outside that interval.

2–78.   Determine the mean of the distribution with c.d.f. $(x + A)/(2A)$, for $|x| < A$.

2–79.   Determine the mean value of the random variable θ whose c.d.f. is $F_\theta(u) = 1 - \cos u$ for $0 \le u \le \pi/2$ (see Example 2–19).

2–80.   Show that if X has a density function $f(x)$ that is symmetrical about $x = a$: $f(a - x) = f(a + x)$ for all x, then if the mean value exists it must be $EX = a$.

2–81.   Given that (X, Y) has a joint density that is constant over the triangle with vertices $(0, 0)$, $(1, 0)$, $(0, 1)$, and zero outside this triangle, determine the conditional mean $E(X \mid y)$ as a function of y and the conditional mean $E(Y \mid x)$ as a function of x (see Example 2–28).

2–82.   Compute the conditional mean $E(X \mid Y = k)$ for the discrete bivariate distribution of Example 2–32:

$$f(x, y) = \tfrac{1}{6} \quad \text{for } x, y = 1, 2, 3, \quad \text{but } x \ne y.$$

2.2.4   *Expectation of a Function of Random Variables*

In discussing simple random variables, in Section 2.2.1, it was found that the expected value of a random variable Y that is defined as a function of another random variable X can be computed on at least two levels—using the distribution of Y, or using the distribution of X:

$$E[g(X)] = \sum_j y_j P(Y = y_j) = \sum_i g(x_i) P(X = x_i).$$

It will now be shown that the same situation obtains more generally, namely, that $E[g(X)]$ can be computed in terms of the distribution of X or in terms of the distribution of Y.

Suppose that $Y = g(X)$ has a distribution contained on the interior of a finite interval $[c, d]$, and that X is similarly restricted to the interior of a finite interval $[a, b]$. The random variable Y is really $Y(\omega) = g(X(\omega))$, where ω is a generic point in an underlying sample space Ω (which, of course, could be the space of X-values, with $X(x) = x$). A partition

$$c = y_0 < y_1 < \cdots < y_m = d$$

of the interval $[c, d]$ induces a partition $A_1, \ldots, A_m$ of Ω:

$$A_j = \{\omega \mid y_{j-1} < Y(\omega) \leq y_j\}.$$

Taking the inf and sup (over all such partitions) of lower and upper approximating sums, as introduced in the preceding section, leads (as it did there) to

$$E(Y) = \int_{-\infty}^{\infty} y \, dF_Y(y).$$

However, suppose instead one considers a partition of $[a, b]$:

$$a = x_0 < x_1 < \cdots < x_n = b.$$

This also induces a partition of Ω, say, $B_1, \ldots, B_n$. For each partition set B_i let M_i denote the sup, and m_i the inf of the values of $g(X(\omega))$. These are also the sup and inf, respectively, of the values of $g(x)$ on (x_{i-1}, x_i). But then if one defines

$$\underline{J} = \sup \sum m_i P(B_i) = \sup \sum m_i [F(x_i) - F(x_{i-1})]$$

and

$$\bar{J} = \inf \sum M_i P(B_i) = \inf \sum M_i [F(x_i) - F(x_{i-1})],$$

taken over all partitions induced by partitions of the interval $[a, b]$, these define, when equal, the Stieltjes integral of $g(x)$ with respect to $F(x)$. But they also include between them the quantities called $\bar{E}$ and $\underline{E}$—the inf and sup over *all* partitions of Ω. That is, if $\underline{J} = \bar{J}$, then $\underline{J} = \underline{E} = \bar{E} = \bar{J}$, and so

$$E(Y) = E(g(X)) = \int_{-\infty}^{\infty} g(x)\, dF_X(x).$$

(According to the development given, this integral should extend over the interval from $x = a$ to $x = b$, although if the entire distribution is contained on that interval, there is no harm in writing the limits as $-\infty$ and ∞, since $dF(x)$ would vanish outside $[a, b]$. However, if the distribution is not confined to a finite interval, the truncation argument used in the preceding section yields the above as a general formula.)

EXAMPLE 2–49.   Suppose that X has a distribution with density function $K \exp(-x^2/2)$, as in Example 2–43. Let $Y = |X|$. The mean value of Y is determined as follows:

$$\begin{aligned}
E\,Y &= \int_{-\infty}^{\infty} |x|\, dF_X(x) = K \int_{-\infty}^{\infty} |x| \exp(-x^2/2)\, dx \\
&= K \int_{0}^{\infty} x \exp(-x^2/2)\, dx - K \int_{-\infty}^{0} x \exp(-x^2/2)\, dx \\
&= 2K \int_{0}^{\infty} x \exp(-x^2/2)\, dx = 2K.
\end{aligned}$$

Since K turns out to be $1/\sqrt{2\pi}$ (as computed in Example 2–22), the result is finally $E|X| = \sqrt{2/\pi}$.

EXAMPLE 2–50.   Let $I_A(x)$ denote the indicator function of the event A:

$$I_A(x) = \begin{cases} 1, & \text{if } x \text{ is in } A, \\ 0, & \text{if } x \text{ is not in } A. \end{cases}$$

The expected value of the random variable $Y = I_A(X)$ is the probability of the event A:

$$E[I_A(X)] = 1 \cdot P(A) + 0 \cdot P(A^c) = P(A).$$

If A is an interval, one can write this expected value as a Stieltjes integral, and so obtain

$$P(A) = \int_A dF_X(x).$$

If this integral is defined to be $E[I_A(X)]$ when A is not an interval, the last relation may be considered as applying to any event A. One defines the integral of a function $g(x)$ over an event A similarly, as

$$\int_A g(x)\, dF_X(x) = \int_{-\infty}^{\infty} I_A(x) g(x)\, dF_X(x),$$

if this last integral exists. When it does, it is equal to an expected value:

$$E[I_A(X) g(X)] = \int_A g(x)\, dF_X(x).$$

In Section 2.1.8, dealing with conditional distributions, it was found that one property of conditional probability functions is this:

$$P(A) = \sum_j P(A \mid Y = y_j) f_Y(y_j),$$

for the case of discrete Y. The analog for the continuous case was used as a criterion to be satisfied by a reasonable definition of conditional density, namely

$$P(A) = \int_{-\infty}^{\infty} P(A \mid Y = y) f_Y(y) \, dy.$$

Upon comparison of these with the formula for the expected value of a function of a random variable, it is seen that these are special cases. That is,

$$P(A) \doteq Eg(Y), \qquad \text{where } g(y) = P(A \mid Y = y).$$

Thus, the conditional probabilities are averaged over the possible values of the conditioning variable to obtain an unconditioned probability. The result is often written:

$$P(A) = E[P(A \mid Y)], \quad \text{or} \quad P(A) = E_Y[P(A \mid Y)].$$

This last result can be used, in turn, to show that averaging conditional expectations with respect to the conditioning variable yields the unconditional expectation. In the above formula, let A denote the event $\{X \le x\}$, and so obtain

$$F_X(x) = P(X \le x) = E[P(X \le x \mid Y)] = \int_{-\infty}^{\infty} F(x \mid y) \, dF_Y(y).$$

It then follows that

$$EX = \int_{-\infty}^{\infty} x \, dF_X(x) = \int_{-\infty}^{\infty} \left\{ \int_{-\infty}^{\infty} x \, dF(x \mid y) \right\} dF_Y(y)$$

$$= \int_{-\infty}^{\infty} E(X \mid y) \, dF_Y(y).$$

This is also written in the condensed form

$$EX = E_Y[E(X \mid Y)],$$

which means

$$EX = E[h(Y)], \qquad \text{where } h(y) = E(X \mid Y = y).$$

EXAMPLE 2–51.   Let (X, Y) have the joint density

$$f(x, y) = \begin{cases} 2, & \text{for } x + y \le 1, \quad x \ge 0, \quad y \ge 0, \\ 0, & \text{elsewhere.} \end{cases}$$

The marginal density of Y (as in Example 2–28) is

$$f_Y(y) = \int_{-\infty}^{\infty} f(x, y)\, dx = \int_0^{1-y} 2\, dx = 2(1 - y), \quad 0 < y < 1,$$

and the conditional density of X given $Y = y$ is

$$f(x \mid y) = \frac{f(x, y)}{f_Y(y)} = \frac{2}{2(1 - y)}, \quad \text{for } 0 < x < 1 - y.$$

The conditional mean of X given $Y = y$ is then

$$E(X \mid y) = \frac{1}{1 - y} \int_0^{1-y} x\, dx = (1 - y)/2.$$

Integrating this with respect to the distribution of Y yields the (unconditional) mean of X:

$$E X = E_Y[E(X \mid Y)] = \int_0^1 [(1 - y)/2]\, 2(1 - y)\, dy = 1/3.$$

A function of two random variables also defines a random variable:

$$Z = g(X, Y),$$

and it is desirable to be able to compute EZ from the joint distribution of (X, Y) without going through the intermediate step of determining the distribution of Z. This is done in a manner similar to that of the case of a function of a single variable, but now the Stieltjes integral is more complicated. Rather than give the derivation, even in outline, it will perhaps suffice for the present purposes to give the results. In the case of a discrete distribution with probability function

$$f(x, y) = P(X = x, Y = y),$$

the formula is

$$E[g(X, Y)] = \sum g(x, y)f(x, y),$$

where the sum extends over all possible pairs (x, y). This result is actually not so hard to derive directly; the more involved derivation is needed for the nondiscrete cases. If (X, Y) has a continuous distribution in the plane with density function $f(x, y)$, the formula is

$$E[g(X, Y)] = \int\int g(x, y)f(x, y)\, dx\, dy,$$

where the double integral extends over the whole xy-plane, and is evaluated in the usual way as an iterated integral (either with respect to the given coordinates, or in terms of some other convenient coordinates).

EXAMPLE 2–52. Consider the joint density $f(x, y) = \exp(-x - y)$, for $x > 0$ and $y > 0$. If (X, Y) is distributed with this density, the expected product is evaluated as follows:

$$E(XY) = \int_0^\infty \int_0^\infty xy\, e^{-x} e^{-y}\, dx\, dy = 1.$$

The sum of two random variables is an instance of a function of two random variables: $Z = X + Y$. It was already pointed out in the preceding section that the expected value of a sum is the sum of the expected values, and this can now be seen as follows, for the continuous case:

$$E(X + Y) = \int\int (x + y)f(x, y)\, dx\, dy$$

$$= \int\int xf(x, y)\, dx\, dy + \int\int yf(x, y)\, dx\, dy$$

$$= EX + EY,$$

where all integrals extend from $-\infty$ to ∞. Thus, the additivity of the expected value is essentially the additivity of the double integral in terms of which $E(\cdot)$ is evaluated. One step in the above reasoning exploits the fact that X is also a special case of a function of (X, Y). For this function, the equivalence of the two ways of evaluating the mean is seen as follows:

$$EX = \int\int xf(x, y)\, dy\, dx = \int x\left\{\int f(x, y)\, dy\right\} dx$$

$$= \int xf_X(x)\, dx = EX.$$

Problems

2–83. Let X have a density that is constant over $-1 \leq x \leq 1$ and zero outside that interval. Determine $E(X^2)$ in two ways—in terms of the distribution of X, and in terms of the distribution of $Y = X^2$.

2–84. Compute $E|X|$, where X is the random variable of the preceding problem.

2–85. Let θ have the density function

$$f_\theta(u) = \sin u, \qquad \text{for } 0 < u < \pi/2,$$

(as in Example 2–10). Determine $E(\cos \theta)$ in two ways—by using the given density of θ, and also by using the density function of the random variable $Y = \cos \theta$.

2–86. Determine $E(\cos^2 \theta)$, where θ is the random variable of the preceding problem.

2–87. Let Y denote a random variable with probability function $f(k) = 1/2^k$, for $k = 1, 2, \ldots$ [This is the variable $U(\omega)$ in Problem 2–3, and is $1 + X$ for the X in Problem 2–27(b).] Try to compute EZ, where $Z = 2^Y$.

2–88. Show that if $P(A) = 0$, and $I_A(x)$ is the indicator function of the event A, then $E[I_A(X)g(X)] = 0$. [*Hint*: Evaluate the upper and lower approximating sums for this expectation using the partition in the sample space defined by the partition of $(-\infty, \infty)$ into A and its complement A^c.]

2–89. Show that if

$$\int_{-\infty}^{\infty} I_A(x)\, g(x)\, dF_X(x)$$

exists but is not zero, then $P(A) > 0$.

2–90. Show that if X and Y are independent, then $E(X \mid y) = EX$.

2–91. Consider the random vector (X, Y) with joint density function

$$f(x, y) = \begin{cases} (4xy)^{-1/2}, & \text{for } 0 < x < y < 1, \\ 0, & \text{elsewhere.} \end{cases}$$

Determine the conditional mean of Y given $X = x$ and then average this with respect to the marginal distribution of X to verify the relation $E[E(Y \mid X)] = EY$.

2–92. Let $E_1, E_2, \ldots$ constitute a partition of the sample space of an experiment. Show that

$$E(X) = \sum E(X \mid E_i) P(E_i).$$

2–93. Let $h(x)$ be a nonnegative function such that on a certain set B, $h(x) \geq b > 0$. By using the partition $\{B, B^c\}$ in the preceding problem, show that $E[h(X)] \geq bP(B)$. (The "X" of that problem can be replaced by the $h(X)$ in this one.)

2–94. Given the joint density of (X, Y) to be

$$f(x, y) = 6(1 - x - y), \qquad 0 < y < 1 - x < 1,$$

compute $E(XY)$.

2–95. If (X, Y) has the joint density $f(x, y) = 2$, for $0 < x < y < 1$,

(a) compute $E(Y - X)$.
(b) compute $E(Y \mid X)$.

2.3 Moments of Probability Distributions

The quantity $E[(X - b)^k]$, when it exists, is called the *k*th *moment* of the random variable X (or of the distribution of X) *about the point* $x = b$. Moments about $x = 0$:

$$\mu_k' = EX^k$$

are sometimes called, simply, "moments," and moments about $\mu_X = \mu_1' = EX$:

$$\mu_k = E[(X - \mu_X)^k],$$

are called *central moments*. The term *absolute moment* denotes the quantity $E(|X - b|^k)$. In any case the integer k is referred to as the *order* of the moment.

The moments of a distribution are descriptive measures computed from the distribution (as characterized by its c.d.f. or density or probability function). The mean or expected value, that is, the first moment, is a measure of centering or location. Higher order moments measure or describe other aspects of a distribution. One of the interesting and well-studied problems of distribution theory is to determine under what circumstances a knowledge of moments determines a distribution (the "moment problem").

The moments of a conditional distribution are called *conditional moments*. The term "conditional" refers to the origin of the distribution—as one obtained from a joint distribution by specifying the condition that some event has occurred.

2.3.1   The Variance

The second central moment is commonly employed as a measure of dispersion or variability, and is called the *variance* of the distribution or of a random variable having the given distribution:

$$\text{var } X = E[(X - \mu_X)^2].$$

This will also be denoted frequently by σ^2, or by $\sigma_X{}^2$ if the extra identification is needed to avoid confusion. Its square root would be measured in the same units as X, and is called the *standard deviation*:

$$\sigma_X = \sqrt{\sigma_X{}^2}.$$

EXAMPLE 2-53.   Consider the continuous random variables X with density e^{-x} for $x > 0$. The mean value is 1, and so the variance is

$$\text{var } X = \int_{-\infty}^{\infty} (x - 1)^2 e^{-x} dx = 1.$$

The standard deviation is then also 1.

An important relation between the variance and other second moments is the following "parallel axis theorem":

$$E[(X - a)^2] = \text{var } X + (\mu - a)^2.$$

This is established by adding and subtracting μ from $X - a$, regrouping and expanding the result as a binomial:

$$(X - a)^2 = [(X - \mu) + (\mu - a)]^2$$
$$= (X - \mu)^2 + 2(X - \mu)(\mu - a) + (\mu - a)^2.$$

The expected value of this is the sum of the expected values of the three terms on the right; the expected value of the first term is the variance, the expected value of $(\mu - a)^2$ is just that constant, and the expected value of the middle term is zero:

$$E[2(X - \mu)(\mu - a)] = 2(\mu - a)E(X - \mu) = 0.$$

A useful special case of the parallel axis theorem is obtained upon setting a equal to 0:

$$\text{var } X = EX^2 - \mu^2.$$

Notice, then, that the expected square of a random variable is *not* the same as the square of the expected value, and that the difference of these two quantities defines the variance.

The parallel axis theorem provides a characterization of the variance of a random variable as the *smallest* second moment, that is, as compared with second moments about other points than μ. For, the mean square deviation about $x = a$ is equal to the variance *plus* the nonnegative quantity $(\mu - a)^2$, which assumes its smallest value (0), when $\mu = a$.

EXAMPLE 2–54.   In the following table of values of a random variable X and corresponding probabilities, columns are also given which are used to calculate the mean and expected square of X:

x_i	p_i	$x_i p_i$	$x_i^2 p_i$
0	8/27	0	0
1	12/27	12/27	12/27
2	6/27	12/27	24/27
3	1/27	3/27	9/27
	1	1	45/27

Thus, $EX = 1$, and $EX^2 = 45/27 = 5/3$. From these values one can compute the variance using the parallel axis theorem:

$$\text{var } X = EX^2 - (EX)^2 = 5/3 - 1^2 = 2/3.$$

The second moment about $x = a$ can be expressed in the form

$$E[(X - a)^2] = 2/3 + (1 - a)^2.$$

This gives $5/3$ when $a = 0$, $2/3$ when $a = 1$ (as computed above), $14/3$ when $a = 3$, etc. The smallest of these is of course $2/3$.

Given a joint distribution of (X, Y), the conditional variance of X given $Y = y$ is

$$\text{var } (X \mid y) = E\{(X - E(X \mid y))^2 \mid y\} = E(X^2 \mid y) - [E(X \mid y)]^2.$$

Although averaging a conditional mean with respect to the distribution of the conditioning variable produces the unconditional mean, this scheme does not quite work with the variance. That is, although one might expect that $E[\text{var}(Y \mid X)]$ would be equal to var Y, the correct relation is

$$\text{var } Y = E[\text{var } (Y \mid X)] + \text{var } [E(Y \mid X)].$$

For, upon using the parallel axis theorem in each term on the right, one obtains

$$E[E(Y^2 \mid X) - (E(Y \mid X))^2] + E\{(E(Y \mid X))^2\} - \{E(E(Y \mid X))\}^2$$

$$= E[E(Y^2 \mid X)] - [E(E(Y \mid X))]^2 = E Y^2 - (E Y)^2 = \text{var } Y.$$

2.3.2   Chebyshev and Related Inequalities

The Chebyshev inequality is a useful theoretical tool, as well as a relation that shows in what sense the variance of a distribution measures the dispersion of probability. It and various other inequalities follow from a somewhat more general and basic inequality.

Let $h(x)$ denote a nonnegative function that is bounded away from 0 in a set A:

$$h(x) \geq b > 0, \qquad \text{for } x \text{ in } A.$$

The integral defining the expected value of the random variable $h(X)$ can be expressed as the sum of an integral over A and an integral over the complement, A^c:

$$E[h(X)] = \int_{-\infty}^{\infty} h(x) \, dF_X(x) = \int_A h(x) \, dF_X(x) + \int_{A^c} h(x) \, dF_X(x).$$

If the second term is dropped, the right-hand side is made smaller; and if in the first term the integrand is replaced by b (which is no larger than $h(x)$ on A), again the effect is to make the right-hand side smaller. Hence,

$$E[h(X)] \geq b \int_A dF_X(x) = bP(A).$$

Division by b yields the *basic inequality*:

$$P(A) \leq \frac{1}{b} E[h(X)].$$

(See Problem 2–93 for an alternative proof.)

Chebyshev's inequality is now obtained by taking $h(x)$ to be the particular function $h(x) = (x - \mu)^2$, and A to be the set on which $|X - \mu| \geq c > 0$, where X is a given random variable with mean μ and variance σ^2. With these particular choices, the basic inequality reduces to

$$P(|X - \mu| \geq c) \leq \frac{1}{c^2} E(|X - \mu|^2) = \frac{\sigma^2}{c^2},$$

since $h(x)$ is surely no smaller than c^2 on the specified A. If $c = k\sigma$, then

$$P(|X - \mu| \geq k\sigma) \leq \frac{1}{k^2}.$$

EXAMPLE 2–55.   If Z has the distribution function given in Table I (see Appendix), in which the mean is zero and the variance is 1, then

$$P(|Z - EZ| > 3\sigma_Z) = P(|Z| > 3) = .0026,$$

which is, indeed, less than $1/3^2 = 1/9$.

   This example shows that the Chebyshev bound is sometimes very crude— depending on how much is thrown away in the proof of the inequality. On the other hand, for *all* distributions (with second moments) the probability outside ± 3 standard deviations on either side of the mean does not exceed 1/9. For some distributions this probability may be zero, and for the one in the preceding example it is .0026. In the next example there is given a distribution in which the Chebyshev bound is actually attained for a certain value of k, showing that in the general inequality the bound could not be improved without further assumptions on the distribution.

EXAMPLE 2–56.   Suppose that X assumes the values 1 and -1, each with probability .5. Then $EX = 0$ and var $X = 1$, and

$$P(|X - EX| \geq \sigma_X) = 1 - P(-1 < X < 1) = 1.$$

But 1 is precisely the Chebyshev bound for this probability, and so the inequality becomes an equality.

   In that at most 1/4 of a distribution can be placed outside the range $\mu \pm 2\sigma$, at most 1/9 outside the range $\mu \pm 3\sigma$, at most .01 outside the range $\mu \pm 10\sigma$, etc., the Chebyshev inequality does indeed relate the standard deviation to the dispersion of probability about the center of the distribution. Problem 2–106 also has to do with this relationship. Yet another aspect of this relationship is the following, which is not an instance of an application of Chebyshev's inequality, but is one in which a similar decomposition of an expected value is employed.

   That a standard deviation is a deviation about the mean that cannot extend beyond the range in which probability is distributed is seen in the fact that if

$P(|X - \mu| > K) = 0$, then $\sigma \leq K$. To prove this it suffices to show that if $\sigma > K$, then $P(|X - \mu| > K) > 0$. To see this, notice that if $\sigma > K$ and B denotes the set $\{|X - \mu| \leq K\}$, then

$$K^2 < \sigma^2 = \int_B (x - \mu)^2 \, dF(x) + \int_{B^c} (x - \mu)^2 \, dF(x)$$

$$\leq K^2 + \int_{B^c} (x - \mu)^2 \, dF(x).$$

Canceling the K^2 one finds that the last integral must be positive, which means (according to Problem 2–89) that the set over which it is taken must have positive probability. And then

$$P(|X - \mu| > K) = P(B^c) > 0,$$

which was to be shown.

Problems

2–96. Determine the variance of the number of defectives among a random selection of four from ten articles of which two are defective (see Problem 2–59).

2–97. Determine the variance of a random variable with c.d.f. x^2 for x in the interval $[0, 1]$ (and 0 for $x < 0$, 1 for $x > 1$).

2–98. Determine the variance of a random variable with density

$$f(x) = \begin{cases} 1 - |x|, & \text{for } |x| < 1, \\ 0, & \text{elsewhere.} \end{cases}$$

(see Problem 2–76.)

2–99. Determine the variance of the distribution defined by the c.d.f.

$$F(x) = \begin{cases} 0, & \text{for } x < 0, \\ 1 - .8e^{-x}, & \text{for } x \geq 0. \end{cases}$$

(see Example 2–41, page 104.)

2–100. Determine the variance of the random variable $Y = (X - \mu)/\sigma$, where μ and σ^2 are the mean and variance of X, respectively. (This is called a "standardizing" transformation.)

2–101. Show that $E[(X - \mu)^3] = E(X^3) - 3\mu\sigma^2 - \mu^3$, where μ and σ^2 are the mean and variance of X, respectively.

2–102. The random variable X takes on values $-a$, 0, a with probabilities $\frac{1}{8}, \frac{3}{4}, \frac{1}{8}$, respectively. Compute $P(|X| \geq 2\sigma)$ and compare with the Chebyshev bound for this probability.

2–103. Referring to Table II, page 481, the row marked "4 degrees of freedom" gives percentiles of a certain distribution. Let X be a random variable having this distribution, and compute $P(|X - 4| > 8)$. Given that $EX = 4$ and var $X = 8$, determine also the Chebyshev bound for this probability.

2–104. Show that for $c > 0$, $P(|X| > c) \leq (1/c) E|X|$, if $E|X|$ exists.

2–105. Show that $E(|X - a|)$ is a minimum, given that X has a continuous distribution, when a is the median of X. [*Hint*: Write the given expectation as an integral, and express it as the sum of the integral over $x \leq a$ and the integral over $x > a$; then minimize by setting the derivative with respect to a equal to zero.]

2–106. Show that $\sigma > K > 0$ implies $P(|X| > K) > 0$. [*Hint:* Observe that $\sigma^2 \leq EX^2$ and decompose this expectation into the sum of integrals over $|x| > K$ and $|x| \leq K$.]

2–107. Show that if var $X = 0$, then $P(X = \mu) = 1$. [*Hint:* The event $X = \mu$ is the intersection of the decreasing sequence of sets $\{|X - \mu| < 1/n\}$, for $n = 1, 2, 3, \ldots$. Use the Chebyshev inequality to bound the probability of each set of this sequence and then pass to the limit as n becomes infinite.]

2–108. Show that $E[\text{var}(Y|X)] = \text{var } Y$ if and only if $E(Y \mid x)$ is essentially independent of x (that is, if $E(Y \mid X) = EY$ with probability 1).

2.3.3   Mixed Moments and Correlation

Given a bivariate distribution of (X, Y), the quantity

$$E[(X - a)^r(Y - b)^s]$$

is called a *mixed moment* if r and s are not zero. Of particular utility and importance is the following second-order mixed moment, called the *covariance* of X and Y:

$$\text{cov}(X, Y) = E[(X - \mu_X)(Y - \mu_Y)] = E(XY) - (EX)(EY).$$

(The second expression given for this covariance is easily derived by multiplying out the product $(X - \mu_X)(Y - \mu_Y)$ and averaging term by term. It corresponds to the parallel axis theorem for the variance.) The covariance will also be denoted by $\sigma_{X,Y}$.

EXAMPLE 2–57.   Consider the discrete distribution of (X, Y) defined in the following table of probabilities:

Y \ X	6	8	10
1	.2	0	.2
2	0	.2	0
3	.2	0	.2

The expected value of X is 8, and that of Y is 2. (These are evident from the symmetry of the marginal distributions.) The expected product is obtained by calculating the sum of the various possible products, each weighted with the probability for that particular pair of values:

$$E(XY) = 6 \times .2 + 10 \times .2 + 16 \times .2 + 18 \times .2 + 30 \times .2 = 16.$$

The covariance is then

$$\text{cov}(X, Y) = E(XY) - (EX)(EY) = 16 - 16 = 0.$$

This last example illustrates the fact that although it might be tempting to assume that independence and a covariance of zero are equivalent, this is not the case. It is true that if X and Y are independent, then the expected product is the product of expectations:

$$E(XY) - (EX)(EY) = 0, \qquad (X \text{ and } Y \text{ independent}).$$

However, in the distribution of (X, Y) in the above example, cov $(X, Y) = 0$, even though (clearly) X and Y cannot be independent (that is, with the zeros in the table corresponding to marginal values with nonzero probabilities). The 0 covariance results from the symmetry of the distribution —there is a positive product $(X - \mu_X)(Y - \mu_Y)$ for each negative one, and they all average out to zero since they carry equal probability weights.

The term "covariance" itself comes from the notion that this quantity purports to measure "covariation"—to be indicative of the degree to which the variables are concordant or coherent. If X tends to be large when Y is large and small when Y is small (in the algebraic sense), then the covariance will be positive; if large values of X tend to correspond to small values of Y, the covariance will be negative; if there is no such tendency—if knowing that X is large does not give much information as to the tendency of Y—the covariance will be close to zero.

The covariance is really a poor measure of coherence, in that it is sensitive to the scale of measurement adopted—being multiplied by any scale factor introduced in one variable or the other. That is, for example, if X and Y are measured in numbers of inches, the covariance will be 144 times what it would be if they were measured in numbers of feet. To obtain a measure of coherence that does not have this defect, the *correlation coefficient* is used, denoted and defined as follows:

$$\rho_{X,Y} = \frac{\sigma_{X,Y}}{\sigma_X \sigma_Y}.$$

Here a scale change in X would introduce a factor in σ_X as well as in $\sigma_{X,Y}$, and these would cancel.

The correlation coefficient will be zero when X and Y are independent, since it is proportional to the covariance. But again, the correlation coefficient can be zero even when there is dependence, and will be near zero when information about the value of one variable does not suggest or imply that the other variable is likely to be on one particular side of its mean. But perhaps it is best to consider directly the significance of a numerically large correlation, and then one question immediately poses itself—how large is "large"? That is, how large can the correlation coefficient be?

That the correlation coefficient is actually limited in magnitude to 1 can be seen from the following inequality:

$$|\sigma_{X,Y}| \leq \sigma_X \sigma_Y,$$

which yields the asserted bound for $\rho_{X,Y}$ upon division by $\sigma_X \sigma_Y$:

$$|\rho_{X,Y}| \leq 1.$$

To prove this, consider the nonnegative random variable $(U - kV)^2$, where U and V are random variables and k is a real constant. The expectation of this variable is surely nonnegative:

$$0 \leq E[(U - kV)^2] = k^2 E(V^2) - 2kE(UV) + E(U^2).$$

In order for a quadratic function of k, such as this, to be nonnegative for all real k, it is necessary and sufficient for its discriminant to be nonpositive:

$$[E(UV)]^2 - E(U^2)E(V^2) \leq 0.$$

This is a form of the *Schwarz inequality*. Setting $U = X - EX$ and $V = Y - EY$ yields the desired result.

The significance of the extreme cases, $\rho = +1$ or -1, is of interest. In either case the discriminant above is actually zero, which would mean that the parabola representing the quadratic in k just touches the k-axis at some point. That is, there is some value of k such that the quadratic is equal to zero:

$$E[(U - kV)^2] = 0, \qquad \text{for some } k.$$

But this in turn implies that

$$P(U = kV) = 1, \qquad \text{for some } k.$$

That is, a correlation of $+1$ or -1 implies that $X - EX$ is, with probability 1, just a multiple of $Y - EY$; in other words, X and Y are linearly related with probability 1. The joint distribution of (X, Y) is then concentrated along the straight line representing that linear relationship. And then, of course, if the value of one variable is given, the value of the other variable can be deduced. (The joint distribution is bivariate only in the singular sense, and one variable is unessential). The correlation $\rho_{X,Y}$ is often, for these reasons, called a coefficient of *linear* correlation.

EXAMPLE 2–58. Consider the density function

$$f(x, y) = \begin{cases} 8xy, & \text{if } 0 \leq x \leq y \leq 1, \\ 0, & \text{otherwise.} \end{cases}$$

The marginal density functions are $4x(1 - x^2)$ and $4y^3$, each defined on $[0, 1]$.

From these can be computed the means and variances: $E(X) = 8/15$, $E(Y) = 4/5$, var $X = 11/225$, and var $Y = 2/75$. The expected product is

$$E(XY) = \int_0^1 \int_0^y xy\, 8xy\, dx\, dy = 4/9,$$

and then

$$\rho_{X,Y} = \frac{E(XY) - E(X)E(Y)}{[(\text{var } X)(\text{var } Y)]^{1/2}} = \frac{4/9 - 32/75}{[(2/75)(11/225)]^{1/2}} = \frac{4}{\sqrt{66}}.$$

Problems

2–109. Show that (as claimed in the text) cov $(X, Y) = E(XY) - (EX)(EY)$.

2–110. Compute the correlation coefficient for the discrete bivariate distribution given in Example 2–47, page 109.

2–111. Show that X and Y are uncorrelated, given their joint distribution according to the following table of probabilities. Are they independent?

X Y	−1	0	1
0	.1	.1	.1
2	.1	.2	.1
4	.1	.1	.1

2–112. Compute the coefficient of correlation in the bivariate distribution with density $f(x, y) = 2$ for $x + y \le 1$, $x \ge 0$, $y \ge 0$.

2–113. Consider the random orientation (θ, ϕ), as considered in Example 2–21 with joint density function $f_{\theta,\phi}(u, v) = (\sin u)/2\pi$ for $0 < \theta < \pi/2$, $0 < \phi < 2\pi$. Show that the variables $X = \cos\phi \sin\theta$ and $Y = \sin\phi \sin\theta$ are uncorrelated, even though (as shown in Problem 2–50) they are not independent.

2–114. Use the Schwarz inequality to show that if $E(X^2)$ is finite, so is EX.

2–115. Given the discrete distribution defined by the following table of probabilities:

X Y	0	2	4
1	1/4	0	1/4
2	1/12	1/3	1/12

(a) Compute the coefficient of correlation.

(b) Compute the covariance of X and Y given $X \ne 4$.

(c) Compute $E(Y \mid X = 0)$.

2–116. Two beads are selected at random (no replacement) from a bowl containing 4 white, 1 red, and 2 black beads. Let X denote the number of red and Y the number of black beads in the selection. Determine cov (X, Y).

2.3.4   *Variance of a Sum*

Consider first a sum of two random variables, $Z = X + Y$. Since the expected value of the sum is the sum of the expectations,

$$Z - EZ = (X - EX) + (Y - EY).$$

The variance of the sum is the average square of this deviation:

$$\text{var}\,(X + Y) = E[(Z - EZ)^2]$$

$$= E[(X - EX)^2 + (Y - EY)^2 + 2(X - EX)(Y - EY)]$$

$$= \text{var}\,X + \text{var}\,Y + 2\,\text{cov}\,(X, Y).$$

So the variance is *not* additive, unless, perchance, the variables are *uncorrelated*, in which case

$$\text{var}\,(X + Y) = \text{var}\,X + \text{var}\,Y, \qquad (X \text{ and } Y \text{ uncorrelated}).$$

And surely if X and Y are independent, this relation holds since they are then also uncorrelated.

If $Z = aX + bY$, the above formula for the variance of a sum is applied to the variables aX and bY to obtain

$$\text{var}\,(aX + bY) = a^2\,\text{var}\,X + b^2\,\text{var}\,Y + 2ab\,\text{cov}\,(X, Y).$$

In particular, notice that if X and Y are uncorrelated, then

$$\text{var}\,(X - Y) = \text{var}\,[X + (-Y)] = \text{var}\,X + \text{var}\,Y,$$

and not (as might be naïvely expected) the difference of the variances.

The preceding discussion provides the possibility of an instructive and helpful geometric representation for random variables (that have finite variances). Consider two vectors in the plane whose lengths are proportional to σ_X and σ_Y, respectively, and separated by an angle θ whose cosine is $\rho_{X,Y}$. The length of the diagonal of the parallelogram determined by them can be computed using the law of cosines (see Figure 2–20):

$$d^2 = \sigma_X{}^2 + \sigma_Y{}^2 - 2\sigma_X\sigma_Y\cos(\pi - \theta) = \sigma_X{}^2 + \sigma_Y{}^2 + 2\sigma_X\sigma_Y\rho_{X,Y}$$

$$= \sigma_X{}^2 + \sigma_Y{}^2 + 2\sigma_{X,Y} = \text{var}\,(X + Y).$$

Thus, the length of the diagonal d is the standard deviation of $X + Y$, and so the addition of the random variables X and Y corresponds to vector addition (according to the parallelogram law) of the vectors representing them. In terms of this representation, a correlation of 0 corresponds to perpendicularity of the vectors X and Y, in which case $\text{var}\,(X + Y) = \text{var}\,X + \text{var}\,Y$. A correlation of 1 corresponds to the pointing of the vectors in the same direction—one is a multiple of the other, and a correlation of -1 corresponds to vectors pointing in opposite directions. All of this may be stated more precisely by saying that random variables with finite variance constitute a linear vector space, with an "inner product" of two random variables defined as their covariance.

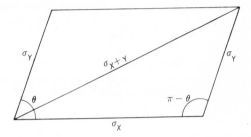

Figure 2–20. Vector representation of random variables.

Consider next the case of n random variables, $X_1, X_2, \ldots, X_n$. Reasoning exactly as in the case of two random variables, one obtains

$$\text{var} (X_1 + \cdots + X_n) = E\{[\sum_i (X_i - E X_i)]^2\}$$

$$= E\{\sum_j \sum_i (X_i - E X_i)(X_j - E X_j)\}$$

$$= \sum_j \sum_i E[(X_i - E X_i)(X_j - E X_j)]$$

$$= \sum_j \sum_i \text{cov} (X_i, X_j),$$

where, of course, $\text{cov} (X_i, X_i) = \text{var } X_i$. The terms in this sum can be thought of as laid out in a square array, corresponding to $i = 1, \ldots, n$ horizontally and to $j = 1, \ldots, n$ vertically, with $i = j$ along the main diagonal. Of the n^2 terms, n are variances and the remaining $n^2 - n$ are covariances; the covariances above the diagonal have matching covariances below the diagonal, since $\text{cov} (X_i, X_j) = \text{cov} (X_j, X_i)$. Finally, then, the variance of the sum can be written as follows:

$$\text{var} (\sum_i X_i) = \sum_i \text{var } X_i + \sum_{i \neq j} \text{cov} (X_i, X_j)$$

$$= \sum_i \text{var } X_i + 2 \sum_{i > j} \text{cov} (X_i, X_j).$$

In the important special cases in which the X's are mutually uncorrelated, each covariance is zero and the variance becomes additive:

$$\text{var} (\sum_i X_i) = \sum_i \text{var } X_i, \qquad (X_i\text{'s pairwise uncorrelated}).$$

One of the important applications of this last result is in the realm of error analysis, in which it is often possible to express a system error as a linear combination of independent, component errors (although sometimes only to a first approximation). The following examples illustrate this.

EXAMPLE 2–59. When resistors are placed in "series," the resistance of the combination is the sum of the individual resistances. Suppose that two 400-ohm and one 200-ohm resistors are placed in series and that they are "5 per cent" resistors. Let us assume that a "5 per cent" resistor is one of a population of resistors whose resistances have a probability distribution about the nominal resistance with a standard deviation that is 5 per cent of the nominal resistance. Then the standard deviations of the given resistances are 20, 20, and 10 ohms, respectively. The standard deviation of the resistance of the series combination is

$$(20^2 + 20^2 + 10^2)^{1/2} = 30 \text{ ohms},$$

which is 3 per cent of the nominal series resistance of 1,000 ohms. The series combination (considered as one of possible series combinations made up at random from the populations of 400-ohm and 200-ohm resistors) has a precision that is better than that of the components.

[It must be admitted that the "5 per cent" label on a resistor is probably not to be interpreted as one standard deviation. This might even vary with the individual manufacturer; but if the measure of variability quoted is *proportional* to the standard deviation, the preceding calculation of percentage would remain valid. At any rate, it is usually not appropriate to add the absolute values of the tolerance figures given (to obtain 50 ohms or 5 per cent in the example cited), since the probability is small that the errors would combine without some cancellation of positive and negative errors.]

EXAMPLE 2–60. Suppose that a quantity is to be computed as the quotient of two measured quantities:

$$A = B/C.$$

If B and C contain errors:

$$B = B_0 + \beta, \qquad C = C_0 + \gamma$$

the computed value of A will be correspondingly in error:

$$A = A_0 + \alpha = B_0/C_0 + \alpha,$$

where then

$$\alpha = A - A_0 = \frac{B_0 + \beta}{C_0 + \gamma} - \frac{B_0}{C_0} \doteq \frac{1}{C_0^2}(C_0\beta - B_0\gamma).$$

This last approximation to the increment in A is just the differential. The variance of the error in A is approximately the variance of this linear combination of β and γ:

$$\operatorname{var}\alpha \doteq \frac{1}{C_0^2}(\operatorname{var}\beta) + \frac{B_0^2}{C_0^4}(\operatorname{var}\gamma).$$

Problems

2–117.   Thirteen cards are drawn at random (without replacement, as in dealing) from a standard bridge deck. Let $X_1, \ldots, X_{13}$ denote the numbers of points
assigned to the cards drawn (as in Problems 2–16 and 2–62: 4 for Ace, 3 for King,
2 for Queen, 1 for Jack, and 0 for anything else).

(a) Compute the expected total number of points.
(b) Determine the variance of the total number of points. [*Hint*: First compute
    var X_i to be 290/169 and cov (X_i, X_j) to be $-290/(169 \cdot 51)$, and then use
    these in the general formula for the variance of a sum.]

2–118.   Gears, A, B, and C have basic widths 0.5, 0.3, and 0.7 in., with standard
deviations of 0.001, 0.004, and 0.002 in., respectively. If these are assembled side
by side on a single shaft, what is the basic width of the assembly and the standard
deviation of this total width?

2–119.   The position error (in nautical miles) in a certain guidance system after
a given time of operation is given by

$$\delta = 5\delta_a + 20\delta_g,$$

where δ_a and δ_g are independent random errors in an accelerometer and in a gyro
(measured in ft/sec² and deg/hr, respectively). Determine the standard deviation of
position error corresponding to standard deviations of 0.1 ft/sec² and 0.05 deg/hr
in δ_a and δ_g, respectively.

2–120.   Show that cov $(X, X + Y) = $ var $X + $ cov (X, Y). More generally,
show that

$$\text{cov} \left(\sum_i a_i X_i, \sum_j b_j Y_j \right) = \sum_i \sum_j a_i b_j \text{ cov } (X_i, Y_j).$$

2–121.   Show that $X + Y$ and $X - Y$ are uncorrelated if and only if var $X = $
var Y.

2–122.   Show that if $\rho^2 = 1$, the variance of $X + Y$ is $(\sigma_X \pm \sigma_Y)^2$, the $+$ or $-$
depending on whether $\rho = 1$ or $\rho = -1$.

2–123.   Obtain an approximate expression for the variance of the error in
computing a product AB using measured values of A and B that involve independent errors α and β about the actual values A_0 and B_0.

2–124.   Show that if var $X = $ var Y, then $\rho_{X, X+Y} = [\frac{1}{2}(1 + \rho_{X,Y})]^{1/2}$. (Interpret this in light of the geometric representation of a random variable as a vector,
discussed in the text above.)

2.4   Generating Functions

A variety of functions that "generate" certain aspects of a probability
distribution can be defined for a given distribution. They are often thought
of as "transforms" of the density function or probability function defining
the distribution, and they have a particular usefulness in connection with
sums of independent random variables—a usefulness that usually stems from
the simple algebraic law: $a^{x+y} = a^x a^y$. Of those considered below, the prob-

ability generating function is particularly useful in certain kinds of combinatorial problems. The factorial moment generating function and the moment generating function can be used to generate the moments of a distribution—a single integration (followed by a series expansion) replacing all of the integrations necessary to obtain the various moments. The characteristic function is most useful as a theoretical tool—proving theorems about sums of independent random variables that will be crucial in obtaining probability distributions of statistics commonly used in inference problems.

2.4.1 Moment Generating Functions

The *moment generating function* of the distribution of a random variable X is defined formally as follows:

$$\psi(t) = E(e^{tX}) = \int_{-\infty}^{\infty} e^{tx}\, dF(x).$$

[If necessary to avoid confusion, a subscript will link this function to the random variable: $\psi_X(t)$.] When it exists, this expectation depends on the choice of t, and so defines (as the notation suggests) a function of t. For $t = 0$ it always exists: $\psi(0) = 1$, but for other values of t it may or may not exist, depending on the distribution.

If the exponential function in the integrand of $\psi(t)$ is replaced by its power series expansion, there follows

$$\psi(t) = \int_{-\infty}^{\infty} \sum_{0}^{\infty} \frac{(tx)^k}{k!}\, dF(x) = \sum_{0}^{\infty} \frac{t^k}{k!} \left(\int_{-\infty}^{\infty} x^k\, dF(x) \right)$$

$$= \sum_{0}^{\infty} E(X^k) \frac{t^k}{k!},$$

provided that the interchange of summation and integral is permitted. If it is, then, the kth moment of a distribution is simply the coefficient of $t^k/k!$ in the power series expansion of the moment generating function. The idea is that in integrating e^{tx} one is simultaneously integrating all powers of x, with the hope of recovering the individual integrals as coefficients in the expansion of the result. The coefficient of $t^k/k!$ in a Maclaurin power series expansion (as derived in differential calculus) is the kth derivative at 0:

$$E(X^k) = \psi^{(k)}(0).$$

Thus, if the function is one whose power series is not well known, the coefficients can be found by differentiation. This result may also be seen by differentiating $\psi(t)$ k times:

$$\frac{d^k}{dt^k} E(e^{tX}) = E(X^k e^{tX}),$$

(differentiating under[6] the $E(\ )$ operation, which is a kind of integral, and then substituting $t = 0$).

EXAMPLE 2–61.   Consider a simple random variable X having just two possible values, 1 with probability p and 0 with probability $1 - p$. The moment generating function is

$$\psi(t) = E(e^{tX}) = e^t \cdot p + e^0 \cdot (1 - p) = pe^t + (1 - p)$$
$$= p(1 + t/1! + t^2/2! + \cdots) + (1 - p)$$
$$= 1 + p(t/1!) + p(t^2/2!) + \cdots.$$

The coefficients of $t^k/k!$ are clearly all equal to p (for $k = 1, 2, \ldots$), and so $E(X^k) = p$, except for $k = 0$. But of course this result can be obtained directly with very little effort, for $X^k = X$ when $X = 0$ or $X = 1$ as is the case here, and hence $EX^k = EX$.

EXAMPLE 2–62.   Consider the distribution for X defined by the following c.d.f.:

$$F(x) = \begin{cases} 0, & \text{if } x < 0, \\ 1 - .8e^{-x}, & \text{if } x \geq 0. \end{cases}$$

In this distribution there is a discrete lump of probability, in the amount .2, at $x = 0$. The moment generating function is

$$\psi(t) = \int_{-\infty}^{\infty} e^{tx} \, dF(x) = e^0(.2) + \int_0^{\infty} e^{tx}(.8e^{-x}) \, dx$$
$$= .2 + .8(1 - t)^{-1} = 1 + .8t + .8t^2 + .8t^3 + \cdots.$$

[This expansion of $(1 - t)^{-1}$ is just an infinite geometric series with common ratio t.] The coefficient of $t^k/k!$ is obtained by writing the term in t^k in the form $(.8)k![t^k/k!]$:

$$EX^k = .8k!$$

Thus, $EX = .8$ and $EX^2 = 1.6$; and the variance is then:

$$\text{var } X = EX^2 - (EX)^2 = 1.6 - .64 = .96.$$

It is to be observed that the integration and expansion used here are only valid for $|t| < 1$, but of course it is the values of $\psi(t)$ near $t = 0$ that are of interest and yield the moments.

If X and Y are *independent* random variables, the moment generating function of the sum $X + Y$ is a particularly simple combination of the moment generating functions of the summands, namely, their product:

$$\psi_{X+Y}(t) = E(e^{t(X + Y)}) = E(e^{tX}e^{tY})$$
$$= E(e^{tX})E(e^{tY}) = \psi_X(t)\psi_Y(t).$$

---

[6] This interchange of the differentiation and averaging operations is permitted when the derivative of the integrand exists and is bounded by an "integrable" function (one whose average or integral exists and is finite). See Loève, M. [15], p. 126.

Thus, the moment generating function of a sum of two independent random variables is the product of their moment generating functions. Finite induction extends this result to the sum of any finite number of independent random variables: if $X_1, \ldots, X_n$ are *independent*, then

$$\psi_{\Sigma X_i}(t) = \prod_{i=1}^{n} \psi_{X_i}(t).$$

If, moreover, the summands have identical distributions, say with common moment generating function $\psi_X(t)$, then

$$\psi_{\Sigma X_i}(t) = [\psi_X(t)]^n.$$

EXAMPLE 2–63.   Let $X_1, \ldots, X_n$ be independent random variables, each with the distribution: $P(X = 1) = p$, $P(X = 0) = 1 - $ p. The moment generating function of this common distribution is

$$\psi_X(t) = E(e^{tX}) = e^t \cdot p + e^0 \cdot q,$$

where $q = 1 - p$, and so the moment generating function of the sum is

$$\psi_{\Sigma X_i}(t) = [\psi_X(t)]^n = (pe^t + q)^n.$$

From this, one can calculate the mean of the sum as the value of the derivative at $t = 0$: $E(\sum X_i) = np$. (This could, of course, also be easily calculated directly as the sum of the means.)

If one obtains the moment generating function of a distribution indirectly (as in the preceding example, where it was found by means other than direct evaluation of its integral formulation), he can then calculate the moments of that distribution; but the question would remain as to the precise density function or probability function of the distribution. There is a "uniqueness theorem" for moment generating functions,[7] which says that there can only be one distribution leading to a given moment generating function (under certain conditions). Thus, if the moment generating function of a random variable Y is obtained indirectly but is recognized as the moment generating function of a known distribution, then that distribution is the distribution of Y.

It is not hard to find examples of distributions for which moment generating functions do not exist. Indeed, a distribution that does not have moments of all orders would not have a moment generating function.

---

[7] Because the characteristic function is more convenient as a theoretical tool, it is the uniqueness theorem for characteristic functions that is usually given—as it is in Section 2.4.4. When it exists, the moment generating function can be expressed in terms of the characteristic function, and its uniqueness then follows that of the characteristic function.

2.4.2   *The Factorial Moment Generating Function*

Closely related to the moment generating function is a function that generates *factorial* moments. This function is defined as follows:

$$\eta_X(t) = E(t^X) = E[e^{X(\log t)}] = \psi_X(\log t).$$

Since $\log 1 = 0$, it is the point $t = 1$ which might be expected to be of interest, and which produces the factorial moments from the derivatives. Formally, one has

$$\eta'(t) = E(Xt^{X-1}), \quad \eta''(t) = E[X(X-1)t^{X-2}], \ldots,$$

and hence

$$\eta'(1) = E(X), \qquad \eta''(1) = E[X(X-1)], \qquad \eta'''(1) = E[X(X-1)(X-2)],$$

and so on. In general, then (assuming that the indicated moments exist, and that the steps of differentiation and averaging can be interchanged),

$$\eta^{(k)}(1) = E[X(X-1) \cdots (X-k+1)].$$

This is what is called the kth *factorial moment*. Because of the awkwardness in writing out k factors starting with n, each factor one less than the preceding, the following notation is sometimes used:

$$(n)_k \equiv n(n-1) \cdots (n-k+1).$$

In terms of this, the kth factorial moment is $E[(X)_k]$

The first factorial moment is the same as the first moment. The second factorial moment is a combination of the first two moments:

$$E[X(X-1)] = E(X^2) - EX,$$

from which the variance can be computed by adding EX to obtain $E(X^2)$ and then subtracting $(EX)^2$:

$$\text{var } X = \eta''(1) + EX - (EX)^2.$$

EXAMPLE 2–64.   For the distribution of the sum $X_1 + \cdots + X_n$ in Example 2–63, the moment generating function was found to be $(pe^t + q)^n$. The factorial moment generating function is then

$$\eta(t) = \psi(\log t) = (pt + q)^n.$$

The second derivative of this is

$$\eta''(t) = n(n-1)(pt + q)^{n-2}p^2,$$

whence

$$E[X(X-1)] = \eta''(1) = n(n-1)p^2,$$

since $p + q = 1$. And then (since $EX = np$, as seen in Example 2–63),

$$\text{var } X = n(n-1)p^2 + np - (np)^2 = np(1-p).$$

The factorial moment generating function also has the property that for a sum of independent random variables it is just the product of the factorial moment generating functions of the summands:

$$\eta_{\Sigma X_i}(t) = E(t^{\Sigma X_i}) = E(\prod t^{X_i}) = \prod \eta_{X_i}(t).$$

2.4.3 Probability Generating Functions

Consider a discrete random variable X whose possible values are non-negative integers: 0, 1, 2, ... The factorial moment generating function of the distribution of X is then

$$\eta_X(t) = E(t^X) = \sum_{k=0}^{\infty} t^k P(X = k).$$

This means that in the MacLaurin power series expansion of $\eta_X(t)$ the coefficient of t^k is the probability that the value of X is k. That is, whereas the expansion of $\eta(t)$ about the point $t = 1$ produces the factorial moments, the expansion about $t = 0$ produces the probabilities. A combination of this property with the one relating to sums of independent random variables provides a technique for calculating probabilities, as shown in the following example.

EXAMPLE 2–65. Let X denote the number of points on a die. The distribution of X, for a fair die, has the generating function

$$E(t^X) = (t + t^2 + t^3 + t^4 + t^5 + t^6)/6 = \frac{t(1 - t^6)}{6(1 - t)}.$$

If this die is tossed three times, with results X_1, X_2, X_3, and if these are independent random variables, then the total number of points thrown is a random variable Y whose factorial moment generating function is the cube of that for the outcome of a single toss:

$$E(t^Y) = E(t^{X_1})E(t^{X_2})E(t^{X_3}) = \left[\frac{t(1 - t^6)}{6(1 - t)}\right]^3$$

$$= \frac{t^3}{216} \sum_{k=0}^{3} \binom{3}{k}(-t)^{6k} \sum_{j=0}^{\infty} \binom{-3}{j}(-t)^j,$$

the last sum being the extension of the binomial expansion to the case of negative integer exponents, where

$$\binom{-n}{k} = \frac{(-n)(-n - 1)\cdots(-n - k + 1)}{k!}.$$

This expansion can be shown to converge to the right value when $|t| < 1$. Writing the expression for $E(t^Y)$ as a double sum, one has

$$E(t^Y) = \frac{1}{216} \sum_{k=0}^{3} \sum_{j=0}^{\infty} (-1)^{j+k}\binom{3}{k}\binom{-3}{j}t^{6k+j+3}.$$

From this one can read, for instance, the probability that the total number of points is 7, as the coefficient of t^7. This power only occurs for $k = 0$ and $j = 4$:

$$P(Y = 7) = \frac{1}{216} \binom{3}{0}\binom{-3}{4} = \frac{(-3)(-4)(-5)(-6)}{216 \cdot 24} = \frac{15}{216}.$$

Problems

2–125. A random variable X assumes the value b with probability 1. Determine the moment generating function of X and from it the moments of X. Determine also the central moments of the distribution.

2–126. Compute the moment generating function of the distribution defined by the density

$$f(x) = e^{-x}, \qquad x > 0.$$

Expand it in a power series and read the moments.

2–127. Compute the factorial moment generating function of the discrete distribution defined by the probability function

$$f(k) = 1/2^{k+1}, \qquad k = 0, 1, 2, \ldots .$$

Determine the mean and variance of the distribution.

2–128. Obtain a formula for the moment generating function of $Y = aX + b$, in terms of the moment generating function of X.

2–129. Determine the moment generating function of the distribution defined by the density $f(x) = 1$, for $0 < x < 1$. Determine from it the mean and variance of the distribution.

2–130. Use the basic inequality of Section 2.3.2, with suitably chosen $h(x)$ and A, to show that $P(X \le 0) \le \psi_X(t)$, for $t < 0$.

2–131. Examine the convergence of the improper integral that would be used in defining a moment generating function for the density

$$f(x) = \frac{1/\pi}{1 + x^2}.$$

2–132. Given $\psi_X(t) = (1 - t^2)^{-1}$, compute var X.

2–133. Given, for any nonnegative integer k, the integral formula

$$\int_0^\infty x^k e^{-x}\, dx = k!,$$

obtain the moment generating function of the density

$$f(x) = x^k e^{-x}/k!, \qquad x > 0.$$

Determine the mean and variance of the distribution from the moment generating function.

2–134. Derive the moment generating function of $Y = X_1 + \cdots + X_n$, where the X's are independent variables each with density e^{-x} (for $x > 0$) as in Problem 2–126. Determine the density function of Y by recognizing the m.g.f. as one derived previously. Compute the mean and variance of Y as a sum of independent random variables, and compare with the values of these moments as obtained from the m.g.f.

2–135.   (*a*) Show the following:

$$(-1)^k \binom{-n}{k} = \binom{n+k-1}{k} = \binom{n+k-1}{n-1}.$$

(*b*) Expand the m.g.f. of *Y* in Problem 2–134 by means of the extended binomial theorem, and read the *k*th moment. Use the result of (*a*) to express this moment as a product.

2–136.   Let $X_1, \ldots, X_r$ be independent, each with the distribution of Problem 2–127. Determine the factorial m.g.f. of $Y = X_1 + \cdots + X_r$. Obtain the power series expansion and read from it the probability that $Y = k$.

2–137.   Derive the m.g.f. of the distribution with density

$$f(x) = K \exp(-x^2/2).$$

(*Hint*: It is not necessary to know or derive the value of *K*. Complete the square in the exponent, and exploit the fact that the integral over $(-\infty, \infty)$ of $\exp(-x^2/2)$ is the same as the integral of $\exp[-(x-a)^2/2]$.)

2–138.   As in Example 2–65, determine the probability that the total number of points in a toss of three dice is 9.

2–139.   Three numbers are drawn at random from the integers $0, 1, 2, \ldots, 9$. Assuming independent identical distributions, determine the probability that the sum of the numbers is 10.

2.4.4   Characteristic Functions

It has been pointed out that the moment generating function of a distribution may or may not exist. A transform that generates moments in just about the same way, but which always exists, is the *characteristic function*:

$$\phi(x) = E(e^{itX}) = \int_{-\infty}^{\infty} \cos tx\, dF(x) + i \int_{-\infty}^{\infty} \sin tx\, dF(x).$$

That these integrals defining $\phi(t)$ always exist can be shown to follow from the fact that

$$\int_{-\infty}^{\infty} |\cos tx|\, dF(x) \le \int_{-\infty}^{\infty} dF(x) = 1,$$

and a similar inequality for the term involving $\sin tx$. The relation connecting the characteristic function with the moment generating function, when the latter exists, is clearly the following:

$$\phi(t) = \psi(it).$$

In such cases the determination of the characteristic function is accomplished by replacing *t* by *it* in the moment generating function—or equivalently, by carrying out the integration of e^{itx} with respect to $F(x)$ as though *it* were a real constant. In other cases, the determination of the characteristic function is not elementary; in Example 2–67, the computation would be carried out using contour integrals (from the theory of functions of a complex variable).

EXAMPLE 2–66.   Consider the distribution defined by the density e^{-x} for $x > 0$. The characteristic function of the distribution is computed as follows:

$$\phi(t) = E(e^{itX}) = \int_{-\infty}^{\infty} e^{itx-x}\, dx = \frac{1}{1-it},$$

which, of course, is the same as $\psi(it)$.

The characteristic function generates moments in much the same way as the moment generating function, except that each differentiation introduces an additional factor of i:

$$E(X^k) = i^{-k}\phi^{(k)}(0).$$

This calculation is possible, of course, only if the kth moment of the distribution exists. If moments up to a certain order, say r, exist, then it is possible to express $\phi(t)$ as a MacLaurin series with a remainder—even though the complete series expansion would not exist. Theorem 4 below asserts that in the case of a characteristic function, the remainder term is better behaved than it is in such expansions generally.

Although the characteristic function does generate moments, its principal use is as a tool in deriving distributions. For this purpose it is necessary to know several facts about characteristic functions. It is beyond the scope of this treatment to present proofs of these, but their statements are not hard to comprehend.

Theorem 1. Inversion Formula.   *If $x - h$ and $x + h$ are any two points of continuity of $F(x)$, the increment over the interval between them is given by the formula*:

$$F(x+h) - F(x-h) = \lim_{T\to\infty} \frac{1}{\pi}\int_{-T}^{T} \frac{\sin ht}{t} e^{-itx}\, \phi(t)\, dt.$$

Theorem 2. Uniqueness Theorem.   *To each characteristic function there corresponds a unique distribution function having that characteristic function.*

Theorem 3. Continuity Theorem.   *If distribution functions $\{F_n(x)\}$ converge to a distribution function $F(x)$, the corresponding characteristic functions $\{\phi_n(t)\}$ converge to the characteristic function of $F(x)$. Conversely, if a sequence of characteristic functions $\{\phi_n(t)\}$ converge to $\phi(t)$ which is continuous at $t = 0$, then $\phi(t)$ is a characteristic function, and the corresponding distribution functions $\{F_n(x)\}$ converge to the distribution function determined by $\phi(t)$.*

Theorem 4. Expansion with Remainder.   *If $E(|X|^k)$ exists, so does $E(|X|^j)$ for $j = 0, 1, \ldots, k - 1$, and*

$$\phi(t) = 1 + E(X)(it) + E(X^2)\frac{(it)^2}{2!} + \cdots + E(X^k)\frac{(it)^k}{k!} + o(t^k),$$

where $o(u)$ denotes a function such that $o(u)/u \to 0$ as $u \to 0$.

The fact that there is an inversion formula implies Theorem 2, that there is a uniqueness property; for, the recovery of $F(x)$ by means of the inversion formula is a uniquely defined operation except at points of discontinuity of $F(x)$, where uniqueness is provided by the requirement of right-continuity of $F(x)$. Other inversion formulas exist.[8] Theorem 3 will permit obtaining limiting distributions by obtaining their characteristic functions as limits of characteristic functions. Theorem 4 relates the existence of moments to the smoothness (existence of derivatives) of the characteristic function.

EXAMPLE 2–67.   Consider again the density function of

$$f(x) = [\pi(1 + x^2)]^{-1}.$$

The characteristic function of the distribution defined by this density is

$$\phi(t) = \frac{1}{\pi}\int_{-\infty}^{\infty}\frac{\cos tx}{1 + x^2}\,dx + \frac{i}{\pi}\int_{-\infty}^{\infty}\frac{\sin tx}{1 + x^2}\,dx = e^{-|t|}.$$

(The evaluation of these integrals is not elementary, but their values can be found in tables of definite integrals.) This characteristic function is not differentiable at $t = 0$, corresponding to the fact that not even the first moment of the distribution exists.

2.4.5   *Multivariate Generating Functions*

Multivariate analogs of univariate moment generating and characteristic functions can be defined so as to serve similar purposes. The *bivariate moment generating function* of the distribution of (X, Y) is defined to be

$$\psi(s, t) = E(e^{sX + tY}).$$

The derivatives of this function evaluated at $(0, 0)$ produce the various moments of the distribution—marginal and mixed:

$$\frac{\partial^{h+k}}{\partial s^h \partial t^k}\psi(s, t)\bigg|_{s=t=0} = E(X^h Y^k),$$

whenever the implied differentiation under the averaging operation is legiti-

---

[8] See Parzen, E. [17], pp. 400 ff.

mate. Again these moments are coefficients in the expansion of the moment generating function.

The moment generating function for the random vector $(X_1, \ldots, X_n)$ is similarly defined:

$$\psi(t_1, \ldots, t_n) = E[\exp(t_1 X_1 + \cdots + t_n X_n)].$$

Notice that in the case of independent variables, this factors into the product of the marginal moment generating functions:

$$\psi(t_1, \ldots, t_n) = E(e^{t_1 X_1}) \cdots E(e^{t_n X_n}) = \psi_{X_1}(t_1) \cdots \psi_{X_n}(t_n).$$

The *characteristic function* of $(X_1, \ldots, X_n)$ is defined to be

$$\phi(t_1, \ldots, t_n) = E[\exp(it_1 X_1 + \cdots + it_n X_n)],$$

which also factors, into the product of marginal characteristic functions, in the case of independent variables.

Problems

2–140.   Determine the characteristic function of the distribution defined by the density function

$$f(x) = \frac{a/\pi}{(x - m)^2 + a^2},$$

for given constants a and m, by making a change of variable in the integral defining it and using the result of Example 2–67.

2–141.   Determine the characteristic function corresponding to the density

$$f(x) = ke^{-kx}, \qquad x > 0,$$

in terms of the given positive constant k.

2–142.   Show that the characteristic function of $X_1 + \cdots + X_n$—where $X_1, \ldots, X_n$ are independent, identically distributed random variables—is the nth power of the characteristic function of the common distribution.

2–143.   Determine the characteristic function of the distribution defined by the density $K \exp(-x^2/2)$. (See Problem 2–137.)

2–144.   Determine the characteristic function of the distribution of the sum in Problem 2–142, if each of the summands has

(a) the distribution of Problem 2–141,
(b) the distribution of Problem 2–143.

2–145.   Given that X has a finite mean μ and variance σ^2, determine the expansion of $\phi_{X-\mu}(t)$ according to Theorem 4 above, carrying it out as far as the assumptions on X permit.

2–146.   Express the characteristic function of $aX + b$ in terms of the characteristic function of X. Use the result to obtain $\phi_{X-\mu}(t)$, and reconcile the result with the answer to the preceding problem by multiplying the series expansions of the factors.

2-147. Obtain the joint characteristic function of (X, Y), where X and Y are independent variates, each with the distribution whose density is $K \exp(-x^2/2)$. (See Problem 2-143.)

2.5 Limit Theorems

The theory of "large" samples in statistical inference makes use of certain results concerning the limiting behaviour of sequences of random variables and probability distributions. The rigorous treatment of such "limit theorems" is usually not elementary, and the mathematical background assumed here permits only a sketchy presentation of useful results. (More complete discussions may be found in Cramér [4], Loève [15], and Gnedenko [8].)

Consider an infinite sequence of random variables defined on a probability space: $Y_1, Y_2, \ldots$. (This space may be taken to be the space of infinite sequences of real numbers, in which case the Y's are coordinate functions.) It is desirable to define what might be meant by the *limit* of the sequence; but random variables are functions, and there are several ways in which a given sequence of functions might be considered to approach a limit function.

The sequence $\{Y_n\}$ is said to approach the random variable Y *in distribution* if, at each point where the distribution function $F(y)$ of Y is continuous, one has

$$\lim_{n \to \infty} F_n(\lambda) = F(\lambda),$$

where $F_n(\lambda)$ is the distribution function of Y_n. The most important example of such convergence is given in Section 2.5.2. The usefulness of such convergence lies in the fact that one can approximate

$$F_n(\lambda) = P(Y_n \leq \lambda) \quad \text{by} \quad F(\lambda) = P(Y \leq \lambda), \quad \text{if } n \text{ is "large."}$$

The sequence $\{Y_n\}$ is said to approach the limit Y *in the mean*, if the mean square difference tends to zero:

$$\lim_{n \to \infty} E[(Y_n - Y)^2] = 0.$$

This is also called convergence *in mean square*, or *in quadratic mean*. It will be used here mainly in the case in which the limiting random variable Y is singular, that is, $Y \equiv k$, with probability 1 concentrated at the value k.

The sequence $\{Y_n\}$ is said to approach Y *in probability* if for each $\epsilon > 0$,

$$\lim_{n \to \infty} P(|Y_n - Y| \geq \epsilon) = 0.$$

Again the special case of particular interest is that in which $Y \equiv k$, in which case convergence in distribution is equivalent to convergence in probability. For, given $\epsilon > 0$, one has

$$P(|Y_n - k| \geq \epsilon) = [1 - F_n(k + \epsilon)] + F_n(k - \epsilon) + P(Y_n = k + \epsilon),$$

and

$$P(|Y_n - k| \geq 2\epsilon) \leq [1 - F_n(k + \epsilon)] + F_n(k - \epsilon) - P(Y_n = k - \epsilon).$$

The first of these relations shows that if Y_n tends to k in probability, then $F_n(k + \epsilon) \to 1$ and $F_n(k - \epsilon) \to 0$, which is convergence to k in distribution. The converse implication follows from the second relation.

That convergence in quadratic mean implies convergence in probability follows by means of the basic inequality of Section 2.3.2. With $h(x) = x^2$, $b = \epsilon^2$, $X = |Y_n - Y|$, and A the set of x's such that $x \geq \epsilon$, the inequality becomes

$$P(|Y_n - Y| > \epsilon) \leq \frac{1}{\epsilon^2} E(|Y_n - Y|^2).$$

If the right-hand side of this inequality tends to zero as n becomes infinite, so does the left-hand side, thereby establishing the assertion.

The sequence Y_n is said to approach Y *with probability one*, or *almost surely* (a.s.), if

$$P[\lim_{n \to \infty} Y_n = Y] = 1.$$

This will be of little use here. It can be shown that a sequence that converges to Y almost surely also does so in probability. The former is sometimes called "strong" convergence and the latter "weak." (For a further discussion of the interrelations among the various types of convergence, see Loève [15].)

2.5.1 Laws of Large Numbers

A basic notion in the formulation of a probability model is that the probability of an event is intended to embody the observed phenomenon of long-run stability in the relative frequency of occurrence of the event in a sequence of trials of the experiment. It is then certainly of interest to determine whether stability is a mathematical consequence of the axioms in the model that has been developed. That this is so is a result referred to as a *law of large numbers*.

Thus, in the particular case of trials in which an event E occurs with probability p and does not occur with probability $1 - p$, the law of large numbers would assert that

$$\lim_{n \to \infty} (Y/n) = p,$$

in some sense, where Y denotes the number of times in n trials that E does occur—the relative frequency of the event. If the trials are independent experiments, the relative frequency of successes does tend towards the probability of the event—in the mean, in probability, and almost surely. The convergence in probability will be demonstrated, as a special case of the following more general law.

Let $X_1, X_2, \ldots$ be a sequence of identically distributed random variables, any finite number of which constitute a set of independent random variables. Let $\mu \equiv EX$ denote the common mean, and $\phi(t)$ the characteristic function:

$$\phi(t) = 1 + i\mu t + o(t).$$

The sequence of random variables

$$Y_n = (X_1 + \cdots + X_n)/n, \qquad n = 1, 2, \ldots$$

converges to μ in probability, as will now be shown. This will be done by showing that Y_n converges in distribution to the constant μ, and this in turn is accomplished by studying the characteristic function of Y_n:

$$\phi_{Y_n}(t) = [\phi(t/n)]^n.$$

The logarithm of this function is

$$\log \phi_{Y_n}(t) = n \log \phi(t/n) = t\, \frac{\log \phi(t/n) - \log \phi(0)}{t/n - 0}$$

$$\to t\left\{\frac{d}{dt} \log \phi(t)\right\}\bigg|_{t=0} = t\, \frac{\phi'(0)}{\phi(0)} = i\mu t.$$

But then

$$\phi_{Y_n}(t) \to e^{i\mu t},$$

which is the characteristic function of the singular distribution that concentrates probability 1 at μ. By the "continuity theorem" for characteristic functions, the sequence Y_n tends in distribution to that singular distribution, thereby establishing the desired result: if the common distribution has a finite mean μ, then the arithmetic average of the results of n independent trials of an experiment approaches μ in probability. This is a form of the *weak law of large numbers*, referred to as "Khintchine's theorem." (A corresponding *strong law*, involving almost sure convergence, is also true but will not be established here.)

The special case referred to earlier is now obtained by setting $X_j = 1$ or 0, according as the jth trial results in an event A or in its complement A^c. Then Y_n is just the relative frequency of E's in n trials, while

$$EX = 1 \cdot P(A) + 0 \cdot P(A^c) = P(A).$$

So the relative frequency of occurrence of A in n independent trials approaches $P(A)$ in probability.

Even though (according to the laws of large numbers) the average, $Y_n = (X_1 + \cdots + X_n)/n$, of independent and identically distributed random variables tends towards the common expected value, it does not follow that the *sum* $S_n = X_1 + \cdots + X_n$ is necessarily close to $nE(X)$. This is because the sum has a large variance:

$$\text{var } S_n = n \text{ var } X,$$

which (as $n \to \infty$) indicates a large dispersion even when var X is finite.

2.5.2   *The Central Limit Theorem*

It is a remarkable fact that the random variable Y_n, defined as the arithmetic mean of a sequence of n-independent replicas (in distribution) of a random variable X, has a distribution whose *shape* tends to a limiting shape that is *independent of the distribution of X*, so long as X has a finite variance, as n becomes infinite. However, to study this limiting shape, it is necessary to modify Y_n so that the limiting distribution is not singular—the limiting distribution function of Y_n itself is a step function with a single step at EX. On the other hand, the variable

$$n Y_n = S_n = X_1 + X_2 + \cdots + X_n$$

has both a mean $(n\mu)$ and a variance $(n\sigma^2$, where $\sigma^2 = \text{var } X)$ that become infinite with n; thus one loses track of the shape of the distribution because it flattens out and moves off to infinity.

A device that keeps the distribution from shrinking or expanding excessively is that of standardization—forming a linear function that has mean zero and variance 1:

$$Z_n = \frac{Y_n - \mu}{\sigma/\sqrt{n}} = \frac{S_n - n\mu}{\sqrt{n}\,\sigma}.$$

It is readily verified that $EZ_n = 0$ and var $Z_n = 1$, since var $Y_n = \sigma^2/n$. Having fixed mean and variance, the random variable Z_n has a distribution whose shape can be examined as n becomes infinite.

The standardized Z_n can be written

$$Z_n = \sum_1^n U_i, \qquad \text{where} \qquad U_i = \frac{X_i - \mu}{\sqrt{n}\,\sigma}.$$

Since $E(X_i - \mu) = 0$ and var $(X_i - \mu) = \sigma^2$, it follows that

$$\phi_{X_i - \mu}(t) = 1 - \sigma^2 t^2/2 + o(t^2),$$

whence

$$\phi_{U_i}(t) = \phi_{X_i - \mu}(t/\sqrt{n\sigma^2}) = 1 - t^2/(2n) + o(t^2/n).$$

The characteristic function of Z_n is then the nth power:

$$\phi_{Z_n}(t) = [\phi_{U_t}(t)]^n = [1 - t^2/(2n) + o(t^2/n)]^n$$

$$= [1 - t^2/(2n)]^n + o(1).$$

By definition, $o(1)$ represents a function that tends to zero as n becomes infinite (so that t^2/n tends to zero). In the first term of the last expression, set $h = -t^2/(2n)$ and pass to the limit as follows:

$$\lim_{n \to \infty} [1 - t^2/(2n)]^n = \lim_{h \to 0} (1 + h)^{-t^2/(2h)}$$

$$= \{\lim_{h \to 0} (1 + h)^{1/h}\}^{-t^2/2} = e^{-t^2/2}.$$

This is the characteristic function corresponding to the density $f(x) = K\exp(-x^2/2)$, as found in Problem 2–143. But then according to the continuity and uniqueness theorems for characteristic functions (Section 2.4.4), the limiting distribution of the standardized sum Z_n is defined by this density—which goes by the name *standard normal*, and will be taken up in more detail in the next chapter. At this point it will be sufficient to refer to Table I (see Appendix) for the values of the corresponding standard normal cumulative distribution function, $\Phi(\lambda)$.

Summarizing the preceding discussion, one has the following theorem:

Central Limit Theorem. *Let $X_1, X_2, \ldots$ be a sequence of identically distributed random variables with mean μ and variance σ^2 (both finite), any finite number of which are independent. Let $S_n = X_1 + \cdots + X_n$. Then for each z,*

$$\lim_{n \to \infty} P\left(\frac{S_n - n\mu}{\sqrt{n}\sigma} \leq z\right) = \Phi(z) = \frac{1}{2\pi} \int_{-\infty}^{z} \exp(-u^2/2)\, du.$$

Since, according to the definition of a limit, the limitand can be made arbitrarily close to the limit by taking n large enough, it follows that the distribution function of the standardized sum can be approximated with the aid of the standard normal table. In particular, setting $z = (y - n\mu)/\sqrt{n\sigma^2}$, one has

$$P(X_1 + \cdots + X_n \leq y) \doteq \Phi\left(\frac{y - n\mu}{\sqrt{n}\sigma}\right),$$

which is the useful formulation of the result.

EXAMPLE 2–68. People using a certain elevator are considered to be drawn randomly from a large population of people with mean 175 lb and standard deviation 20 lb. What is the probability that 16 persons would have a combined weight exceeding the load limit of 3,000 lb?

Assuming the total weight W of 16 persons to be approximately normally distributed with mean $16 \times 175 = 2{,}800$ lb and variance $16 \times 400 = 80^2$ lb^2, one finds

$$P(W > 3{,}000 \text{ lb}) = 1 - P(W < 3{,}000 \text{ lb}) = 1 - F_W(3{,}000)$$

$$\doteq 1 - \Phi\left(\frac{3{,}000 - 2{,}800}{80}\right) = 0.0062.$$

The Central Limit Theorem is called "central" because it is central to the distribution theory necessary for statistical inference. It is a remarkable result in that the limiting distribution is the same no matter what the common distribution of the summands, so long as the variance is finite. This common distribution can be discrete, or not symmetric, or not unimodal (that is, with more than one maximum in its density). However, the more nearly normal the summands, the fewer the number of summands necessary to achieve approximate normality. In particular, it will be shown in the next chapter that if the summands are normal themselves, then the sum is exactly normal for any finite number of terms. Because of this dependence on the rate of approach to normality on the underlying distribution of the summands, it is not easy to specify the size of n for a good approximation. However, in most cases an n of 25 or more is adequate for approximations to two decimal places. Experience with problems and examples will help to give some idea as to what one can get away with.

The form of central limit theorem given above is not the most general in that the same conclusion of asymptotic normality of a sum is valid under weaker conditions. It is not necessary that the terms in the sum be identically distributed, provided their third moments satisfy a certain mild condition, for instance.[9] There are also circumstances under which the assumption of independence of the terms can be relaxed.[10]

Problems

2–148. Deduce the weak law of large numbers for the case in which the variance is finite by showing that the arithmetic mean approaches the expected value in quadratic mean.

2–149. Apply Khintchine's theorem to show that if $X_1, X_2, \ldots$ are independently and identically distributed with finite kth moment, then $(X_1{}^k + \cdots + X_n{}^k)/n$ converges in probability to $E(X^k)$, where X refers to the common distribution of the X_i's.

2–150. Booklets are packaged in bundles of 100 by weighing them. Suppose that the weight of each booklet is a random variable with mean 1 oz. and standard deviation .05 oz. What is the probability that a bundle of 100 booklets weighs

[9] See Cramér, H. [4], p. 213 ff.
[10] See Fraser, D. A. S. [7], p. 215.

more than 100.5 oz. (and so would be considered to have more than 100 booklets)?
Assume independence of the weights.

2–151. In adding n real numbers, each is rounded off to the nearest integer.
Assuming that the round-off error is a continuous random variable with constant
density on the interval $(-.5, .5)$, determine the probability that the error in the
sum is no greater than $\sqrt{n}/2$ in magnitude, for large n. (Assume independence of the
errors.)

2–152. A sign in an elevator reads: "Capacity, 3,000 lb or 20 persons."
Assume a standard deviation of 20 lb for the weight of a person drawn at random
from all the people who might ride this elevator, and calculate approximately this
person's expected weight, given that the probability that a full load of 20 persons
weighs more than 3,000 lb is .20.

CHAPTER 3

SOME PARAMETRIC FAMILIES
OF DISTRIBUTIONS

A number of probability distributions have been encountered in the problems and examples of the preceding chapter that are sufficiently important to warrant an identification by name and a more systematic study of certain of their properties and applications. Their significance lies in their utility as workable models for many important practical situations. Although useful in practice, they represent idealizations, as do most mathematical models, implying conditions that cannot really be met in practice. Or perhaps a safer generality would be that one simply cannot know whether the conditions are or are not met in practice. Indeed, it is one of the purposes of statistical inference to exploit experimental data to decide whether a certain ideal model can be assumed to be the one representing an actual phenomenon.

Specific names for probability models are usually assigned not to particular distributions but to "classes" of distributions. The distributions in a class would have certain aspects in common and be related, ordinarily, through their representation by a density or probability function involving a "parameter"—an extra variable in the formula whose particular values define the particular distributions in the class. The parameter values then serve to index the various members of the class or family, and so it is called a parametric class or parametric family.

Although many important classes of distributions arise in the study of the distributions of statistics used in inference, the classes taken up in this chapter are more directly related to the basic experiment at hand.

3.1   Distributions for Bernoulli Trials

A *Bernoulli* experiment is one in which there are just two outcomes of interest—some event A either happens or does not happen. Some examples of such experiments include tossing a coin (resulting in Heads or Tails), determining the sex of a randomly drawn person or animal (male or female), testing a product (good or defective), playing a game (win or lose), comparing one variable with another (larger or smaller), giving an inoculation (takes or does not take), carrying out a mission (success or failure), and so on.

The indicator function of an event is a *Bernoulli random variable*:

$$X(\omega) = \begin{cases} 1, & \text{if } A \text{ occurs,} \\ 0, & \text{if } A^c \text{ occurs.} \end{cases}$$

Thus, whether the sample space is discrete or continuous, the distribution of $X(\omega)$ is discrete, having just two values, and is completely defined by specification of the quantity $P(A)$, which will be called p, with $1 - p$ defined to be q:

$$P(A) = p, \qquad P(A^c) = q, \qquad p + q = 1.$$

Thus, the probability table for X is particularly simple:

k	$f(k)$
0	q
1	p

This probability function can also be given by a formula:

$$f(k) = P(X = k) = p^k q^{1-k}, \qquad \text{for } k = 0 \text{ or } 1.$$

This may appear to make a simple thing complicated, but the formula is convenient in some manipulations.

The moments are particularly simple, since for either $X = 0$ or $X = 1$ and $k > 0$ it is true that $X^k = X$:

$$EX^k = EX = 1 \cdot p + 0 \cdot q = p.$$

The moment generating function of the distribution is

$$\psi(t) = E(e^{tX}) = e^t \cdot p + e^0 \cdot q = pe^t + q$$

$$= 1 + pt + pt^2/2! + \cdots.$$

The variance can be computed from the first two moments:

$$\text{var } X = EX^2 - (EX)^2 = p - p^2 = pq.$$

EXAMPLE 3–1.   An urn contains four white beads and six black beads. When one bead is drawn at random from the urn, it can be classified as either white or black, and the random variable

$$X(\omega) = \begin{cases} 1, & \text{if the bead is black,} \\ 0, & \text{if the bead is white,} \end{cases}$$

is a Bernoulli variable. This bead and urn situation can be considered as a prototype for many sampling problems, particularly in the realm of public opinion sampling. (For example, do you favor candidate A or candidate B? Do you call yourself a Republican or a Democrat?, etc.)

When a Bernoulli experiment is performed over and over again, this is said to be a sequence of *Bernoulli trials*. If it is really the same experiment each time, the value of p is constant over the sequence of trials, and one speaks of them as *identical* Bernoulli trials. (This does *not* mean that the results are the same, but simply that the experiments are the same.) In a finite sequence of Bernoulli trials, the indicator functions for the trials keep count of the event A of interest, and their *sum* over n trials is precisely the number of "successes" among those trials. (The term "success" is convenient to use, in the general discussion, for the event A that is being counted.) The notation will be $\sum X_i(\omega)$ or just $\sum X_i$ for the number of successes in n trials.

3.1.1   The Binomial Distribution

Suppose now that the random variables $X_1, \ldots, X_n$ denoting the results of n Bernoulli trials are *independent* random variables, that is, the trials are independent experiments. With a constant p the X's are identically distributed with factorial moment generating function

$$\eta(t) = \psi(\log t) = pt + q,$$

and so the distribution of the sum S_n has the generating function

$$\eta_{S_n}(t) = [\eta(t)]^n = (pt + q)^n$$

$$= \sum_{k=0}^{n} \binom{n}{k} p^k q^{n-k} t^k.$$

The probabilities for the various possible values of S_n (namely, $0, 1, 2, \ldots, n$) are then the coefficients of corresponding powers of t:

$$P(S_n = k) = P(k \text{ successes in } n \text{ trials}) = \binom{n}{k} p^k q^{n-k}.$$

This result is known as the *binomial formula*. A random variable with this distribution is said to be *binomially distributed*.

The binomial formula can be deduced more directly from the independence of the trials. The probability of a particular pattern of k successes among the n trials is just the product of n factors, a p for each success and a q for each failure: $p^k q^{n-k}$. The number of distinct patterns in which there are exactly k successes is $\binom{n}{k}$, and each of these has probability $p^k q^{n-k}$. Hence, the probability of k successes in n independent trials is $\binom{n}{k} p^k q^{n-k}$, as obtained above.

The moments of S_n can be obtained from its factorial moment generating function; in particular,

$$ES_n = \eta'(1) = np$$

and

$$\text{var } S_n = \eta''(1) + ES_n - (ES_n)^2 = n(n-1)p^2 + np - n^2p^2 = npq.$$

The mean and variance can also be computed from the moments of the common distribution of the results of the individual trials:

$$ES_n = EX_1 + \cdots + EX_n = p + \cdots + p = np,$$

and

$$\text{var } S_n = \text{var } X_1 + \cdots + \text{var } X_n = pq + \cdots + pq = npq,$$

the latter exploiting the assumed independence of the trials.

EXAMPLE 3–2.   Let X denote the number of sixes thrown in 12 tosses of a die. Assuming independence, the "binomial formula" derived above gives

$$P(X = k) = \binom{12}{k} \left(\frac{1}{6}\right)^k \left(\frac{5}{6}\right)^{12-k},$$

since p, the probability of a six in a single toss, is $1/6$. The expected number of sixes is

$$E(X) = np = 12 \cdot 1/6 = 2.$$

The variance of the distribution is $npq = 5/3$. The probability of any event described in terms of X can be computed as a suitable sum of binomial probabilities. For instance,

$P(\text{at least 3 sixes}) = 1 - P(\text{2 or fewer sixes})$

$$= 1 - \left[\binom{12}{2}\left(\frac{1}{6}\right)^2\left(\frac{5}{6}\right)^{10} + \binom{12}{1}\left(\frac{1}{6}\right)^1\left(\frac{5}{6}\right)^{11} + \binom{12}{0}\left(\frac{1}{6}\right)^0\left(\frac{5}{6}\right)^{12} \right]$$

$$\doteq .32.$$

3.1.2   *The Negative Binomial Distribution*

Suppose, instead of performing a fixed or given number of trials, one performs independent Bernoulli trials repeatedly, until a given number of successes are observed, and then stops. In this setting, the total number of trials required is *random*, equal to the (random) number of failures encountered before the given number of successes plus that number of successes.

Consider, to attack a simpler problem first, the number of failures encountered prior to the *first* success, and call this X. The probability that k failures occur in a row followed by a success is the probability that X takes on the value k:

$$P(X = k) = q \cdots q \cdot p = q^k p, \qquad \text{for } k = 0, 1, \ldots$$

The distribution defined by these probabilities is said to be *geometric*, since the probabilities are terms in a geometric series:

$$p + pq + pq^2 + \cdots = p\,\frac{1}{1 - q} = 1.$$

The factorial moment generating function is

$$\eta(t) = E(t^X) = \sum_0^\infty t^k q^k p = \frac{p}{1 - tq}$$

$$= \frac{1}{1 - (t - 1)q/p} = \sum_0^\infty \left(\frac{q}{p}\right)^k (t - 1)^k.$$

The factorial moments, $\eta^{(k)}(1)$, are the coefficients of $(t - 1)^k/k!$ in this Taylor expansion about $t = 1$:

$$E[(X)_k] = E[X(X - 1) \cdots (X - k + 1)] = k!(q/p)^k.$$

Thus, the mean is q/p and the variance q/p^2.

The random variable $X + 1$, the number of trials needed to get the first success, has mean $q/p + 1 = 1/p$, which is an intuitively appealing result. For example, if the probability of success at each trial is $1/6$, then the mean number of trials to get the first success is the reciprocal, 6.

Consider next S_r, the number of failures encountered prior to the rth success. This is the number X_1 encountered prior to the first success plus the number X_2 encountered after the first but prior to the second success, ..., plus the number X_r encountered after the $(r-1)$st, but prior to the rth success:

$$S_r = X_1 + X_2 + \cdots + X_r.$$

This is a sum of r independent variables, each having the geometric distribution. The generating function is therefore the rth power:

$$\eta_{S_r}(t) = [\eta(t)]^r = p^r(1 - qt)^{-r} = p^r \sum_{k=0}^{\infty} \binom{-r}{k}(-qt)^k.$$

The coefficient of t^k gives the probability that k failures are encountered prior to the rth success:

$$P(S_r = k) = (-1)^k \binom{-r}{k}p^r q^k = \binom{r + k - 1}{k}p^{r-1}q^k p,$$

in which the result of Problem 2–135 has been used to express the "negative binomial coefficient" $\binom{-r}{k}$ in terms of an ordinary binomial coefficient. The sum S_r is said to have a *negative binomial* distribution, since the probabilities for its values are terms in the expansion of a negative power of a binomial. The last expression above giving the probability function for S_r can be obtained more directly, with the realization that there will be exactly k failures prior to the rth success if and only if the first $r + k - 1$ trials are made up of k failures and $r - 1$ successes in some order, and the $(r + k)$th trial results in success.

The mean and variance of S_r can be obtained (as in the case of the binomial variable) either from the mean and variance of the X's that make it up:

$$ES_r = rEX = rq/p, \qquad \text{var } S_r = r \text{ var } X = rq/p^2,$$

or as coefficients in the expansion of the factorial moment generating function about $t = 1$.

EXAMPLE 3–3.   Let T denote the number of trials necessary to obtain a number of twos and threes totaling twelve, in independent tosses of an ordinary die. Here "success" is the throwing of a two or a three, with probability $\frac{1}{3}$ at each trial. The variable T can be expressed as $S + 12$, where S is the number of "failures" prior to 12 successes. Thus, the values of T are 12, 13, ..., with probabilities

$$P(T = k + 12) = \binom{11}{k}(1/3)^{12}(2/3)^k, \qquad \text{for } k = 0, 1, \ldots$$

The expected value of T is $ES + 12$, or

$$ET = 12 \cdot \frac{2/3}{1/3} + 12 = 36.$$

(The number of trials needed to get each of the twelve successes is three, on the average.)

Problems

3–1. Determine the mean and variance of the binomially distributed variable that counts the number of successes in 100 independent trials, if the probability of success at each trial is .2.

3–2. A person attempts predicting the fall of a coin in each of several successive trials. If he really has no clairvoyant powers and is only guessing, what is the probability that he will predict correctly in four out of four successive trials? In at most two out of ten trials? In eight or more out of ten successive trials?

3–3. Let X have the density $f(x) = [\pi(1 + x^2)]^{-1}$, and let Y denote the indicator function of the event $\{X \geq 1\}$. What is the distribution of Y?

3–4. The reliability (probability of successful functioning) of a certain automatic cutoff device is assumed to be $\frac{11}{12}$. What is the reliability of a system consisting of four such devices so arranged that any one would provide the "cutoff" if functioning properly?

3–5. Determine the reliability of a certain piece of equipment which consists of four components, each having reliability 0.9 so arranged that each component must work if the equipment is to work.

3–6. A random variable X is binomially distributed with mean 3 and variance 2. Compute $P(X = 7)$.

3–7. Determine the probability that all of five articles taken from a production line are good, given that the probability of a defective article's being produced is 0.1. What is the probability that at most one of five has a defect? What is the average number of defectives in a lot of 50 articles?

3–8. Determine the rth factorial moment of a binomial distribution.

3–9. Evaluate:

$$\sum_{0}^{20} k^2 \binom{20}{k} (.3)^k (.7)^{20-k}.$$

3–10. (a) A die is cast repeatedly until a 6 shows. What is the expected number of throws necessary?

(b) Two dice are cast repeatedly. What is the expected number of casts required to obtain a 7? To obtain a 7 or an 11?

3–11. Make a table of values and probabilities for the negative binomial variable defined as the number of failures encountered prior to the fifth success in a series of independent Bernoulli trials with $p = \frac{1}{2}$. What are the most likely values?

3–12. Show:

$$\sum_{0}^{\infty} \binom{4 + k}{k} / 2^k = 32.$$

3–13. Show that the sum of two independent binomial random variables with a common p is again binomial by means of generating functions. (What is the interpretation in terms of Bernoulli trials?)

3–14. Show that the sum of two independent, negative binomial random variables with a common p again has a negative binomial distribution by means of generating functions. (What is the interpretation in terms of Bernoulli trials?)

3–15. Let $X_1, X_2, \ldots, X_n$ be independent and identically distributed with common c.d.f. $F(x)$. Let S_n denote the number of these observations that do not exceed x, a given, fixed value. What is the distribution of S_n? [*Hint:* Define Y_i to be the indicator function of the event $X_i \leq x$ and examine the sum $\sum Y_i$.] Show that S_n/n approaches $F(x)$ in quadratic mean, and therefore in probability.

3.1.3 Sampling without Replacement

One situation in which Bernoulli trials are encountered is that in which an object is drawn at random from a collection of objects of two types—say black and white beads in an urn, as in Example 3–1. In order to repeat this experiment so that the results are independent and identically distributed it is necessary to replace each bead drawn and to mix the beads before the next one is drawn. This process is referred to as *sampling with replacement.* If the sampling is done *without* replacement of the beads drawn, the resulting "trials" are still of the Bernoulli type but no longer independent.

EXAMPLE 3–4. Four balls are drawn, one at a time, at random and without replacement from ten balls in a container, three black and seven white. The probability that the third ball drawn is black can be computed as follows:

$$P(\text{3rd ball black}) = P(WWB) + P(WBB) + P(BWB) + P(BBB)$$

$$= \frac{7}{10} \cdot \frac{6}{9} \cdot \frac{3}{8} + \frac{7}{10} \cdot \frac{3}{9} \cdot \frac{2}{8} + \frac{3}{10} \cdot \frac{7}{9} \cdot \frac{2}{8} + \frac{3}{10} \cdot \frac{2}{9} \cdot \frac{1}{8}$$

$$= 3/10,$$

which is the same as the probability that the first ball drawn is black. (The symbol "WWB," for example, means the event that the first ball drawn is white, the second is white, and the third is black.) It should not be surprising that this probability for black is the same on the third draw as on the first, when it is realized that the probability referred to is the marginal probability or absolute probability, and *not* a conditional probability given the results of the first two drawings. When each drawing is considered by itself, it may as well be thought of as made from the whole collection initially available—when no information is at hand concerning the results of previous trials.

The constancy of "p," or probability of obtaining a black ball in a single drawing, shown in the preceding example, is actually general. Even though some balls are removed from the container, they may as well still be there (so far as odds are concerned) if their colors are not known. This can be demonstrated as a property of the probability model being used, and this demonstration is called for in Problem 3–28.

The general situation, then, is that n objects are to be drawn from a collection of M objects of one kind and $N - M$ of another, making N in all. The random variable of interest is again the number of objects of the one type (corresponding to "success") among the n drawn. The selection is made either by drawing a group of n simultaneously, at random (that is, with all $\binom{N}{n}$ combinations equally likely), or one at a time at random and without replacement. (See Example 1–43 and Problem 1–51 for the equivalence of these schemes.)

Coding the two types of objects with 1 and 0, respectively, and selecting the n objects one at a time, one has n identical Bernoulli variables, $X_1, \ldots, X_n$, where X_i is the result of the ith drawing. The number of objects of the type coded "1" is then the sum of these:

$$S_n = X_1 + X_2 + \cdots + X_n.$$

The probability function for S_n was essentially derived in Chapter 1, and depends on the parameters N, M, and n:

$$f(k; N, M, n) = \frac{\binom{M}{k}\binom{N-M}{n-k}}{\binom{N}{n}}.$$

The possible values of S_n are included in the list $0, 1, \ldots, n$, and the given formula works for these values; but it also is valid for any nonnegative integer, even impossible values, if it is understood that $\binom{a}{b}$ is zero when $b > a > 0$. A random variable with the above probability function is said to have a *hypergeometric* distribution.

The mean of the hypergeometric distribution is easily obtained from the representation of a hypergeometric variable as a sum of the Bernoulli trials that make it up:

$$E(S_n) = E(X_1 + \cdots + X_n) = p + p + \cdots + p = np = n \cdot M/N.$$

That is, whether the objects drawn are replaced or not, the expected number of type "1" among the n objects drawn is the same, just the number drawn times the probability of success at each trial. However, the variance of S_n is not the sum of the variances of the X's, since the latter are not independent. One method of calculation of var S_n is suggested in Problem 3–29, but it can also be obtained from a calculation of the general factorial moment.

The factorial moments of the hypergeometric distribution can be computed as follows:

$$E[(S_n)_r] = \sum_{k=r}^{N} (k)_r f(k; N, M, n) = \sum_{k=r}^{N} (k)_r \frac{\binom{N-M}{n-k}\binom{M}{k}}{\binom{N}{n}}.$$

By using the identity

$$(k)_r \binom{M}{k} = (M)_r \binom{M-r}{k-r},$$

one obtains

$$\sum_{k=r}^{N} (k)_r \binom{N-M}{n-k}\binom{M}{k} = \sum_{k=r}^{N} (M)_r \binom{M-r}{k-r}\binom{N-M}{n-k}$$

$$= (M)_r \sum_{j=0}^{N} \binom{M-r}{j}\binom{(N-r)-(M-r)}{(n-r)-j}$$

$$= (M)_r \binom{N-r}{n-r} \sum_{j=0}^{N} f(j; N-r, M-r, n-r)$$

$$= (M)_r \binom{N-r}{n-r} = \frac{(M)_r (n)_r}{(N)_r} \binom{N}{n}.$$

Thus,

$$E[(X)_r] = \frac{(M)_r (n)_r}{(N)_r}.$$

In particular,

$$EX = \frac{nM}{N}, \quad \text{and} \quad E[X(X-1)] = \frac{M(M-1)n(n-1)}{N(N-1)}.$$

From these one can compute

$$\text{var } X = E[X(X-1)] + EX - (EX)^2 = n \cdot \frac{M}{N} \cdot \frac{N-M}{N} \cdot \frac{N-n}{N-1}$$

$$= npq \, (N-n)/(N-1),$$

where $p = M/N$, the probability at each trial that the object drawn is of the type of which there are initially M.

This last formula differs from the formula for the variance of S_n when drawing is done with replacement and mixing (the binomial case) by the extra factor $(N-n)/(N-1)$. This factor is 1, when $n = 1$ (in which case there is no distinction between the two schemes), and is zero for $n = N$. In this case the entire group of available objects is drawn; and the random variable S_n is no longer variable but constantly equal to M, so that its variance is zero.

EXAMPLE 3–5.   A lot of ten contains three defective and seven good articles. Suppose that four articles are drawn from the lot without replacement. The probability function for the number of defective articles in the sample of four is,

$$f(k; 10, 3, 4) = \frac{\binom{3}{k}\binom{7}{4-k}}{\binom{10}{4}}.$$

In the following table are given the values of this function (multiplied through by the denominator for simplicity) for the possible values $k = 0, 1, 2, 3$ (notice that 4 is not possible), together with computations needed for computing the mean and variance directly:

k	$30f(k)$	$30kf(k)$	$30k^2f(k)$
0	5	0	0
1	15	15	15
2	9	18	36
3	1	3	9
	30	36	60

The expected value is then

$$E(S_4) = 36/30 = 4 \cdot 3/10,$$

and the variance

$$\text{var } S_4 = 60/30 - (36/30)^2 = 4 \cdot \frac{3}{10} \cdot \frac{7}{10} \cdot \frac{10-4}{10-1}.$$

These results are seen to be the same as what would be obtained using the formulas for mean and variance derived above.

Another interesting feature of the factor that distinguishes the variance in the no-replacement case from the variance in the replacement case is that for fixed p (that is, a fixed proportion M/N of the objects of type "1") and fixed n, the factor tends to 1 as N becomes infinite. This is not surprising, when it is realized that when the population of objects is very large, the removal of a small number of them does not appreciably alter the proportions in what is left, and these proportions are then almost independent of precisely what was drawn in the earlier trials.

Indeed, it will now be demonstrated that the hypergeometric probability function tends towards the binomial probability function:

$$f(k; N, M, n) \rightarrow f(k; n, p),$$

for fixed k and n, and fixed $p = M/N$. (Both M and N become infinite in a fixed ratio.) It is simply a matter of expressing the hypergeometric probability in terms of factorials, judiciously grouping factors, and observing what happens:

$$\frac{\binom{M}{k}\binom{N-M}{n-k}}{\binom{N}{n}} = \frac{(M)_k(N-M)_{n-k}n!}{k!(n-k)!(N)_n}$$

$$= \frac{M}{N}\frac{M-1}{N-1}\cdots\frac{M-k+1}{N-k+1}\frac{N-M}{N-k}\cdots$$

$$\frac{N-M-n+k+1}{N-n+1}\binom{n}{k}$$

$$\rightarrow p\cdot p\cdots p\cdot q\cdots q\binom{n}{k} = p^kq^{n-k}\binom{n}{k}.$$

The usefulness of the approach of the hypergeometric to the binomial distribution lies in the possibility of estimating a hypergeometric probability with an easier-to-compute binomial probability, when the number of objects drawn is considerably less than the number available. From a practical point of view, it is important to know "how fast" the hypergeometric distribution tends to the binomial. To give some hint of this, the calculations in the next example are presented.

EXAMPLE 3–6.   Presented in the table below are hypergeometric probabilities of 0, 1, 2, 3, 4, and 5 "defectives" in a selection of ten articles from populations of sizes $N = 50, 100, 200$, and ∞, half of which are defective. The last, $N = \infty$, is really the binomial case for $n = 10$ and $p = 0.5$.

k	$N = 50$	$N = 100$	$N = 200$	$N = \infty$ (Binomial)
0	.0003	.0006	.0008	.0010
1	.0050	.0072	.0085	.0098
2	.0316	.0380	.0410	.0439
3	.1076	.1131	.1153	.1172
4	.2181	.2114	.2082	.2051
5	.2748	.2539	.2525	.2461

3.1.4 Approximate Binomial Probabilities (Moderate p)

The central limit theorem is useful in providing a means of approximate computation of binomial probabilities when a direct computation is tedious. This application hinges upon the fact that a binomially distributed random variable has the distribution of a sum of independent, identical Bernoulli variables. That is, if $X_i = 0$ with probability $1 - p$ and $X_i = 1$ with probability p, and if $X_1, \ldots, X_n$ are independent, then their sum has the binomial distribution (n, p), with mean np and variance $np(1 - p)$. According to the central limit theorem, then, the distribution of the sum S_n, and hence the binomial distribution, is asymptotically normal for large n. More precisely, for fixed p,

$$\lim_{n \to \infty} P\left(\frac{S_n - np}{\sqrt{np(1 - p)}} \leq z\right) = \Phi(z).$$

Hence

$$P(S_n \leq x) = P\left\{\frac{S_n - np}{\sqrt{np(1 - p)}} \leq \frac{x - np}{\sqrt{np(1 - p)}}\right\} \doteq \Phi\left(\frac{x - np}{\sqrt{np(1 - p)}}\right).$$

EXAMPLE 3-7.   Consider a binomial distribution with $n = 8$ and $p = \frac{1}{2}$. The actual distribution function is

$$P(X \leq x) = \sum_{k \leq x} \binom{8}{k}\left(\frac{1}{2}\right)^k\left(\frac{1}{2}\right)^{n-k},$$

and the normal approximation is

$$P(X \leq x) \doteq \Phi\left(\frac{x - 4}{\sqrt{2}}\right).$$

The graphs of these two functions are shown in Figure 3–1.

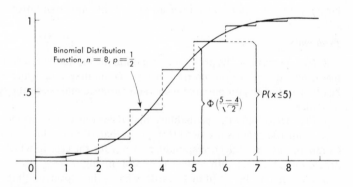

Figure 3–1.

It is seen in this figure that the normal approximation to the binomial is good when x is about halfway between integers; but it is *at* the integers that the value of $F(x)$ is needed. A better approximation to the value $F(k)$ is obtained by taking the ordinate on the continuous curve one-half unit to the right of k:

$$F(k) = P(X \leq k) \doteq \Phi\left(\frac{k + \frac{1}{2} - np}{\sqrt{np(1 - p)}}\right).$$

With this "continuity correction," the normal approximation can be quite good even for rather small values of n, as in the next example.

EXAMPLE 3–8.   Consider a binomial distribution with $n = 4$ and $p = \frac{1}{2}$:

$$P(X \le k) \doteq \Phi \left(\frac{k + \frac{1}{2} - 2}{\sqrt{1}} \right).$$

These approximate values and the values computed from the actual distribution function are given in the following table.

k		0	1	2	3	4
$F_X(k)$		.0625	.3125	.6875	.9375	1.0000
Normal approx.	With cont. corr.	.0668	.3085	.6915	.9332	.9938
	Without cont. corr.	.0228	.1587	.5000	.8413	.9772

When p is near .5, the binomial distribution is rather symmetric, and the normal approximation is useful even for quite small n, as seen above. However, values of p near 0 or 1 result in a somewhat skewed distribution, and a larger value of n is required for an acceptable approximation.

Problems

3–16.   Determine the probability function for the number of white beads among five beads drawn at random from a bowl containing four white and seven black beads. Use this to compute the mean and variance and check the results using the formulas.

3–17.   Determine the probability that three out of five articles drawn at random from 100 articles are defective, given that 10 in the lot of 100 are defective. Compare this with the corresponding answer for the case in which the articles are drawn one at a time with replacement and mixing.

3–18.   In a bridge hand of 13 cards, what is the expected number of Aces? The expected number of face cards? (Of the 52 cards in the deck, 4 are Aces and 12 are face cards.)

3–19.   In a population of 10,000 voters, 45 per cent favor a certain proposal. What is the probability that among ten voters chosen at random without replacement, six or more favor the proposal?

3–20.   Show that for fixed n and fixed $p = M/N$ the rth factorial moment of the hypergeometric distribution tends to that of a binomial distribution as N becomes infinite.

3–21.   Of 20 cups of coffee, 15 are brewed in the usual way and 5 are made from instant coffee. After tasting all 20 cups, a taster selects 5 which he thinks are the ones made from instant coffee. What is the probability that if his selection is random (made by "pure chance"), exactly k of the 5 he selects are made from instant coffee?

3–22. Let X have a hypergeometric distribution with parameters N, n, and M. Let $P(X = k)$ be denoted by $p(k; M)$. Show that if $M' > M$,

$$\frac{p(k; M)}{p(k; M')} \geq \frac{p(k + 1; M)}{p(k + 1; M')}.$$

(Express each probability in terms of factorials and start canceling.)

3–23. Evaluate:

$$\sum_{0}^{4} k \binom{4}{k}\binom{8}{6 - k}.$$

3–24. A coin is to be tossed 100 times. Determine approximately probabilities that

(a) less than 50 Heads turn up;
(b) exactly 50 Heads turn up;
(c) more than 40 but less than 60 Heads turn up.

3–25. Determine approximately the probability that in at least 28 of 72 tosses of a die the outcome is a 1 or a 2.

3–26. Given that 55 per cent of the votes in a city of 50,000 voters will vote for candidate A, what is the probability that a random selection of 100 voters would not show a majority in favor of A?

3–27. A bowl contains three white and seven black beads, from which one at a time is drawn. Determine the distribution of the number of black beads drawn before a white one is drawn (a) if the beads drawn are replaced and mixed with the rest after each drawing, and (b) if the beads drawn are not replaced.

3–28. In sampling without replacement from M black and $N - M$ white beads, show that the probability of black on the jth draw is M/N. [Express this as the average of conditional probabilities, given k black beads among the first $j - 1$ trials. This, in turn, can be evaluated by recognizing it as an average of $M - k$ with respect to the number k drawn in the first $j - 1$ trials.]

3–29. Calculate the variance of the hypergeometric S_n using the formula for the variance of a sum of dependent variables, and evaluating cov (X_i, X_j) as cov (X_1, X_2) (since it is the same for all $i \neq j$).

3.2   The Poisson Process

An experiment of chance that continues in time (or in space) and is observed as it unfolds is sometimes called a *stochastic process*, or a *random process* (or, simply, a *process*). A snapshot or observation at each instant of time (or at each point in space) is an experiment of chance. If one is observing the time variation of some numerical variable, the instantaneous values make up a family of random variables indexed by time as a parameter. An observation on the complete process is a *function* of time.

One important process is the *Poisson process*, used to describe a wide variety of phenomena that share certain characteristics, phenomena in which some kind of "happening" takes place sporadically over a period of time in a manner that is commonly thought of as "at random." Examples of happenings for which the model is found useful include arrivals at a service counter, flaws in a long manufactured tape or wire, clicks or counts recorded by a Geiger counter near a radioactive substance, and breakdowns or failures of a piece of equipment or a component (when failures are corrected as they occur and the equipment is put back into operation). Just to have a convenient reference term in the general discussion, the happening will be referred to as a "failure." And, even though in some cases the observed functions are functions of position in space (or on a line or plane), the general discussion will be phrased in terms of time variation.

The particular model for such processes that goes by the name *Poisson* is that in which the following postulates can be assumed to hold. In stating them the notation $P_n(h)$ will be used for the probability that n failures occur in an interval of width h.

Poisson Postulates

1. Events defined according to the numbers of failures in nonoverlapping intervals of time are *independent*.

2. The probability structure of the process is time invariant.

3. The probability of exactly one failure in a small interval of time is approximately proportional to the size of the interval:

$$P_1(h) = \lambda h + o(h), \qquad \text{as } h \to 0.$$

4. The probability of more than one failure in a small interval is negligible in comparison with the probability of one failure in that interval:

$$\sum_{n>1} P_n(h) = o(h), \quad \text{as} \quad h \to 0.$$

The assumption of time invariance means that the probability distribution of any set of observations on the process is dependent only on the timespacing of the observations and not on the location of the reference origin on the time-axis. (This justifies using only the *width* of the time-interval in the notation for the probability of n failures in an interval of given width.) The notation $o(h)$, read "little oh of h," was introduced in Section 2.5.2, and stands for any function of h that "goes to zero faster than h" in this sense:

$$\lim_{h \to 0} \frac{o(h)}{h} = 0.$$

[In particular, h^2, $\sin^2 h$, and $1 - \exp(-h^2)$ all have this property, and might be symbolized by $o(h)$. Notice that $a[o(h)] + b[o(h)] = o(h)$.] The third and fourth postulates could then be written in the following form:

3. $[P_1(h) - \lambda h]/h \to 0$ as $h \to 0$, for some $\lambda > 0$.
4. $P_n(h)/h \to 0$ as $h \to 0$.

Postulates 1–4 will be shown to define $P_n(t)$.

3.2.1   The Poisson Random Variable

Of particular interest in connection with a Poisson process is the random variable

$$X = \text{number of failures in an interval of width } t,$$

for a given t. The probability function for this discrete random variable is, in the above notation,

$$f(n) = P(n \text{ failures in time } t) = P_n(t).$$

The derivation of $P_n(t)$ from the Poisson postulates uses a differential approach, since the postulates deal with small increments of time. Consider then the interval $(0, t + h)$, decomposed into the intervals $(0, t)$ and $(t, t + h)$. The event that n failures occur in $(0, t + h)$ can be expressed as a union of $n + 1$ events, according to how many fall in $(0, t)$ and how many in $(t, t + h)$. Thus,

$$P_n(t + h) = P[n \text{ failures in } (0, t + h)]$$

$$= P[n \text{ failures in } (0, t) \text{ and none in } (t, t + h)]$$

$$+ P[(n - 1 \text{ failures in } (0, t) \text{ and } 1 \text{ in } (t, t + h)]$$

$$+ \cdots + P[0 \text{ failures in } (0, t) \text{ and } n \text{ in } (t, t + h)].$$

By postulate 1, each probability on the right can be factored and written as the probability of a certain number of failures in $(0, t)$ times the probability of a certain number in $(t, t + h)$, since these intervals are nonoverlapping. Hence, for $n > 0$,

$$P_n(t + h) = P_n(t)[1 - \lambda h + o(h)] + P_{n-1}(t)[\lambda h + o(h)]$$

$$+ P_{n-2}(t)o(h) + \cdots + P_0(t)o(h),$$

and for $n = 0$:

$$P_0(t + h) = P_0(t)[1 - \lambda h + o(h)].$$

Transposing the $P_n(t)$, dividing by h, and passing to the limit as $h \to 0$ one obtains the derivative of $P_n(t)$:

$$\begin{cases} P_n'(t) = -\lambda P_n(t) + \lambda P_{n-1}(t), & n = 1, 2, 3, \ldots \\ P_0'(t) = -\lambda P_0(t). \end{cases}$$

The appropriate initial conditions are $P_0(0) = 1$ and $P_n(0) = 0$ for $n > 0$.

Since $P_0'/P_0 = -\lambda$, it follows (in view of the initial condition) that

$$P_0(t) = e^{-\lambda t}.$$

Substitution of this in the equation for $P_1'(t)$ yields

$$P_1'(t) + \lambda P_1(t) = \lambda e^{-\lambda t}.$$

This becomes integrable upon multiplication by $e^{\lambda t}$, with the result

$$e^{\lambda t}P_1(t) = \lambda t + \text{(const.)}.$$

The initial condition $P_1(0) = 0$ then implies

$$P_1(t) = \lambda t e^{-\lambda t}.$$

Substitution of this into the equation for $P_2'(t)$ results in still another first order linear differential equation, for P_2, and so on. The results can be summarized in the following expression for $P_n(t)$, which can be derived by induction as outlined above, or shown to satisfy the differential relations for $P_n(t)$ by direct substitution:

$$P_n(t) = e^{-\lambda t}(\lambda t)^n/n!.$$

For a given time interval t, the quantities λ and t always occur in the combination λt, so there is essentially just this single parameter, $m \equiv \lambda t$. The probabilities for $X = 0, 1, 2, \ldots$ add up to 1, as they must:

$$e^{-m} + e^{-m}m + e^{-m}(m^2/2!) + \cdots = e^{-m} \sum_{k=0}^{\infty} (m^k/k!) = e^{-m}e^m = 1.$$

That is, the Poisson probabilities are proportional to the terms in the series expansion of the function e^m. Poisson probabilities are given in Table XII for a number of values of m. More precisely, it gives *cumulative* probabilities:

$$F(c) = \sum_{k=0}^{c} e^{-m}m^k/k!.$$

Probabilities of individual values can be obtained by taking differences in successive tabulated probabilities:

$$P(X = c) = F(c) - F(c - 1) = P(X \leq c) - P(X \leq c - 1).$$

The moments of the distribution are readily calculated from the factorial moment generating function:

$$\eta(t) = E(t^X) = \sum_{0}^{\infty} t^k f(k) = \sum_{0}^{\infty} e^{-m} \frac{(tm)^k}{k!} = e^{m(t-1)}.$$

From the rth derivative:

$$\eta^{(r)}(t) = m^r e^{m(t-1)},$$

the rth factorial moment is obtained by substituting $t = 1$:

$$E[(X)_r] = \eta^{(r)}(1) = m^r,$$

so that

$$EX = m, \quad E(X^2 - X) = m^2, \qquad \text{var } X = m^2 + m - m^2 = m.$$

The mean and variance are seen to be equal, each having the value m, the parameter that indexes the family of Poisson distributions.

The parameter λ in the Poisson process can now be interpreted in terms of the number of failures in a unit interval; for, since

$$E(\text{number of failures in } t) = EX = \lambda t,$$

it follows with $t = 1$ that

$$E(\text{number of failures in unit time}) = \lambda.$$

Thus, although the probability of a failure in an interval is proportional to the width of the interval only for very tiny intervals, the *expected* number of failures in an interval is porportional to the width of the interval, for intervals of any size. Cutting the interval in half, for instance, halves the expected number of failures.

EXAMPLE 3–9.   Customers enter a waiting line "at random" at a rate of four per minute. Assuming that the number entering the line in any given time interval has a Poisson distribution, one can determine, say, the probability that at least one customer enters the line in a given half-minute interval. Taking a minute as the unit of time, one has $\lambda = 4$, and hence the average number of arrivals per half minute is $\lambda/2 = 2$. Therefore,

$$P(\text{at least one arrival in a half-minute interval})$$

$$= 1 - P(\text{none arrives in a half-minute interval})$$

$$= 1 - e^{-\lambda t}\frac{(\lambda t)^0}{0!} = 1 - e^{-2} \doteq 0.865.$$

Problems

3–30.   Weak spots occur in a certain manufactured tape on the average of one per 1,000 ft. Assuming a Poisson distribution of the number of weak spots in a given length of tape, what is the probability that (a) a 2,400-ft roll will have at most two defects? (b) A 1,200-ft roll will have no defects? (c) In a box of five 1,200-ft rolls, two have just one defect and the other three have none?

3–31.   Given that X has a Poisson distribution with variance 1, calculate $P(X = 2)$.

3–32. A Geiger counter records on the average of 40 counts per minute when in the neighborhood of a certain weakly radioactive substance. Determine the probability that (a) there will be two counts in a 6-second period. (b) There will be k counts in a T-second period.

3–33. Telephone calls are being placed through a certain exchange at random times on the average of four per minute. Assuming a Poisson law, determine the probability that in a 15-second interval there are three or more calls.

3–34. Flaws in the plating of large sheets of metal occur at random on the average of one in a section of area 10 square feet. What is the probability that a sheet 5 ft by 8 ft will have no flaws? At most one flaw?

3–35. Show directly that the Poisson formula obtained for $P_n(t)$ does satisfy postulates (3) and (4) which were used in deriving it.

3–36. Evaluate:

$$\sum_{0}^{\infty} (k^2 - k)3^k/k!\,.$$

3–37. Show that the sum of independent Poisson variables has a Poisson distribution.

3–38. Men arrive at a service counter according to a Poisson process at an average of 6/hour, women arrive also according to a Poisson process at an average of 12/hour, and children according to a Poisson process at an average of 12/hour. Determine the probability that at least two customers (without regard to sex or age) arrive in a five-minute period.

3.2.2 *The Negative Exponential Distribution*

In a Poisson process with parameter λ, let L denote the time to the next failure as measured from any given instant of time, which may as well be called $t = 0$. This is the "future life" of the equipment "now" in operation. The distribution of L is readily obtained by expressing the event $L > t$ in terms of a Poisson random variable:

$$F_L(t) = P(L \leq t) = 1 - P(L > t)$$

$$= 1 - P(\text{no failure in } (0, t)) = 1 - e^{-\lambda t}, \qquad \text{for} \quad t > 0.$$

The distribution defined by this c.d.f. is called an exponential, or a negative exponential, or a Laplace distribution. It is a continuous distribution, with density

$$f_L(t) = F_L'(t) = \lambda e^{-\lambda t}, \qquad \text{for } t > 0.$$

Its moment generating function, defined for $|t| < 1$, is

$$\psi_L(s) = E(e^{sL}) = \int_0^{\infty} e^{st}(\lambda e^{-\lambda t})\, dt$$

$$= \frac{1}{1 - s/\lambda} = \sum_{0}^{\infty} (1/\lambda)^k s^k,$$

and the kth moment is therefore

$$E(L^k) = k!/\lambda^k.$$

The mean and variance are then

$$EL = 1/\lambda, \quad \text{and} \quad \text{var } L = 1/\lambda^2.$$

Notice that the mean time to failure is the reciprocal of the mean number of failures per unit time! If, for instance, the mean number of failures per hour is 6, then the mean time to failure is $\frac{1}{6}$ hour, or ten minutes.

Although possibly unnoticed, it is significant that in the above derivation, the time L was measured from any instant at which a watch was placed on the equipment, whether just after the equipment was put in operation following a previous failure, or after it had been operating for a long time. That is, the future life of equipment whose breakdown pattern follows the Poisson law is a random variable whose distribution is independent of how long the equipment has been operating. In such a case, preventive maintenance involving replacement of the equipment or component while it is still working would be of no advantage. This can come about only because failures in such cases are caused by external sources, and not by a wearing out of the equipment. If wear-out is a cause of failure, the Poisson model is not appropriate.

The time to the rth failure after a given instant of time (say, $t = 0$), is a random variable which is the sum of the exponential variables measuring the time to the first failure, the time to the second failure measured from the first, etc. Denoting this total time by S_r, one can express it as

$$S_r = L_1 + L_2 + \cdots + L_r,$$

where L_i is the time from the $(i - 1)$st to the ith failure and has the exponential distribution. Because the inequalities in the event $\{L_1 > t_1, \ldots, L_r > t_r\}$ are equivalent to events relating to nonoverlapping intervals of time, the random variables $L_1, \ldots, L_r$ are independent, and the moment generating function of their sum S_r is therefore

$$\psi_{S_r}(s) = [\psi_L(s)]^r = (1 - s/\lambda)^{-r}.$$

From the results of Problems 2–133 and 2–134 it follows that the density of the total time to the rth failure is

$$f_{S_r}(t) = \lambda^r t^{r-1} e^{-\lambda t}/(r - 1)! \quad \text{for } t > 0.$$

The distribution defined by this density is called a *gamma distribution*. The mean and variance, of course, are just

$$ES_r = rEL = r/\lambda, \quad \text{and} \quad \text{var } S_r = r \text{ var } L = r/\lambda^2.$$

EXAMPLE 3–10.   Consider the Poisson process describing the arrivals of customers at a service counter, as in Example 3–9, with an average of four arrivals per minute. The average time to an arrival is then $\frac{1}{4}$ minute, and the density of the time to an arrival is $4e^{-4t}$, for $t > 0$. The time to the 10th arrival has the density

$$f_{S_{10}}(t) = 4^{10}t^9 e^{-4t}/9! \qquad \text{for} \qquad t > 0,$$

with mean 2.5 minutes (that is, 10 times $\frac{1}{4}$ minute).

3.2.3   Approximating Binomial Probabilities (Small p)

Besides being a useful probability model in its own right, the Poisson distribution can be used in approximating binomial probabilities in those skewed cases in which an unusually large n would be required for a successful use of the Central Limit Theorem. Perhaps the most natural way to see this is through an alternative derivation of the Poisson formula from the Poisson postulates, a bit more heuristic than the one given earlier.

Consider a Poisson process characterized by the constant λ as the mean number of "arrivals" (or whatever happenings are being observed) per unit time. Let Y denote the number of arrivals in an interval $(0, t)$, and let this interval be subdivided into n equal parts, of width $h = t/n$. Consider now the n "Bernoulli trials" corresponding to these n subdivision intervals—"success" corresponding to an arrival in a given subinterval, and "failure" corresponding to no arrival. The trials are not exactly Bernoulli, since there could be *more* than one arrival in a subinterval. But n will be allowed to increase without limit, so that the subinterval length h will shrink to zero; and for small h it is approximately true that either one arrival or no arrivals occur in an interval of width h, with probabilities:

$$p = P(1 \text{ arrival in } h) \doteq \lambda h,$$

$$1 - p = P(\text{no arrivals in } h) \doteq 1 - \lambda h.$$

There will be k arrivals in $(0, t)$, then, if there is one arrival in each of k subintervals. The probability of this is approximately binomial:

$$P(k \text{ "successes" in } n \text{ trials}) = \binom{n}{k} p^k (1 - p)^{n-k}.$$

As n becomes infinite, the approximations become better and better. Putting $p = \lambda h = \lambda t/n$, one obtains

$$P[k \text{ arrivals in } (0, t)] \doteq \binom{n}{k}(\lambda t/n)^k (1 - \lambda t/n)^{n-k}$$

$$= \frac{n}{n} \cdot \frac{n-1}{n} \cdots \frac{n-k+1}{n} \cdot \frac{(\lambda t)^k}{k!} (1 - \lambda t/n)^{-k}(1 - \lambda t/n)^n.$$

As n becomes infinite, the first k factors on the right tend to 1, the next is fixed, the next tends to 1, and the last factor can be written

$$[(1 - \lambda t/n)^{-n/\lambda t}]^{-\lambda t},$$

which tends to $\exp(-\lambda t)$, since the quantity in brackets converges to e^{-1}. Hence,

$$P(Y = k) = P[k \text{ arrivals in } (0, t)] = [(\lambda t)^k/k!]e^{-\lambda t},$$

as was derived earlier.

The practical significance of the present derivation is in the approximate equality (for large n)

$$e^{-\lambda t}(\lambda t)^k/k! \doteq \binom{n}{k}(\lambda t/n)^k(1 - \lambda t/n)^{n-k},$$

which follows from the fact that the left member is the limit of the right. With $\lambda t/n = p$, this becomes

$$\binom{n}{k}p^k(1 - p)^{n-k} \doteq (np)^k e^{-np}/k!,$$

a useful approximation for large n and small p. The following example will give some indication as to the success of the approximation.

EXAMPLE 3–11.   In the table below are given values of the probability function for each of two binomial distributions, one in which $n = 10$ and $p = .1$, and the other in which $n = 20$ and $p = .05$ In each case $np = 1$, and the Poisson approximations using $\lambda t = np = 1$ are also given. (The table is clearly not quite complete.)

k	Poisson, $m = 1$	Binomial (10, .1)	Binomial (20, .05)
0	.368	.349	.358
1	.368	.387	.377
2	.184	.194	.187
3	.061	.057	.060
4	.015	.011	.013
5	.0031	.0015	.0022

Although the approximation scheme discussed above is given for the case of small p, it applies equally well for values of p near 1—just by interchanging the basic Bernoulli coding so that p becomes q and vice versa. When p is near 1, then q is small.

EXAMPLE 3–12.   Consider the binomial distribution for $n = 20$ and $p = .8$. If

X denotes the number of successes in 20 independent Bernoulli trials, and the probability of success is .8 in each trial, then

$$
\begin{aligned}
P(X = 16) &= P(16 \text{ successes in 20 trials}) \\
&= P(4 \text{ failures in 20 trials}) \\
&= \binom{20}{4}(.2)^4(.8)^{16} \\
&= e^{-4}(4^4/4!) = .629 - .433 = .196.
\end{aligned}
$$

The Poisson parameter here is $20 \times .2 = 4$, and Table XII was used to obtain the cumulative probabilities at 4 and at 3 (whose difference gives the probability for 4).

It is of course true that when n is "large," the normal distribution can be used to approximate binomial probabilities. But when p is small or close to 1, the binomial distribution is quite skewed (one way or the other), and it takes a larger n to get a reasonable degree of approximation than when p is moderate. The next example gives both the normal and Poisson approximations in one case, for comparison.

EXAMPLE 3–13. In the table below are given cumulative probabilities for a binomial distribution with $n = 8$ and $p = \frac{1}{8}$. In addition to the actual probabilities (exact to four decimal places) are given the Poisson approximations with $m = np = 1$ and the normal approximations with $\mu = np = 1$ and $\sigma^2 = npq = \frac{7}{8}$.

k	Binomial	Normal	Poisson
0	.3436	.2965	.3679
1	.7363	.7035	.7358
2	.9327	.9456	.9197
3	.9888	.9962	.9810
4	.9988	.9999	.9963
5	.9999	1.0000	.9994

Even in this instance in which p is not really very small, the Poisson approximation is much better for small k and almost as good for large k. The smaller the p, the more preferable is the Poisson approximation.

The Poisson process has been seen to be a continuous-time analog of a sequence of Bernoulli trials with small p—in the one case arrivals or breakdowns or flaws occur at random, unpredicted instants of time, and in the other Heads or "success" occurs occasionally as the trials proceed, in unpredictable fashion. The analogy can be carried further. The geometric distribution describes the "waiting time" to Heads in a Bernoulli sequence, and the negative exponential distribution describes the waiting time to an arrival or breakdown in a Poisson process. The negative binomial distribution describes the "waiting time" to the rth Heads in a Bernoulli sequence, and the gamma distribution describes the waiting time to the rth arrival in a Poisson process. Thus, in a sense:

geometric:binomial:negative binomial

$$= \text{negative exponential:Poisson:gamma}.$$

Problems

3–39. Determine the median of the negative exponential distribution.

3–40. Customers join a waiting line according to the Poisson law, with an average time between arrivals of 2 minutes.

(a) What is the probability that 5 minutes will elapse with no customers arriving?

(b) What is the probability that in a 5-minute interval at most two customers arrive?

3–41. In a certain electronic device there are ten tubes each having a life distribution that is negative exponential with mean 50 hours. The device fails if any one of the tubes fails, and when it fails, the tube that has caused the failure is replaced and the device turned on again. Determine the distribution of the time from one failure of the device to the next, assuming that tubes fail independently of one another.

3–42. Let the times between failures of a certain device have a common distribution function $F(x)$; the probability of successful operation (no failures) for a period t is called the *reliability* of the device:

$$R(t) = 1 - F(t).$$

The *hazard* is defined in terms of reliability:

$$H(t) = -\frac{d}{dt}[\log R(t)].$$

(This can be interpreted as the rate of "dying" among many such systems relative to the number still operating.) Show that if the hazard is constant, the distribution of system life (or time between failures) is the negative exponential, and conversely.

3–43. Show that if the times between successive "events" have the negative exponential distribution with parameter λ, then

$$P(\text{one or more events in } h) = \lambda h + o(h).$$

3–44. A certain machine manufactures bolts and turns out defective bolts on the average of one per 200 bolts. They are packaged in boxes of 50. Determine the probability that a box has at most one defective bolt. Determine also the probability that of the 100 boxes in a carton, no box has more than one defective bolt.

3–45. Given that 1,500 out of 50,000 people in a certain city are watching a certain television program, what is the probability that of 200 people called at random fewer than four are watching the program?

3–46. A man holds 5 tickets in a lottery in which 1,000 tickets are sold. Ten tickets are to be drawn for prizes. What is the probability that the man wins at least one prize?

3-47. Use appropriate approximations and tables to evaluate each of the following:

(a) $P(X = 52)$, where X is binomial, $n = 100, p = \frac{1}{2}$;

(b) $P(X \leq 3)$, where X is binomial, $n = 100, p = .05$;

(c) $P(X \leq 50)$, where X is Poisson, $m = 64$.

[*Hint:* A Poisson variable with $m = 64$ is approximately normal.]

3-48. Each of two units has an exponential distribution of time to failure with mean 1 hour and is placed in a system so that the system fails if and only if *both* units fail. What is the expected time to failure of the system?

3-49. Let L denote the life (or time to failure) of a certain piece of equipment, and suppose that it follows the negative exponential law with mean $1/\lambda$. Determine the conditional distribution of future life, $L - L_0$, given that the equipment is still operating after L_0 units of time have elapsed. (That is, compute

$$P\{L - L_0 \leq x \mid L > L_0\}.)$$

3-50. Show that the distribution function of S_r, the time to the rth "failure" in a Poisson process, is the following:

$$F_{S_r}(x) = 1 - \sum_{k=0}^{r-1} e^{-\lambda x}(\lambda x)^k/k!, \qquad x > 0,$$

in two ways:

(a) Differentiate $F_{S_r}(x)$ to obtain the previously given density of S_r and check that the additive constant is correct.

(b) Calculate $P(S_r \leq x)$ by expressing the event $\{S_r \leq x\}$ in terms of a Poisson random variable.

3-51. Given that the times between successive "failures" are independent, identical negative exponential random variables, show that the probability of more than one failure in time h is $o(h)$ as h tends to zero. (That is, that Poisson Postulate 4 is satisfied.) [*Hint:* Let X_1 be the time to the first, and X_2 the subsequent time to the second failure after the beginning of the interval of width h and evaluate $P(X_1 + X_2 < h)$.]

3.3 The Normal and Related Distributions

The "standard normal" distribution was encountered in the Central Limit Theorem as the limiting distribution of a standardized sum of independent, identically distributed summands, as the number of terms increases without limit. The adjective "normal" will also be applied to distributions related to the standard normal distribution by a change of scale and/or a translation. The form of the density of these distributions is such as to permit an extensive analysis of distributions occurring in inference about normal populations. This in itself would not be sufficient justification for the prominent role of normal inference in statistical theory, but it happens that the normal model is often a workable representation for actual phenomena. It has been said that the Central Limit Theorem tends to account for the occurrence of approximately normal distributions in practice, since random phenomena are often additive combinations of several contributory variables.

To review, the *standard normal* density function is the following:

$$f(z) = \frac{1}{\sqrt{2\pi}} \exp\left(-z^2/2\right).$$

The constant multiplier, which makes the area under the graph of the density function equal to 1, is most easily determined as what is needed to make the volume under the joint density surface of a pair of independent, standard normal variables equal to 1. This joint density is just the product of marginal densities:

$$f(x, y) = \frac{1}{2\pi} \exp\left[-(x^2 + y^2)/2\right],$$

and the volume under the surface that represents it is

$$\int_{-\infty}^{\infty} \int_{-\infty}^{\infty} f(x, y)\, dx\, dy = (1/2\pi) \int_{-\infty}^{\infty} \int_{-\infty}^{\infty} \exp\left[-(x^2 + y^2)/2\right] dx\, dy$$

$$= (1/2\pi) \int_{0}^{2\pi} \int_{0}^{\infty} \exp\left(-r^2/2\right) r\, dr\, d\theta = 1.$$

The distribution function of a standard normal distribution will be denoted by $\Phi(z)$:

$$\Phi(z) = \int_{-\infty}^{z} \frac{\exp\left(-u^2/2\right)}{\sqrt{2\pi}}\, du,$$

and is tabulated for $-4 \leq z \leq 4$ in Table I of the Appendix. Graphs of the standard normal density $\phi(z)$ and the standard normal c.d.f. $\Phi(z)$ are shown in Figure 3–2. Certain percentiles are given in Table Ia, and certain two-tail

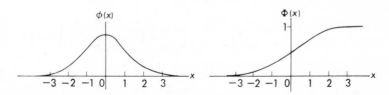

Figure 3–2. Standard normal density and C.D.F.

probabilities are given in Table Ib. The corresponding moment generating function was found in Problem 2–137 to be

$$\psi_Z(t) = e^{t^2/2} = \sum_{0}^{\infty} \frac{(t^2/2)^k}{k!} = \sum_{0}^{\infty} \frac{(2k)!}{2^k k!}\, \frac{t^{2k}}{(2k)!},$$

from which it is seen that the odd order moments are zero and that the even order moments are given by the formula

$$E(Z^{2k}) = (2k - 1)(2k - 3) \cdots 5 \cdot 3 \cdot 1, \quad \text{for } k = 1, 2, \ldots .$$

3.3.1 The General Normal Distribution

A random variable is said to be *normally distributed* if it can be expressed as a linear transformation of a standard normal variable. Thus, if Z is standard normal, any variable of the form

$$X = aZ + b,$$

for $a \neq 0$, is normally distributed. Clearly,

$$EX = b, \quad \text{and} \quad \text{var } X = a^2.$$

Moreover, a can be taken as positive without loss of generality, since $-Z$ is standard normal if Z is standard normal (see Problem 3–54). The expression for X in terms of Z can then be written in the form

$$X = \sigma Z + \mu, \quad \text{or} \quad Z = (X - \mu)/\sigma,$$

where $\mu = EX$ and σ is the standard deviation of X. Central moments of X are as follows:

$$E[(X - \mu)^n] = \sigma^n E(Z^n) = \begin{cases} 0, & \text{if } n \text{ is odd}, \\ (2k - 1) \cdots 5 \cdot 3 \cdot 1 \sigma^{2k}, & \text{if } n = 2k, \end{cases}$$

for $k = 1, 2, \ldots .$

The general normal density function is the derivative of the general normal distribution function:

$$f_X(x) = \frac{d}{dx} P(\sigma Z + \mu \leq x) = \frac{d}{dx} P\left(Z \leq \frac{x - \mu}{\sigma}\right)$$

$$= \frac{d}{dx} \Phi\left(\frac{x - \mu}{\sigma}\right) = \frac{1}{\sigma} f_z\left(\frac{x - \mu}{\sigma}\right) = \frac{1}{\sqrt{2\pi}\sigma} \exp\left[-\frac{1}{2\sigma^2}(x - \mu)^2\right].$$

Notice that an expression for the value of the general normal c.d.f. in terms of the standard normal c.d.f. was used in the above computation, namely

$$P(X \leq x) = \Phi\left(\frac{x - \mu}{\sigma}\right).$$

From this it is evident that a single table, for the *standard* normal distribution, suffices for the calculation of general normal probabilities. One enters the standard table at the "standardized" argument, which measures x according to its deviation from the mean in standard deviation units.

EXAMPLE 3–14. Consider the computation of $P(|X - 9| > 1)$, where X is normally distributed with mean 10 and variance 4. [This is sometimes written as follows: $X \stackrel{d}{=} \mathcal{N}(10, 4)$.] Table I can be used if one first expresses the event in terms of events of the type $X < c$ and then evaluates their probabilities by expressing them in terms of the standard normal c.d.f.:

$$
\begin{aligned}
P(|X - 9| > 1) &= 1 - P(|X - 9| < 1) = 1 - P(8 < X < 10) \\
&= 1 - [F_X(10) - F_X(8)] = 1 - \Phi[(10 - 10)/2] \\
&\qquad\qquad\qquad\qquad\qquad\qquad\quad + \Phi[(8 - 10)/2] \\
&= 1 - .5 + .1587 = .6587.
\end{aligned}
$$

(Here, as in other instances in which tables are used, the equality is only approximate—up to the accuracy of the table.)

The density function of a general normal distribution has been seen to be essentially an exponential function of a quadratic exponent in which the coefficient of the square term is negative. Any such function, with suitable normalization by a multiplicative constant, can serve as a normal density, as will be evident from the following example.

EXAMPLE 3–15. Consider the function $\exp(-3x^2 + 6x)$. This can be used as the basis of a density. For, the exponent can be rewritten by completing the square:

$$
-3x^2 + 6x = -3(x - 1)^2 + 3 = -\frac{(x - 1)^2}{1/3} + 3.
$$

Upon comparison with the exponent of the general normal density, it is apparent that this is a special case in which $\mu = 1$ and $2\sigma^2 = \frac{1}{3}$. Thus, the following function, which is a constant times the given one, is a normal density:

$$
\frac{1}{\sqrt{2\pi}\,\sqrt{1/6}} \exp\left\{-\frac{(x - 1)^2}{2(1/6)}\right\}.
$$

The moment generating function of a general normal distribution is readily obtained from that of the standard normal distribution:

$$
\psi_X(t) = E[\exp(tX)] = E[(\exp t(\sigma Z + \mu)] = \exp(t\mu + \sigma^2 t^2/2),
$$

and the characteristic function of the distribution is then

$$
\phi_X(t) = \psi_X(it) = \exp(it\mu - \sigma^2 t^2/2).
$$

With this one can determine the distribution of a sum of independent, normal random variables. For, if $X_1, X_2, \ldots, X_n$ are independent, identically random variables with a common normal distribution (μ, σ^2), and S_n denotes their sum, then

$$
\phi_{S_n}(t) = [\phi_X(t)]^n = \{\exp(it\mu - \sigma^2 t^2/2\}^n = \exp[i(n\mu)t - (n\sigma^2)t^2/2],
$$

which is the characteristic function of a normal distribution with mean $n\mu$ and variance $n\sigma^2$. This, then, is the distribution of S_n. (See also Problem 3–65).

3.3.2 The Lognormal Distribution

The random variable X is said to have a *lognormal* distribution if $\log X$ is normally distributed; that is, if X is of the form e^Y where Y is normal. The pertinent properties of a lognormal distribution can then be derived from properties of the normal distribution. In particular, the density function is computed as follows for $x > 0$:

$$f_X(x) = \frac{d}{dx} P(e^Y < x) = \frac{d}{dx} F_Y(\log x)$$

$$= \frac{1}{x} f_Y(\log x) = \frac{1}{\sqrt{2\pi}\sigma x} \exp\left\{\frac{-(\log x - \mu)^2}{2\sigma^2}\right\}.$$

(The density is zero for negative x.)

The kth moment of X about zero is expressible in terms of the moment generating function of $\log X$:

$$E(X^k) = E(e^{kY}) = \psi_Y(k) = \exp(k\mu + \sigma^2 k^2/2).$$

In particular,

$$EX = \exp(\mu + \sigma^2/2),$$

and

$$\operatorname{var} X = E(X^2) - (EX)^2 = \{\exp(\sigma^2) - 1\}\{\exp(2\mu + \sigma^2)\}.$$

The median is that number M such that

$$P(e^Y < M) = 1/2, \quad \text{or} \quad P(Y < \log M) = 1/2.$$

Clearly, then, $\log M = \mu$, and $M = e^{\mu}$.

The lognormal distribution finds application in a wide variety[1] of fields: physics, engineering, economics, biology, astronomy, sociology, and even philology. It is used as the distribution of incomes, of household size, of particle size, body weight, results of endurance tests, and so on.

3.3.3 Rayleigh and Maxwell Distributions

A number of other distributions arise in connection with normal distributions. Those encountered in inference problems are taken up in a later chapter. Here mention will be made of two distributions encountered in model building with normal components.

---

[1]See Aitchison, J., and Brown, J. A. C., *The Lognormal Distribution*. New York: Cambridge Univ. Press, 1957.

The bivariate distribution defined by two independent, normal variates with mean zero and common variance is sometimes called *circular normal*, with density

$$f(x, y) = \frac{1}{2\pi\sigma^2} \exp\left[-(x^2 + y^2)/(2\sigma^2)\right].$$

The radial distance out to the point (X, Y):

$$Z = (X^2 + Y^2)^{1/2}$$

has a distribution whose density is found by differentiating the c.d.f.:

$$f_Z(z) = \frac{d}{dz} P(X^2 + Y^2 < z^2) = \frac{1}{2\pi\sigma^2} \frac{d}{dz} \int\int_A \exp\left[-\frac{1}{2\sigma^2}(x^2 + y^2)\right] dx\, dy$$

$$= \frac{1}{\sigma^2} \frac{d}{dz} \int_0^z r \exp\left[-\frac{r^2}{2\sigma^2}\right] dr = \frac{z}{\sigma^2} \exp\left[-\frac{z^2}{2\sigma^2}\right], \quad \text{for } z > 0.$$

(The region denoted by A is the interior of a circle of radius z and center at the origin. The integral over this region was expressed in terms of polar coordinates and the θ-integration performed before differentiating with respect to z.) The distribution with this density is called a *Rayleigh* distribution.

A trivariate distribution for (X, Y, Z) in which these components are independent normal variates with mean zero and common variance σ^2 might be called a spherical normal distribution. The distance from the origin out to the point (X, Y, Z):

$$R = (X^2 + Y^2 + Z^2)^{1/2}$$

is a random variable whose distribution can be derived in just about the same way as the Rayleigh distribution was derived above. The result is the density

$$f_R(u) = \sqrt{2/\pi}\,(u^2/\sigma^3) \exp\left[-u^2/(2\sigma^2)\right], \quad \text{for } u > 0,$$

defining what is sometimes called the Maxwell distribution. The derivation is called for in Problem 3–62.

Problems

3–52. Given that X is normal with mean 10 and variance 4, compute

$$P(|X - 10| > 3).$$

3–53. Given that X is normally distributed with mean 10 and that $P(X > 12)$ is .1587, determine $P(9 < X < 11)$.

3–54. Given that X is normal with mean 30 and variance 25, compute

(a) $P(X > 27)$,
(b) $P(|X - 28| < 2)$.

3–55. Show that if Z has a normal distribution with zero mean, so does $-Z$.

3–56. Determine the first and third quartiles (that is, the twenty-fifth and seventy-fifth percentiles) of a standard normal distribution. From these determine the first and third quartiles of a normal distribution with mean 10 and variance 4.

3–57. Suppose that in tabulating observations on a normal random variable with mean 10 and variance 4, the range of possible values is divided into ten parts by the points 6, 7, ..., 14. (The first "class interval" goes from $-\infty$ to 6, the next from 6 to 7, etc.) Determine the probabilities of each interval.

3–58. Using characteristic functions, show that if X is normal, so is $Y = aX + b$ for any constants a and b, with $a \neq 0$.

3–59. Determine the density function and expectation of the random variable $|X - \mu|$, where X is normal with mean μ and variance σ^2.

3–60. Show that if X is log-normal, so is X^r.

3–61. It is found that in a certain rock-crushing process, the "diameters" d of the crushed rocks have approximately a lognormal distribution, with mean diameter 1.5 in. and standard deviation .3 in.

(a) What percentage of rocks would have diameters exceeding 2 in.? Less than 1 in.?

(b) Assuming rock weights to be proportional to d^3, what is the expected weight of a rock (in terms of the constant of proportionality)?

3–62. Derive the density of Maxwell distribution.

3–63. Obtain formulas for the mean and variance of the Rayleigh distribution.

3–64. Discuss the distribution of Z^2, where Z is standard normal. (Obtain the density, m.g.f., mean, and variance.)

3–65. Using characteristic function, show that any linear combination of independent, normal variables is again normal.

3.3.4   The Chi-Square Distribution

The chi-square distribution is defined as the distribution of a sum of squares of independent standard normal variables. Beginning with the special case of the square of a *single* standard normal variable, let X be normally distributed with zero mean and unit variance. The characteristic function of X^2 is then

$$E[\exp(itX^2)] = \frac{1}{\sqrt{2\pi}} \int_{-\infty}^{\infty} \exp(itx^2 - x^2/2)\, dx = (1 - 2it)^{-1/2}.$$

From this can be obtained the distribution of a sum of squares of k independent standard normal variables $X_1, \ldots, X_k$:

$$\chi^2 = X_1^2 + X_2^2 + \cdots + X_k^2.$$

The characteristic function of the distribution of χ^2 is the kth power of the characteristic function of a single term:

$$\phi_{\chi^2}(t) = (1 - 2it)^{-k/2}.$$

The density of this distribution will be derived in Chapter 7. Its cumulative distribution function is given in Table II, which is a table of percentiles for various values of k, called the number of *degrees of freedom*.

The mean and variance of a chi-square distribution can be read from the series expansion for the characteristic function:

$$\phi_{\chi^2}(t) = (1 - 2it)^{-k/2} = 1 + k(it) + (k^2 + 2k)\frac{(it)^2}{2!} + \cdots .$$

They are as follows:

$$E(\chi^2) = k, \quad \text{and} \quad \text{var } \chi^2 = 2k.$$

In Figure 3–3 are sketched the graphs of the chi-square density functions for several values of the parameter k. Observe that for $k = 1$, the density is infinite at $x = 0$, and that for $k = 2$, the density is that of the negative exponential distribution. As k increases, the mean shifts to the right and the variance

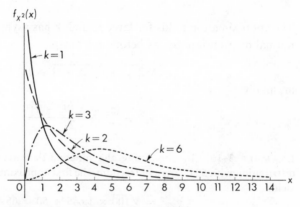

Figure 3–3.   Chi-square densities.

increases. As $k \to \infty$, the *shape* approaches that of the normal density, for according to the central limit theorem the distribution of the sum of k independent, identically distributed variables is asymptotically normal. The mean and variance of this asymptotic distribution are, respectively, k and $2k$.

Tables of chi-square percentiles (like Table II, Appendix) take advantage of the fact that the distribution is asymptotically normal. Chi-square percentiles can be approximated, using normal percentiles as follows: For any given probability p,

$$p = P(\chi^2 < \chi_p{}^2) = P\left(\frac{\chi^2 - k}{\sqrt{2k}} < \frac{\chi_p{}^2 - k}{\sqrt{2k}}\right)$$

$$\doteq P\left(Z < \frac{\chi_p{}^2 - k}{\sqrt{2k}}\right),$$

where Z is standard normal. Thus, if z_p is the 100 pth percentile of the standard normal distribution,

$$z_p \doteq (\chi_p{}^2 - k)/\sqrt{2k} \qquad \text{or} \qquad \chi_p{}^2 \doteq \sqrt{2k}\, z_p + k.$$

A somewhat better approximation results from a modification using the variable

$$Y = \sqrt{2\chi^2} - \sqrt{2k - 1}.$$

This has the distribution function

$$P(Y < x) = P(\sqrt{2\chi^2} < \sqrt{2k - 1} + x)$$

$$= P\left(\chi^2 < \frac{2k - 1}{2} + x\sqrt{2k - 1} + \frac{x^2}{2}\right)$$

$$\doteq P(\chi^2 < k + \sqrt{2k}\, x) = P\left(\frac{\chi^2 - k}{\sqrt{2k}} < x\right).$$

The approximation holds for large k, and Y has asymptotically the standard normal distribution. So, as before, for any p,

$$\sqrt{2\chi_p{}^2} - \sqrt{2k - 1} \doteq z_p,$$

or, finally

$$\chi_p{}^2 \doteq \frac{(z_p + \sqrt{2k - 1})^2}{2}.$$

EXAMPLE 3–16. In computing the ninety-fifth percentile of the chi-square distribution with 50 degrees of freedom, the first approximate formula given above yields

$$\chi_{.95}{}^2 = \sqrt{100} \times 1.645 + 50 = 66.45.$$

The modified formula yields

$$\chi_{.95}{}^2 = \tfrac{1}{2}(1.645 + \sqrt{100 - 1})^2 = 67.2,$$

which is more nearly correct, the actual value being closer to 67.5.

The chi-square distribution has a number of uses in problems of statistical inference concerning normal distributions and also in problems of goodness of fit and in contingency tables.

Problems

3–66. Using a normal approximation, estimate:

(a) The eightieth percentile of a chi-square distribution with 60 degrees of freedom.

(b) $P(\chi^2 > 60)$, where χ^2 has the chi-square distribution with 50 degrees of freedom.

3–67. Suppose that Y/σ^2 has a chi-square distribution with ten degrees of freedom. Determine the density function, mean, and variance of Y.

3–68. Show that a sum of independent chi-square variables has again the chi-square distribution, the number of degrees of freedom of the sum being the sum of the numbers of degrees of freedom of the summands.

3–69. Show that if U is uniform on $[0, 1]$, the variable $-2 \log U$ has a chi-square distribution with two degrees of freedom.

3–70. Show that if Z has the Maxwell distribution with parameter σ^2, then Z^2/σ^2 has the chi-square distribution with 3 degrees of freedom.

3.4 The Multinomial Distribution

The multinomial distribution is a generalization of the binomial distribution to instances in which the independent, identical "trials" involved are experiments with more than two outcomes. The binomial distribution arose in connection with a sequence of independent Bernoulli trials, each of which has two possible outcomes, as the number of times one particular outcome occurs in a given number of trials. Consider now a sequence of independent trials of an experiment that has k outcomes, $A_1, A_2, A_3, \ldots, A_k$ with corresponding probabilities $p_1, p_2, \ldots, p_k$. These probabilities are of course related:

$$p_1 + p_2 + \cdots + p_k = 1,$$

so that if $k - 1$ of them are specified, the remaining one is automatically determined.

Consider the random variables $X_1, \ldots, X_k$, where

$$X_i = \text{frequency of } A_i \text{ among } n \text{ trials},$$

which is of course binomially distributed (n, p_i). Since

$$X_1 + \cdots + X_k = n,$$

it follows that the joint distribution of $(X_1, \ldots, X_k)$ would be concentrated on this hyperplane. That is, there are really essentially only $k - 1$ variables, the remaining one being determined from the fact that they all must add up to n. (In the case $k = 2$, only the number of successes was studied; the joint distribution of the number of successes (X_1) and the number of failures (X_2) would be singular.) Thus, either the singular joint distribution of $(X_1, \ldots, X_k)$ or the nonsingular distribution of $k - 1$ of these, say, $(X_1, \ldots, X_{k-1})$, would be called *multinomial*.

The probability function of the k-nomial distribution is obtained along the lines of the derivation of binomial probabilities. For a *particular* sequence of results, of which f_1 are A_1, f_2 are $A_2, \ldots,$ and f_k are A_k, the probability is just the product of corresponding p's:

$$p_1{}^{f_1} p_2{}^{f_2} \cdots p_k{}^{f_k}.$$

But such a sequence of results can come in many patterns—the number of which is the number of ways of arranging n objects, f_1 of one kind, $\ldots,$ and f_k of the kth kind, namely, $n!$ divided by a factorial for each group of like objects. The total probability for all sequences with the given frequencies is then

$$P(X_1 = f_1, \ldots, \text{ and } X_k = f_k)$$

$$= \frac{n!}{f_1! \cdots f_k!} p_1{}^{f_1} p_2{}^{f_2} \cdots p_k{}^{f_k},$$

provided, of course, $f_1 + \cdots + f_k = n$. This is the joint probability function of the distribution.

The term "multinomial" is appropriate since (as in the particular case $k = 2$) these probabilities just derived are terms in a multinomial expansion:

$$(p_1 + \cdots + p_k)^n = \sum \frac{n!}{f_1! \cdots f_k!} p_1{}^{f_1} \cdots p_k{}^{f_k} = 1,$$

the sum extending over all sets of nonnegative integers that sum to n.

The moment generating function of the distribution of $(X_1, \ldots, X_k)$ is

$$\psi(t_1, \ldots, t_k) = E[\exp(t_1 X_1 + \cdots + t_k X_k)]$$

$$= (p_1 e^{t_1} + \cdots + p_k e^{t_k})^n.$$

The marginal m.g.f. of $(X_1, \ldots, X_{k-1})$ is obtained by setting $t_k = 0$:

$$\psi(t_1, \ldots, t_{k-1}, 0) = (p_1 e^{t_1} + \cdots + p_{k-1} e^{t_{k-1}} + p_k)^n.$$

This distribution (unlike that of $(X_1, \ldots, X_k)$) is nonsingular, and has marginal distributions of the same type. In particular, the univariate marginals are binomial:

$$E(e^{t_i X_i}) = (p_i e^{t_i} + 1 - p_i)^n.$$

(This is clear also from the definition of X_i as the number of times A_i occurs in n independent trials.)

EXAMPLE 3–17. A die is tossed 12 times. Let X_i denote the number of tosses in which i dots turn up, for $i = 1, \ldots, 6$. Then $p_i = 1/6$, and $E(X_i) = 12/6 = 2$, for each i. A sample probability computation is

$$P(X_1 = 2, X_2 = 2, \ldots, X_6 = 2) = \frac{12!}{2!2! \cdots 2!} \left(\frac{1}{6}\right)^2 \left(\frac{1}{6}\right)^2 \cdots \left(\frac{1}{6}\right)^2$$

$$= \frac{1{,}925}{549{,}872}$$

(which shows, incidentally, that the "expected" outcome is not very likely). The marginal distribution, say, of X_1 and X_2 is the trinomial distribution defined by

$$P(X_1 = f_1 \quad \text{and} \quad X_2 = f_2) = \sum_{f_1 + f_2 \le 12} \frac{12!}{f_1! f_2! (12 - f_1 - f_2)!} p_1^{f_1} p_2^{f_2} p^f,$$

where $p = 1 - p_1 - p_2 = 4/6$ and $f = 12 - f_1 - f_2$.

EXAMPLE 3–18.   In recording the value of a continuous random variable X it is necessary to "round off," a process which in effect divides the value space of X into mutually disjoint intervals $I_1, I_2, \ldots, I_k$. These constitute a partition of the value space, and as a succession of values of X are obtained, in repeated trials of the underlying experiment, one notes only the interval in which each value falls. The number of observations in a given interval I_j, called the frequency f_j of that interval, is a binomial variable if the observations are independent. The *joint* distribution of the frequencies $(f_1, \ldots, f_k)$ is multinomial, with

$$p_j = P(X \text{ falls in } I_j) = \int_{I_j} f(x) \, dx,$$

where $f(x)$ is the density of the distribution of X.

3.5   The Exponential Family

A one-parameter family of distributions that can be written (by suitable choice of functions) in the form

$$f(x; \theta) = B(\theta) e^{Q(\theta) R(x)} h(x)$$

is said to belong to the *exponential family* of distributions. Most of the distributions encountered so far belong to this family. The table on page 184 indicates the choice of functions corresponding to each of these various distributions. [Although the name θ for the indexing parameter is used at the head of the columns, the names (p, λ, m) used in the earlier discussions of particular cases appear in the table.]

Besides showing why it is that these models have so much in common when it comes to inference about them, recognizing them to be just special cases of a more general model makes it possible to derive once and for all many results that would otherwise have to be obtained in each particular case.

There is also an "exponential family" of distributions indexed by a multi-dimensional parameter $\boldsymbol{\theta} = (\theta_1, \ldots, \theta_k)$, namely, that defined by densities of the form

$$f(x; \boldsymbol{\theta}) = B(\boldsymbol{\theta}) h(x) \exp \left[Q_1(\boldsymbol{\theta}) R_1(x) + \cdots + Q_k(\boldsymbol{\theta}) R_k(x) \right].$$

Name	$f(x; \theta)$	$B(\theta)$	$Q(\theta)$	$R(x)$	$h(x)$
Bernoulli	$p^x(1-p)^{1-x}$	$1-p$	$\log\dfrac{p}{1-p}$	x	1
Binomial	$\binom{n}{x}p^x(1-p)^{n-x}$	$(1-p)^n$	$\log\dfrac{p}{1-p}$	x	$\binom{n}{x}$
Geometric	$p(1-p)^x$	p	$\log(1-p)$	x	1
Negative binomial	$\binom{r+x-1}{x}p^r(1-p)^{x-1}$	$p^r(1-p)^{-1}$	$\log(1-p)$	x	$\binom{r+x-1}{x}$
Poisson	$e^{-m}m^x/x!$	e^{-m}	$\log m$	x	$1/x!$
Negative exponential	$\lambda e^{-\lambda x}$	λ	$-\lambda$	x	1
Normal $(0, \theta)$	$(2\pi\theta)^{-1/2}\exp[-x^2/(2\theta)]$	$(2\pi\theta)^{-1/2}$	$-(2\theta)^{-1}$	x^2	1
Normal $(\theta, 1)$	$(2\pi)^{-1/2}\exp[-(x-\theta)^2/2]$	$(2\pi)^{-1/2}\exp(-\theta^2/2)$	θ	x	$\exp(-x^2/2)$
Gamma	$\lambda^n x^{n-1}\dfrac{e^{-\lambda x}}{(n-1)!}$	$\dfrac{\lambda^n}{(n-1)!}$	$-\lambda$	x	x^{n-1}
Rayleigh	$\dfrac{x}{\theta^2}\exp[-x^2/(2\theta^2)]$	$1/\theta^2$	$-1/(2\theta^2)$	x^2	x

The beta distribution (see Problem 3–77) and the normal distribution (see the following example) belong to this family.

EXAMPLE 3–19.   The general normal distribution is defined by the following density function, depending on the vector parameter $\theta = (\mu, \sigma^2)$:

$$f(x; \mu, \sigma^2) = \frac{1}{\sqrt{2\pi\sigma^2}} \exp\left[-(x - \mu)^2/(2\sigma^2)\right]$$

$$= \frac{1}{\sqrt{2\pi\sigma^2}} \exp\left[-\mu^2/(2\sigma^2)\right] \exp\left[-x^2/(2\sigma^2) + x(\mu/\sigma^2)\right].$$

This is seen to belong to the exponential family, with the following identifications:

$$B(\theta) = \frac{1}{\sqrt{2\pi\sigma^2}} \exp\left[-\mu^2/(2\sigma^2)\right], \qquad h(x) = 1,$$

$$Q_1(\theta) = -1/(2\sigma^2), \qquad\qquad R_1(x) = x^2,$$

$$Q_2(\theta) = \mu/\sigma^2, \qquad\qquad R_2(x) = x.$$

A multivariate density for the random vector $X = (X_1, \ldots, X_n)$ is said to belong to the exponential family of distributions if it is of the following form, in which $\theta = (\theta_1, \ldots, \theta_k)$ and $x = (x_1, \ldots, x_n)$:

$$f(x; \theta) = B(\theta)h(x) \exp\left[Q_1(\theta)R_1(x) + \cdots + Q_k(\theta)R_k(x)\right].$$

The joint density of n independent observations on a random variable X whose distribution belongs to the univariate exponential family is of the above form. For, if the density of X (in the case of a single parameter) is

$$f_X(x) = C(\theta)g(x) \exp\left[Q(\theta)S(x)\right],$$

then the joint density of n independent replicas of X is

$$f(x; \theta) = \prod f(x_i; \theta) = [C(\theta)]^n \exp\left[Q(\theta) \sum S(x_i)\right]\prod g(x_i),$$

in which the sum and product extend from $i = 1$ to $i = n$. Clearly, with $B(\theta) = [C(\theta)]^n$, $R(x) = \sum S(x_i)$, and $h(x) = \Pi g(x_i)$, this multivariate density belongs to the exponential family.

To avoid the conclusion that all distributions belong to the exponential family mention should be made of some that do not: the Cauchy family of distributions (Problem 2–140), and the family of distributions uniform on $[0, \theta]$.

Problems

3–71.   One black, three white, and two red balls are placed in a container. One ball is selected at random and replaced, and then a second ball is selected at random. Let X and Y denote, respectively, the number of red and white balls that turn up. Construct a probability table for (X, Y) and determine from it the marginal distributions of X and Y. (Notice that these are binomial distributions.)

3–72. Four independent observations are to be made on a random variable with density $f(x) = 1 - |x|, -1 < x < 1$. Suppose that the interval from -1 to 1 is divided into four class intervals of equal length. What is the probability that one observation will fall in the left-most class interval, one in the next, two in the next, and none in the right-most class interval?

3–73. A group of students consists of five from each of the four classes (freshman, sophomore, junior, senior). Determine the probability that a committee of eight chosen at random from these twenty students represents the classes equally.

3–74. Determine an approximate answer to the preceding problem with the change that the selection is made from the whole school which has 5,000 in each of the four classes.

3–75. Show that the Maxwell distribution belongs to the exponential family (see Section 3.3.3).

3–76. Given that $(X_1, \ldots, X_k)$ has a multinomial distribution with parameters $(p_1, \ldots, p_k)$, where $\sum p_i = 1$, use the moment generating function to derive the covariance of X_1 and X_2 to be $-np_1 p_2$.

3–77. The *beta distribution* with parameters (r, s) is defined by the density

$$f(x; r, s) = \text{(const.)} \, x^{r-1} (1 - x)^{s-1}, \qquad \theta < x < 1.$$

The constant multiplier is a function of r and s, call it $1/B(r, s)$ (see Section 7.1.5). Show that this distribution belongs to the exponential family by identifying the various functions in the general form of density.

3–78. Show that if X_1 and X_2 are independent, discrete, and identically distributed with density $B(\theta)h(x)e^{Q(\theta)R(x)}$, then $R(X_1) + R(X_2)$ has a distribution in the exponential family.

CHAPTER 4

STATISTICAL PROBLEMS
AND PROCEDURES

In dealing with some physical, social, biological, industrial, or psychic phenomenon, the governing laws or relations—the "way things really are"—will be called the *state of nature*. This term will refer not to all of nature but to that portion which governs the immediate phenomenon. It is to discover something about the state of nature that experiments are conducted and data are gathered. The making of inferences (direct or implicit) about the state of nature on the basis of data is called *statistical inference* when, as is usually the case, the state of nature is represented by a stochastic model and the data involve randomness.

Whether statistics coincides with or is a part of the general area of data analysis is a matter of opinion, but certainly statistical problems include such as these: making a decision between accepting or rejecting a lot of drugs on the basis of tests on a sample from the lot; announcing that the value of a certain physical constant is contained within a certain interval of values with a specified degree of assurance; ranking the effectiveness of several agricultural treatments based on an experiment involving all treatments; predicting the degree of success of a college student based on entrance tests and high school rank; and so on.

Statistics, then, deals with making decision or pronouncements or predictions under uncertainty as to how things really are, but based on the data from experimentation. The experimentation is actually a form of "spying" on nature in order to educate the guesses and actions.

Viewed broadly, statistical problems and procedures include those of designing the experiment which is to yield pertinent data—determining what experiment to perform and how much data to gather; of gathering data in such a way that the results are representative of the experiment one thinks he is performing; and of drawing inferences or taking action on the basis of the data. Of these three broad aspects of a statistical problem, the third is the one that has the most highly developed mathematical theory and with which this book is mainly concerned.

Some statistical problems, notably in business and industry, are *decision* problems, in which the partial information about the state of nature provided by data from experimentation is used as the basis of making an immediate decision. Others, in scientific areas, have to do with the exploitation of data to add to scientific knowledge for future unknown uses—to advance the understanding of the laws of "nature." Yet it is possible to consider the various existing statistical problems and procedures in a framework of decision theory; and it is the point of view of this book that so doing unifies and clarifies the processes of inference, and gives a better understanding of the claims that can and cannot be made about these processes.

In a general decision problem one is faced with a set or "space" $\mathscr{A}$ of possible actions that might be taken, the individual "points" a of this space being the individual actions. The problem then is the selection of one of these actions without knowing the state of nature (at least, not knowing it in every pertinent detail). The most intensively studied problems are (a) those in which the space of actions consists of just two points, called *hypothesis-testing* problems, and (b) those in which the action space $\mathscr{A}$ is identical with the space of parameter values that index the family of possible states of nature, called *estimation* problems. Chapters 5 and 6, respectively, deal with these two classes of problems in detail. This chapter will deal with the general problem, although many illustrations will be problems of hypothesis-testing or estimation.

4.1 Preliminaries

The space of possible states of nature will be denoted by Θ and the individual states by θ. A particular θ refers to a particular probability model. The problem lies in the fact that the "true" or "correct" or "actual" state of nature is unknown, except that it is one of the states in Θ. In many instances θ will be a real-valued parameter of a family of probability distributions, but in general it is simply a label of some kind for a particular model.

A rational approach to the making of decisions under uncertainty must take into account the *consequences* of decisions, and one of the major difficulties in making the theory practical lies in trying to evaluate these consequences on a quantitative and meaningful scale. Nevertheless, it will be assumed that one is given or determines at the outset a measure of loss $\ell(\theta, a)$ corresponding to each combination of a state of nature θ and an action a. That is, $\ell(\theta, a)$ denotes the loss incurred upon taking action a when the state of nature is actually θ. It is called the *loss function*. (It can be negative, in which case the "loss" is really a gain.)

4.1.1 Convex Combinations

For a graphical representation of losses in decision procedures in simple cases, a background in certain simple geometrical notions is needed. These will be presented for the case of the plane, or two-dimensional geometry, but much of the discussion would apply equally well in spaces of n dimensions.

Given points P and Q in the plane, in which a cartesian coordinate system is established, multiplication by a scalar (or real number) and the addition of points are defined as follows:

(a) kP is the point whose coordinates are k times those of P;

(b) $P + Q$ is the point whose coordinates are the sums of corresponding coordinates of P and Q.

These can be interpreted as multiplication of a vector by a scalar and addition of vectors, when one identifies the point P with the vector from the origin out to P (that is, with the "position vector" of P). A *linear combination* of points $P_1, \ldots, P_k$ is defined to be the point

$$P = a_1 P_1 + \cdots + a_k P_k,$$

where the a's are real constants (scalars).

EXAMPLE 4–1.   Consider the three points $P = (4, 4)$, $Q = (5, 0)$, $R = (2, 5)$. A linear combination of these is a point $S = (x, y)$ of the form

$$S = a_1 P + a_2 Q + a_3 R,$$

This is also written in the following form, with (x, y) written as a column matrix:

$$\binom{x}{y} = a_1\binom{4}{4} + a_2\binom{5}{0} + a_3\binom{2}{5}.$$

The relation is equivalent, according to the definitions of the operations used, to two equations:

$$\begin{cases} x = 4a_1 + 5a_2 + 2a_3 \\ y = 4a_1 + 0a_2 + 5a_3. \end{cases}$$

In the applications to follow, linear combinations of particular interest will be those in which the coefficients are nonnegative and add up to 1:

$$a_1 + \cdots + a_k = 1, \qquad a_i \geq 0 \text{ for all } i.$$

Another way of saying this is that the coefficients constitute a discrete probability distribution. Such a linear combination will be called a *convex combination*, for reasons yet to be seen.

Convex combinations arise naturally in determining the center of gravity of a system of finitely many point masses. Suppose that there is a mass m_1 at the point P_1, a mass m_2 at $P_2, \ldots$, and a mass m_k at P_k. The center of gravity of this system of masses is defined to be the following point:

$$P = (m_1 P_1 + \cdots + m_k P_k)/m, \qquad \text{where} \quad m = m_1 + \cdots + m_k.$$

(And it is found in the study of mechanics that this is the *balance point* when the masses are affixed to a weightless stiff wire.) The coefficients in this linear combination are nonnegative and add up to 1, so P is a convex combination of $P_1, \ldots, P_k$. From this it follows that any convex combination can be interpreted as a center of gravity of a mass distribution in which the points are assigned masses proportional to the constants in the combination.

One is often interested in the set of *all* convex combinations of a given collection of points, and the interpretation in terms of centers of gravity gives the clue as to the nature of this set of convex combinations. In particular, the convex combinations of two points define, in their totality, the *line segment* joining those two points. The combination $(P + Q)/2$ is the midpoint of that segment, corresponding to equal masses at P and Q. Increasing the weight assigned to P shifts the center of gravity towards P.

EXAMPLE 4-2. The line segment joining $(-1, 3)$ and $(3, -5)$ consists of linear combinations of the form

$$\binom{x}{y} = \alpha\binom{-1}{3} + (1 - \alpha)\binom{3}{-5}.$$

The weight α that corresponds to a particular point on the line, say $(0, 1)$ is found by solving one of the two equations implied by

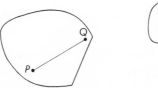

$$\binom{0}{1} = \alpha\binom{-1}{3} + (1 - \alpha)\binom{3}{-5}.$$

Thus,

$$0 = -\alpha + 3(1 - \alpha) = 3 - 4\alpha,$$

from which $\alpha = \frac{3}{4}$. Three times as much mass at $(-1, 3)$ as at $(3, -5)$ yields $(0, 1)$ as the center of gravity.

A set of points is said to be *convex* if it includes the entire line segment joining any pair of its points. A line segment is itself a convex set, and Figure 4–1 shows a plane set that is convex and one that is not; in the latter case a

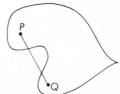

Figure 4–1.

pair of points is indicated for which the line segment joining them is not in the set. The set of all convex combinations of points $P_1, \ldots, P_k$ is a convex set, a fact that will now be demonstrated. Consider any two points P and Q that are convex combinations:

$$P = \sum a_i P_i, \quad \text{and} \quad Q = \sum b_i P_i.$$

Each point of the segment joining P and Q is of the form

$$R = \alpha P + (1 - \alpha)Q = \alpha \sum a_i P_i + (1 - \alpha) \sum b_i P_i$$

$$= \sum (\alpha a_i + [1 - \alpha]b_i)P_i.$$

But these coefficients of P_i also add up to 1:

$$\sum (\alpha a_i + [1 - \alpha]b_i) = \alpha \sum a_i + (1 - \alpha) \sum b_i = \alpha + (1 - \alpha) = 1.$$

Hence, R is also a convex combination of $P_1, \ldots, P_k$, showing that the set of convex combinations contains every point on the line segment joining each pair of its points—and so is a convex set.

EXAMPLE 4–3.   Consider the set of all convex combinations of the three points $(4, 4)$, $(5, 0)$, and $(2, 5)$. This set consists of all possible centers of gravity corresponding to various weights at the three points, and is the set of points in the triangle whose vertices are the given points, indicated by the shaded region in Figure 4–2. If the mass at one point is zero, then the corresponding center of gravity lies on the side of the triangle defined by the other two points. To move the center of gravity outside the triangle would take a negative mass at some point, which is ruled out.

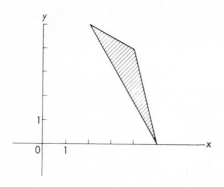

Figure 4–2. Convex combinations of three points.

The set of convex combinations of a given collection of points is the smallest convex set containing those points and is called the convex set *generated* by those points (or their *convex hull*). In the case of a finite collection of points, the convex set they generate consists of points that lie within or on a *polygon*, whose vertices are points in that collection. This polygon is formed by a rubber band stretched to include all of the points and released to rest on pegs inserted at the various points. Figure 4–3 illustrates this.

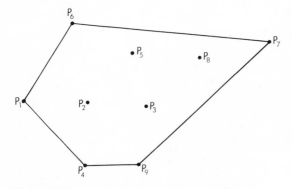

Figure 4–3. Convex set generated by nine points.

Problems

4–1. Show that $k(P + Q) = kP + kQ$. (Multiplication by a scalar is distributive over addition of points.)

4–2. Obtain (by eliminating α) the rectangular equation of the line through the points $(-1, 3)$ and $(3, -5)$ from the representation of the line segment as a set of linear combinations as given in Example 4–2. (Where does the point (x, y) lie when α does *not* lie on the range $0 \leq \alpha \leq 1$?)

4–3.   Determine the point in which the line $x = y$, thought of as issuing from the origin, would first meet the convex set in Example 4–3, generated by (4, 4), (5, 0), and (2, 5). What probability weights would produce this point?

4–4.   Determine the center of gravity of a system of masses consisting of 2 gm at $(1, 2, -3)$, 4 gm at $(0, 2, 0)$, 3 gm at $(1, -4, 3)$, and 1 gm at $(2, 5, -1)$.

4–5.   Which of the following three-dimensional sets are convex?

(a) The set of points within a sphere.
(b) The set of points on a plane.
(c) The set of points within a tetrahedron.
(d) The set of points within a right cylinder defined by a convex base.
(e) The set of points on the surface of a sphere.

4–6.   Determine the point, and corresponding probability weights, in which the ray $x = y = z$ issuing from the origin of a three-dimensional rectangular coordinate system first strikes the convex set generated by the points $(0, 4, 0)$, $(3, 1, 0)$, $(0, 0, 4)$, and $(4, 3, 5)$.

4.1.2   Utility

Loss is not necessarily monetary. It can be as vague as loss of prestige, comfort, or goodwill. But to be useful, loss must be measured on at least an ordered, if not a numerical, scale. The term *utility* has come to be used to denote a kind of measure of gain (or negative loss) which appears to be appropriate for decision problems.

Specifically, *utility* denotes a real-valued function on prospects with which one is faced that (a) is bounded, (b) orders prospects according to preference, (c) is computed as an expected value for prospects that are random. In terms of the notation $u(\mathscr{P})$ for the utility of a prospect $\mathscr{P}$, property (b) says that if $\mathscr{P}_1$ is preferred to $\mathscr{P}_2$, then $u(\mathscr{P}_1) \geq u(\mathscr{P}_2)$. The essence of property (c) is that if $\mathscr{P}$ is the random prospect of facing prospect $\mathscr{P}_1$ with probability α and prospect $\mathscr{P}_2$ with probability $1 - \alpha$, then $\mathscr{P}$'s utility is

$$u(\mathscr{P}) = \alpha u(\mathscr{P}_1) + (1 - \alpha)u(\mathscr{P}_2),$$

or the weighted average that defines the expected value of the random variable $u(\mathscr{P})$. The boundedness of property (a) is a condition that avoids certain paradoxes, like that of the following example.

EXAMPLE 4–4.   The following proposition is offered, for a fee: You will be given a reward of 2^k dollars if in repeated tosses of a coin the first Heads turns up on the kth toss. How large a fee would *you* pay to enter this arrangement?

Ordinarily entry fees (apart from the "overhead" for the "house") are determined to be the expected monetary gain—at least, such a determination makes the game "fair." Here the expected gain is

$$E(2^X) = \sum_{1}^{\infty} 2^k(1/2^k) = \infty,$$

which would not only be prohibitive as an entry fee, but is not even approached by what people are actually willing to pay to play this game. The paradox is resolved by the fact that people's attitudes are not determined solely by dollar amounts—that their utility in this situation is not proportional to amount of money.

It is not easy for one to determine whether he actually has a utility function, satisfying the above properties, and it is usually even harder to determine what the function is, given that there is one. The existence of a utility function can be shown to follow as a consequence of certain reasonable axioms for preference patterns.[1]

Utility is clearly a personal matter, but it is not uncommon that two people have similar utility functions. If they do, a reasonable theory of decisions based on utility as a measure of gain should lead them to similar behavior rules in a given problem. On the other hand, if they have quite different utility functions, they might well be led to opposite behaviors, and still both be considered rational.

It will be assumed that loss functions to be used will measure utility—except that it will sometimes be mathematically convenient to use a loss function that is not bounded (whereas utility has been assumed to be bounded). In such instances the unboundedness will not play a crucial role or lead to a behavior significantly different from what is obtained by using a bounded modification of loss.

The notion of utility helps to explain why people sometimes enter into an unfair betting situation. A bet resulting in a new total capital M_W with probability p and with new total capital M_L with probability $1 - p$ is said to be *fair* if the expected total capital after the bet is equal to the initial capital M_0:

$$M_0 = pM_W + (1 - p)M_L.$$

The utility U_B of the random prospect consisting of taking the bet is computed by taking the expected value of the possible utilities after the bet:

$$U_B = pu(M_W) + (1 - p)u(M_L).$$

Putting these two equations together:

$$\binom{M_0}{U_B} = p\binom{M_W}{u(M_W)} + (1 - p)\binom{M_L}{u(M_L)},$$

[1] See Blackwell, D., and Girshick, M. [2], pp. 104–111.

one finds that the quantity U_B can be interpreted as the ordinate of that point whose abscissa is M_0 and which is a convex combination of $[M_W, u(M_W)]$ and $[M_L, u(M_L)]$, lying therefore on the line segment joining these two points. The bet will be worthwhile, then, if the utility curve at M_0 is below that line segment, as in Figure 4–4. That is, if $U_B > u(M_0)$, one is better off taking the bet than not taking it.

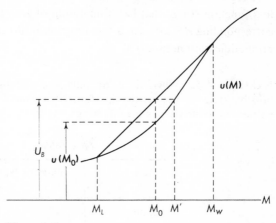

Figure 4–4.

The bet is disadvantageous (and advantageous to the one offering the bet) if

$$M_0 > pM_W + (1 - p)M_L,$$

which implies that the expected net gain is negative:

$$p(M_W - M_0) + (1 - p)(M_L - M_0) < 0.$$

Inspection of the graph shows how much to the right of its present value one could move M_0 and still keep $u(M_0) > U_B$, so that the bet would be still worthwhile. (Note that U_B, depending only on M_L, M_W, and p, does not change as one considers larger M_0's or more disadvantageous bets.) The largest M_0 that one could consider before the bet becomes disadvantageous is indicated on the graph in Figure 4–4 as M'.

4.1.3   Regret

It is felt by some that actions should be based on what is called *regret* instead of on *loss*. The regret function $r(\theta, a)$ is defined as the result of subtracting from the loss $\ell(\theta, a)$ the minimum loss for the given θ:

$$r(\theta, a) = \ell(\theta, a) - \min_a \ell(\theta, a).$$

That is, for each state of nature, one determines the smallest loss he could get by with if that state of nature were known to be the true state; this is a contribution to loss that even a *good* decision cannot avoid, and so, to obtain a quantity more appropriate to the decision process, it is subtracted from the loss. The difference $r(\theta, a)$ represents the loss that could have been avoided had the state of nature been known—hence the term *regret*.

A regret function has a minimum value of zero for each θ. Conversely, a loss function $\ell(\theta, a)$ that has a minimum of zero for each θ is equal to the corresponding $r(\theta, a)$; such a loss function is already a regret function, with no modification necessary.

EXAMPLE 4–5. When there are only two actions available and only two possible states of nature, the loss function is completely described by the four entries in a table such as the following:

Loss Table

	States of Nature	
	θ_1	θ_2
Actions: a_1	10	10
a_2	15	0

The table of corresponding regrets is obtained by subtracting from each entry in a column the minimum in that column. The result is as follows:

Regret Table

	States of Nature	
	θ_1	θ_2
Actions: a_1	0	10
a_2	5	0

The correct action for state θ_1 (according to either table) is a_1, since the loss is smaller for that action. This minimum loss for θ_1 cannot be avoided when nature is in state θ_1; it is not the fault of the decision. On the other hand, the loss of 15 for action a_2 can be reduced to 10 by taking action a_1 instead—if the state is θ_1. The difference of 5 would be "regretted."

It will be seen that whether regret or loss is used can make a difference in the procedure to which one is led, depending on what guiding principles are used in arriving at the procedure. Most classical statistical procedures imply loss functions that are actually regret functions.

Problems

4-7.   A man needs $6.00 to buy a ticket to a certain ball game, but he has only
$3.00. He wants to see the game badly. Are the numbers of dollars good repre-
sentatives of his utility? Devise a graph that would better indicate his utility as a
function of how much money he has at the time. In terms of this utility scale,
determine his utility in tossing a coin for his $3.00, double or nothing. Is his
utility improved in playing this game—that is, should he play it?

4-8.   Referring to Example 4–4, suppose that utility for money (x in dollars)
is defined as follows:

$$u(x) = \begin{cases} x/2^b, & \text{if } x \le 2^b, \\ 1, & \text{if } x > 2^b. \end{cases}$$

Determine the expected utility in playing the game, and by translating this into
dollars, determine the most a person with the above utility function ought to be
willing to pay as an entry fee.

4-9.   Determine the regret table corresponding to the loss table shown.

	θ_1	θ_2	θ_3
a_1	2	-3	-1
a_2	4	0	5
a_3	1	1	-1
a_4	0	2	-2

4-10.   Determine the regret function corresponding to the loss function
$\ell(\theta, a) = (\theta - a)^2$, where θ and a are both real numbers.

4-11.   Is an unfair bet ever worthwhile if one's utility function for money is
$1 - e^{-x}$?

4-12.   A man is considering a bet in which he will end up with $10.00 if he
wins and with nothing if he loses. His utility for money is

$$u(x) = \begin{cases} 0, & \text{if } x < 1, \\ (x - 1)/9, & \text{if } x > 1, \end{cases}$$

over the range of values of x (in dollars) of interest. Determine the utility in his
taking the bet. Is there any probability of success so unfavorable that he should
not take the bet, assuming that his initial capital is $1.00? Assuming that his
initial capital is $2.00?

4-13.   Given the bet of the preceding problem, what probability of winning
makes it a "fair" bet if the man has initially $1.00? Given this probability of
winning, what is the most that the man could start with and still consider the bet
worthwhile?

4.2   The No-Data Decision Problem

Although statistical inference ordinarily involves data, the problem of
making a decision in the absence of data is simpler, and serves to introduce

the basic concepts. Moreover, the techniques developed later in the case of data amount to a reduction to the no-data case.

Consider, then, the problem of choosing an action from the set $\mathscr{A}$ of available actions, given only the set Θ of possible states of nature and the loss function $\ell(\theta, a)$, which gives the loss incurred when action a is taken and nature is in state θ. By definition, loss is something to be avoided, and it would be desirable to choose a in such a way as to minimize the loss. When the state of nature is known, this is possible, and amounts to an ordinary minimization problem—minimizing $\ell(\theta, a)$ as a function of a for fixed θ. When the state of nature is unknown, the best action cannot be determined by a simple minimization, since the action best for one state of nature is usually not best for another state of nature.

Choosing an action without knowing the state of nature can be likened to a two-person game, in which the "opponent" is Nature. In the theory of games, it is assumed that both players are trying to "win." But although it may sometimes seem to be so, it is certainly dubious that Nature is really trying to get the better of the statistician. Nevertheless, the terminology and concepts of game theory are found in decision theory. For instance, a choice of action is sometimes called a *strategy*, and a state of nature (or choice by the player called Nature) is a strategy of the opponent.

In game theory it is found that it pays to consider what are called *mixed* strategies, or procedures that employ an extraneous random device to make the choice of action. A choice of a mixed strategy is a choice of a particular random device. The original strategies are then called *pure* strategies, and are special cases of mixed strategies in which the random device chosen is really deterministic. For instance, if there are two available actions, mixed strategies are Bernoulli experiments—tossing a (biased) coin with probability p of Heads. One action is taken if it falls Heads, the other if it falls Tails. The choice of coin or choice of p is a strategy, and choosing $p = 1$ (or using a two-Headed coin) is a pure strategy, as is $p = 0$.

If the action to be taken is chosen by a random device, the loss function becomes a random variable, being a function of the action taken. Accepting the assumed property of utility that calls for treating random prospects according to their expected utilities, one is led to consider the *expected loss*

$$L(\theta, P^{\mathscr{A}}) = E[\ell(\theta, a)],$$

where $P^{\mathscr{A}}$ denotes a particular probability distribution (that is, a mixed strategy) on the action space $\mathscr{A}$.

EXAMPLE 4-6. Consider a problem in which there are two states of nature and three possible actions. To have a concrete (though possibly fanciful) illustration in mind, think of the states of nature as "rain" (θ_1) and "no rain" (θ_2), and the actions as "stay at home" (a_1), "go out without an umbrella" (a_2), and "go out with an umbrella," (a_3). That is, one has an errand to do and must decide whether to take an umbrella and face the possible mortification of carrying it in the sunshine, leave the umbrella home and possibly get soaked, or just give up on the errand. The following table gives losses (negative utility) that represent the dilemma which constitutes the decision problem.

	States of Nature	
	θ_1 (rain)	θ_2 (no rain)
Actions: a_1 (stay home)	4	4
a_2 (go, no umbrella)	5	0
a_3 (go with umbrella)	2	5

A mixed strategy is now a vector of probabilities:

$$p = (p_1, p_2, p_3), \qquad (\textstyle\sum p_i = 1, \quad p_i \geq 0).$$

That is, a random device is used that has three outcomes ω_1, ω_2, and ω_3 with probabilities p_1, p_2, and p_3, respectively; action a_i is taken if outcome ω_i is observed. The strategy $(1, 0, 0)$ is then the pure strategy a_1, $(0, 1, 0)$ is a_2, and $(0, 0, 1)$ is a_3. For a given mixed strategy p, the expected loss $L(\theta, p)$ depends on θ; let $L_i = L(\theta_i, p)$. These losses are computed as follows:

$$\begin{cases} L_1 = 4p_1 + 5p_2 + 2p_3, \\ L_2 = 4p_1 \qquad\quad + 5p_3, \end{cases}$$

or

$$\begin{pmatrix} L_1 \\ L_2 \end{pmatrix} = p_1 \begin{pmatrix} 4 \\ 4 \end{pmatrix} + p_2 \begin{pmatrix} 5 \\ 0 \end{pmatrix} + p_3 \begin{pmatrix} 2 \\ 5 \end{pmatrix}.$$

Plotting (L_1, L_2) as a point in the plane one sees (from this last relation) that this point—which corresponds to the mixed strategy p—is a convex combination of $(4, 4)$, $(5, 0)$, and $(2, 5)$. It lies, therefore, somewhere in the triangle with these three points as vertices; it is a center of gravity corresponding to masses proportional to the components of p. This triangle, shown in Figure 4–5, includes points each of which represents a particular mixed strategy or probability vector p. The coordinates of the points are the losses under θ_1 and θ_2, respectively.

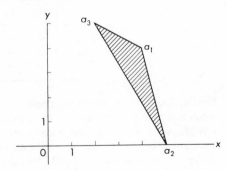

Figure 4–5. Set of mixed actions in Example 4–6.

4.2.1 The Minimax Principle

It has been seen that even in the simplest problems the desire to choose an action to minimize loss is not an adequate guide, since the action that minimizes the loss for one state of nature does not necessarily do so for another. It should come as no surprise, then, that no single method or principle for selecting an action has been universally accepted as "best." Two principles are considered in this and the following section; each principle proposes a way of assigning a single number to each action, and so *ordering* them according to this number. The one assigned the smallest number is presumed to be "best," and is the action called for by that particular ordering.

The *minimax principle* is that one should expect the worst and prepare for it. That is, for each action determine the maximum possible loss that might be incurred under the various states of nature. This number is assigned to that action and serves to order the actions. The one with the smallest (or minimum) maximum loss is the one taken.

EXAMPLE 4–7.   Consider again the loss table of Example 4–6; a column has been added, listing the maximum loss for each action:

	θ_1	θ_2	$\max \ell(\theta, a)$
a_1	4	4	4
a_2	5	0	5
a_3	2	5	5

If action a_1 is selected, the maximum loss is 4, incurred for either state of nature. This maximum is smaller than the maximum of 5 encountered for a_2 or a_3, and so a_1 is the minimax action.

The minimax principle can also be applied to the regret function. The regret table corresponding to the above loss table is the following, in which a column of maximum regrets for the various actions is given:

	θ_1	θ_2	$\max r(\theta, a)$
a_1	2	4	4
a_2	3	0	3
a_3	0	5	5

The minimum of the maximum regrets is 3, achieved for action a_2. The minimax regret action is not the same as the minimax loss action in this example.

A graphical representation is enlightening. As in Example 4–6, the actions are represented by the points (L_1, L_2), with $L_i = \ell(\theta_i, a)$. Now, for any point (x, y) above the line $x = y$, the second coordinate (y) is the maximum one; for a point below the line $x = y$, the first coordinate (x) is maximum. To choose between two actions *both above* $x = y$, take the one with the smaller y—the lower one, or the one first met by a horizontal line moving upward. To choose between two actions *both below* $x = y$, take the one first met by a vertical line moving to the right. For points some of which lie above, some on, and some below the line $x = y$, take (for the minimax action) the one first hit in moving together a horizontal line up *and* a vertical line to the right—the point first met by a wedge moving with its vertex on $x = y$, as shown in Figure 4–6.

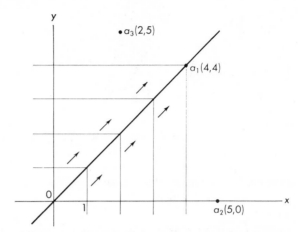

Figure 4–6.   Graphical   determination   of   miminax
action.

The above example illustrates the fact that if one follows the minimax principle, he can be led to different actions according as he considers *loss* or *regret* as the proper way of assessing the consequences of decisions. In the case of two actions, subtracting the minimum loss for each state of nature makes one entry zero and the rest nonnegative for each state. This has the effect, graphically, of moving the set of strategies without rotation so that at least one point falls on each coordinate axis and the rest are in the first quadrant.

In selecting a strategy from among mixed strategies the minimax principle is applied to the expected loss. That is, a mixed strategy or probability distribution $P^{\mathscr{A}}$ on the action space $\mathscr{A}$ is selected so as to minimize the maximum over θ of the loss averaged with respect to $P^{\mathscr{A}}$. The following example illustrates this in a simple case.

EXAMPLE 4–8.   For the loss table in Examples 4–6 and 4–7 there was computed in Example 4–6 the following expected losses, $L_i = E[\ell(\theta_i, a)]$:

$$\begin{cases} L_1 = 4p_1 + 5p_2 + 2p_3, \\ L_2 = 4p_1 \qquad\quad + 5p_3, \end{cases}$$

corresponding to the mixed strategy (p_1, p_2, p_3). The minimax mixed strategy can be determined graphically just as in the case of the pure strategies (Example 4–7), except that the actions considered are all mixtures of a_1, a_2, and a_3. As seen in Figure 4–7, the first point of this set of mixtures hit by a wedge moving out

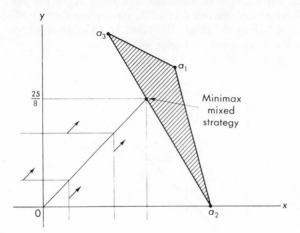

Figure 4–7.   Graphical   determination   of   minimax
mixed   action.

along $x = y$ is $(25/8, 25/8)$. This point is the center of gravity of weights 0 at a_1, 3/8 at a_2, and 5/8 at a_3. The minimax mixed strategy is therefore $(0, 3/8, 5/8)$. Notice that, as in the case of pure strategies, the minimax mixed action would be different if the above process were applied to the expected regrets.

The graphical analysis given above in the case of two states of nature makes it clear that only boundary points of the set of mixed strategies could ever be minimax strategies. Moreover, not all of the boundary points can be minimax strategies. Only the boundary points between the points in which a line moved up parallel to the x-axis and a line moved to the right parallel to the y-axis first meet the set of strategies can be minimax strategies. Actually, there will only be one minimax strategy unless the wedge first strikes the strategy set in an edge parallel to one of the axes; this one point will lie on the "lower left" portion of the boundary, as just described.

In particular, if the losses for one action are all greater than the losses for another action, the former would not be a minimax action nor be a part of a minimax mixed strategy.

The analytical determination of minimax mixed strategies is a matter that will not be investigated here in general, or even in the relatively simple example just treated. Such an investigation would be in order if the minimax principle were a major tool in determining good statistical procedures. However, although the principle provides a means of selecting a procedure, it is felt by many to be overly pessimistic, guarding against all possibilities no matter how remote. A means of incorporating feelings about "remoteness" of possible states is taken up in the next section.

Problems

4–14. Given the loss table below, determine the minimax loss (pure) action and also the minimax regret (pure) action.

	θ_1	θ_2	θ_3
a_1	2	-3	-1
a_2	4	0	5
a_3	1	1	-1
a_4	0	2	-2

4–15. Investigate the minimax strategies (pure and mixed, using loss and then regret) for the following loss table:

	θ_1	θ_2
a_1	10	10
a_2	15	0

4-16. Given the following loss table, plot points corresponding to the various actions and determine the minimax strategy (mixed). Determine the corresponding regret table and determine the minimax regret strategy.

	a_1	a_2	a_3	a_4	a_5
θ_1	-1	1	0	2	5
θ_2	3	2	5	3	2

4-17. Which actions in Problem 4–16 are automatically out of the running in view of the comment in the next to the last paragraph of the preceding text?

4-18. In estimating a Bernoulli parameter p, $0 \leq p \leq 1$, the actions are the possible values a that might be announced as the estimates of p. That is, $0 \leq a \leq 1$. Given the loss function $\ell(p, a) = (p - a)^2$, determine the maximum loss for each a and then determine the a that minimizes this maximum loss.

4.2.2 Bayes Solutions

Although the state of nature is ordinarily unknown in a decision problem, it is unusual not to have some information about the state of nature—information that could and should be taken into account in the decision process. This *a priori* information about nature can be used to set up a weighting for the states of nature, called a *prior* distribution (or an *a priori* distribution). It is used to represent the relative "likelihood" of the various states of nature for the particular decision problem at hand.

Suppose then that a distribution is given for Θ, the set of all possible states of nature. If this is actually a probability distribution, the average or expected loss can be computed for each action:

$$B(a) = E[\ell(\theta, a)].$$

This will be referred to as the *Bayes loss* corresponding to the given prior distribution. It serves to order the various possible actions, and the *Bayes principle* calls for taking that action which minimizes this Bayes loss.

In case the set Θ is discrete, the Bayes loss for a given action is computed as a weighted sum of the various losses for the action. If the weight $g(\theta)$ is assigned to the state θ, the Bayes loss is

$$B(a) = \sum \ell(\theta, a) g(\theta).$$

If θ is a real parameter and is assigned a continuous prior distribution with density $g(\theta)$, the Bayes loss is

$$B(a) = \int \ell(\theta, a) g(\theta) \, d\theta.$$

Notice that this is a second possible meaning of the phrase "expected loss." In the earlier case of a mixed strategy the phrase referred to an average with respect to a distribution of probability on the set of actions; here the average is taken with respect to a distribution on the set of states—and this latter distribution could be thought of as a mixed strategy for Nature.

EXAMPLE 4–9.   Consider the loss table for the three-action, two-state problem of Example 4–6:

	a_1	a_2	a_3
θ_1	4	5	2
θ_2	4	0	5

Suppose that past experience shows that it rains on the date in question 40 per cent of the time. To incorporate this into the problem, one assigns weights .4 to θ_1 and .6 to θ_2. The Bayes losses are as follows:

$$B(a_1) = 4 \times .4 + 4 \times .6 = 4,$$
$$B(a_2) = 5 \times .4 + 0 \times .6 = 2,$$
$$B(a_3) = 2 \times .4 + 5 \times .6 = 3.8.$$

The smallest of these is 2, incurred by taking action a_2, which action is then the Bayes solution.

The Bayes solution can be determined graphically, using the plot of (L_1, L_2) introduced in Example 4–6. The Bayes loss for an action with losses (L_1, L_2) is

$$B(a) = .4L_1 + .6L_2.$$

All actions with a given Bayes loss K would satisfy the condition

$$.4L_1 + .6L_2 = K,$$

and so be represented by points on the line having this equation. For various K's, the equation defines a *family* of lines with slope $-.4/.6$, higher lines corresponding to larger K's. (The intercept on the vertical axis is $K/.6$.) Thus, to compare two actions it is only necessary to determine which action lies on the lower line in this family of lines. Or, if there are several actions to compare, move a line with slope $-.4/.6$ (which is the slope common to all of the lines $.4L_1 + .6L_2 = K$) from below all of the points representing actions until it first hits one of those points. The corresponding action is the Bayes solution. Figure 4–8 illus-

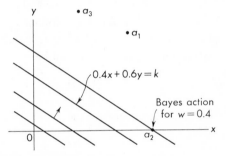

Figure 4–8. Graphical determination of Bayes action.

trates this, and examination of that figure also shows that for different prior weights, which would give families of lines with slopes other than $-.4/.6$ (but always nonpositive), the Bayes solution would be always either a_2 or a_3. (For *one* choice of prior weights, the line would hit a_2 and a_3 simultaneously, in which case it does not matter which of these actions is taken.)

EXAMPLE 4–10.   Another kind of graphical representation is instructive in the situation of the above example. Consider the loss table as given there, and assume a prior distribution defined by $g(\theta_1) = w$ and $g(\theta_2) = 1 - w$. The expected losses are as follows:

$$B(a_1) = 4w + 4(1 - w) = 4,$$

$$B(a_2) = 5w + 0(1 - w) = 5w,$$

$$B(a_3) = 2w + 5(1 - w) = 5 - 3w.$$

These functions of w are plotted in Figure 4–9. At each value of w the action with the smallest Bayes loss can be seen by inspection as the action whose line is lowest at that point. Notice that for any prior probability for θ_1 up to $w = \frac{5}{8}$

action a_2 is best; for $w > \frac{5}{8}$ action a_3 is best. Action a_1 is not best for any prior distribution.

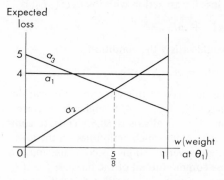

Expected
loss

Figure 4–9. Graphical determination
of Bayes action.

If both the decision maker and Nature use mixed strategies, the average must be taken with respect to the joint distribution of the vector (θ, a). The random variables θ and a would usually be independent (with no collusion between Nature and the decision maker), so that in the case of discrete θ and discrete a, the expected loss corresponding to prior probability function $g(\theta)$ and mixed strategy $p(a)$ would be

$$E\ell(\theta, a) = \sum_i \sum_j \ell(\theta_i, a_j) g(\theta_i) p(a_j).$$

This is the Bayes loss for the mixed strategy $p(a)$. It can be written in the form

$$E[\ell(\theta, a)] = \sum_i E[\ell(\theta_i, a)] g(\theta_i),$$

where the expectation on the left is with respect to the joint distribution of (θ, a) and the expectation inside the sum on the right is with respect to the distribution of a that defines the mixed strategy. That is, the Bayes procedure is simply applied to the expected loss, or loss averaged with respect to the mixed strategy used.

EXAMPLE 4–11. In the decision problem of the preceding two examples, in which there are just two states of nature, the same graphical procedure used to determine the Bayes pure action (Example 4–9 and Figure 4–8) can be used to determine the Bayes mixed action. This strategy is the probability vector (p_1, p_2, p_3) that minimizes

$$E[\ell(\theta, a)] = w(4p_1 + 5p_2 + 2p_3) + (1 - w)(4p_1 + 5p_3)$$

$$= wL_1 + (1 - w)L_2,$$

where L_1 and L_2 are the expected losses under θ_1 and θ_2, respectively, and (L_1, L_2) is the point in the graphical representation corresponding to the mixed action (p_1, p_2, p_3). The Bayes strategy is found to be that corresponding to the point first hit by a line moving upward with slope $-w/(1 - w)$. Figure 4–10 shows the set of mixed strategies, and lines with various slopes and corresponding w-values as they meet the set of strategies. One important observation is that nothing is really accomplished by including non-pure strategies in the competition. Only the pure

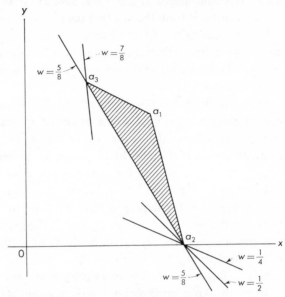

Figure 4–10.   Bayes solutions (Example 4–11).

strategy a_2 or the pure strategy a_3 will be the Bayes solution, with one exception —the case in which w defines a family of lines parallel to the line through a_2 and a_3. In that instance, any *mixture* of a_2 and a_3 would give the same Bayes loss— but there is no particular point to using such a mixture in preference to either a_2 or a_3.

The last observation of the preceding example is certainly applicable to any decision problem with two states of nature and finitely many actions. The set of mixed strategies in such problems is polygonal and a line moving upward first meets the set either in a vertex or along a whole edge (including the vertices defining that edge). Thus, nothing is gained by including mixtures of actions as strategies. This is in contrast to the fact that in using the minimax principle, mixed strategies can lead to a smaller minimax loss than can pure actions alone. It should be pointed out that in determining Bayes solutions it does not matter whether one uses the loss function or the regret function. For, since

$$r(\theta, a) = \ell(\theta, a) - \min_a \ell(\theta, a),$$

it follows that for any prior distribution on Θ with c.d.f. $W(\theta)$,

$$\int_\Theta r(\theta, a) \, dW(\theta) = \int_\Theta \ell(\theta, a) \, dW(\theta) - \int_\Theta \min \ell(\theta, a) \, dW(\theta).$$

And then because the second term is independent of a, the action that minimizes the expected regret minimizes also the expected loss.

In the graphical procedure that applies in problems with two states of nature this equivalence of regret and loss, as far as Bayes solutions are concerned, is evident from the fact that the determination of regret from loss involves translating the set of strategies without rotation. But the process of moving up a line with given slope until it hits the set of strategies does not depend on the location of the origin and therefore yields the same solution or solutions in both cases.

The set of Bayes solutions is the set of points that are first encountered, for lines of nonpositive slope, as a line is moved up to the convex set of possible strategies from beneath—in the case of two states of nature. This would include all points that could be the minimax strategy, and so the minimax strategy is a Bayes strategy for some prior distribution. This particular prior distribution is said to be *least favorable*. This terminology is appropriate in view of Figure 4–9, referring to Example 4–10, in which the least favorable prior distribution is that defined by $w = \frac{5}{8}$. (Inspection of Figure 4–10 shows that the minimax strategy would be the same as the Bayes strategy for this prior distribution.) The minimum Bayes loss for $w = \frac{5}{8}$ is larger than the minimum Bayes loss for any other prior distribution.

To use the Bayes principle it is not really essential that the prior distribution be a bona fide probability distribution. The total "mass" need not be 1, nor even finite, in order for the technique to lead to a solution of the decision problem. However, unless it *is* 1, the Bayes loss $B(a)$ is not comparable to the loss—not measured on the same scale. If the mass used is finite, it may as well be normalized to 1 by dividing all masses by this finite total mass. But if it is infinite, the distribution cannot be made into a *probability* distribution and the state of nature is not a random phenomenon according to the definitions of Chapter 1.

EXAMPLE 4–12.   If the state of nature is a parameter θ defined for $\theta \geq 0$, the particular prior density $g(\theta) = 1$ would not have a finite total area under its graph; and yet this distribution could be used to define a "Bayes loss,"

$$B(a) = \int_0^\infty \ell(\theta, a) \cdot 1 \cdot d\theta,$$

that serves to order the actions and define a Bayes solution. On the other hand, the notion that equal portions of the positive axis should be equally likely (tenable or not) can be approached by defining a sequence of legitimate, uniform prior distributions on $0 \leq \theta \leq M$, for which the Bayes loss is

$$B_M(a) = \frac{1}{M} \int_0^M l(\theta, a)\, d\theta.$$

The action a_M that minimizes this would also minimize the integral from 0 to M (without the $1/M$ in front), and in some instances would approach the action a that minimizes the integral from 0 to ∞, or $B(a)$ above.

A distribution that does not have a finite total weighting cannot represent probability if probability is conceived of as a limit of relative frequencies over a long sequence of trials. Although there are instances in which the state of nature can reasonably be thought of as random (that is, arising as the result of an experiment for which a standard probability model is appropriate), there are situations in which the state of nature is not easily thought of as coming from a repeatable experiment, so that the relative frequency approach does not have meaning. Assuming a probability distribution for θ is a way of expressing beliefs or convictions about θ, which is then inherently personal or subjective; and this is the basis for objections to the Bayes approach by some people, who feel that the decision process should be objective—particularly in scientific work. Indeed, the Bayes principle is perhaps best suited to decision problems in which an immediate action is to be taken by some person—the statistician or his client. Taking personal considerations into account in such instances is perhaps not irrational.

Another objection to the Bayes principle is that it requires specification of a prior distribution, a process that is about as difficult and fuzzy as a specification of the loss function. However, this objection is not so serious when, as is often the case, the Bayes strategy is not particularly sensitive to minor modifications in the prior distribution.

4.2.3   Dominance and Admissibility

An action a is said to *dominate* the action a_1 if, for all states θ,

$$\ell(\theta, a) \leq \ell(\theta, a_1).$$

If a dominates a_1 and if the inequality is strict for some θ, then a is said to dominate a_1 *strictly*. An action is called *admissible* if it is not strictly dominated by any other action. Mixed actions are similarly compared on the basis of *expected* loss.

For the special case in which nature has but two possible states, θ_1 and θ_2, the actions can be represented graphically (as in earlier examples) by the points (L_1, L_2) with $L_i = E[\ell(\theta_i, a)]$. In this representation an action a strictly dominates an action a^* if both coordinates of a are not larger than those of a^* and if at least one is smaller. In Figure 4–11 the action a strictly dominates a^* and a^{**}, as well as any action in the upper right quadrant with a as vertex. If the available pure and mixed actions are those in the

shaded set, the heavy portion of the boundary is the set of admissible strategies. Notice that this is precisely the set of Bayes strategies.

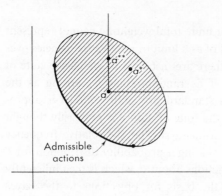

Figure 4–11.

EXAMPLE 4–13. Consider a no-data problem with two states of nature and four
actions, the losses being those in the following table:

	Actions			
	a_1	a_2	a_3	a_4
States: θ_1	4	5	2	3
θ_2	4	0	5	5

Action a_4 is strictly dominated by action a_3 and so is inadmissible; for, the loss in
taking a_4 is always at least as large as the loss in taking a_3, and it is actually larger
for state θ_1. There is no dominance relation among a_1, a_2, and a_3, but if *mixed*
actions are allowed, some mixtures of a_2 and a_3 dominate a_1 strictly. For example, the mixed action $(0, .5, .5, 0)$ does. In Figure 4–12 the heavy line indi-

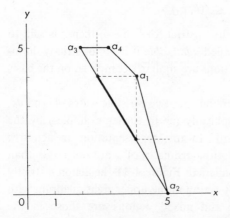

Figure 4–12.

cates the mixtures of a_2 and a_3 which dominate a_1. In the set of mixed actions, only mixtures of a_2 and a_3 are admissible.

A class of strategies is called a *complete class* if any strategy not in the class is strictly dominated by some strategy in the class. Such a class contains all admissible strategies, since if a strategy is not in the class, it is strictly dominated by one which is, and is therefore inadmissible. A *minimal complete class* is a complete class that does not contain a complete proper subclass. If the class of admissible strategies is complete, it is the minimal complete class; and if a minimal complete class exists, it is identical with the class of admissible strategies.

Admissibility appears to be a good property, since it would seem pointless to consider one procedure if another has no larger losses and actually a smaller loss for some states. However, an "inadmissible" procedure that is only a little bit inadmissible might still be very useful. In Figure 4–11, for instance, there are clearly actions that are arbitrarily close to being admissible. As loss functions are usually far from precise, one might find it hard to argue that a slight amount of inadmissibility should condemn a procedure.

For a discussion of conditions under which the class of Bayes strategies is complete, and other relevant matters (such as ϵ-admissibility), refer to Blackwell and Girshick [2] and Wald [21].

Problems

4–19. Determine the Bayes action for the loss table of Problem 4–15 using prior probabilities $g(\theta_1) = w$ and $g(\theta_2) = 1 - w$.

4–20. Determine the Bayes solution for Problem 4–16 for the prior probabilities $g(\theta_1) = w$ and $g(\theta_2) = 1 - w$.

4–21. Determine the Bayes action for Problem 4–14 given prior probabilities $(1/6, 1/3, 1/2)$ for $(\theta_1, \theta_2, \theta_3)$.

4–22. A lot of five articles is to be accepted or rejected (with no data). Suppose that the loss is taken to be twice the number of defectives for lots that are passed and equal to the number of good articles in lots that are rejected.

(a) Determine the minimax mixed strategy.
(b) Determine also the Bayes pure strategy corresponding to a prior probability for k defectives in the lot which is binomial with parameter $p = 1/5$.

4–23. Assume a uniform prior distribution for p on $[0, 1]$ and determine the Bayes action, when the action space is also the interval $[0, 1]$ and the loss function is $(p - a)^2$ (see Problem 4–18).

4–24. Show that if a strictly dominates a_1, a Bayes solution does not require a_1.

4–25. Look for dominance relations in the loss table of Problem 4–14 and show that a_2 and a_3 are not admissible in the class of mixed actions.

4–26. Determine the admissible strategies for the loss table of Problem 4–16.

4.3 Sampling

The process of gathering data or of obtaining results from several performances of an experiment of chance is called *sampling*. The results themselves
are called *observations*, and the collection of observations is called a *sample*.

Although the result of an experiment of chance may be more general,
attention will be focused on the case in which the result of each performance
of the experiment is a single random variable.

4.3.1   *Random Sampling*

Some of the terminology of sampling stems from the following situations
that are frequently encountered in statistics:

(1) Objects are drawn one at a time from an actual, finite collection of
objects called a *population*, and a particular characteristic of interest is
determined for each object drawn. After each observation, and before the
next drawing, the object just drawn is replaced and the population of objects
is thoroughly mixed.

(2) Objects are drawn from an actual, finite population as in (1) except that
the objects are *not* replaced.

The population of objects is frequently a collection of people, and the
observed characteristic may be such a thing as weight, eye color, political
preference, etc., or a combination of these. The basic probability space—the
experiment of chance—is this collection of people or objects, although probability would naturally be transferred to the space of "values" of the characteristic of interest; and this value space itself can be conceived of as the basic
probability space.

When objects are drawn in such a way that at each drawing all remaining
objects are equally likely to be chosen, the sampling is called *random*, a usage
that conforms to the layman's notion of "selecting at random." It is to make
each drawing random that the population should be mixed when objects
drawn are replaced. With this understanding that each selection is random,
the sampling in (1) is called *random sampling with replacement*; and in (2),
random sampling without replacement.

In a sense, random sampling without replacement is better than random
sampling with replacement, since in the former case objects that have been
drawn are not put back into the pool of available objects to confound things.
To take an extreme case, suppose that there are only two objects in
the population; when one is drawn, selection of a second object would
furnish complete information about the original population *if* the first were

not replaced. Drawing without replacement is also sometimes more convenient in that the mixing required with the replacement of objects is not always easy to achieve. On the other hand, as will be seen in a moment, the mathematically simpler process is sampling with replacement. Of course, if a population is enormous with respect to the size of the sample to be drawn, it is practically immaterial whether the objects drawn are or are not replaced; sampling without replacement merges into sampling with replacement as the population size becomes infinite. The theory of one could then be used with the practice of the other.

Suppose that when an object is drawn, the characteristic measured or otherwise ascertained is X. This is a random quantity whose distribution is determined by the proportions of the various values of X among the objects in the population and the agreement that the objects are equally likely. It is this distribution of X that will be called the *population distribution*.

EXAMPLE 4–14.   In a group of 100 freshmen, 73 are 18, 22 are 17, 4 are 19, and 1 is 16 years old. Selecting one freshman from the group at random is represented by assigning probability .01 to each freshman. The population random variable X that is of interest is the age of a freshman drawn, and this variable has the following probability table:

Age	16	17	18	19
Probability	.01	.22	.73	.04

The following notation will be used consistently: X_1 denotes the characteristic X of the first object drawn; X_2 denotes the characteristic X of the second object drawn; and so on. A random sample is then written in the form $(X_1, X_2, \ldots, X_n)$, listing the values of the observed characteristic as they are obtained, where n is the size of the sample. This vector of the n observations in a sample will also be written as X.

It is clear that in either (1) or (2), the quantity X_1 is a random variable with the population distribution—the distribution of X. It is also clear that in (1), *all* observations $X_1, \ldots, X_n$ have this population distribution as a common distribution because prior to each drawing the population of objects is restored to its original condition. It is not quite so clear, but true, that also in (2) the observations share a common distribution. This statement refers to the marginal distributions of the observations—to the distribution of X_7, for instance, unconditioned by information as to the values of any previous or subsequent X's.

EXAMPLE 4–15.   A bowl contains four beads numbered from 1 to 4. Two are drawn at random, one at a time. Let X_1 denote the number on the first bead drawn and X_2 the number on the second bead drawn. There are 12 possible samples:

$$(1, 2), \quad (1, 3), \quad (1, 4), \quad (2, 3), \quad (2, 4), \quad (3, 4),$$

$$(2, 1), \quad (3, 1), \quad (4, 1), \quad (3, 2), \quad (4, 2), \quad (4, 3).$$

As discussed in Example 1–5, each of these 12 outcomes has probability 1/12. From this, one can compute the distributions of X_1 and X_2. For instance,

$$P(X_1 = 1) = P[(1, 2), (1, 3), \text{ or } (1, 4)] = \tfrac{1}{4}.$$

Similarly,

$$P(X_2 = 1) = P[(2, 1), (3, 1), \text{ or } (4, 1)] = \tfrac{1}{4}.$$

In like fashion it is found that for X_1, each of the possible values 1, 2, 3, and 4 has probability 1/4, and that X_2 has exactly the same distribution—the population distribution.

Thus the basic difference between sampling of types (1) and (2) is not in the marginal distributions of the individual observations, for in both cases these observations are identically distributed. However, in case (1) the result of any one observation is not affected by the results of any other observations; the observations are *independent* random phenomena. In case (2) the observations are *not* independent.

There is another kind of commonly occurring situation, mechanically different from (1) and (2), in which the results are mathematically of the same type as (1), random sampling with replacement:

(3) Observations are obtained as the result of repeated, independent performances of an experiment, under conditions that are identical with respect to those factors that can be controlled.

This description includes (1) as a special case, but now does not necessarily refer to a tangible "population" from which an object is to be selected. However, one may imagine an infinite population of possible results. Performing the experiment selects one of these results, and performing the experiment again selects a result from the same collection of possible results as was available in the first trial. That is, repeating the experiment under "identical" conditions means that the first result is "replaced" and is again one of the candidates to be "drawn" the next time. In both (1) and (3), then, the observations are identically distributed and independent. The term *random sampling* without further qualification will denote such a process:

Definition. A *random sample* from a population random variable X is a a set of independent, identically distributed, random variables $X_1, \ldots, X_n$, each with the distribution of X.

A random sample (with replacement) is simpler to treat mathematically than is a sample obtained without replacement from a finite population. This is a result of the independence in a random sample, which implies that the joint density function of the sample observations is a product of their marginal distribution densities:

$$f_X(u_1, \ldots, u_n) = f_{X_1}(u_1) \cdots f_{X_n}(u_n) = \prod_{i=1}^{n} f_X(u_i),$$

where X denotes the population random variable, whose distribution is shared by each of the observations.

EXAMPLE 4–16.   The life of a certain type of electron tube in a given application has a negative exponential distribution with mean life of 10 hours. The life of each tube operated in this way then has the density

$$f_X(u) = .1e^{-.1u}, \qquad u > 0.$$

The joint density function of the lives $X_1, \ldots, X_n$ of n such tubes operated independently is

$$f_X(u_1, \ldots, u_n) = (.1)^n \prod_{i=1}^{n} e^{-.1u_i} = (.1)^n \exp\left[-.1 \sum_{i=1}^{n} u_i\right].$$

Whether an actual sampling process is faithfully described by a mathematical model for sampling is usually a moot question, one that will not be considered here. In the last analysis it is really unanswerable, and about all one can do is to make every effort to see that the process used in collecting data conforms as nearly as can be determined to a definite mathematical model; otherwise the grounds for inference are wobbly indeed. How to make such efforts will not be considered in this book; in the case of scientific experiments their consideration would require knowledge of the field of application, and in the case of sampling from actual populations, the subject is so extensive as to be beyond our scope.[1]

4.3.2   Statistics

In assimilating the information contained in a sample, in describing and comparing samples, and in making decisions on the basis of the results of a sample, it is convenient to be able to use, rather than the complete list of observations as they were obtained, some more readily comprehended measures computed from the sample. It will be seen subsequently that there are principles that lead naturally to certain measures as being appropriate to certain problems. Here are presented some of the sample measures or characteristics

[1]See Hanson, M., Hurwitz, W., and Madow, W. [9].

that actually do find many useful applications. This will provide a "vocabulary" of some of the simpler, common sample characteristics for purposes of illustration. For the present these can be thought of as being constructed by using intuition, and historically this is usually the way they were introduced. Actually, more than just furnishing illustrations, intuitively derived sample measures and procedures based on them frequently turn out to work pretty well. But they can and should be compared with others developed more systematically.

The term *statistic* denotes a descriptive measure computed from the observations in a sample. The value of a given statistic then depends on the values of the observations; hence the following:

Definition. A *statistic* is a function of the observations in a sample.

(In particular, computation of a statistic does not require knowledge of any unknown population characteristics.)

The term *statistic* applies to the *relationship* between independent and dependent variables—or to the random variable defined by the functional relation. If $(x_1, \ldots, x_n)$ is a possible sample point (a possible list of observations in a sample), the functional relationship

$$y = t(x_1, \ldots, x_n)$$

provides a transformation or mapping from the space of all sample points to the space of values of the function. This mapping induces a probability distribution in the latter space and thereby defines a random variable:

$$Y = t(X_1, \ldots, X_n) = t(X).$$

Computation of a statistic from a set of observations constitutes a reduction of the data to a single number, or to a vector of numbers, if the function defining the statistic is vector valued. In the process of such reduction certain information about the population may be lost; but ideally the measure computed would be chosen so that the information lost is not pertinent to the particular problem at hand, so that the measure is still sufficient to handle the problem. This notion of "sufficiency" of a statistic for a given problem will be made more precise in Section 4.5.

Frequently, in an attempt to create order out of the chaos of a mass of data, the observations are put in *numerical* order. The result is a permutation of the original observations and will be denoted by $[X_{(1)}, \ldots, X_{(n)}]$. That is, $X_{(1)}$ is the smallest observation, $X_{(2)}$ is the next smallest, and so on. The vector of these ordered observations is sometimes referred to as the *order statistic*. Various other quantities based on order are also thought of as order statistics;

thus, for example, any component $X_{(i)}$, the ith smallest observation, and $[X_{(1)} + X_{(n)}]/2$, the average of the smallest and largest observations, are order statistics.

The *range* of a sample is defined as the difference between the largest and smallest observations:

$$R = X_{(n)} - X_{(1)}.$$

The *median* of a sample is defined as the midvalue (if there is an odd number of observations) or as the average of the two middle values (if there is an even number of observations), in the list of *ordered* observations. That is,

$$\text{Median} = \begin{cases} X_{((n+1)/2)}, & \text{for } n \text{ odd,} \\ \frac{1}{2}[X_{(n/2)} + X_{(n/2+1)}], & \text{for } n \text{ even.} \end{cases}$$

Both the range and the median involve a reduction of the order statistic, the range being appropriate in certain problems of dispersion and the median in certain problems of location.

EXAMPLE 4–17.   Consider the following observations:

$$31, 28, 27, 32, 36, 33, 29, 35, 24, 33.$$

The smallest is $x_{(1)} = 24$, the largest is $x_{(10)} = 36$, and the order statistic is

$$(24, 27, 28, 29, 31, 32, 33, 33, 35, 36),$$

or, to indicate the permutation of the original order of observation:

$$(x_9, x_3, x_2, x_7, x_1, x_4, x_6, x_{10}, x_8, x_5).$$

The range is the difference $36 - 24 = 12$, and the median is the average of the fifth smallest and sixth smallest observations:

$$\tfrac{1}{2}(31 + 32) = 31.5.$$

Corresponding to a given sample, there is defined a *sample distribution function* (which is not to be interpreted as the model for any chance experiment): Let a "mass" of amount $1/n$ be placed at each observed value. The distribution function of this mass distribution is

$$F_n(x) = \frac{1}{n} \times \text{(number of observations not exceeding } x).$$

This is the sample distribution function. It is intended to mimic the population distribution function, and it will be seen to provide a natural estimate of the population distribution function. The sample distribution function can be computed from the order statistic, and conversely.

The sample distribution function is mathematically just like a probability distribution function for a discrete distribution and shares the mathematical properties of such a function. For instance, $F_n(x)$ has moments, at least the first two of which turn out to be rather useful. The first moment about zero is called the *sample mean*:

$$\bar{X} = \frac{1}{n} \sum_{i=1}^{n} X_i,$$

with the usual property that the first moment about this value is zero:

$$\frac{1}{n} \sum_{i=1}^{n} (X_i - \bar{X}) = 0.$$

The second moment of the sample distribution function about the sample mean is called the *sample variance*:

$$s_x^2 = \frac{1}{n} \sum_{i=1}^{n} (X_i - \bar{X})^2 = \frac{1}{n} \sum_{i=1}^{n} X_i^2 - \bar{X}^2.$$

The positive square root of the sample variance is called the *sample standard deviation*:

$$s_x = \sqrt{s_x^2}.$$

It is useful to observe and easy to show that under the important particular kind of transformation of data called *linear*, the sample mean undergoes exactly the same transformation, and the sample variance is multiplied by the square of the scale factor. That is, if $Y_i = aX_i + b$, then $\bar{Y} = a\bar{X} + b$ and $s_y^2 = a^2 s_x^2$. These relations can be seen directly, but they follow from the fact that a sample distribution can be considered mathematically as a probability distribution. They have already been seen to hold for probability distributions. This same reasoning shows that the "parallel axis theorem":

$$s_x^2 = \frac{1}{n} \sum (X_i - a)^2 - (\bar{X} - a)^2$$

holds as a special case of the parallel axis theorem for probability distributions.

In large samples it is often convenient to gather or present the data in the form of a *frequency table*. In such a table, the original measurements or observations are grouped: The *distinct* values in the sample are listed in numerical order with a number called *frequency*, giving the number of times the corresponding value occurs in the data. The data will usually have such multiplicities of values because of the roundoff required in recording a measurement.

The data might also be regrouped by what is effectively a coarser rounding off of the original data. To regroup, one selects nonoverlapping (and usually equal sized) *class intervals* which cover the range of values in the data. The observations in each class interval are represented by, say, the midpoint of that interval; a frequency is assigned to that midpoint value according to the number of the original observations that fall in the interval. The regrouped data are patently different data from the original data but may serve to give a more digestible delineation of the sample's coarser features, if the regrouping is not carried to the extreme.

Given below is the type of array usually used to exhibit the data in grouped (or regrouped) form, and to compute the sample moments. The frequency of the class interval represented by x_i is denoted by f_i.

x_i	f_i	$f_i x_i$	$f_i x_i^2$
x_1	f_1	$f_1 x_1$	$f_1 x_1^2$
$\vdots$	$\vdots$	$\vdots$	$\vdots$
x_k	f_k	$f_k x_k$	$f_k x_k^2$
Sums	n	$\sum f_i x_i$	$\sum f_i x_i^2$

In this tabulation, $x_1, \ldots, x_k$ represent the distinct values among the n observations, and the summations extend from $i = 1$ to $i = k$. The sum of the frequencies is necessarily the sample size n.

Computations of the sample mean and variance proceed as follows: For the mean,

$$\bar{X} = \frac{1}{n} (\text{sum of the observations}) = \frac{1}{n} \sum_{i=1}^{k} f_i x_i,$$

and for the variance,

$$s_x^2 = \frac{1}{n} \sum_{i=1}^{k} f_i x_i^2 - (\bar{X})^2.$$

(If the frequencies in these computations are those resulting from regrouping the original data into wider class intervals, the computed mean and variance are not quite the mean and variance of the original data. Sometimes "Sheppard's corrections" are applied, which for the above moments amount to leaving the mean as it is and subtracting from the computed variance $h^2/12$, where h is the class interval width.[2])

Computation is often simpler if the data are transformed so that the new origin is near the mean and the new unit is the class interval width, as in the following example.

EXAMPLE 4–18.   In the following tabulation, x_i denotes dial tension in grams

[2]See Chernoff, H., and Moses, L. [3], p. 361 ff.

and f_i the corresponding frequency among 200 observations. The quantities y_i are given by

$$y_i = \frac{x_i - 9.0}{.5} \quad \text{or} \quad x_i = 9.0 + .5y_i.$$

x_i	y_i	f_i	$f_i y_i$	$f_i y_i^2$
6.5	-5	3	-15	75
7.0	-4	2	-8	32
7.5	-3	30	-90	270
8.0	-2	42	-84	168
8.5	-1	36	-36	36
9.0	0	28	0	0
9.5	1	28	28	28
10.0	2	15	30	60
10.5	3	8	24	72
11.0	4	3	12	48
11.5	5	1	5	25
12.0	6	1	6	36
12.5	7	1	7	49
13.0	8	0	0	0
13.5	9	1	9	81
14.0	10	1	10	100
Totals:		200	-102	1080

$$\bar{Y} = -\frac{102}{200} = -.51$$

$$\bar{X} = 9.0 + .5\bar{Y}$$
$$= 9.0 - .255 = 8.745$$

$$s_y^2 = \frac{1080}{200} - (-.51)^2$$

$$= 5.4 - .26 = 5.14$$

$$s_x^2 = (.5)^2 s_y^2$$

$$= 1.285.$$

The various quantities associated with a sample distribution—the sample median, sample range, sample mean, sample variance, and so on—are often useful in particular in studying related parameters of the distribution of probability in the population from which the sample was taken. It should be kept in mind, though, that statistics are random variables; they vary from sample to sample according to the observations one happens to obtain. Population parameters are constants, albeit frequently unknown.

Problems

4-27. Compute the median, mean, range, and standard deviation of the following observations: $-3, 2, 5, 0, -4$.

4-28. Given that $X_1^2 + \cdots + X_{10}^2 = 160$ and that $s_x^2 = 12$, determine two possible values of $\bar{X}$, with $n = 10$.

4-29. Given the following 30 test scores: 51, 52, 52, 58, 59, 59, 61, 62, 63, 69, 72, 74, 76, 80, 80, 80, 81, 81, 82, 83, 83, 84, 86, 87, 87, 88, 88, 89, 90, 94.

(a) Determine the mean and standard deviation and plot the sample distribution function.

(b) Round off the above scores to the nearest multiple of 5 and compute the mean and standard deviation of the rounded-off data.

4-30. The mean and standard deviation of the numbers $x_1, \ldots, x_n$ are 5 and 2, respectively. Determine the average of their squares and the mean and standard deviation of $y_1, \ldots, y_n$, where $y_i = 3x_i + 4$.

4-31. Write out the joint density or probability function of the observations $X_1, \ldots, X_n$ in a random sample from (a) a uniform distribution on $[a, b]$; (b) a normal distribution (μ, σ^2); (c) a Bernoulli distribution (p); (d) a Poisson distribution with expectation m; (e) a geometric distribution with parameter p.

4-32. Write the joint probability function of $X_1, \ldots, X_n$, the results of random sampling *without* replacement from a population of size N including M objects coded 1 and $N - M$ coded 0.

4-33. (a) Show that

$$\frac{1}{n} \sum_{i=1}^{n} X_i^2 - \bar{X}^2 = \frac{1}{n} \sum_{i=1}^{n} (X_i - \bar{X})^2.$$

(b) Show that if $Y_i = aX_i + b$, then $\bar{Y} = a\bar{X} + b$ and $s_y = |a| \, s_x$.

(c) Show that the second moment of a set of observations is smallest when taken about their mean.

4-34. Carry out the computations in Example 4–18 using as "origin" the value 8.5. (That is, using $z_i = (x_i - 8.5)/.5$.)

4.3.3 *Distributions of Statistics*

Being a random variable a statistic has a probability distribution, a distribution induced by the population distribution. If (as has been hinted) a statistic is to provide information concerning the population, it is essential to know what there is about the distribution of a statistic that has to do with the population distribution.

The statistic $\bar{X}$, to consider a very important example, has a distribution whose characteristic function is readily expressed in terms of the characteristic function of the population, assuming a random sample:

$$\phi_{\bar{X}}(t) = E(e^{it\bar{X}}) = E[e^{it(X_1 + \cdots + X_n)/n}]$$

$$= E[e^{itX_1/n}] \cdots E[e^{itX_n/n}]$$

$$= [\phi_X(t/n)]^n.$$

From this, or from the linearity of the expectation operation (even when the observations are *not* independent), it follows that

$$E(\bar{X}) = E(X),$$

which says that the "center" of the distribution of $\bar{X}$ is the population mean. Further, since the observations in a random sample are uncorrelated:

$$\text{var } \bar{X} = \text{var } (\sum X_i/n) = \sigma^2/n,$$

where σ^2 is the population variance. The *asymptotic* distribution of the mean of a random sample is (according to the central limit theorem) normal with mean μ and variance σ^2/n. That is, the limiting distribution of

$$\frac{\bar{X} - \mu}{\sigma/\sqrt{n}},$$

as n becomes infinite, is *standard normal*—independent of the population distribution as long as the latter has second moments. Another limit theorem, Khintchine's theorem, says that $\bar{X}$ tends in probability to $E(X)$.

The sample variance s_x^2 is by no means so easy to treat as is the sample mean. The expected value of s_x^2 is readily computed:

$$E(s_x^2) = E\left\{\frac{1}{n}\sum(X_i - \mu)^2 - (\bar{X} - \mu)^2\right\}$$

$$= \sigma^2 - \text{var } \bar{X} = \sigma^2\left(1 - \frac{1}{n}\right).$$

The variance of s_x^2 is considerably more complicated:

$$\text{var } s_x^2 = \frac{\mu_4 - \mu_2^2}{n} - \frac{2(\mu_4 - 2\mu_2^2)}{n^2} + \frac{\mu_4 - 3\mu_2^2}{n^3},$$

where μ_k denotes the kth population moment about the population mean. It will be convenient to have a reduction of this expression for the particular case of a normal population, in which case $\mu_4 = 3\mu_2^2$:

$$\text{var } s_x^2 = \frac{2\sigma^4(n - 1)}{n^2} \qquad \text{(random sample from normal population)}.$$

Higher order sample central moments can be treated with ever increasing complexity of detail.[3]

Sample moments about 0 are simpler to analyze, since for a random sample each $\sum X_i^k/n$ is a sum of independent random variables. The mean is clearly $E(X^k)$, and the variance is easily expressible (Problem 4–36) in terms of $E(X^{2k})$ if the latter exists. Further, the limiting distribution is normal (by the central limit thorem) and the limit in probability is $E(X^k)$ (by Khintchine's theorem).

By using the fact that sample central moments are expressible as polynomial functions of sample moments about zero, one can show that the sample central moments are asymptotically normal and tend in probability to the corresponding population moments.[4]

The sample distribution function is known to converge to the population

[3] See Cramer, H. [4], p. 348.
[4] *Ibid.*, p. 365.

distribution function with probability one, uniformly in x. Here it will only be shown that the sample distribution function approaches the population distribution function at each x in quadratic mean (or "in the mean"), and therefore in probability. This follows from the fact that $nF_n(x)$ is just the number of observations not exceeding x and is therefore binomial (n, p), where

$$p = P(X \le x) = F(x).$$

For, then

$$E[nF_n(x)] = nF(x) \quad \text{and} \quad \text{var } [nF_n(x)] = nF(x)[1 - F(x)],$$

and consequently,

$$E[F_n(x)] = F(x) \quad \text{and} \quad \text{var } F_n(x) = \frac{F(x)[1 - F(x)]}{n}.$$

Since the expectation is $F(x)$ and the variance tends to zero, the assertion is established.

Problems

4–35. A population consists of four chips numbered 1, 2, 3, 4. Let (X_1, X_2) denote a random sample without replacement and let $(X_{(1)}, X_{(2)})$ denote the corresponding order statistic.

(a) Determine the probability table for the joint distribution of $X_{(1)}$ and $X_{(2)}$.
(b) Determine the distribution of the range.
(c) Determine the distribution of $\bar{X}$.
(d) Use (first show) the identity $s_x^2 = R^2/4$, for samples of size 2, to compute $E s_x^2$ from (b).

4–36. Express the variance of the kth sample moment about zero in terms of $E(X^{2k})$ and $E(X^k)$.

4–37. Two independent random samples are taken from a normal population with mean 150 and variance 28.6. The sample sizes are 10 and 25, and the corresponding sample mean are $\bar{X}_1$ and $\bar{X}_2$. Determine

(a) $E(\bar{X}_1 - \bar{X}_2)$,
(b) var $(\bar{X}_1 - \bar{X}_2)$,
(c) $P(|\bar{X}_1 - \bar{X}_2| > 4)$.

[*Hint*: The sample means and hence their difference are all normal.]

4–38. Determine the density function of the mean of a random sample from a negative exponential population, using the results of Problems 2–133 and 2–144(a).

4–39. What is the asymptotic distribution of $\sum (X_i - E(X))^2/n$?

4–40. Consider a random sample of size n without replacement from a finite population of size N. Given[5]

$$\text{var } \bar{X} = \frac{\sigma^2}{n} \frac{N - n}{N - 1},$$

[5] See Wilks, S. S. [22], p. 219.

where σ^2 is the population variance, show that

$$E(s_x{}^2) = \frac{n-1}{n} \frac{N}{N-1} \sigma^2.$$

4–41. Derive an expression in terms of the population distribution function $F(x)$ for the distribution function of $X_{(n)}$, the largest observation.

4–42. Use characteristic functions to show that the mean of a random sample from a normal population is normal.

4.4 Using Data in Decisions

Looking at data resulting from performing the experiment whose model is under study can be thought of as a form of "spying" on the "opponent," Nature. Such spying usually costs something, so that the amount of spying permitted or desired is not necessarily infinite. How much should be done depends on the extent to which spying increases one's information about nature; if he is spying in the wrong way—doing the wrong experiment—a large amount of it may be futile. Before a balance of cost of experimentation and gain of information can be made, it is necessary to see what information is to be gained by experimenting, and for a given amount of experimenting, how to get the most out of the data. For the present, then, the size of the sample used will be considered fixed.

The general discussion will be given in terms of "data" Z, where Z may be the value of a single observation on a univariate distribution or on a multi-variate distribution; or it may be a vector of the values in a sample, or the value of some statistic computed from the sample. In any case there is a corresponding distribution of Z.

4.4.1 The Risk Function

A decision rule or strategy that is to lead to a decision based on the data Z must take into account that Z can have many values. A rule for choosing an action is not then complete until it prescribes an action a for each conceivable value z of Z. Such a rule is called a *statistical decision function*:

$$a = d(z).$$

This is a mapping from the space of possible data points to the space of actions. The statistician's task is then the selection of a suitable decision rule, or decision function, $d(z)$.

The action taken is random, since the data to which the decision rule is applied are random. Hence, the loss is random: $\ell(\theta, d(Z))$. It is customary, and consistent with rules for utility, to base the analysis on the *expected value* of this loss:

$$R(\theta, d) = E_\theta[\ell(\theta, d(Z))].$$

Notice that this gives a third possible meaning of the phrase *expected loss*. First it was used to denote an average with respect to a randomized action; then it was used to denote an average with respect to a prior distribution (or randomized strategy for Nature); and in the present usage, the average is computed with respect to the distribution of the data Z. This distribution of Z depends on θ, so the dependence of the function $R(\theta, d)$ on θ enters through the θ in $\ell(\theta, a)$ and also through the θ in the distribution of Z. The expected loss $R(\theta, d)$ is called the *risk function*.

Some use the term *risk function* to denote the expected value of the *regret* function. If the loss function used is already a regret function, as will be the case in many of the important statistical applications to be discussed, there is no difference in usage. It is interesting that the expected regret is the same as what would be obtained by applying the "regret-izing" process to the risk function:

$$E_\theta[r(\theta, d(Z))] = R(\theta, d) - \min_d R(\theta, d).$$

(To show this is an exercise in inequalities and minima.)

The data have thus been used to change the problem of the statistician from one of selecting an action in view of a certain loss function, to one of selecting a decision function d in view of a certain risk function. Interpreting an "action" as a *decision function* and "loss" as *risk*, the problem is now like the original no-data problem, and the concepts developed for no-data problems can be applied to the present situation.

EXAMPLE 4–19.   Consider the rain problem of Example 4–6, with loss function as follows:

	θ_1 (rain)	θ_2 (no rain)
(Stay home) a_1	4	4
(Go, no umbrella) a_2	5	0
(Go with umbrella) a_3	2	5

A single observation of a rain indicator (or a weather report) will make up the "datum" Z. If this datum is to be useful, one must know the way in which the distribution of the datum depends on the state of nature. For this problem assume the following, in which z_1 indicates an observation (or prediction) of "rain," and z_2, of "no rain":

	θ_1 (rain)	θ_2 (no rain)
z_1 (rain)	.8	.1
z_2 (no rain)	.2	.9

That is, assume as known from past experience that when it is going to rain, the probability is .8 that the indicator will show "rain," and .2 that it will show "no rain."

Since there are finitely many possible actions and possible values of Z, the number of decision functions is finite. Indeed, it is $3^2 = 9$, since there are three actions and two values of Z (a decision function assigns an action to each value of Z). These nine decision functions are listed as follows:

	d_1	d_2	d_3	d_4	d_5	d_6	d_7	d_8	d_9
If outcome is z_1, take action	a_1	a_2	a_3	a_1	a_2	a_1	a_3	a_2	a_3
If outcome is z_2, take action	a_1	a_2	a_3	a_2	a_1	a_3	a_1	a_3	a_2

The computation of the risk function $R(\theta, d)$ proceeds as follows: For $\theta = \theta_1$ and $d = d_5$,

$$R(\theta_1, d_5) = E_{\theta_1}[\ell(\theta_1, d_5(Z))]$$

$$= \ell(\theta_1, d_5(z_1))p_{\theta_1}(z_1) + \ell(\theta_1, d_5(z_2))p_{\theta_1}(z_2)$$

$$= \ell(\theta_1, a_2) \times .8 + \ell(\theta_1, a_1) \times .2 = 5 \times .8 + 4 \times .2 = 4.8.$$

In similar fashion one can compute $R(\theta, d)$ for each combination of decision function d and state θ. The results are tabulated:

	θ_1	θ_2
d_1	4	4
d_2	5	0
d_3	2	5
d_4	4.2	0.4
d_5	4.8	3.6
d_6	3.6	4.9
d_7	2.4	4.1
d_8	4.4	4.5
d_9	2.6	0.5

This array can now be attacked as though it gave the loss function in a no-data problem. For instance, d_1, d_5, d_6, and d_8, are *inadmissible*, even in the set of pure strategies, and can be eliminated from the competition. Similarly, d_4 and d_7 are dominated by mixtures of other strategies, but there is still no clear choice among d_2, d_3, and d_9.

Figure 4–13 shows graphically the effect of the data. Points (L_1, L_2) are plotted for each decision function, where $L_i = R(\theta_i, d)$.

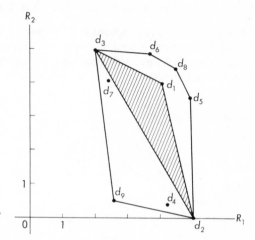

Figure 4–13.   Decision rules for
              Example 4–19.

The original no-data points appear as d_1, d_2, and d_3, which essentially ignore the data. The set of no-data strategies is shown as the shaded region, and the strategies available using data correspond to points inside the larger polygon. The use of the datum Z provides strategies that dominate most of the no-data strategies—as well as some that do worse, because they use the datum in an unreasonable way. Improvement is possible because the distribution of Z is related to the state of nature. Problems 4–44 and 4–43 show that no improvement is possible if the datum is independent of θ and that the regret can be reduced to 0 if the datum is "perfectly" related to θ.

EXAMPLE 4–20.   The problem is to estimate the value of the parameter θ in a negative exponential density with mean θ. That is, it is assumed that nature is in one of the states described by this family of distributions. The actions here are the various possible choices of an estimated value of θ, so the action space is the same as the state space. For purposes of this example, assume that the loss function is quadratic and has a zero minimum for each action:

$$\ell(\theta_0, a) = (a - \theta_0)^2,$$

the loss incurred upon choosing a as the estimate when the state is θ_0.

A decision procedure is to be based on the result of n performances of the negative exponential experiment, a sample of size n from the population. As illustrations of the computation of risks, consider the following (arbitrarily selected) decision procedures:

$$d_1(X) = \bar{X}, \qquad d_2(X) = \bar{X} + 1, \qquad d_3(X) = X_n.$$

The risk functions for these procedures are as follows:

$$R(\theta, d_1) = E_\theta(\bar{X} - \theta)^2 = \text{var } \bar{X} = \theta^2/n,$$

$$R(\theta, d_2) = E_\theta(\bar{X} + 1 - \theta)^2 = \text{var } \bar{X} + 1 = \theta^2/n + 1$$

$$R(\theta, d_3) = E_\theta(X_n - \theta)^2 = \text{var } X = \theta^2.$$

These are plotted as functions of θ in Figure 4–14. It is clear from the figure that d_1 dominates both d_2 and d_3 strictly but that d_2 and d_3 are not comparable with each other. All three risk functions are unbounded because the loss function given is unbounded.

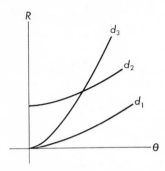

Figure 4–14. Risk functions for Example 4–20.

EXAMPLE 4–21.   Flash bulbs come in "lots" of ten, and one is taken from each lot and tested (a process that ruins it). The remaining nine are either to be sold at fifteen cents each, with a double-your-money-back guarantee, or to be junked at a cost of ten cents for the lot. Thus, one of two actions is to be selected: sell the lot or junk it. The state of nature is described by the number k of defective bulbs among the ten.

Since the experiment has only two outcomes, assigning one of the two actions to each outcome can be done in four distinct ways; these are the possible decision functions:

d_1 : Sell the lot if the test bulb is good; junk if defective.
d_2 : Junk the lot if the test bulb is good; sell if defective.
d_3 : Sell the lot if the test bulb is good; sell if defective.
d_4 : Junk the lot if the test bulb is good; junk if defective.

Consider first $d_1(X)$, where X denotes the outcome of the test. The loss is

$$\ell(k, d_1(X)) = \begin{cases} -1.35 + (.30)k, & \text{if } X = \text{good}, \\ .10 & \text{if } X = \text{defective}, \end{cases}$$

and the risk function is then

$$R(k, d_1) = E_k[\ell(k, d_1(X))]$$

$$= (-1.35 + .3k)(1 - k/10) + .10(k/10)$$

$$= -.01(3k^2 - 44.5k + 135).$$

For $d_2(X)$,

$$\ell(k, d_2(X)) = \begin{cases} .10, & \text{if } X = \text{good,} \\ -1.35 + .30(k - 1), & \text{if } X = \text{defective,} \end{cases}$$

and

$$R(k, d_2) = .01(3k^2 - 17.5k + 10).$$

Similarly,

$$R(k, d_3) = -.09(15 - 3k),$$

$$R(k, d_4) = .10.$$

These four risk functions are plotted (as though k were continuous, for ease in following the graphs) in Figure 4–15. For some states the best decision function

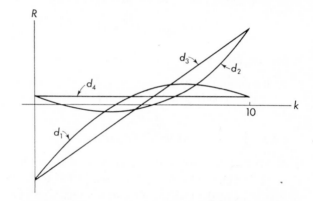

Figure 4–15.   Risk functions for Example 4–21.

is d_3; for others it is d_2; and for still others it is d_4. And d_1, which is never best, is not far from being best at all states.

Problems

4–43.   Calculate the risk for the rain problem (Example 4–19) when a decision function is used based on an observation Y (with two possible values) that is "perfectly" related to the state of nature: $P(Y = y_1 \mid \theta_1) = 1$, $P(Y = y_2 \mid \theta_2) = 1$. Compare the graphical plot with that of Figure 4–13.

4–44.   Calculate the risk table for the rain problem (Example 4–19) when one has an observation X (with two possible values) that is "independent" of the state of nature:

$$P(X = x_1 \mid \theta_1) \;=\; P(X = x_1 \mid \theta_2) \;=\; p.$$

Is the observation of value?

4–45.   A coin is known to be biased, with probability of heads either $\frac{1}{4}$ or $\frac{3}{4}$. After two tosses of the coin, one is required to choose between $\frac{1}{4}$ and $\frac{3}{4}$. Given the loss function $\ell(p, a) = (p - a)^2$, where p is the actual probability of heads and *a* is the statistician's choice, determine the possible decision functions and the risk function for each.

4-46. In the problem of estimating the mean μ in a normal population with unit variance, determine the risk function for the procedure that takes the mean of a sample of size n as the estimate of μ, first using the loss function $(\mu - a)^2$ and then using $|\mu - a|$. Observe the dependence of risk on n in each case.

4-47. Referring to Example 4–20, consider the class of decision functions of the form $d_A(X) = A\bar{X}$, where A is a positive constant. Determine the value of A such that the risk function corresponding to d_A is (uniformly) smallest, and determine that smallest risk function.

4-48. Referring to Problem 4–45, determine the risk (under each state of nature) corresponding to the mixed strategy $(0, 0, 0, 0, \frac{1}{2}, 0, 0, \frac{1}{2})$. Describe how this strategy would be carried out using a coin.

4-49. In estimating the parameter p of a Bernoulli distribution (as in Problem 4–18) a decision function based on Y is to be used, where

$$P(Y = k) = \binom{2}{k} p^k (1 - p)^{2-k}, \qquad (k = 0, 1, 2).$$

If the loss, when the estimate a is announced, is $(p - a)^2$, determine the risk for

(a) the decision function $d(Y) = Y/2$.
(b) the decision function $d(Y) = \frac{1}{4}(Y + 1)$.

4.4.2 Minimax and Bayes Procedures

A minimax decision function is selected from the available decision functions on the basis of the risk function, just as a minimax action was selected on the basis of the loss function in a no-data problem. That is, the decision function that makes

$$M(d) = \max_\theta R(\theta, d)$$

smallest is the minimax decision function. As mentioned before, such an approach is rather pessimistic—guarding against situations that are "unlikely" to arise.

The minimax risk is $M(d^*)$, where d^* is the minimax decision rule. The experimentation has served a purpose if the minimax risk is less than the minimax loss with no data, and the gain can be balanced against the cost of obtaining the data.

EXAMPLE 4–22. Referring to Figure 4–15 in the flash-bulb problem of Example 4–21, it is apparent that d_4 has the risk function with the lowest maximum point. The minimax decision function is that which rejects all lots. It would be an unusual manufacturer who would manufacture flash bulbs and then junk everything he made for fear of the large loss he might incur if the proportion of defectives in the lots were quite high. The manufacturing process would be developed, rather, so that a lot with more than, say, half defective would "practically" never occur.

Thus, in a realistic situation, the maximum risk would be considered over small values of k, where the smallest maximum would be achieved by using d_3. Actually, this focusing of the attention on certain practically possible states is perhaps better handled using Bayes' principle.

The minimax risk is $.10 = M(d_4)$. This can be compared with the minimax loss with no data, where

$$\ell(k, \text{sell}) = .30k - 1.50$$

$$\ell(k, \text{junk}) = .10.$$

Since

$$\max_{0 \leq k \leq 10} \ell(k, \text{sell}) = 1.50 > .10 = \max_{0 \leq k \leq 10} \ell(k, \text{junk}),$$

the minimax action is to junk, and the minimax loss is .10. The testing of one bulb has not reduced this and is therefore pointless (or worse, if it costs something) in this instance.

The Bayes principle can be used to select a decision function for a problem with data by applying it to the risk function. For a given prior distribution on the space of states of nature, the corresponding *Bayes risk* is the expectation with respect to the prior distribution:

$$B(d) = E[R(\theta, d)].$$

The Bayes decision procedure is that which minimizes this quantity. If θ is a real parameter with values on I, the weighting defines a "distribution function" $G(\theta)$, where then

$$B(d) = \int_I R(\theta, d) \, dG(\theta),$$

with further reductions if G has a "density" or is discrete.

EXAMPLE 4–23.   In the flash-bulb problem of Example 4–21, consider a weighting on k (the number of defectives in a lot) which is uniform for $k = 0, 1$, and 2. If a unit weight is assigned to each of these values, then

$$B(d_1) = -.01 \sum_{k=0}^{2} (3k^2 - 44.5k + 135) = -2.865,$$

$$B(d_2) = .01 \sum_{k=0}^{2} (3k^2 - 17.5k + 10) = -.075,$$

$$B(d_3) = -.09 \sum_{k=0}^{2} (15 - 3k) = -3.24,$$

$$B(d_4) = \sum_{k=0}^{2} (.10) = .30.$$

The minimum of these is obtained by using d_3, which is then the Bayes procedure for the assumed prior weighting: Sell the lot, regardless of the outcome of the test. The same minimizing procedure is obtained by using a weighting 1/3 for each of $k = 0, 1, 2$; the only difference would be that the $B(d)$ in each case would be divided by 3, the result being then comparable to values of the original risk function.

Although a distribution on the states of nature weights the possible states according to one's pleasure—or more accurately, according to one's past experience or other information, there may be situations in which it is not unreasonable to think of the state of nature as random. Perhaps the state came to pass by a random process and, though now fixed, is still unknown (as in the toss of a coin: after the coin has fallen the result is not really random, but now *knowing* the outcome, one is forced to behave as though it were random).

EXAMPLE 4-24. Referring once more to the flash-bulb problem of Example 4–21, one could think of the "population parameter" k as the number of defectives in a sample of ten bulbs from a production line that is "in control," putting out flash bulbs with a constant probability p_0 of a defective. The appropriate prior distribution would then be binomial, with parameters $(10, p_0)$. The expected risks for the four decision functions considered are then as follows:

$$B(d_1) = -.05(54p_0^2 - 83p_0 + 27),$$

$$B(d_2) = .05(54p_0^2 - 29p_0 + 2),$$

$$B(d_3) = -1.35(1 - 2p_0),$$

$$B(d_4) = .10.$$

For a given p_0 (that is, a given prior distribution), the Bayes solution is to choose the d with the smallest $B(d)$. Examining the above as functions of p_0, one finds that the Bayes solution would be d_3 over a broad range of small values of p_0. Thus d_3 would appear to be appropriate even though p_0 is unknown and possibly changing from lot to lot—if it can be assumed small.

The value of experimenting or obtaining data can be defined, when the Bayes principle is used, as the amount of reduction from minimum Bayes loss with no data to minimum Bayes risk with the data. If this reduction does not at least equal the cost of obtaining the data, it is pointless to obtain it.

EXAMPLE 4-25. Consider the prior distribution for k, in the flash-bulb Example 4-24, that is binomial with $p_0 = .1$. The minimum Bayes risk is

$$B(d_3) = -1.08.$$

The Bayes losses with no data are (see Example 4–22)

$$B(\text{sell}) = E(.30k - 1.50) = .30 \times 10p_0 - 1.50 = -1.20,$$

$$B(\text{junk}) = E(.10) = .10.$$

The minimum Bayes loss with no data is then -1.20, which is less than the -1.08 obtained using the result of a test of one bulb. Apparently the information gained in the test does not offset the loss in revenue from the sale of the untested bulb, and so testing would not pay (with *this* p_0!).

Problems

4–50. Determine the Bayes rule for the loss table

	θ_1	θ_2	θ_3
a_1	0	4	5
a_2	3	2	6
a_3	4	0	3

corresponding to prior probabilities $(.1, 0, .9)$

(a) when no data are used.
(b) when the value of Z is observed, where Z has distributions under θ_1, θ_2, θ_3 given in this table:

	θ_1	θ_2	θ_3
z_1	.2	.4	.7
z_2	.8	.6	.3

4–51. Determine the minimax decision rule for Problem 4–45.

4–52. Determine the minimax loss decision rule for the rain problem of Example 4–19.

4–53. In estimating the parameter p of a Bernoulli population, consider only decision functions that take as the estimated value the quantity $k/n + b$, where k is the number of "successes" among the n independent trials and b is a constant. Select b according to the minimax risk principle, taking the loss function to be $(p - a)^2$, where a is the estimate.

4–54. In the flash-bulb problem, Example 4–21, determine the decision function that minimizes the maximum risk, not over all k but over $k \leq 5$.

4–55. Determine the Bayes decision function for Problem 4–45 corresponding to a prior distribution that weights the two possible values of p equally.

4–56. Determine the Bayes procedure for the rain problem of Example 4–19, assuming equal weights for the two states of nature. How much is the experiment worth?

4–57. Verify the expression for Bayes risk given in Examples 4–23 and 4–24.

4–58. Referring to the flash-bulb problem (Example 4–21) determine the loss table for the no-data case (that is, either sell all 10 bulbs or junk the lot, without any testing). Does the testing pay if the prior distribution is that of Example 4–23?

4.4.3 Posterior Distributions

Treating the state of nature θ as a random variable means that the probability function or density function $f(z; \theta)$ is actually a *conditional* probability or density, the condition being that nature is in state θ. Thus, when using a probability distribution for θ, it is more appropriate to use the notation $f(z \mid \theta)$ for the probability or density function of the data Z. From the conditional distribution of Z and the given prior distribution for θ one can calculate the joint distribution of (Z, θ):

$$f_{Z, \theta}(z, \theta) = f(z \mid \theta)g(\theta),$$

and the corresponding marginal or absolute distribution of Z, with density or probability[6]

$$f_Z(z) = E_g[f(z \mid \theta)] = \begin{cases} \displaystyle\int f(z \mid \theta)g(\theta)d\theta, & (\theta \text{ continuous}) \\ \displaystyle\sum f(z \mid \theta_i)g(\theta_i), & (\theta \text{ discrete}). \end{cases}$$

Bayes' formula can now be put to use to give the conditional distribution of the state of nature, given the data $Z = z$, according to its density or probability function:

$$h(\theta \mid z) = \frac{f(z \mid \theta)g(\theta)}{f_Z(z)}.$$

(Here f and f_Z are both probability functions or both density functions, according as Z is discrete or continuous, and h and g are likewise both probability functions or both density functions, according as θ is discrete or continuous.)

EXAMPLE 4–26. The probability table giving the conditional distribution of the data in Example 4–19 (the rain problem again) is repeated below, with a row of prior probabilities (.7, .3) assumed here to represent beliefs based on past experience or hunches.

	$f(z; \theta_1)$	$f(z; \theta_2)$	$f_Z(z)$
z_1 (rain)	.8	.1	$.8 \times .7 + .1 \times .3 = .59$
z_2 (no rain)	.2	.9	$.2 \times .7 + .9 \times .3 = .41$
$g(\theta)$	.7	.3	

The last column in this table gives the computation of the unconditional or absolute probability of each value of Z, as averages of the conditional probabili-

---

[6] One discovers that the hope for notational consistency fades. Here the sin has been committed of using the same letter θ for both the random quantity and the dummy variable in its density or probability function. Also, the symbol E_g has been slipped in to mean that the average of $f(z \mid \theta)$ is taken with respect to the density or probability of θ, as defined by the formulas that follow its use.

ties with respect to the prior probabilities. The posterior probabilities are now ratios of the terms composing the sum to the value of the sum, in each case:

$$h(\theta_1 \mid z_1) = \frac{.8 \times .7}{.59} = 56/59, \qquad h(\theta_2 \mid z_1) = \frac{.1 \times .3}{.59} = 3/59,$$

$$h(\theta_1 \mid z_2) = \frac{.2 \times .7}{.41} = 14/41, \qquad h(\theta_2 \mid z_2) = \frac{.9 \times .3}{.41} = 27/41.$$

(Of course, the posterior probabilities, for a given z, must add up to 1, as they do here.) Thus, an indication of "rain" (z_1) alters the odds from 7 to 3 in favor of rain (prior) to 56 to 3 in favor of rain (posterior). And an indication of "no rain" (z_2) alters the odds to 14 to 27 against rain. The amount by which the odds are altered depends on the strength of the relationship between the data and the state of nature—on the quality of the data. Problems 4–61 and 4–62 point up this last statement even more strikingly.

EXAMPLE 4–27.   Consider the estimation of p in the Bernoulli probability function $p^x(1 - p)^{1-x}$, $x = 0$ or 1, using the statistic k, the number of "successes" in n independent trials. Given p, the probability function for k is binomial:

$$f(k \mid p) = \binom{n}{k} p^k (1 - p)^{n-k}, \qquad k = 0, 1, \ldots, n.$$

Assuming a uniform prior distribution for p on [0, 1], one finds[7] the following absolute probability function for k:

$$f(k) = \binom{n}{k} \int_0^1 p^k (1 - p)^{n-k} \, dp = \frac{1}{n + 1}, \qquad k = 0, 1, \ldots, n.$$

The posterior distribution of p, given k, is then the integrand of $f(k)$ divided by $f(k)$:

$$h(p \mid k) = \frac{1 \cdot f(k \mid p)}{f(k)} = \binom{n}{k}(n + 1)p^k(1 - p)^{n-k}.$$

For instance, if the n trials all result in "success," then $k = n$, and the distribution function for p is

$$H(p \mid k = n) = p^{n+1}, \qquad 0 \le p \le 1.$$

For large n, a sequence of n successes would put most of the weight near $p = 1$ in the posterior distribution.

It is of interest to observe that if the posterior distribution is used as a prior distribution for a second experiment, the resulting new posterior distribution based on the outcome of the second experiment is the same as the posterior distribution that would have been obtained based on the *combined*

---

[7] The integration is performed using the following formula to be derived in Chapter 7:

$$\int_0^1 x^r(1 - x)^s \, dx = \frac{r!s!}{(r + s + 1)!},$$

where r and s are nonnegative integers.

data from the two experiments and the initial prior distribution. For, let the outcomes of the experiments be (X, Y), with joint density

$$f(x, y \mid \theta) = f(x \mid \theta)f(y \mid x, \theta).$$

The posterior density of θ, given $X = x$ and assuming a prior density $g(\theta)$, is

$$h(\theta \mid x) = \frac{g(\theta)f(x \mid \theta)}{\int g(\theta)f(x \mid \theta)\, d\theta},$$

and using this as a prior distribution together with the result $Y = y$, one obtains the posterior distribution:

$$k(\theta \mid x, y) = \frac{h(\theta \mid x)\, f(y \mid x, \theta)}{\int h(\theta \mid x)f(y \mid x, \theta)\, d\theta}$$

$$= \frac{g(\theta)f(x \mid \theta)f(y \mid x, \theta)}{\int g(\theta)f(x \mid \theta)f(y \mid x, \theta)\, d\theta} = \frac{g(\theta)f(x, y \mid \theta)}{\int g(\theta)f(x, y \mid \theta)\, d\theta},$$

which is what would have been obtained by using the combined result $X = x$ and $Y = y$ together with the prior distribution given by $g(\theta)$. This property of posterior distributions is illustrated in Problem 4–64.

The posterior distribution can be used as a tool in computing Bayes' strategies. The method is to compute the posterior expected loss:

$$E_h[\ell(\theta, a)] = \int \ell(\theta, a)h(\theta \mid z)\, d\theta,$$

and then to select the action a (for the given z) that minimizes this quantity. The dependence of the chosen a on the given z provides a decision function $a = d^*(z)$, which is precisely the Bayes decision function for the given prior distribution.

To establish this claim, the expression for the Bayes risk corresponding to a decision function $d(z)$ is manipulated as follows:

$$B(d) = E_g[R(\theta, d)] = \int R(\theta, d)g(\theta)\, d\theta$$
$$= \int\int \ell(\theta, d(z))f(z \mid \theta)\, g(\theta)\, dz\, d\theta$$
$$= \int f(z)\{\int \ell(\theta, d(z))h(\theta \mid z)\, d\theta\}\, dz$$
$$= \int f(z)E_h[\ell(\theta, d(z))]\, dz.$$

From the last representation of $B(d)$ it is apparent that $B(d)$ is minimized by a function $d(z)$ whose value a for each z is selected to minimize the expected posterior loss, $E_h[\ell(\theta, a)]$.

The method, then, is equivalent to the following: Determine the posterior distribution, given $Z = z$, and use it as a prior distribution for θ in a no-data problem with the original loss function. The Bayes solution for this no-data problem is the desired Bayes action for the given problem.

The significance of this method of determining $d(z)$ is that it is only necessary to compute the value of $d(z)$ for the z actually obtained as the result of experimentation. Computing $d(z)$ as a Bayes strategy or decision function from the basic definition involves a determination of the whole function—the value of $d(z)$ for each foreseeable z. Mathematically, a problem in the calculus of variations (minimizing over a set of possible functions) is replaced by a problem in the calculus (minimizing over a set of numbers). It may prove helpful to consider the schematic diagrams for computation of Bayes strategies according to the two methods, as shown in Figures 4–16 and 4–17.

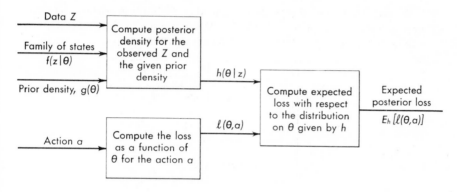

Bayes action for data Z is the a which yields a minimum expected posterior loss

Figure 4–16. Schematic for obtaining Bayes action from posterior distribution.

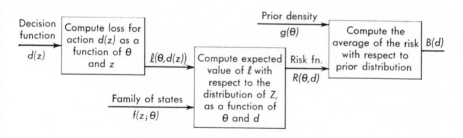

Bayes decision function is the d(z) which yields the minimum B(d)

Figure 4–17. Schematic for obtaining Bayes rule from risk.

EXAMPLE 4–28.   The two methods of computing a Bayes strategy will now be applied to the rain problem, with data Z and prior probabilities as in Example 4–26. It was seen earlier (Example 4–6) that the only admissible strategies are

d_2:   go without umbrella, no matter what Z is;
d_3:   go with the umbrella, no matter what Z is;
d_9:   go with it if Z = "rain," go without it if Z = "no rain."

The risk table for these three decision rules, together with a column giving the Bayes risk for each computed by weighting the risks with prior probabilities, is as follows:

	θ_1	θ_2	$B(d)$
d_2	5	0	3.5
d_3	2	5	2.9
d_9	2.6	.5	1.97
$g(\theta)$	.7	.3	

The Bayes rule is d_9, since this produces the smallest $B(d)$. The alternative computation is to apply posterior probabilities to the original loss table. This is done in the following table, for each of the possible observations:

	θ_1	θ_2	$B(a \mid z_1)$	$B(a \mid z_2)$
a_1	4	4	236/59	164/41
a_2	5	0	280/59	70/41
a_3	2	5	127/59	163/41
$h(\theta \mid z_1)$	56/59	3/59		
$h(\theta \mid z_2)$	14/41	27/41		

To illustrate the computations, the Bayes loss $B(a \mid z_2)$ using the posterior probabilities given $Z = z_2$ is

$$B(a \mid z_2) = 2 \times 14/41 + 5 \times 27/41 = 163/41.$$

The Bayes action given $Z = z_1$ is a_3 (which gives the minimum Bayes loss of 127/59), and the Bayes action given $Z = z_2$ is a_2 (which gives the minimum Bayes loss of 70/41). These results—take a_3 (go with umbrella) if $Z = z_1$ ("rain"), and take a_2 (go without umbrella) if $Z = z_2$ ("no rain")—constitute what was identified as decision rule d_9, seen above to be the Bayes rule.

Exploiting the computations of previous examples has perhaps served to mask the comparison in the amounts of computation needed for each method. In applying prior probabilities to risks, the risk for each of the nine decision rules must be obtained, whereas in applying posterior probabilities to losses, only the posterior probabilities corresponding to the observed value of Z need be computed. Making the entire set of necessary computations in each case "from scratch" would make the comparison more convincing.

EXAMPLE 4–29.   In Example 4–27 there was computed the posterior distribution for the parameter p in a Bernoulli family, assuming a uniform prior distribution on $[0, 1]$. The result, given k "successes" in n trials, is

$$h(p \mid k) = \binom{n}{k} (n + 1)p^k(1 - p)^{n-k}.$$

Given the quadratic loss function $(p - a)^2$ for an estimate a when the actual value is p, the posterior expected loss is

$$E_h[\ell(p, a)] = E_h[(p - a)^2].$$

This is a second moment, and the smallest such second moment is that taken about the *mean* of the distribution; that is, about $E_h(p)$. This mean is therefore the Bayes action:

$$E_h(p) = \int_0^1 p\binom{n}{k} (n + 1)p^k(1 - p)^{n-k} \, dp$$

$$= \frac{k + 1}{n + 2},$$

computed by using again the integration formula given in the footnote on page 235. In particular, for instance, the Bayes estimates of p corresponding to $k = 0$, $1, \ldots, 8$ successes in eight trials are, respectively, $\frac{1}{10}, \frac{2}{10}, \ldots, \frac{9}{10}$.

A *restricted Bayes procedure* is one that minimizes the Bayes risk among the class of procedures whose risk functions do not exceed some constant C, where C is greater than the minimum–maximum risk. The idea is that in using such a procedure, one guards to some extent against a catastrophic loss that might be caused by a poor or imprecise prior distribution used in an ordinary Bayes process. The more certain is the prior distribution, the larger the C that would be used.[8]

Problems

4–59. Determine the posterior probabilities for θ_1 and θ_2 and the Bayes action, given $Z = z_1$, and prior probabilities $g(\theta_1) = .9$ and $g(\theta_2) = .1$, in the rain problem of Examples 4–26 and 4–28 above.

4–60. Show that if one state has priority probability $g(\theta) = 1$, then the posterior distribution is the same as the prior, provided the data are not "perfectly" related to θ. (That is, no amount of data can convince a statistician whose mind is already made up.)

4–61. Show that if the data have a distribution that is independent of θ, then the posterior distribution is the same as the prior. (Data that have nothing to do with the state of nature do not help in making inferences.)

4–62. Referring to the rain problem of Example 4–28, show that if a perfect indicator is available, that is, an observation Y with probabilities $f(y_1 \mid \theta_1) = f(y_2 \mid \theta_2) = 1$, then the posterior probabilities are $(1, 0)$ given y_1 and $(0, 1)$ given y_2, no matter what the prior probabilities are (so long as neither one is zero). More generally, in any problem with discrete θ, show that if $f(z_0 \mid \theta)$ is 1 for $\theta = \theta_0$ and 0 for other states, then $h(\theta_0 \mid z_0) = 1$, if no prior probability is zero.

4–63. Compute the posterior distribution of p for Problem 4–55, given that the outcomes of both tosses are Heads. Determine the corresponding posterior

[8]See Hodges, J. L., Jr., and Lehmann, E. L., "The use of previous experience in reaching statistical decisions," *Ann. Math. Stat.* **23**, 396–407 (1952).

expected loss and the action that minimizes it. Compare this with the action determined by the Bayes decision function obtained in Problem 4–55.

4–64. Consider a uniform prior distribution on the parameter p in a Bernoulli family. Using the posterior distribution determined in Example 4–27 based on k successes in the first n trials as a prior distribution for m additional trials, compare the posterior distribution based on j successes in these m trials with the posterior distribution based on $j + k$ successes in $n + m$ trials (using a uniform distribution on p in the latter computation).

4–65. Show that the prior weighting $1/(pq)$ for $0 < p < 1$ and $p + q = 1$ yields the Bayes estimate k/n for the p in a Bernoulli distribution, based on k successes in n independent trials, using a quadratic loss. (This weighting does not define a probability distribution because its integral over $[0, 1]$ is not convergent.)

4–66. (a) Compute for Example 4–28 the minimum Bayes risk using Z, in two ways—as the minimum $B(d)$ for the Bayes rule d, and as the weighted sum of the expected posterior losses $B(a \mid z_i)$ using absolute probabilities of the z_i's as weights.

   (b) Determine the value of the data Z in Example 4–28, as measured by the reduction in minimum Bayes loss obtained by its use. Compare this with the value of the data Z in Problem 4–59.

4–67. Compute the minimum Bayes risk for Example 4–29 in two ways: (1) as the minimum expected value of the risk function, using the Bayes decision function to obtain this minimum; (2) as the average with respect to the absolute distribution of k of the posterior expected loss, again using the estimate that minimizes this posterior expected loss.

4.4.4   Maximum Likelihood Procedures

Suppose first that the population of interest is discrete, so that it is meaningful to speak of the probability that $X = x$, where X denotes a sample $(X_1, \ldots, X_n)$ and x a possible realization $(x_1, \ldots, x_n)$. This probability that $X = x$ depends on x, of course, but it also depends on the state of nature θ which governs. As a function of θ for given x, it is called the likelihood function:

$$L(\theta) = P_\theta(X = x).$$

Thinking of a state of nature as a possible "explanation" of observed data, the *maximum likelihood principle* considers the "best" explanation to be the state of nature $\hat{\theta}$ that maximizes the likelihood function—that maximizes the probability of getting what was actually observed. A maximum likelihood procedure is then one that is best when the state of nature is the maximum likelihood state, $\hat{\theta}$. This is determined from the loss function as the action that minimizes $\ell(\hat{\theta}, a)$.

The best explanation $\hat{\theta}$ of a given observation $X = x$ depends on x, and so defines a function of x or a statistic. The rule that says take the action that minimizes $\ell(\hat{\theta}, a)$ assigns this action to the x that leads to $\hat{\theta}$, and so the maximum likelihood principle defines a decision function, called the maximum likelihood decision function.

EXAMPLE 4–30.   The likelihood function for the rain problem of Example 4–26 is given by the same table as the probability function; the difference is that instead of holding θ fixed, one holds z fixed. Thus, the columns in the following table give $f(z \mid \theta)$ and the *rows* give $L(\theta)$:

	$f(z \mid \theta_1)$	$f(z \mid \theta_2)$
z_1	.8	.1
z_2	.2	.9

Given $Z = z_1$, the larger probability is .8, when θ is θ_1, and this is the maximum likelihood state for $Z = z_1$. Similarly, the maximum likelihood state for $Z = z_2$ is θ_2, for which the likelihood function is .9. The maximum likelihood decision rule then calls for action a_3 if $Z = z_1$ [which minimizes $\ell(\theta_1, a)$] and action a_2 if $Z = z_2$ [which minimizes $\ell(\theta_2, a)$]. The maximum likelihood decision function is that previously called d_9.

EXAMPLE 4–31.   Consider once again the flash-bulb problem: Flash bulbs come in lots of ten, and one bulb is selected from the lot for testing (cf. Example 4–21). Let k denote the number of defective bulbs in a lot of ten, let $p = k/10$, and let X denote the outcome of the test (X = good or X = defective). The likelihood function is

$$L(p) = P_p(X = x) = \begin{cases} 1 - p, & \text{if } x = \text{good}, \\ p, & \text{if } x = \text{defective}. \end{cases}$$

The maximizing value of p for a given x is then

$$\hat{p} = \begin{cases} 0, & \text{if } x = \text{good}, \\ 1, & \text{if } x = \text{defective}. \end{cases}$$

From the loss function given in Example 4–21 are found the following:

$$\ell(0, \text{sell}) = -1.35, \qquad \ell(1, \text{sell}) = 1.35,$$

$$\ell(0, \text{junk}) = .10, \qquad \ell(1, \text{junk}) = .10.$$

If p is really 0, the minimum loss is achieved by selling; if p is really 1, the minimum loss is achieved by junking. Hence, the maximum likelihood decision function is to sell the lot if the bulb tested is good and to junk the lot if the bulb tested is bad.

In the case of a continuous population, maximizing the probability that $X = x$ accomplishes nothing, since each such probability is zero. Instead, one maximizes the "probability element" for given dx; that is, a value of θ is chosen which maximizes the density function of X at the point x. The maximizing value of θ is again the state assumed to be correct in choosing an action to minimize the loss.

The joint density function of the sample observations at x is called (as a function of θ) the *likelihood function*:

$$L(\theta) = f(x; \theta) = f(x_1, \ldots, x_n; \theta).$$

In the case of a random sample, with identically distributed, independent observations, this becomes

$$L(\theta) = \prod_{i=1}^{n} f(x_i; \theta),$$

where $f(x; \theta)$ is the population density function.

EXAMPLE 4–32.   Consider, from the point of view of maximum likelihood, the estimation problem considered in Example 4–20, in which it was desired to estimate θ in the negative exponential density $(1/\theta) \exp(-x/\theta)$, $x > 0$, on the basis of a random sample of size n. For a given sample X, the likelihood function is

$$L(\theta) = \prod_{i=1}^{n} \frac{1}{\theta} \exp\left(\frac{-X_i}{\theta}\right) = \frac{1}{\theta^n} \exp\left(\frac{-n\bar{X}}{\theta}\right).$$

This function has a maximum at $\theta = \bar{X}$. If, then, the loss function has the natural property of being smallest when $a = \theta$, the right choice of action would be to take $\bar{X}$ (now assumed to be the true state) as the estimate of θ. Hence, for such loss functions, the sample mean is the maximum likelihood estimate of θ.

The quantity $\hat{\theta}$ that maximizes $L(\theta)$ and which is used as the true state in determining the right action can be thought of as the number that maximizes the density of the posterior distribution of θ, assuming a uniform prior distribution. For

$$h(\theta \mid z) = \frac{f(z; \theta)g(\theta)}{f(z)},$$

where $g(\theta)$ is the prior density and $f(z)$ the absolute density of Z. Clearly, if $g(\theta)$ is constant, the maximum of $L(\theta) = f(z; \theta)$ is attained for the value of θ that maximizes $h(\theta \mid z)$. (The maximum of a density function, when it has a single maximum, is called the *mode* of the distribution; it may or may not coincide with the mean or the median of the distribution.)

It is to be observed that the quantity θ (which indexes the states of nature), although frequently a real parameter, can be a vector-valued parameter—$(\theta_1, \ldots, \theta_k)$—or it could be nonnumerical.

Since it is possible to index a given family of states of nature in different ways, it should be observed that the maximum likelihood state does not depend on the parametrization. Consider the family $\{f(z; \theta)\}$, with likelihood function

$$L(\theta) = f(z; \theta).$$

And suppose that $\xi = g(\theta)$ is a one to one correspondence between the values of θ and the values of a new indexing parameter ξ. Let $g^{-1}(\xi)$ denote the inverse function, with the properties

$$g(g^{-1}(\xi)) = \xi, \quad \text{and} \quad g^{-1}(g(\theta)) = \theta.$$

The probability or density function f, in its dependence on θ, becomes a new function of ξ:

$$f^*(z; \xi) = f(z; g^{-1}(\xi)),$$

and the likelihood function of ξ is then

$$L^*(\xi) = f(z; g^{-1}(\xi)) = L(g^{-1}(\xi)).$$

Suppose now that $\hat{\theta}$ maximizes $L(\theta)$, and consider the new likelihood function at $g(\hat{\theta})$:

$$L^*(g(\hat{\theta})) = L(g^{-1}(g(\hat{\theta}))) = L(\hat{\theta}) \geq L(g^{-1}(\xi)) = L^*(\xi),$$

for *any* ξ. Hence, $\hat{\xi} = g(\hat{\theta})$ maximizes $L^*(\xi)$, and this $\hat{\xi}$ identifies the same state of nature as does $\hat{\theta}$:

$$f^*(z; g(\hat{\theta})) = f(z; g^{-1}(g(\hat{\theta}))) = f(z; \hat{\theta}).$$

Problems

4-68. Determine the maximum likelihood rule for the decision problem of Problem 4–50.

4-69. Write out likelihood functions for a random sample of size n from each of the following populations:

(a) normal (μ, σ^2);
(b) Poisson (m);
(c) Bernoulli (p).

4-70. Let M denote the number of defectives in a lot of five articles, and let the possible actions be a_1, accept the lot, and a_2, reject the lot. Let the loss function be M for action a_1 and $2(5 - M)$ for a_2. Determine the maximum likelihood action for the results of tests on samples of size two from the lot.

4-71. Determine the decision procedure for Problem 4–70 which calls for the action that is best when the state of nature is one that maximizes the posterior probability function,

(a) given equal prior probabilities for $M = 0, 1, \ldots, 5$, and
(b) given prior probabilities $g(0) = 1/2$, $g(1) = 1/3$, and $g(2) = 1/6$.

4-72. Let the observation X have a uniform distribution on $0 \leq x \leq \theta$, where θ is the parameter indexing the family of states of nature. Given $X = x$, what is the maximum likelihood state of nature?

4-73. Let $X_1, \ldots, X_5$ be independent observations each with the distribution of X in the preceding problem. Determine the maximum likelihood state of nature,

(a) given $X_1 = 17$, $X_2 = 9$, $X_3 = 13$, $X_4 = 10$, $X_5 = 16$;
(b) given $X_1 = x_1, \ldots, X_5 = x_5$.

4-74. Consider an observation X with density $\lambda e^{-\lambda x}$, for $x > 0$, where λ is a positive parameter. Determine the maximum likelihood state $\hat{\lambda}$ and compare with the maximum likelihood state $\hat{\theta}$, where $\theta = 1/\lambda$. (That is, determine the relation between $\hat{\lambda}$ and the maximum likelihood state for the family with density $(1/\theta)e^{-x/\theta}$, $x > 0$.)

4.5 Sufficiency

The notion of sufficiency was discussed rather imprecisely earlier in this chapter in considering the reduction of the data in a sample to more manageable measures—a reduction hopefully not so drastic as to throw away information in the sample pertinent to the problem at hand. Although the notion will now be made more precise, a rigorous treatment of sufficiency in the general case requires a rigorous treatment of conditional probability as a basis. Not having this, one can only reason intuitively and simply state results (except in the discrete case, in which it is possible to be quite precise and rigorous with the background assumed).

4.5.1 Statistics and Partitions

In Section 1.1.6 the notion of a *partition* as induced by a function on a sample space was introduced. A statistic, being a function on the space of values of the data Z (whether this be a single random variable, or a vector of observations as in a random sample), defines a *partition* of that space— into mutually disjoint "partition sets" whose union is the whole space. A *partition set* is determined and identified by a particular value of the function, or in the present case, by a value of the statistic, as the set of points on which the function assumes that value. Distinct values define distinct partition sets.

Two statistics $T_1 = g(Z)$ and $T_2 = h(Z)$ that define the same partition are in 1-1 correspondence—there is a function $T_1 = s(T_2)$ with a unique inverse, $T_2 = s^{-1}(T_1)$. This function may not be easy to write down, but it does exist; for, given any value of T_2, one can go to the corresponding partition set and obtain as the value of $g(T_2)$ the T_1-value that defines that partition set.

Given a partition, any assignment of a number to each set such that no two sets have the same number assigned defines a statistic. For that number is simply assigned to each point of the set it identifies.

EXAMPLE 4–33.   Consider a random variable Z with four possible values, z_1, z_2, z_3, z_4. The statistic T_1 defined by

$$T_1 = \begin{cases} 0, & \text{if } Z = z_1 \text{ or } z_2, \\ 1, & \text{if } Z = z_3, \\ 2, & \text{if } Z = z_4, \end{cases}$$

defines the partition of the Z-space into the sets $\{z_1, z_2\}$, $\{z_3\}$, $\{z_4\}$. The same partition would be defined by

$$T_2 = \begin{cases} 3, & \text{if } Z = z_1 \text{ or } z_2, \\ 17, & \text{if } Z = z_3, \\ 7, & \text{if } Z = z_4, \end{cases}$$

or, indeed, by any statistic that has distinct values on the sets $\{z_1, z_2\}$, $\{z_3\}$, $\{z_4\}$. The statistic T_1 is a function of T_2 and vice versa, with the following correspondences between values of one and values of the other: $0 \leftrightarrow 3$, $1 \leftrightarrow 17$, $2 \leftrightarrow 7$.

A partition Π_1 is said to be a *reduction* of a partition Π_2 if each partition set of Π_1 is precisely the union of sets of Π_2. In such a case, a statistic T_1 that defines Π_1 must be a function of any statistic T_2 that defines Π_2, but not a function with a unique inverse unless the two partitions are exactly the same. That is, each value of T_2 leads to and so defines a corresponding value of T_1— a value of T_2 picks out one of the partition sets of Π_2 which in turn is contained entirely in some partition set of Π_1 and is then assigned the value that T_1 has on that set. If Π_1 is a reduction of Π_2, one says that the statistic T_1 is a reduction of T_2—meaning, then, that it is a function of T_2.

If T_1 is a reduction of T_2 and T_2 is a reduction of T_1, then these statistics must define the same partition and so be related by a function that is a 1–1 correspondence. Given any two statistics (or corresponding partitions) it is not always the case that one is a reduction of the other. Thus, partitions of a given space are only partially ordered.

EXAMPLE 4–34.   Continuing Example 4–33, let T_3 be defined by

$$T_3 = \begin{cases} 4, & \text{if } Z = z_1 \text{ or } z_2, \\ 5, & \text{if } Z = z_3 \text{ or } z_4. \end{cases}$$

The partition determined by T_3 consists of the sets $\{z_1, z_2\}$ and $\{z_3, z_4\}$, which is clearly a reduction of the partition defined by T_2 (or by T_1) in the preceding example, since $\{z_3, z_4\}$ is the union of $\{z_3\}$ and $\{z_4\}$. On the other hand, the statistic

$$T_4 = \begin{cases} 6, & \text{if } Z = z_1 \text{ or } z_3, \\ 8, & \text{if } Z = z_2 \text{ or } z_4. \end{cases}$$

is not a reduction of T_2—nor is T_2 a reduction of T_4.

EXAMPLE 4–35.   Consider a sample (X_1, X_2, X_3) from a continuous population. The statistic $S = X_1 + X_2 + X_3$ defines a partition consisting of planes of the form $x_1 + x_2 + x_3 = $ const. Precisely the same partition is defined by the sample mean, $\bar{X} = S/3$; the $\bar{X}$-label for any set is just $\frac{1}{3}$ of the S-label for that set, but sets with distinct $\bar{X}$-labels have distinct S-labels. The statistic $T = X_1^2 + X_2^2 + X_3^2$ defines the partition whose sets are spheres centered at the origin, each sphere being labeled by the square of its radius. The statistic $(\bar{X}, T)$ defines partition sets that are loci of the simultaneous system

$$\begin{cases} x_1 + x_2 + x_3 = a \\ x_1^2 + x_2^2 + x_3^2 = b \end{cases}$$

for various choices of the two constants. When the two surfaces defined by these two equations (namely, a plane and a sphere) intersect, the intersection is a circle; the union of all the circles in this two-parameter (a, b) family of circles is the whole sample space.

The conditional probability of an event, given $T = t$, where T is some statistic, or function of the observations $X = (X_1, \ldots, X_n)$, is the same as the conditional probability given $U = u$, where U is any statistic defining the same partition as T [so that U is some function of T, say $h(T)$, and then $u = h(t)$]. That is to say, the conditional probability is really *defined by the partition set* that is known to have "occurred," and is not dependent on the particular statistic that is used to define that partition set. The quantity $P(A \mid T = t)$ can thus be interpreted as the probability that condition A is satisfied by the sample point X given that X falls in the partition set whose T-label happens to be t.

4.5.2 Sufficient Statistics

Before taking up the general definition, consider the following example, a discrete case that illustrates the main idea without the complications of general notation.

EXAMPLE 4-36.   Consider the family of Bernoulli distributions indexed as usual by the probability p of "success" in a single trial:

$$P(X = x) = p^x(1 - p)^{1-x}, \quad x = 0 \text{ (failure), } 1 \text{ (success).}$$

There are eight distinct samples of size three, and the probability function of (X_1, X_2, X_3) is

$$P(X = x) = P(X_1 = x_1, X_2 = x_2, X_3 = x_3) = p^k(1 - p)^{3-k},$$

where $x_1 + x_2 + x_3 = k$, the number of 1's among the values (x_1, x_2, x_3). Let the statistic T denote the number of successes in three trials: $T = X_1 + X_2 + X_3$, with probability function

$$P(T = k) = P(k \text{ successes in 3 trials}) = \binom{3}{k}p^k(1 - p)^{3-k}.$$

The *conditional* probability of obtaining (x_1, x_2, x_3), given that $T = k$, is the quotient

$$p(x \mid T = k) \;=\; P(X = x \mid T = k) \;=\; \frac{P(X = x \text{ and } T = k)}{P(T = k)}.$$

The numerator is zero unless $x_1 + x_2 + x_3 = k$, in which case the condition $T = k$ is redundant; hence,

$$p(x \mid T = k) = \begin{cases} 0, & \text{if } x_1 + x_2 + x_3 \neq k, \\[2mm] \dfrac{p^k(1 - p)^{3-k}}{\binom{3}{k} p^k (1 - p)^{3-k}} = \dfrac{1}{\binom{3}{k}}, & \text{if } x_1 + x_2 + x_3 = k. \end{cases}$$

These probabilities for the various samples and conditions are itemized in the following tabulation:

Sample	T	Prob.	Prob. given $T = 0$	Prob. given $T = 1$	Prob. given $T = 2$	Prob. given $T = 3$
(0, 0, 0)	0	$(1 - p)^3$	1	0	0	0
(0, 0, 1)	1	$p(1 - p)^2$	0	$\frac{1}{3}$	0	0
(0, 1, 0)	1	$p(1 - p)^2$	0	$\frac{1}{3}$	0	0
(1, 0, 0)	1	$p(1 - p)^2$	0	$\frac{1}{3}$	0	0
(0, 1, 1)	2	$p^2(1 - p)$	0	0	$\frac{1}{3}$	0
(1, 0, 1)	2	$p^2(1 - p)$	0	0	$\frac{1}{3}$	0
(1, 1, 0)	2	$p^2(1 - p)$	0	0	$\frac{1}{3}$	0
(1, 1, 1)	3	p^3	0	0	0	1

Notice in particular that the distribution of (X_1, X_2, X_3), given any particular value of T, *does not involve the parameter p.*

One can imagine that a sample point, say (1, 1, 0), is obtained in this way: First a game is played that gives the value of T, namely $T = 2$. Then, among the three samples for which the sample sum is 2, the particular result (1, 1, 0) comes from playing a second game—tossing a three-sided object with equal probabilities. This second game does not depend on p, and it would seem quite pointless to play the second game whose outcome depends in no way on the parameter of interest. That is, the information relevant to p in a particular sample is contained in the sample sum, and it does no good to know which particular sample with that sum is the one that was actually observed.

The statistic T is said to be *sufficient* for the family of Bernoulli distributions because knowing T is just as good as knowing the actual sample insofar as knowledge of p is concerned. But notice that the same would be true of $T/3$, or of T^2, or of any other function of T that defines the same partition. Sufficiency is basically a property of the partitioning of the space of possible samples into these four sets:

$$\{(0, 0, 0)\}$$
$$\{(0, 0, 1), (0, 1, 0), (1, 0, 0)\}$$
$$\{(0, 1, 1), (1, 0, 1), (1, 1, 0)\}$$
$$\{(1, 1, 1)\}.$$

On any one of these partition sets T is constant—a different constant each—and so T serves to identify the sets. Similarly, $T/3$ would also serve to identify them, etc. But no matter how these partitions sets are coded, the conditional distribution of X, given that the result is in a particular partition set, does not depend on p, and one is no better off knowing exactly which sample point occurred than he is knowing which partition set occurred.

Consider a family of states of nature, or the equivalent family of distributions of the sample point X. The statistic $T = t(X)$ is said to be *sufficient* for the family if the conditional distribution of X, given the value of T, is the same for all members of the family. If the family is indexed by a (real or vector) parameter θ, the conditional distribution of X, given the value of T, is to be independent of θ.

The statement that $T = t(X)$ has a certain value, say, $T = k$, is interpreted geometrically to mean that the sample point X lies on the partition set $t(x_1, \ldots, x_n) = k$, which is the set of *all* points for which $t(x) = k$. Sufficiency of T for a family of distribution means that the conditional distribution of probability on such partition sets induced by one member of the family is the same as that induced by any other. Knowledge of X in more detail than just the value of $t(X)$ does not help in chasing down the particular member of the family that is the true state of nature. It is actually the *partition* that is sufficient, and any function $g(x)$ that has distinct values on distinct partition sets is a sufficient statistic. The most that a sample can say regarding the underlying state of nature is contained in the statement that the sample point is on some one of the partition sets, and no pertinent information is discarded in a reduction $T = t(x)$ that defines the partition.

The statistic T in this definition of sufficiency can be a vector. It might be, for instance, the order statistic $(X_{(1)}, \ldots, X_{(n)})$, or even the original sample point itself: $(X_1, \ldots, X_n)$. With this understanding, it is clear that the sample itself is trivially a sufficient statistic for any family of distributions. The partitioning of the sample space is into sets, each consisting of just one point.

The significance of a sufficient statistic T in statistical problems is that by restricting attention to procedures based on T, no information is overlooked. For, as was argued in the illustrative example, the original experiment of chance which determines a sample point x can be thought of as first an experiment that determines the value of T, followed by one that does not depend on which member of the family of distributions is the one that governs. That is, to determine the sample and hence any other statistic, one can first play the game to find T and then play the second game, which is the same for all states of nature considered. This implies that *any decision procedure can be viewed as a randomized (mixed) decision procedure based on the sufficient statistic T.*

If T is sufficient for a family of distributions and is a function of a statistic U, then U is also sufficient. (Equivalently, if a statistic is not sufficient, no reduction of it can be sufficient.) This is clear intuitively, since a reduction could not possibly add "information" about the population, and usually reduces the informative value of a sample; moreover, if the value of T can be computed from the value of U, then knowing U must be at least as good as knowing T. A more rigorous argument using the factorization criterion of the next section will be given there.

Problems

4–75. Consider a statistical problem with just three states of nature, and with data Z having the following probability table:

z_i	$f(z_i \mid \theta_1)$	$f(z_i \mid \theta_2)$	$f(z_i \mid \theta_3)$
z_1	.4	.6	.2
z_2	.2	.3	.1
z_3	.4	.1	.7

Consider the partition whose partition sets are $A = \{z_3\}$ and $B = \{z_1, z_2\}$.

(a) Determine the conditional distributions in the sample space defined by $f(z_i \mid A)$ and $f(z_i \mid B)$.

(b) Construct a statistic that defines the partition A, B; is it sufficient?

(c) Consider the statistic:

$$T(Z) = \begin{cases} 0, & \text{if} \quad Z = z_1, \\ 1, & \text{if} \quad Z = z_2 \quad \text{or} \quad z_3. \end{cases}$$

Is this sufficient?

4–76. Determine the partition of the plane defined by the order statistic for a sample (X_1, X_2), that is, by $T = (X_{(1)}, X_{(2)})$. Determine also the partition sets defined by $U = X_1 + X_2$. Is T a reduction of U, or conversely?

4–77. Describe the partitions defined by $\bar{X}$ and $\bar{X}^2$, where $\bar{X}$ is the mean of a sample of size three, and observe how one is a reduction of the other.

4–78. An urn contains five beads, marked 1, 2, 3, 4, 5, respectively. Three are drawn, one at a time, without replacement. Let X_i be the number on the ith bead drawn.

(a) List the points in the sample space (X_1, X_2, X_3) that lead to the particular order statistic (1, 2, 5).

(b) List the ten possible order statistic vectors and their corresponding probabilities of occurrence.

(c) Determine the partitions of the sample space for the order statistic [in (b)] corresponding to each of these statistics:

(i) $(X_{(1)}, X_{(3)},)$ (ii) $X_{(1)}$,   (iii) $X_{(3)}$,   (iv) $X_{(3)} - X_{(1)}$.

4-79.   In sampling without replacement from N objects of which M are black and $N - M$ are white, the probability of a particular sequence of n observations was found in Problem 1–51 to be given by the formula

$$\frac{\binom{M}{k}\binom{N - M}{n - k}}{\binom{n}{k}\binom{N}{n}}, \qquad k = 0, 1, \ldots, n,$$

where k is the number of black objects in the sequence. Determine the conditional distribution in the sample space (that is, the conditional probability of any given sample sequence) given the value of Y, the number of black objects in the sequence of n observations. Is Y sufficient? (The population parameter here is M, the numbers N and n being given constants.)

4-80.   A sample (X_1, X_2) has the distribution given in the accompanying table. The parameter M can take on any of the values 0, 1, 2, 3, 4.

Sample	Probability
(0, 0)	$(12 - 7M + M^2)/12$
(0, 1)	$(4M - M^2)/12$
(1, 0)	$(4M - M^2)/12$
(1, 1)	$(M^2 - M)/12$

(a) Is (X_1, X_2) a *random* sample?
(b) Is $X_1 + X_2$ sufficient?
(c) Is $X_1 X_2$ sufficient?
(d) For each sample point, determine the maximum likelihood action given the following loss table:

	0	1	2	3	4
a_1	0	1	2	3	3
a_2	3	2	1	2	3
a_3	5	4	3	2	1

(e) Calculate the risk $R(M, d^*)$, where d^* is the maximum likelihood rule determined in (d). Can the rule d^* be expressed as a procedure based on the sufficient statistic $X_1 + X_2$? (Do it.)
(f) Determine a randomized rule based on $X_1 + X_2$ having the same risk function as the following rule: Take action a_1 if the sample is (0, 0) or (0, 1), and take action a_3 if the sample is (1, 0) or (1, 1).

4.5.3   The Factorization Criterion

To determine whether a given statistic is sufficient, it is usually easier, rather than to determine the conditional distribution given the value of the statistic, to use the following criterion:

In order that the statistic $T = t(X)$ be sufficient for the family $f(x; \theta)$, it is necessary and sufficient that the sample joint density function factor:

$$f(x; \theta) = g[t(x), \theta]h(x),$$

where g depends on the observations only through the value of $t(x)$, and h does not involve the parameter θ.

In this statement we have omitted certain regularity conditions that must be imposed for the continuous case.[9] However, in the discrete case (in which $f(x, \theta)$ is interpreted as a probability function), the argument runs as follows: If a factorization is assumed,

$$P_\theta(X = x) = g[t(x), \theta]h(x),$$

then for any given t_0,

$$P(T = t_0) = \sum_{t(x)=t_0} P_\theta(X = x) = \sum_{t(x)=t_0} g[t(x),\theta]h(x)$$

$$= g[t_0, \theta] \sum_{t(x)=t_0} h(x).$$

The conditional distribution of X, given $T = t_0$, is then

$$P(X = x \mid T = t_0) = \frac{P(X = x \text{ and } T = t_0)}{P(T = t_0)} = \begin{cases} 0, & \text{if } t(x) \neq t_0, \\ \dfrac{P(X = x)}{P(T = t_0)}, & \text{if } t(x) = t_0, \end{cases}$$

where, if $t(x) = t_0$,

$$\frac{P(X = x)}{P(T = t)} = \frac{g[t_0,\theta]h(x)}{g[t_0, \theta] \sum\limits_{t(x)=t_0} h(x)},$$

which is independent of θ. Hence, T is sufficient.

Conversely, if the conditional probability that $X = x$, given $T = t_0$, is independent of θ:

$$P(X = x \mid T = t_0) = c(x, t_0),$$

then for a given x, with t_0 defined to be $t(x)$,

$$P(X = x) = P(X = x \quad \text{and} \quad t(X) = t_0)$$

$$= c(x, t_0)P[t(X) = t(x)],$$

the first factor on the right being independent of θ and the second depending on x only through the values of $t(x)$.

A proof for the case of a continuous population will not be given. The criterion is applicable in the cases to which it will be applied here.

[9] See Lehmann, E. [13], p. 19, and references given therein.

The factorization criterion is often used in the following way: A joint density function $f(x; \theta)$ is inspected to determine whether there is any factorization of the type required, in terms of some function $t(x)$. If there is, then $T = t(X)$ is a sufficient statistic.

EXAMPLE 4–37.   Consider a random sample $(X_1, \ldots, X_n)$, where each observation has the geometric distribution, defined (for $0 < p < 1$) by

$$f(x; p) = p^x(1 - p), \qquad x = 0, 1, \ldots.$$

The joint probability function of the observations is

$$f(x; p) = \prod_{1}^{n} p^{x_i}(1 - p) = (1 - p)^n p^{\Sigma x_i} = g(\textstyle\sum x_i, p) h(x),$$

where $h(x) = 1$ and

$$g(t, p) = (1 - p)^n p^t.$$

Because $f(x; p)$ factors in this way, the factorization criterion asserts the sufficiency of the statistic $\sum X_i$.

EXAMPLE 4–38.   Consider a problem with two states of nature, θ_0 and θ_1, and with data X. Let $f_0(x)$ and $f_1(x)$ be the density function of X under θ_0 and θ_1, respectively. (In the discrete case the f's would be probability functions.) Then, setting

$$g(\lambda, \theta) = \begin{cases} \sqrt{\lambda}, & \text{if } \theta = \theta_0, \\ 1/\sqrt{\lambda}, & \text{if } \theta = \theta_1, \end{cases}$$

and

$$h(x) = [f_0(x)f_1(x)]^{1/2},$$

one finds that $T = t(X)$, where

$$t(x) = f_0(x)/f_1(x),$$

is sufficient, by the factorization criterion. For,

$$g(t(x), \theta)h(x) = \begin{cases} [f_0(x)f_1(x)]^{1/2} \left(\dfrac{f_0(x)}{f_1(x)}\right)^{1/2} = f_0(x), & \text{if } \theta = \theta_0, \\[3mm] [f_0(x)f_1(x)]^{1/2} \left(\dfrac{f_1(x)}{f_0(x)}\right)^{1/2} = f_1(x), & \text{if } \theta = \theta_1, \end{cases}$$

which is precisely the density of the data, for each state. The statistic T whose sufficiency is herewith established is called the *likelihood ratio* statistic.

The factorization criterion shows easily that if $T = c(U)$ and T is sufficient, then U is sufficient. For, sufficiency of T implies

$$f(X; \theta) = g(T, \theta)h(X) = g(c(U), \theta)h(X) = \tilde{g}(U, \theta)h(X),$$

which shows the sufficiency of U.

It is not usually easy to use the factorization criterion to show that a statistic T is *not* sufficient, since this would mean showing that $f(x, \theta)$ cannot be factored in the right way. But if one can't seem to factor $f(x; \theta)$, it might be just that he is not clever enough. To show that T is not sufficient, it is usually easier to show that the conditional distribution of X, given $T = t$, *does* depend on θ.

EXAMPLE 4–39. Consider a random sample $(X_1, \ldots, X_n)$ from a discrete population with probability function $f(x; \theta)$. The statistic

$$T = (X_1, \ldots, X_{n-1})$$

is *not* sufficient. For,

$$P[X = x \mid T = (k_1, \ldots, k_{n-1})] = \frac{P(X = x)}{P(T = (k_1, \ldots, k_{n-1}))} = P(X_n = x_n),$$

because the observations are independent. (This formula holds if $x_1 = k_1$, $\ldots, x_{n-1} = k_{n-1}$; otherwise the probability is zero.) But this conditional probability given the value of T is just the probability function of the nth observation, $f(x_n, \theta)$, which *does* depend on θ.

Moreover, any function of the $n - 1$ observations in T is also not sufficient, being a further reduction of an already insufficient statistic. Thus, an observation cannot be thrown away without giving up sufficiency.

Problems

4–81. Determine in each case a sufficient one-dimensional statistic (that is, a single real valued function of the observations) based on a random sample of size n; using the factorization criterion:

(a) from a Bernoulli population, $f(x; p) = p^x(1 - p)^{1-x}$, $x = 0, 1$;
(b) from a geometric population, $f(x; p) = p(1 - p)^x$, $x = 0, 1, \ldots$;
(c) from a negative exponential population, $f(x; \lambda) = \lambda e^{-\lambda x}$, $x > 0$;
(d) from a uniform population, $f(x; \theta) = 1/\theta$, $0 < x < \theta$.

4–82. Determine a sufficient statistic for a sample obtained by sampling without replacement from a finite Bernoulli population, using the factorization criterion (see Problem 4–79).

4–83. Determine, by use of the factorization criterion, a sufficient statistic based on a random sample of size n for the Rayleigh family (Section 3.3.3), with density

$$f(z; \sigma^2) = (z/\sigma^2) \exp[-z^2/(2\sigma^2)], \qquad z > 0.$$

4–84. Use the factorization criterion to determine a two-dimensional statistic (that is, two real-valued functions of the observations) based on a random sample of size n that is sufficient for the normal family of distributions with parameters (μ, σ^2).

4–85. Use the factorization criterion to determine a sufficient statistic based on a random sample from the family of distributions for a random variable with a finite list of possible values: $x_1, \ldots, x_k$, with corresponding probabilities:

$p_1, \ldots, p_k$. (The joint probabilitity function of the observations is discussed in Section 3.4 on the multinomial distribution.)

4.5.4   Minimal Sufficient Statistics

Having seen that it is often possible to "reduce" the data in a sample by the calculation of some statistics without losing information needed in the inference problem at hand, and also possible to reduce the data too far—by calculating some statistic that is no longer sufficient, one would naturally want to know just how far a sample can be reduced *without* losing sufficiency. Reduction of the data certainly simplifies the methodology and makes it easier to understand, but reducing the data so far as to sacrifice sufficiency essentially throws away some information that could make the inference more precise.

A statistic is said to be *minimal sufficient* if it is sufficient and if any reduction of the partition of the sample space defined by it is not sufficient. A technique for obtaining a minimal sufficient partition has been devised by Lehmann and Scheffé[10] and will be presented next. Once the partition is obtained, of course, a minimal sufficient statistic can be defined by assigning distinct numbers to distinct partition sets.

In constructing sets of a partition that is to be sufficient for the family of sample densities (or probability functions) $f(x; \theta)$, for θ in some parameter space Θ, there is associated with each point x in the sample space a *set* $D(x)$:

$$D(x) = \{y \,|\, f(y; \theta) = k(y, x)f(x; \theta)\},$$

where $k(y, x)$ is not zero and is not dependent on θ. That is, $D(x)$ is the set of all sample points y "equivalent" to x in the sense that the ratio of the densities at y and at x does not involve the state of nature. The reason for writing the definition in terms of a product rather than a ratio is to take into account the points for which $f(x; \theta)$ is zero. Indeed, all points such that $f(x; \theta) = 0$ for all θ will be equivalent, and so lie in the same "D", call it D_0. Every x will lie in some D, namely, in $D(x)$, and there is no overlapping of the D's—so that they do indeed constitute a partition of the sample space. For, if two D's, say $D(x)$ amd $D(y)$, have a point z in common, then z is equivalent to both x and y, which are then equivalent to each other and define the same D. (The "equivalence" of sample points being used here is an equivalence relation in the mathematical sense, being reflexive, symmetric, and transitive. The partition sets are then *equivalence classes* under this relation.)

[10] Lehmann, E., and Scheffé, H., "Completeness, Similar Regions, and Unbiased Estimation," in *Sankhya*, **10**, 327ff (1950).

Defining the D's thus defines a partition of the sample space, and this partition is asserted to be the minimal sufficient partition. A rigorous proof of this assertion requires measure theory and will not be attempted. However, the basic idea of the proof is not difficult. It involves showing (a) that the partition is sufficient, and (b) that any reduction of it is not sufficient.

To show sufficiency, choose for each set D of the partition a representative point x_D. Let $G(x)$ denote the mappings from a given point x to the set $D(x)$ in which it lies and then to the representative point x_D of that set. That is, $G(X)$ is a statistic and defines the partition. Now for any partition set D except D_0, and for any x in D,

$$f(x; \theta) = k(x, x_D)f(x_D; \theta) = k[x, G(x)]f[G(x); \theta].$$

But then for all x,

$$f(x; \theta) = h(x)g[G(x), \theta],$$

where

$$h(x) = \begin{cases} 0, & \text{if } x \text{ is in } D_0, \\ k[x, G(x)], & \text{otherwise,} \end{cases}$$

and

$$g[G(x), \theta] = f[G(x); \theta].$$

The function $h(x)$ does not involve θ, and the function $g[G(x), \theta]$ depends on x only through the values of the function $G(x)$. Thus $G(X)$ is sufficient, as is the given partition, which it defines.

To see the minimality of the sufficient statistic $G(X)$ and the corresponding partition, consider any other sufficient statistic $t(X)$ with corresponding partition sets E. The minimality follows when it is shown that each set E is contained in some D of the constructed partition (except possibly for points in a set of probability zero). Let x and y be points in E so that $t(x) = t(y)$. Since $t(X)$ is sufficient, the joint density at x can be factored in the form

$$f(x; \theta) = r(x)s[t(x), \theta] = r(x)s[t(y), \theta],$$

and, likewise, at y:

$$f(y; \theta) = r(y)s[t(y), \theta].$$

If $r(x) \neq 0$,

$$f(y; \theta) = r(y)\frac{f(x; \theta)}{r(x)} = k(y, x)f(x; \theta),$$

where

$$k(y, x) = \frac{r(y)}{r(x)}$$

is not zero if $r(y)$ is not zero. Hence, if $r(y) \neq 0$, x and y belong to the same D. Thus, all E is contained in D, except possibly for those points x such that

$r(x) = 0$; but for such points, $f(x; \theta) = 0$ for all θ, and the totality of all such points has probability zero.

EXAMPLE 4–40. Consider the Bernoulli family with probability function

$$f(x; p) = p^x(1 - p)^{1-x}, \qquad x = 0, 1.$$

For a sample X of independent observations, the joint probability function at x is

$$f(x; p) = p^{\Sigma x_i}(1 - p)^{n - \Sigma x_i},$$

and at the point y it is

$$f(y; p) = p^{\Sigma y_i}(1 - p)^{n - \Sigma y_i}.$$

The ratio is

$$\frac{f(x; p)}{f(y; p)} = \left\{\frac{p}{1 - p}\right\}^{\Sigma x_i - \Sigma y_i},$$

which is independent of p if and only if $\Sigma x_i = \Sigma y_i$. Thus, points whose coordinates have the same sum lie in the same set of the minimal sufficient partition. The sum $X_1 + \cdots + X_n$ is therefore a minimal sufficient statistic.

EXAMPLE 4–41. Consider the random sample X, where each observation is normal (μ, σ^2). The ratio of the joint density function at x to its value at a point y is

$$\frac{f(x; \mu, \sigma^2)}{f(y; \mu, \sigma^2)} = \exp\left\{-\frac{1}{2\sigma^2}\left[\Sigma x_i^2 - \Sigma y_i^2 - 2\mu(\Sigma x_i - \Sigma y_i)\right]\right\}$$

This is independent of the parameters (μ, σ^2) if and only if *both* $\Sigma x_i^2 = \Sigma y_i^2$ and $\Sigma x_i = \Sigma y_i$. Therefore, $(\Sigma X_i^2, \Sigma X_i)$ is a minimal sufficient statistic for the normal family. Since these uniquely determine $\bar{X}$ and s_x^2 and conversely, the pair $(\bar{X}, s_x^2)$ is also minimal sufficient.

In each of the above examples there is a minimal sufficient statistic of the same dimension as the parameter indexing the family of states. This is not always the case; in the case of a Cauchy family, for instance, the minimal sufficient statistic is the order statistic, and any further reduction sacrifices sufficiency.

4.5.5   The Exponential Family

The *exponential family* of distributions (introduced in Section 3.5) consists of those distributions with densities or probability functions expressible in the following form:

$$f(x; \theta) = B(\theta) \exp[Q(\theta)R(x)] \, h(x).$$

The Bernoulli, binomial, Poisson, geometric, and gamma distributions, for instance, were seen to be included in this family.

A minimal sufficient statistic for the family is found by using the technique given in Section 4.5.4. The joint density function (or probability function) for a random sample X is

$$f(x; \theta) = B^n(\theta) \exp [Q(\theta) \sum R(x_i)] \prod h(x_i).$$

The ratio of this density at x to its value at y is

$$\frac{f(x; \theta)}{f(y; \theta)} = \exp [Q(\theta)\{\sum R(x_i) - \sum R(y_i)\}] \prod \frac{h(x_i)}{h(y_i)}.$$

This is independent of θ if and only if $\sum R(x_i) = \sum R(y_i)$, and therefore $t(X) = \sum R(X_i)$ is minimal sufficient.

The statistic $t(X)$ has itself a distribution that belongs to the exponential family. To show this in the continuous case would require transformation of a multiple integral; the verification in the discrete case is simpler and proceeds as follows. The probability function for $t(X)$ is

$$p(t; \theta) = P(\sum R(X_i) = t)$$

$$= \sum_{R(x_i)=t} B^n(\theta) \exp [Q(\theta) \sum R(x_i)] \prod h(x_i)$$

$$= b(\theta) \exp [tQ(\theta)]H(t),$$

where $b(\theta) = B^n(\theta)$ and

$$H(t) = \sum_{R(x_i)=t} \prod h(x_i).$$

Clearly, then, $p(t; \theta)$ belongs to the exponential family.

EXAMPLE 4–42.   The number of trials preceding the first "Heads" in a sequence of independent Bernoulli trials has the probability function

$$f(x; p) = p(1 - p)^x = pe^{x \log (1-p)}.$$

The statistic $X_1 + \cdots + X_n$, the sum of n independent observations, is then minimal sufficient, and has a probability function that is again of the exponential family. This sum is the number of "Tails" occurring before the nth "Heads", and has the negative binomial distribution—which has been shown to be in the exponential family in Section 3.5.

For the case of a multidimensional parameter $\boldsymbol{\theta} = (\theta_1, \ldots, \theta_k)$, the exponential family of distributions has a density (or probability function) of the form

$$f(x; \boldsymbol{\theta}) = B(\boldsymbol{\theta}) \exp [Q_1(\boldsymbol{\theta})R_1(x) + \cdots + Q_k(\boldsymbol{\theta})R_k(x)]h(x).$$

Given a random sample X, the k-dimensional statistic

$$[\sum R_1(X_i), \ldots, \sum R_k(X_i)]$$

(sums extending from $i = 1$ to $i = n$, the sample size) is a minimal sufficient statistic for the family.

It is interesting that under certain regularity assumptions, and if the set on which $f(x; \boldsymbol{\theta})$ is positive does not depend on $\boldsymbol{\theta}$, then[11] if there exists a k-dimensional sufficient statistic on a random sample of size n from $f(x; \boldsymbol{\theta})$ with $n > k$, the distribution $f(x; \boldsymbol{\theta})$ must belong to the exponential family. In this sense the exponential family consists of those distributions for which there is a sufficient statistic of the same dimension as that of the parameter.

Problems

4-86. Determine a minimal sufficient statistic for each of the following families of distributions, assuming a random sample

(a) Bernoulli ($p^x(1 - p)^{1-x}$, $x = 0, 1$);
(b) normal with known variance;
(c) negative exponential ($\lambda e^{-\lambda x}$, $x > 0$);
(d) normal with mean 0 $\left\{ \dfrac{1}{(2\pi v)^{1/2}} \exp\left[-x^2/(2v) \right] \right\}$.
(e) Rayleigh $\{(z/v) \exp\left[-z^2/(2v) \right]\}$;
(f) Maxwell $\{(2u^2/\pi\sigma^3) \exp\left[-u^2/(2\sigma^2) \right]\}$.

4-87. Obtain the minimal sufficient partition for the family of distributions in Problem 4-75. (The three distributions in the family were as follows: (.4, .2, .4), (.6, .3, .1), (.2, .1, .7) for (z_1, z_2, z_3), respectively.)

4-88. Determine the minimal sufficient statistic for sampling without replacement from a finite Bernoulli population.

4-89. Show that the sufficient statistic obtained in Problem 4-85 is actually minimal sufficient.

4-90. Derive the likelihood ratio (see Example 4-38) as the *minimal* sufficient statistic for a problem with just two states of nature.

4.6 Some Properties of Procedures

A number of properties of statistical procedures have been formulated over the years, including those of *admissibility, efficiency, consistency*, and *unbiasedness*. These have been proposed and treated as good properties, and it is evident that the names were chosen to suggest goodness. Actually, none of them (by itself) guarantees a uniformly small risk function. It is essential to understand the significance and limitations of each, and they will be treated in more detail in the next two chapters, in problems of estimation and testing hypotheses.

General definitions are possible for most of the listed properties, definitions

---

[11] See Lehmann, E. [13], p. 51.

that serve to unify the notions and provide for problems *other* than the testing of hypotheses (two action problems) or the estimation of parameters.

The notion of *admissibility* was defined in Section 4.2.3 for the no-data problem. In general, the definition is the same, except that it is applied to the risk function. That is, d dominates d_1 if

$$R(\theta, d_1) \geq R(\theta, d), \qquad \text{for all } \theta.$$

A procedure would be called *inadmissible* if it were strictly dominated by some other procedure. However, whether this is bad or not depends on the degree to which it is dominated, as discussed in Section 4.2.3.

If two procedures d and d' are both based on samples of a given size, and if d dominates d' strictly, d can be thought of as more *efficient* than d', since in general it would take more observations using d' to equalize the risks. The relative efficiency of d' with respect to d might be defined as the ratio of the risk of d to that of d' for a given sample size, or as the ratio of sample sizes needed to make the risks equal, if this be possible. (These ratios need not agree and would usually depend on the state θ.) Further, the risk then often has a lower bound or minimum achievable risk (in restricted classes of procedures) that can be used as the basis of a measure of "absolute" efficiency. This will be discussed in Chapter 5.

A procedure d is said to be *consistent* if the expected regret tends to zero as the sample size becomes infinite. This implies that the "procedure" include instructions as to how to apply it to samples of different sizes. That is, consistency applies to a *sequence* of procedures, one for each sample size. Presumably, if the expected regret tends to zero, it will be small for "large" samples; this is of little comfort if a large sample is expensive. Indeed, one is always forced to work with finite samples. Nevertheless, consistent procedures frequently turn out to have good properties even for small samples.

A procedure based on the statistic Z is said to be *unbiased* if for all states of nature θ and θ',

$$E_\theta[\ell(\theta', d(Z))] \geq E_\theta[\ell(\theta, d(Z))],$$

where again the subscript on E denotes the states to be used in computing the expectation. This can be interpreted to sound very plausible: Thinking of $\ell(\theta, a)$ as related to how close the action a comes to the action, which should correspond to θ, the relation states that the decision procedure d comes closer *on the average* to the correct decision than to an incorrect one. Yet, despite the appealing sound of this statement, fulfillment of the condition of unbiasedness by no means guarantees a good procedure.

For instance, if a sample of 1,000 is to be used, a procedure based on only the first observation in the sample can be unbiased even though it ignores the remaining 999 observations. Indeed, it can and does happen that by restricting his attention to unbiased procedures, one eliminates procedures that are better in terms of risk than those he keeps.

EXAMPLE 4-47.   In Problem 4-47 it was seen that for the problem of estimating the mean μ of a negative exponential distribution with quadratic regret, the decision function $d(\bar{X}) = n\bar{X}/(n + 1)$ has the risk

$$R(\mu, d) = \frac{\mu^2}{n + 1}.$$

This is uniformly smaller than the risk μ^2/n found in Example 4-20 for the procedure $d^*(\bar{X}) = \bar{X}$. Yet (Problem 4-91) d is biased and d^* is unbiased.

4.7   Monotone Problems and Procedures

Many statistical problems are concerned with families of distributions indexed by a *single* real parameter. Of these, some are of a type called *monotone*—problems in which the loss function has a monotone character and in which the family of distributions has a monotone likelihood ratio.

A regret function $r(\theta, a)$ defines a function of θ for each action—a family of regret curves each identified by a particular action. These curves will lie above the θ-axis, except that some will be zero for certain states θ. When a regret is zero, the corresponding action is optimal or best for that state. The set of θ-values for which a given regret curve is zero will be called the *optimality set* for that action. A regret function $r(\theta, a)$ will be called a monotone regret function if the regret curve it defines satisfy the following conditions:

(1) The optimality sets for the various actions are intervals (finite, infinite, single point, or empty) which constitute a partition of the parameter space.

(2) For each action, the regret curve does not decrease as θ moves away from the optimality set in either direction.

(3) Any two regret curves intersect at most once. (That is, the difference $r(\theta, a_1) - r(\theta, a_2)$ changes sign at most once for a given pair of actions a_1 and a_2.)

Figure 4-18 gives three examples of a monotone regret function. In Figure 4-18 (a) is shown a quadratic regret $(\theta - a)^2$ for the estimation problem, although curves are drawn for only three values of a. For each action a, there is just one parameter value $(\theta = a)$ for which a is the correct action, and these points of zero regret fill out the θ axis; it is also clear that the other two conditions are fulfilled. Figures 4-18 (b) and (c) show monotone regret functions for the two- and three-action cases, respectively.

In Figure 4–19 are shown regret functions that are *not* monotone. In (a), the first two conditions are fulfilled but (3) is not, since $r(\theta, a_1) - r(\theta, a_2)$ changes sign twice. In (b), all three conditions are violated.

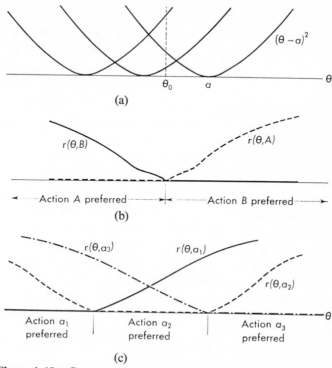

(a)

(b)

(c)

Figure 4–18.   Some monotone regret functions.

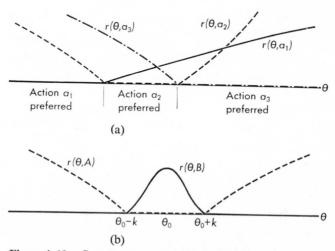

(a)

(b)

Figure 4–19.   Some nonmonotone regret functions.

EXAMPLE 4-48.   Lots of a certain product (say, eggs) are to be classified into three grades according to the average lot quality θ. That is, if $\theta > \theta_2$, the lot is grade A. If $\theta_1 < \theta < \theta_2$, it is grade B; and if $\theta < \theta_1$, it is grade C. The classification is to be done on the basis of a sample from each lot. Suppose that the penalties for misclassifications are those given in the following regret table:

		Lot Quality (State of Nature, θ)		
		$\theta < \theta_1$	$\theta_1 < \theta < \theta_2$	$\theta > \theta_2$
	A	2	1	0
Actions	B	1	0	1
(grade assigned)	C	0	1	2

This regret function satisfies (1)–(3), and so is monotone.

A family of distributions indexed by a real parameter θ is said to have a *monotone likelihood ratio* if for each sample X with joint density $f(x;\theta)$ there is a statistic $t(X)$ such that for each pair of states θ and θ' with $\theta > \theta'$ the likelihood ratio $f(x;\theta)/f(x;\theta')$ is a nondecreasing function of $t(x)$. (The "nondecreasing" could be replaced by "monotone," since a nonincreasing function of $t(x)$ would be a nondecreasing function of $-t(x)$. However, it is convenient to make the monotoneity specifically nondecreasing.)

EXAMPLE 4-49.   Consider the family of negative exponential distributions, with density $\lambda e^{-\lambda x}$, $x > 0$. The likelihood ratio, for two parameter values λ_1 and λ_2 is

$$\prod \frac{\lambda_1 \exp(-\lambda_1 x_i)}{\lambda_2 \exp(-\lambda_2 x_i)} = \left(\frac{\lambda_1}{\lambda_2}\right)^n \exp[-(\lambda_1 - \lambda_2)\sum x_i] = g(-\sum x_i),$$

where $g(u)$ is $\exp[(\lambda_1 - \lambda_2)u]$, an increasing function of u if $\lambda_1 > \lambda_2$. Hence, the family has a monotone likelihood ratio in terms of the statistic $-\sum x_i$. Observe that the likelihood ratio could also be expressed as $h(1/\sum x_i)$, where $h(v)$ is $\exp[-(\lambda_1 - \lambda_2)/v]$, again an increasing function of $\lambda_1 > \lambda_2$. Notice, too, that if the family had been parametrized by $\theta = 1/\lambda$, the likelihood ratio would be monotone in terms of the statistic $\bar{X}$.

If a likelihood ratio $f(x;\theta)/f(x;\theta')$ is monotone in terms of a statistic $T = t(X)$, then the larger the value of T that is observed, the greater is the advantage (in the sense of Section 4.4.4) of the explanation provided by state θ over the explanation given by θ'. This suggests the kind of linking of the parameter values to the values of the statistic that is needed in inference. Thus, whereas what can often be said is that the larger the θ the larger T tends to be, what is needed is justification for the inference that a large T-value means a large θ-value.

EXAMPLE 4–50.   Consider sampling without replacement from a population of N objects, M of type 1 and $N - M$ of type 0. The family of distributions for a sample of size n is indexed by M, and it was shown in Problem 3–22 that the likelihood ratio is monotone in terms of the number Y of objects of type 1 in the sample. The larger the Y, then, the "better" the explanation by a large value of M than a small value of M. (Again, "better" is based on the notion that the size of the likelihood function measures the success of a state of nature in explaining an observed result.)

EXAMPLE 4–51.   Consider a one-parameter exponential family of distributions:

$$f(x; \theta) = A(\theta) \exp [Q(\theta)R(x)] h(x),$$

and a sample with joint density function

$$f(x; \theta) = B(\theta) \exp[Q(\theta)S(x)] h(x).$$

The likelihood ratio for θ and θ' is

$$\frac{f(x; \theta)}{f(x; \theta')} = \frac{B(\theta)}{B(\theta')} \exp \{[Q(\theta) - Q(\theta')]S(x)\}.$$

If $Q(\theta)$ is a nondecreasing function of θ, then $Q(\theta) - Q(\theta') \geq 0$ if $\theta > \theta'$, and the likelihood ratio is an increasing function of $S(x)$. Thus, the family has a monotone likelihood ratio for such Q's. If the sample is a random sample, then $S(x) = \sum R(x_i)$.

To describe the known results concerning monotone problems it is necessary to define the notion of a *monotone procedure*. In a monotone decision problem, in which the likelihood ratio is monotone in terms of the statistic $T = t(X)$, a decision function $d(X)$ is said to be monotone provided that the inequality $t(X) \leq t(Y)$, for any two given samples X and Y, is equivalent to the statement that the optimality set for the action $d(X)$ is not to the right of the optimality set for $d(Y)$. This means simply that the axis of values of $t(X)$ is partitioned by the decision rule in a manner that corresponds to the partition of the parameter axis by the optimality sets. Thus, if there are just *two* actions, the parameter axis is partitioned by the regret function into two sets, $\theta < \theta^*$ and $\theta > \theta^*$ (with $\theta = \theta^*$ put into either one); and a monotone procedure is defined by a value t^* that divides the T-axis into $T \leq t^*$ and $T > t^*$, the former inequality calling for the action corresponding to $\theta < \theta^*$, and the latter for the action corresponding to $\theta > \theta^*$. If there are *three* available actions, a monotone rule is defined by points t_1 and t_2 such that $T < t_1$ calls for the action that is best for small θ, $T > t_2$ calls for the action that is best for large θ, and $t_1 < T < t_2$ calls for the action that is best for intermediate θ. And so on, for any finite number of actions. For an estimation problem, a monotone procedure announces as an estimate of θ the value of a statistic that is a monotone increasing function of $t(X)$.

The action corresponding to one of the $n - 1$ boundary points can be given by putting the boundary point into one or the other of the contiguous sets, either by specifying this at the outset or by the toss of a (biased) coin. The decision rule in the latter case would be a randomized or mixed strategy, and would be defined by a set of probabilities, one for each boundary point (together with the specification of those points).

EXAMPLE 4–52.   Consider again the (egg) classification problem of Example 4–48, and suppose that the classification is to be made on the basis of the weight of a single egg taken from the lot. If this weight X is (for practical purposes) normally distributed with given variance and mean μ, the family of distributions of X (as indexed by μ) has a monotone likelihood ratio in terms of X, since these distributions are in the exponential family with $R(x) = x$. A *monotone procedure* is then defined by four constants: x_1, x_2, p_1, p_2, and carried out as follows: If $X < x_1$, classify the lot as C; if $x_1 < X < x_2$, classify it as B; if $X > x_2$, classify it as A; if $X = x_1$, classify it as C or B according to the toss of a "coin" with $p = p_1$; if $X = x_2$, classify it as B or A according to the toss of a "coin" with $p = p_2$.

The class of all monotone procedures has been found[12] to be *essentially complete* for monotone problems with finitely many actions, and for the monotone estimation problem. That is, for any procedure *not* in the class there is one *in* the class that is at least as good (as measured by risk) for all θ. It can also be shown,[12] subject to increasingly less general conditions as n increases, that the monotone procedures for a monotone problem with n actions are admissible. (That is, not only do the monotone procedures include essentially all of the admissible ones, they include nothing but admissible ones.) These matters will not be investigated further here. Indeed, although the existence of such results should give some assurance that restricting candidate procedures for monotone problems to monotone procedures is justifiable, the concepts of this section will be used in the remaining chapters only to obtain uniformly most powerful tests for certain testing problems.

Problems

4–91.   Using the definition of an unbiased procedure, show that the procedures d^* and d in Example 4–47 are, respectively, unbiased and biased (assuming a quadratic regret), as claimed.

4–92.   Show that the regret function $r(\theta, a) = |\theta - a|^\alpha$ for $\alpha > 0$ is monotone. (The state θ and the action a are both real numbers.)

---

[12] These results are obtained by S. Karlin and H. Rubin in "The theory of decision procedures for distributions with monotone likelihood ratios," *Annals Math. Stat.* **27**, 272–299 (1956). They discuss the results in a paper at a somewhat more elementary level in *Jour. Amer. Stat. Assn.* **51**, 637–643 (1956).

4-93. Obtain a statistic in terms of which the likelihood ratio is monotone in the case of a random sample from

(a) The Bernoulli family;
(b) The Poisson family;
(c) The normal family with known variance;
(d) The normal family with known mean.

4-94. Show that for a single observation from the Cauchy family with density $f(x; \theta) = [\pi(1 + (x - \theta)^2)]^{-1}$ the likelihood ratio is not a monotone function of x. [*Hint*: This can be seen geometrically, interpreting $1 + y^2$ with the aid of the Pythagorean theorem.]

4-95. Given the two possible distributions for Z (labeled θ_1 and θ_2) in the following table of probabilities, determine a statistic $T = t(Z)$ such that the likelihood ratio is monotone in terms of T.

	z_1	z_2	z_3	z_4	z_5
θ_1	.2	.3	.1	.3	.1
θ_2	.3	.1	.3	.2	.1

4-96. Suppose that nature is in one of states θ_1, θ_2, θ_3, and that an observation X is made having a normal distribution with unit variance and mean -2 under θ_1, mean 0 under θ_2, and mean $+2$ under θ_3. Let the loss function be as given in the following table:

		θ_1	θ_2	θ_3
Action	A	0	1	2
	B	1	0	1
	C	2	1	0

Consider the following decision rules:

$d_1(X) = A$, if $X < -1$; B, if $-1 < X < 1$; C, if $X > 1$.
$d_2(X) = A$, if $X < -1.5$; B, if $-1.5 < X < 1.5$; C, if $X > 1.5$.
$d_3(X) = A$, if $X > 0$; C, if $X < 0$.
$d_4(X) = B$, if $X < -1$; C, if $-1 < X < 1$; A, if $X > 1$.

Calculate the risk function for each rule. Which rules are monotone?

CHAPTER **5**

ESTIMATION

The problem of estimation will now be treated in greater detail. Although such problems have been introduced in Chapter 4 as special decision problems, it will be noticed that the development of this chapter is not always completely in the spirit of statistical decision theory. The unifying notions of decision theory were introduced after the estimation problem had already been intensively studied.

The estimation problems to be considered are those called *parametric*. It is known or assumed in these problems that the distribution of probability in an experiment of chance is one of a family of distributions indexed by one or more real parameters. The problem is that of determining estimates for the unknown parameters of the model on the basis of observations on the experiment. The framework of decision theory is thought of as including the estimation problem by considering the "action" to be taken as the announcement of the estimated value. The action space is then coincident with the parameter space.

Thus, it is desired to estimate the parameter vector $(\theta_1, \ldots, \theta_k)$ in the density function (or probability function, in a discrete case)

$$f(x; \theta_1, \ldots, \theta_k)$$

on the basis of the observations $X_1, \ldots, X_n$. A "decision function" in this problem is a function associating with each possible sample point $(x_1, \ldots, x_n)$ an estimate $(T_1, \ldots, T_k)$, T_j being the estimate for θ_j. This function defines a *statistic*

$$(T_1, \ldots, T_k) = t(X_1, \ldots, X_n)$$

called an *estimator* of $(\theta_1, \ldots, \theta_k)$. In the common case of a single parameter, an estimator is a real-valued function $T = t(X_1, \ldots, X_n)$.

Much of the traditional practice in estimation problems involves implicitly a *quadratic* loss function of the form (in the case of a single parameter)

$$\ell(\theta, a) = A(\theta)(\theta - a)^2,$$

where $A(\theta)$ is a specified weighting factor, frequently assumed for simplicity to be a constant. This quadratic loss function has a zero minimum in a for each state θ, and so the regret is the same as the loss. The risk function then is the expected loss or regret:

$$R(\theta, T) = A(\theta)E_\theta[(\theta - T)^2].$$

Strictly speaking, this quadratic loss cannot measure utility, in view of the earlier agreement that utility be bounded. It can happen with a quadratic loss that the maximum risk is infinite for all estimates, which would mean that all estimates are minimax. For minimax considerations, then, the loss must be modified; but for other purposes the unboundedness of a quadratic loss does not seem to be troublesome.

5.1 Properties of Estimators

Of the properties of procedures defined in Chapter 4, three are discussed here—bias, consistency, and efficiency, in terms of a quadratic loss and for the case of a single parameter. These three properties are not necessarily the most significant, but they are the most commonly encountered in treatments of estimation. It is important to know what the properties do and do not mean.

Given the simple loss $(T - \theta)^2$, incurred when the estimate $T = t(X)$ is used and the actual parameter value is θ, the risk function is the expected value:

$$R(\theta, t) = E[(t(X) - \theta)^2] = \operatorname{var} T + (ET - \theta)^2.$$

The quantity $ET - \theta$ is called the *bias* in T as an estimate of θ, and denoted by $b_T(\theta)$. With this notation the risk is

$$R(\theta, t) = \text{var } T + [b_T(\theta)]^2.$$

The risk will be small, then, if and only if both the variance of the estimate and the bias in the estimate are small. However, choosing T to minimize one term does not necessarily minimize the other; what is really wanted is a small sum—a small mean squared error between the announced and actual values of θ.

5.1.1 Bias

A procedure for an estimation problem is a statistic. A statistic T, then, is *unbiased* according to the definition of Chapter 4 if

$$E_\theta[\ell(\theta_1, T)] \geq E_\theta[\ell(\theta, T)], \qquad \text{for all } \theta, \theta_1.$$

Using the quadratic loss $A(T - \theta)^2$ for an estimator T of θ, this condition for unbiasedness becomes

$$E_\theta[(T - \theta_1)^2] \geq E_\theta[(T - \theta)^2], \qquad \text{for all } \theta, \theta_1.$$

The condition is satisfied by an estimator T whose mean is θ, since the right member is then the variance of T, which is indeed the smallest second moment of T. Conversely, if the condition is satisfied, it follows (upon expanding the squares, averaging term by term, cancelling, and forming squares again) that

$$[E_\theta(T) - \theta_1]^2 \geq [E_\theta(T) - \theta]^2, \qquad \text{all } \theta_1;$$

and therefore since this *is* true for $\theta_1 = E_\theta(T)$, the right member must be zero—which implies that $E_\theta(T) = \theta$. That is, under the assumption of a quadratic loss function, the property of unbiasedness becomes equivalent to the property that the distribution of the estimator T be "centered" at the parameter θ in the sense of expectation.

Using the loss function $|T - \theta|$, one would find that the condition of unbiasedness is equivalent to the condition that the distribution of the estimator T be centered at θ in the sense of the median; that is, that the median of T be θ. An estimator with this property[1] is sometimes called *median unbiased*.

The condition that $E(T) = \theta$ is often taken as the *defining* condition for an unbiased estimator, and what has just been shown is that this is consistent with the general definition of Chapter 4 in the case of a quadratic loss function.

[1] See Lehmann, E. [13], p. 22.

EXAMPLE 5–1.   Because

$$E\left(\frac{1}{n} \sum X_i^k\right) = E(X^k),$$

it follows that the sample kth moment about zero is an unbiased estimate of the population kth moment about zero.

EXAMPLE 5–2.   In Section 4.3.3, the expected value of the sample variance was computed, with the result

$$E\left[\frac{1}{n} \sum (X_i - \bar{X})^2\right] = \sigma^2(1 - 1/n).$$

The sample variance is therefore biased as an estimate of the population variance. The amount of the bias is $-\sigma^2/n$, which is negligible for large samples.

If an estimator has a bias proportional to the parameter estimated, multiplication by a constant yields an unbiased estimator. For, if $E(T) = k\theta$, then $E(T/k) = \theta$.

EXAMPLE 5–3.   Consider the statistic

$$\check{s}_x^2 = \frac{1}{n-1} \sum_{i=1}^{n} (X_i - \bar{X})^2.$$

This is just $n/(n - 1)$ times what has been termed the sample variance, and its expectation is therefore

$$E(\check{s}_x^2) = \frac{n}{n-1} E(s_x^2) = \sigma^2.$$

The statistic $\check{s}_x^2$ is then unbiased as an estimate of σ^2.

Despite the un-American connotations of the word "bias," a biased estimator is not necessarily to be rejected as inferior. Indeed, there are slightly biased estimates that are very good in other respects, and certainly there are unbiased estimates which no one in his right mind would use (see Problem 5–1). The point is that arranging things so that the center of gravity of the distribution of an estimator is at θ is not enough to obtain an estimated value that is close to θ.

5.1.2   Standard Error of Estimate

One classical approach to estimation has been to consider estimates with zero bias, and then in this class to choose the one with smallest variance. At any rate, given $b_T(\theta) = 0$ the variance of the estimate is a measure of its success. Its positive square root, or the standard deviation of the estimate, is also a measure of success of the estimation and is measured in the same units as the parameter being estimated. Unfortunately, however, this standard deviation often depends on unknown population moments. For large samples, these population moments are approximated quite closely by corresponding sample moments. The *standard error of estimate* in using an estimator with zero bias is defined to be the approximation to the standard deviation of the estimator obtained by replacing any population moments that are involved in it by corresponding sample moments. It is a measure of reliability of the estimation process.

EXAMPLE 5–4. Consider a large sample from a population with unknown mean μ and unknown variance σ^2. Because the sample mean converges in probability to the population mean, it is reasonable to approximate the latter by the former for a large sample. The estimator $\bar{X}$ is unbiased, having mean μ, so the risk is the variance of $\bar{X}$, which involves σ^2:

$$\text{var } \bar{X} = \sigma^2/n \doteq s_x^2/n.$$

The standard error of estimate using $\bar{X}$, called also the standard error of the mean, is the square root: $s_x/\sqrt{n}$.

5.1.3 Consistency

A sequence of procedures was called *consistent* in Chapter 4 if the expected regret approaches zero for each state, as the sample size becomes infinite. With the assumption of a quadratic risk function, consistency of a sequence of estimators $\{T_n\}$ means that $T_n \to \theta$ in quadratic mean:

$$\lim_{n \to \infty} E[(T_n - \theta)^2] = 0.$$

This condition can be written

$$\lim_{n \to \infty} [\text{var } T_n + b^2(T_n)] = 0,$$

(where again $b(T_n)$ is the bias in T_n) and is satisfied if and only if *both* the variance and the bias of T_n tend to zero as n becomes infinite.

It was seen in Section 2.5 that convergence in quadratic mean to a constant implies convergence in probability to that constant. Thus, if $\{T_n\}$ is consistent in the above sense, it is also true that T_n tends to θ in probability:

$$\lim P(|T_n - \theta| \geq \epsilon) = 0, \quad \text{for any } \epsilon > 0.$$

This convergence in probability of T_n to θ is the condition that traditionally defines consistency of $\{T_n\}$. Since existence of second moments is not required, it is more widely applicable. (Of course, if T_n does not have second moments, quadratic loss should not be used.) If it becomes necessary to distinguish between consistency in the sense of convergence in probability and consistency in the sense of convergence in quadratic mean one can write "consistent (in prob.)" for the former and "consistent (in q.m.)" for the latter.

EXAMPLE 5–5.   The fact that sample moments tend in probability to corresponding population moments was discussed in Section 4.3.3. The sample moments are therefore consistent (in prob.) estimates of the corresponding population moments.

EXAMPLE 5–6.   Consider the estimate $\tilde{s}_x^2$ of σ^2, which was seen in Example 5–3 to be unbiased. Since this differs from the consistent estimate s_x^2 by a factor that tends to 1, it, too, is consistent.

If a statistic T_n has a variance that tends to zero while its expectation converges to k, a number different from θ, then T_n converges in probability—but to the wrong value, k. Consequently, even though the significance of bias has been mimimized, an estimator that has a bias which does not disappear as n becomes infinite would have to be modified to remove the bias in order to obtain an estimator which is consistent (in q.m.).

EXAMPLE 5–7.   Consider the one-parameter family of Cauchy distributions defined by the density

$$f(x; \theta) = \frac{1/\pi}{1 + (x - \theta)^2}.$$

This is symmetrical about θ, but $\bar{X}$ is not a consistent estimate of θ. For, the characteristic function of the sample mean is

$$\exp\left[-n|t/n| + n(it\theta/n)\right] = \exp\left[-|t| + it\theta\right],$$

which is the characteristic function of the population itself (according to Problem 2–140). That is, the distribution of the sample mean is the same as that of the population, no matter how large the sample. The sample mean cannot converge in probability to any constant, let alone θ.

Problems

5–1.   Show that in a random sample of size n, the first observation obtained, X_1, is an unbiased estimate of the population mean. Show also that the average of any two sample observations is an unbiased estimate of the population mean.

5–2.   Determine the bias of $\sum (X_i - \mu)^2/n$ as an estimate of σ^2, in a problem in which $\mu = E(X)$ is given.

5–3.   Determine the condition under which $\sum a_i X_i$ is an unbiased estimate of $E(X)$.

5–4.   Show that if T is an unbiased estimate of θ, $aT + b$ is an unbiased estimate of $a\theta + b$. Is T^2 an unbiased estimate of θ^2?

5–5.   Determine the standard error of estimate in the relative frequency of success in n independent trials of an experiment as an estimate of the probability of success (p) in a single trial.

5–6. Determine the standard error of the mean as an estimate of the mean of a negative exponential population.

5–7. Show that the estimates of Problem 5–1 are not consistent.

5–8. Show that the estimate of Problem 5–2 is consistent.

5–9. Consider a random sample from a uniform population on $[0, \theta]$. Given that the density of the largest of the observations in the sample is $f_{X_{(n)}}(u) = nu^{n-1}/\theta^n$, $0 < u < \theta$ (you might try to derive this!), show that the statistic $X_{(n)}$ is a consistent estimate of θ.

5.1.4   *Efficiency*

A procedure d was said in Chapter 4 to be more efficient than a procedure d' based on a sample of the same size if

$$R(\theta, d) \leq R(\theta, d'),$$

with strict inequality for some θ. With quadratic loss, this condition would say that an estimator T of θ is more efficient than T' if

$$E[(T - \theta)^2] \leq E[(T' - \theta)^2],$$

with strict inequality for some θ. The relative efficiency of T' with respect to T is the ratio

$$e(T', T) = \frac{E[(T - \theta)^2]}{E[(T' - \theta)^2]}.$$

This would generally depend on θ, but it turns out frequently to be independent of θ. In the case of unbiased estimators it is just the ratio of their variances, and the most efficient such estimator would be the one with minimum variance.

EXAMPLE 5–8.   The linear combination of observations $\sum a_i X_i$ is an unbiased estimate of $E(X)$ if $\sum a_i = 1$. The particular combination that is most efficient is the one which minimizes

$$\text{var}\left(\sum a_i X_i\right) = \sum a_i^2 \text{ var } X_i = (\text{var } X) \sum a_i^2,$$

or the one that minimizes $\sum a_i^2$, subject to $\sum a_i = 1$.

For such restricted minimization problems it will be convenient to have the tool of the method of Lagrange's multipliers. It is shown in advanced calculus that the minimum of $g(y)$ subject to $h(y) = K$ is found by locating the minimum of the function $g(y) - \lambda h(y)$. This will not be proved here; but it is easily seen that if y satisfies $h(y) = K$ and minimizes $g(y) - \lambda h(y)$ for some λ, then for any other y' such that $h(y') = K$,

$$g(y) - \lambda h(y) \leq g(y') - \lambda h(y'),$$

or, since $h(y) = h(y')$,

$$g(y) \leq g(y').$$

Thus y is the desired minimizing quantity.

Applying this method in the case at hand, one minimizes the quantity $\sum a_i^2 - \lambda \sum a_i$. The derivative of this with respect to a_j must vanish:

$$2a_j - \lambda = 0, \qquad j = 1, \ldots, n.$$

The minimizing a's are therefore all equal, and equal to $1/n$. The sample mean is thus the most efficient unbiased linear combination of the observations in a random sample.

An absolute measure of efficiency of an estimate would require that its mean square deviation from the parameter being estimated be compared with a lower bound or absolute minimum of such mean square deviations, if one that is not zero exists. The "information inequality" is aimed at providing such a lower bound.

The level of presentation here precludes a rigorous derivation of the information inequality, but the following manipulations for the continuous case indicate the line of reasoning used to establish the inequality.[2]

The statistic $T = t(X)$ based on a sample X from $f(x; \theta)$ is considered as an estimator for the parameter θ, assumed now to be one-dimensional. Let the joint density function of the sample observations be

$$f(x_1, \ldots, x_n; \theta) = f(x; \theta),$$

and let V denote the following random variable:

$$V = \frac{\partial}{\partial \theta} \log f(X; \theta).$$

The expected value of V is zero:

$$E(V) = \int \frac{1}{f(x; \theta)} \left(\frac{\partial}{\partial \theta} f(x; \theta)\right) f(x; \theta) \, dx = \frac{d}{d\theta} \int f(x; \theta) \, dx = 0.$$

The variance of V is therefore its expected square, and the covariance of the random variables V and T is their expected product:

$$\mathrm{cov}\,(V, T) = E(VT) = E\left[T \frac{\partial}{\partial \theta} \log f(X; \theta)\right]$$

$$= \int t(x) \frac{1}{f(x; \theta)} \left(\frac{\partial}{\partial \theta} f(x; \theta)\right) f(x; \theta) \, dx$$

$$= \frac{d}{d\theta} E(T) = \frac{d}{d\theta} [\theta + b_T(\theta)] = 1 + b_T'(\theta),$$

where $b_T(\theta)$ is the bias in T.

[2] See Cramer, H. [4], Section 32.3.

The information inequality now results from the fact that a correlation is numerically bounded by 1—that is, from Schwarz' inequality (see Section 2.3.3):

$$\text{var } T \geq \frac{[\text{cov }(V, T)]^2}{\text{var } V} = \frac{[1 + b_T{}'(\theta)]^2}{I(\theta)},$$

where

$$I(\theta) = \text{var } V = E\left\{\left[\frac{\partial}{\partial \theta} \log f(X;\theta)\right]^2\right\}.$$

The quantity $I(\theta)$ is called the *information* in the sample. (The information inequality is also known as the Cramér–Rao inequality, or the Frechét inequality.)

The validity of the above derivation depends on fulfillment of conditions that permit interchange of integration and differentiation operations, on the existence and integrability of the various partial derivatives, on the differentiability of $b_T(\theta)$, and on the nonvanishing of $I(\theta)$. In the case of a discrete random variable with finitely many values, the $f(x; \theta)$ is a probability, the expectations are finite sums, and the interchange of differentiation and summation is permitted.

If X and Y are independent samples from $f(x; \theta)$, the information in the combined sample is the sum of the information in X and that in Y. To see this, it is convenient to have another expression for $I(\theta)$. Let a prime denote differentiation with respect to θ, and consider V':

$$\frac{\partial V}{\partial \theta} = \frac{ff'' - (f')^2}{f^2} = \frac{f''}{f} - V^2.$$

Since

$$E\left(\frac{f''}{f}\right) = \frac{d^2}{d\theta^2} \int f(x; \theta) \, dx = 0,$$

it follows that

$$I(\theta) = E(V^2) = -E\left(\frac{\partial}{\partial \theta} V\right).$$

If now $f_1(x; \theta)$ and $f_2(y; \theta)$ are densities for X and Y, the joint density of (X, Y) is the product $f_1(x; \theta) f_2(y; \theta)$. And then

$$I_{X,Y}(\theta) = -E\left(\frac{\partial}{\partial \theta} V_{X,Y}\right) = -E\left(\frac{\partial^2}{\partial \theta^2} [\log f_1 + \log f_2]\right)$$

$$= -\left[E\left(\frac{\partial}{\partial \theta} V_X\right) + E\left(\frac{\partial}{\partial \theta} V_Y\right)\right] = I_X(\theta) + I_Y(\theta).$$

If X is a random sample from $f(x; \theta)$, the information in the sample is the sum of the informations for the individual observations, or n times the information in a single observation:

$$I(\theta) = nE\left\{\left[\frac{\partial}{\partial \theta} \log f(X; \theta)\right]\right\}^2.$$

In the class of unbiased estimators, the lower bound in the information inequality is $1/I(\theta)$, independent of which estimator is considered. The *efficiency* of an unbiased estimate T is therefore defined as

$$e(T) = \frac{1/I(\theta)}{\text{var } T}.$$

An estimator of efficiency 1 is said to be *efficient*.

EXAMPLE 5-9.   Consider a normal population with given mean μ and unknown variance v. The population density has the logarithm

$$\log f(x; v) = \frac{-(\log 2\pi)}{2} - \frac{(\log v)}{2} - \frac{(x - \mu)^2}{2v}.$$

This is differentiated with respect to v:

$$\frac{\partial}{\partial v} \log f(x; v) = \frac{-1}{2v} + \frac{(x - \mu)^2}{2v^2}$$

to obtain

$$E\left\{\left[\frac{\partial}{\partial v} \log f(X; v)\right]^2\right\} = \frac{1}{4v^4} [E(X - \mu)^4 - 2vE(X - \mu)^2 + v^2]$$

$$= \frac{1}{4v^4} (3v^2 - 2v^2 + v^2) = \frac{1}{2v^2}.$$

For a random sample of size n, then, $I(v) = n/2v^2$.

The estimate

$$v^* = \sum \frac{(X_i - \mu)^2}{n}$$

is unbiased and has variance

$$= \frac{1}{n^2} \sum \text{var } [(X_i - \mu)^2]$$

$$= \frac{1}{n} [E(X - \mu)^4 - (E[X - \mu]^2)^2].$$

Since this is equal to $1/I(v)$, the efficiency of v^* is 1.

EXAMPLE 5-10.   Consider the estimation of μ in a normal population with unit variance. The information $I(\mu)$ based on a random sample of size n is readily shown to be n. The estimate $T \equiv 0$, on the other hand, has a risk equal to μ^2 which is less than $1/I\mu) = 1/n$ for any μ between $1/\sqrt{n}$ and $-1/\sqrt{n}$. The "Cramér–Rao lower bound" might appear to be violated, except that the estimate $T \equiv 0$ is *biased* for any $\mu \neq 0$. The information inequality is just $0 \geq 0$, since var $T = 0$ and $1 + b_T'(\mu) = 0$.

The situation in which the lower bound in the information inequality is achieved proves interesting. The "inequality" is an equality if the correlation between V and T is $+1$ or -1. If this is the case, then either T is identically constant or V is a linear function of T with probability one, and conversely. The coefficients in the linear relationship between V and T can be functions of θ (written for convenience as derivatives):

$$V = A'(\theta)T + B'(\theta),$$

where again the prime denotes differentiation with respect to θ. Integrating with respect to θ, one obtains

$$\log f(X; \theta) = A(\theta)T + B(\theta) + K(X),$$

where the "constant" of integration $K(X)$ does not depend on θ but might depend on X. Equivalently:

$$f(X; \theta) = \exp [A(\theta)T + B(\theta) + K(X)]$$
$$= C(\theta) \exp[A(\theta)T] h(X),$$

which shows that $f(x; \theta)$ is in the exponential family and that T is sufficient. Conversely, if $f(x; \theta)$ is in the exponential family, the statistic T that occurs in the exponent is such that the lower bound in the information inequality is achieved. Among the class of estimators with the same bias, T has minimum variance and hence minimum risk (with a quadratic loss). If this T is unbiased, it is efficient.

By *asymptotic efficiency* is meant the limit of the efficiency as the sample size becomes infinite. In order for this limit to be a finite positive number, it is necessary that the variance of the estimator behaves asymptotically as $1/n$. The limiting or asymptotic efficiency is then

$$\lim_{n\to\infty} e(T) = \lim_{n\to\infty} \frac{1/I(\theta)}{\text{var } T} = \frac{1}{c^2 E([(\partial/\partial\theta) \log f(X; \theta)]^2)},$$

where
$$c^2 = \lim_{n\to\infty} n \text{ var } T.$$

When the asymptotic efficiency is 1, the estimator is said to be asymptotically efficient.

Asymptotic efficiency is sometimes defined even when the efficiency for finite samples is not defined for one reason or another. (The estimator may be biased or may not have moments.) If T is asymptotically normal with mean θ and variance c^2/n, the asymptotic efficiency of T is defined to be an expression given as the limit of $e(T)$ above. Whether this is meaningful in a given situation depends on the loss function; this question will not be investigated here.

Problems

5–10. Determine the efficiency of the estimates in Problem 5–1 relative to the sample mean.

5–11. Show that the sample mean is efficient in estimating the mean of a normal population with given variance.

5–12. Show that the sample mean is efficient as an estimate of p in a Bernoulli population.

5–13. Show that the sample mean is efficient in estimating the mean of a negative exponential distribution.

5–14. Determine the lower bound of the variance of unbiased estimates of the location parameter θ in the Cauchy family with density $[\pi(1 + [x - \theta]^2)]^{-1}$.

5.1.5 On Quadratic Loss

An excuse usually offered for using quadratic loss in estimation problems—assessing estimates according to their variances—is that the mathematical manipulations entailed in its use are simpler than with other loss functions. This excuse, of course, only carries weight if there are other reasons. One such reason is presented here. It applies only to the case of estimates that are normally distributed and unbiased. It will be shown that in this case a comparison of estimators on the basis of risk computed from a monotone regret function is equivalent to a comparison on the basis of risk computed from a quadratic regret function.

The monotone regret function $r(\theta, a)$ has the property that for every θ, $r(\theta, b) > r(\theta, a)$ if $b > a > \theta$ or if $b < a < \theta$. Let the risk based on this regret be denoted $R_r(\theta, T)$; the risk based on quadratic regret (since the discussion deals only with unbiased T) is just var T. Consider a normal estimator T and another normal estimator T' which is not as good as T as measured by (quadratic) risk: var $T' >$ var T. Then

$$R_r(\theta, T) = E[r(\theta, T)] = \int_{-\infty}^{\infty} r(\theta, t) \, dF_T(t)$$

$$= \int_0^1 r(\theta, F_T^{-1}(u)) \, du,$$

the last integral being obtained by a change of variable, $F_T(t) = u$. Similarly,

$$R_r(\theta, T') = \int_0^1 r(\theta, F_{T'}^{-1}(u)) \, du.$$

Now if T and T' are both unbiased and normal, the inverse functions both have the value θ at $u = 1/2$; and if var $T' >$ var T, these inverse functions are as pictured in Figure 5-1. Observe in this figure that

$$F_{T'}{}^{-1}(u) < F_T{}^{-1}(u) < \theta, \qquad \text{for } u < 1/2,$$

and

$$F_{T'}{}^{-1}(u) > F_T{}^{-1}(u) > \theta, \qquad \text{for } u > 1/2.$$

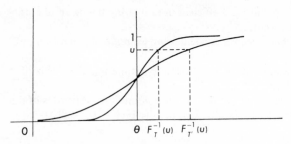

Figure 5-1.

In either case, and hence for the whole interval $0 < u < 1$,

$$r(\theta, F_T{}^{-1}) < r(\theta, F_{T'}{}^{-1}),$$

from which it follows that $R_r(\theta, T) < R_r(\theta, T')$. That is, the estimator T' which was assumed worse than T using quadratic regret is also worse than T using the monotone regret $r(\theta, a)$.

5.2 Determination of Estimators

As in the general decision problem, there is no single, best procedure for estimating the parameter of a distribution. In a given problem, it pays to consider intuitively derived estimates, Bayes estimates, minimax estimates, maximum likelihood estimates. (Of course, the minimax method does not work in the case of a quadratic or any other such unbounded loss function.) In this section the emphasis will be on the traditional method of maximum likelihood, with passing reference to the Bayes method and certain other methods not yet introduced.

5.2.1 The Method of Moments

The oldest method of determining estimates (devised by K. Pearson in about 1894) is the method of moments. If there are k parameters to be estimated, the method consists of expressing the first k population moments in terms of these k parameters, equating them to the corresponding sample moments and taking the solutions of the resulting equations as estimates of the parameters. The method usually leads to relatively simple estimates.

The estimates obtained in this way are clearly functions of the sample moments. Since the sample moments are consistent estimates of population moments, the parameter estimates will generally be consistent.

Although the asymptotic efficiency of estimates obtained by the method of moments is often less than 1, such estimates may conveniently be used as first approximations from which more efficient estimates may be obtained by other means.

EXAMPLE 5–11.   The estimate of μ^2 in any population having a mean would be the square of the sample mean, $\bar{X}^2$, according to the method of moments. This is biased but consistent. Efficiency could not be discussed without further assumptions as to the nature of the population.

EXAMPLE 5–12.   The estimate of the parameter m in the Poisson family would be, according to the method of moments, the sample mean. For, m is the population mean, and although m is also the population variance, the lowest order population moment is used.

5.2.2   Bayes Estimates

It has been seen that the Bayes action for a given observation $Z = z$ is that which minimizes the expected value of the loss with respect to the posterior distribution. This expected loss, assuming a quadratic loss function $(\theta - a)^2$, is

$$E_H(\theta - a)^2 = \int_{-\infty}^{\infty} (\theta - a)^2 \, dH(\theta),$$

where $H(\theta)$ is the distribution function for the posterior distribution. Since this expected loss is a second moment of a distribution, it is minimized when taken about the mean of the distribution. That is, the minimizing action—and hence the Bayes estimate of θ—is

$$E_H(\theta) = \int_{-\infty}^{\infty} \theta \, dH(\theta).$$

EXAMPLE 5–13.   A sequence of independent, Bernoulli trials is carried out until m successes are obtained. The joint probability function for a given sequence of results is

$$p^m(1 - p)^{\Sigma x_i},$$

where x_1 is the number of failures prior to the first success, x_2 the number between the first and second successes, and so on. (Clearly $\sum X_i$ is minimal sufficient.)

Assuming a uniform prior distribution for p on $0 < p < 1$, the unconditional probability function is

$$f(x) = \int_0^1 p^m (1 - p)^{\Sigma x_i} \, dp = \frac{m! \, (\sum x_i)!}{(m + \sum x_i + 1)!}.$$

The posterior density for p is the integrand divided by the value of the integral, and the mean of p with respect to this posterior distribution is the Bayes estimate:

$$E_h p = \int_0^1 p \cdot \frac{p^m (1 - p)^K}{f(x)} \, dp = \frac{(m + 1)! \, (m + K + 1)!}{m! \, (m + K + 2)!} = \frac{m + 1}{m + K + 2},$$

where $K = \sum x_i$ is the number of failures prior to the mth success. (Upon referring to Example 4–29, it is seen that the Bayes estimate with this type of sampling, called *inverse* sampling, is precisely the same as in the case of a fixed number of trials, namely, one more than the number of successes divided by two more than the number of trials. The equivalence would hold, with different answers, for any prior distribution.)

Problems

5–15.   Use the method of moments to determine the estimate of the parameter v in the Rayleigh distribution, with density

$$\frac{x}{v} \exp\left[-x^2/(2v)\right], \qquad \text{for } x > 0.$$

(See Problem 3–63 for the population moments).

5–16.   Use the method of moments to obtain estimates of the mean and variance of a normal population.

5–17.   Use the method of moments to obtain an estimate of the parameter θ in the uniform distribution on $(0, \theta)$.

5–18.   Determine the Bayes estimate of the Bernoulli parameter based on a sequence of n independent trials, assuming a prior density proportional to $p(1 - p)$, and a quadratic loss.

5–19.   Determine the Bayes estimate for the Poisson parameter m, assuming a random sample of size n from a Poisson population, a quadratic loss, and

(a) a uniform prior weighting for m,

(b) a prior density $g(m) = \lambda \exp(-\lambda m)$.

5–20.   Determine the Bayes estimate for λ in a negative exponential population with density $\lambda \exp(-\lambda x)$, $x > 0$, assuming a quadratic loss, a random sample of size n, and a uniform prior distribution for λ on $0 < \lambda < 1$.

5–21.   Given a single observation $X = x$ from a normal population with unknown mean and unit variance, a quadratic loss function and a prior density for μ that is normal with mean μ_0 and unit variance, show that the Bayes estimate of μ is the average of the observation and the center of the prior distribution, $(x + \mu_0)/2$.

5.2.3   Maximum Likelihood Estimates

According to the maximum likelihood principle given in Section 4.4.4, a state $\hat{\theta}$ is found that "best explains" a given sample X in the sense that the likelihood function

$$L(\theta) = f(X; \theta)$$

is maximized for that value $\hat{\theta}$. The action taken, then, is the one that would be best if $\hat{\theta}$ were known to be the actual state.

A reasonable regret function for estimation has the property that $r(\theta, \theta) = 0$, which means that the most appropriate action to take if $\hat{\theta}$ is the actual state is to announce $\hat{\theta}$ as the state. In particular, the quadratic regret $A(\theta)(\theta - a)^2$ has this property. A *maximum likelihood estimate*, therefore, is a value of θ that maximizes the likelihood function. If θ is *multi*dimensional, so is $\hat{\theta}$, and the components are said to be *joint* maximum likelihood estimates of the corresponding components of θ.

EXAMPLE 5–14.   Consider a system that will either operate or fail in a certain mission, and let p denote the probability of successful operation. Eight trials are conducted, with these results: S, F, S, S, S, F, S, S. The probability of observing this sequence, assuming independence of the trials, is

$$L(p) = p^6(1 - p)^2.$$

This is positive for $0 < p < 1$ and zero at $p = 1$ and at $p = 0$, so the maximum occurs in the interior of the interval $[0, 1]$ at a point where $L'(p)$ vanishes. Now,

$$L'(p) = p^5(1 - p)(6 - 8p),$$

and this is clearly zero at $p = 3/4$, which is the relative frequency of successes among the eight trials. This is the maximum likelihood estimate of p. If it were the actual value of p, the probability of the given sequence of six successes would be $(6/8)^6(2/8)^2$, and this is larger than the probability of six successes using any other value of p.

If the sample is a random sample, the likelihood function is a product of the population densities for each value in the sample:

$$L(\theta) = \prod_{i=1}^{n} f(X_i, \theta).$$

Consequently, the manipulation is frequently simpler if the *logarithm* of the likelihood function is maximized:

$$\log L(\theta) = \sum_{i=1}^{n} \log f(X_i; \theta).$$

Since the logarithm function is monotone increasing, $L(\theta)$ and its logarithm are maximized by the same value θ. If $L(\theta)$ is a differentiable function [as is, also, then, $\log L(\theta)$], and if its maximum is attained at a point $\hat{\theta}$ which is interior to the range of values of θ, it follows that

$$\left[\frac{\partial}{\partial \theta} \log L(\theta)\right]_{\theta = \hat{\theta}} = 0.$$

This is called the *likelihood equation*. If $\theta = (\theta_1, \ldots, \theta_k)$, the necessary condition for a maximum is really k equations:

$$\begin{cases} \frac{\partial}{\partial \theta_1} \log L(\theta_1, \ldots, \theta_k) = 0 \\ \qquad \vdots \qquad\qquad \vdots \\ \frac{\partial}{\partial \theta_k} \log L(\theta_1, \ldots, \theta_k) = 0. \end{cases}$$

A solution $(\hat{\theta}_1, \ldots, \hat{\theta}_k)$ of this system, assuming it corresponds to a maximum of L, is a maximum likelihood estimate of $(\theta_1, \ldots, \theta_k)$.

One might wonder whether an estimate obtained as the solution of the likelihood equation actually maximizes the likelihood function when the vanishing of $L'(\theta)$ does not by itself guarantee this. When there is any doubt on this point, it should be investigated. The usual situation is that the likelihood function (being a product of probabilities or densities) is bounded above and continuous in θ, and that the likelihood equation has only one solution, which then must maximize $L(\theta)$.

EXAMPLE 5–15.   Consider a normal population, first with *known* mean μ and unknown variance v. The logarithm of the likelihood function is

$$\log L(v) = -\frac{n}{2} \log (2\pi v) - \frac{1}{2v} \sum (X_i - \mu)^2,$$

and its derivative is

$$-\frac{n}{2v} + \frac{1}{2v^2} \sum (X_i - \mu)^2.$$

This vanishes when v is given the value

$$\hat{v} = \frac{1}{n} \sum (X_i - \mu)^2,$$

which is the maximum likelihood estimate of v when μ is known.

Suppose next that *both* μ and v are *unknown*; the likelihood function is now a function of these two parameters, but in fact it is given by the same expression as $L(v)$ above:

$$\log L(\mu, v) = -\frac{n}{2} \log (2\pi v) - \frac{1}{2v} \sum (X_i - \mu)^2.$$

The likelihood equations are obtained by setting equal to zero the partial derivatives of $\log L$ with respect to μ and v:

$$\begin{cases} \dfrac{1}{\hat{v}} \sum (X_i - \hat{\mu}) = 0, \\[2mm] -\dfrac{n}{2\hat{v}} + \dfrac{1}{2\hat{v}^2} \sum (X_i - \hat{\mu})^2 = 0. \end{cases}$$

From the first equation it is seen that $\hat{\mu} = \bar{X}$, and substitution of this into the second equation yields $\hat{v} = s_x^2$. That is, $\bar{X}$ and s_x^2 are joint maximum likelihood estimates of μ and v. Recall that these estimates have been found to be sufficient for the normal family.

EXAMPLE 5–16.   Consider the basic experiment of a multinomial distribution, one that can result in any of k ways: $A_1, \ldots, A_k$. The parameters of the distribution are the corresponding probabilities $p_1, \ldots, p_k$, where $\sum p_i = 1$. Suppose that among n independent observations on this experiment there are f_i outcomes of type A_i, $i = 1, \ldots, k$. The probability of such a result is the required likelihood function

$$L(p_1, \ldots, p_k) = p_1^{f_1} \cdots p_k^{f_k},$$

with logarithm

$$\mathscr{L} = \log L(p_1, \ldots, p_k) = \sum_{i=1}^{k} f_i \log p_i.$$

In maximizing this, the probability vector $(p_1, \ldots, p_k)$ is restricted by the condition that $\sum p_i = 1$ Using the Lagrange method, one maximizes $\mathscr{L} - \lambda \sum p_i$, differentiating this with respect to each p_j:

$$\frac{\partial}{\partial p_j} [\mathscr{L} - \lambda \sum p_i] = \frac{f_j}{p_j} - \lambda.$$

These derivatives vanish for $j = 1, \ldots, k$ only if f_j/p_j is the same (equal to λ) for all j. That is, the maximum likelihood estimates must be proportional to the frequencies f_j. With the condition that $\sum p_j = 1$, this means that $\hat{p}_j = f_j/n$, the relative frequency of outcomes of type A_j.

Suppose that it is desired to estimate some function of a population parameter, $g(\theta)$. The loss function (assumed to be quadratic) would be $(g(\theta) - a)^2$; and the maximum likelihood estimate is the value a that minimizes this loss when the state of nature is assumed to be the maximum likelihood state $\hat{\theta}$, that is, that minimizes $(g(\hat{\theta}) - a)^2$. The minimizing a is clearly $g(\hat{\theta})$, which is then the maximum likelihood estimate of $g(\theta)$.

EXAMPLE 5–17.   Consider a normal population with mean 0 and unknown variance v. The maximum likelihood estimate of v is $\sum X_i^2/n$, and therefore the maximum likelihood estimate of the population standard deviation is $(\sum X_i^2/n)^{1/2}$. (This is not the sample standard deviation.)

One property of the method of maximum likelihood is that if there is a statistic T sufficient for the family $f(x; \theta)$, any solution of the likelihood equation is a function of T. For, the likelihood function factors, according to the factorization criterion for sufficiency:

$$L(\theta) = f(X; \theta) = g[T, \theta]h(X).$$

But then

$$\log L(\theta) = \log g[T, \theta] + \log h(X),$$

and

$$\frac{\partial}{\partial \theta} \log L(\theta) = \frac{\partial}{\partial \theta} \log g[T, \theta].$$

Any quantity $\hat\theta$ that makes this zero depends on the observations only through the value of T.

Another property is that if there is an unbiased, efficient estimator T, the maximum likelihood method will produce it. This is seen as follows: The information inequality for T is an equality (if T is efficient), so that

$$V = \frac{\partial}{\partial \theta} \log f(X; \theta) = A'(\theta)T + B'(\theta).$$

This has (as shown in Section 5.1.4) mean zero for all θ:

$$E(V) = A'(\theta)E(T) + B'(\theta) = A'(\theta)\theta + B'(\theta) \equiv 0.$$

The derivative of the logarithm of the likelihood function is

$$\frac{\partial}{\partial \theta} \log f(X; \theta) = A'(\theta)T + B'(\theta),$$

and this is zero for $\theta = \hat\theta$, a maximum likelihood estimate:

$$-\frac{B'(\hat\theta)}{A'(\hat\theta)} = T.$$

But since for *all* θ, $-B'(\theta)/A'(\theta) = \theta$, the left member is $\hat\theta$. That is, the statistic T is the maximum likelihood estimate $\hat\theta$.

A third property, which will not be derived here, is that a maximum likelihood estimate is asymptotically normally distributed with variance $1/I(\theta)$ under certain conditions of regularity. That is, it is asymptotically efficient.[3]

EXAMPLE 5–18. Consider the density function that is uniform on the interval $[0, b]$, where b is unknown, and is therefore a parameter of the distribution:

$$f(x, b) = \begin{cases} 1/b, & \text{for } 0 \le x \le b, \\ 0, & \text{elsewhere}. \end{cases}$$

[3] See Cramer [4], p. 500.

Given a set of observations in a random sample X, we have $f(X_i; b) = 1/b$ if $X_i < b$; but if any $X_i > b$, the corresponding density function is zero, as is then the likelihood function:

$$L(b) = \prod_{i=1}^{n} f(X_i; b) = \begin{cases} 1/b^n, & \text{if } b > \text{all } X_i, \\ 0, & \text{otherwise.} \end{cases}$$

The graph of this function of b for given X is shown in Figure 5–2. The maximum is clearly achieved for $\hat{b}$ equal to the largest observation in the sample. But the

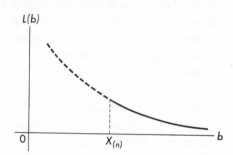

Figure 5–2.

derivative of $L(b)$ does not vanish at this maximum. In this example the conditions for the standard theorems on maximum likelihood are not satisfied, the density function being discontinuous at a point whose location depends on the parameter being estimated.

Problems

5–22. Determine the maximum likelihood estimate of λ in the negative exponential density, $\lambda e^{-\lambda x}$, $x > 0$, assuming a random sample of size n. Determine also maximum likelihood estimates of the population mean and variance.

5–23. A lot contains ten articles, and a sample of four is drawn without replacement from the lot. Given that one of the four articles drawn is defective, what number of defectives in the lot would give the largest probability of this result?

5–24. Determine the maximum likelihood estimate of the parameter b in the density function

$$f(x; b) = \begin{cases} \exp(-|x - b|), & \text{for } x > b, \\ 0, & \text{for } x < b. \end{cases}$$

5–25. Show that the maximum likelihood estimates of p in a Bernoulli population based on a sequence of n independent trials, and based on a sequence of independent trials sufficient to obtain a specified number of successes agree (because the likelihood functions agree).

5–26. Determine the maximum likelihood estimate of the Poisson parameter m based on a sequence of n independent observations.

5–27. Determine the maximum likelihood estimates of the mean of a normal population with known variance and of the variance of a normal population with known mean, assuming a random sample.

5–28. Determine the maximum likelihood estimate of the common variance of

X, assumed to be normal with mean μ and variance σ^2, and Y, assumed normal with mean ν and variance σ^2, based on a random sample of size m from X and a random sample of size n from Y. Assume independent samples.

5.2.4 Other Devices

Brief mention will be made of certain other techniques for obtaining estimators—brief because they are slightly beyond the scope at this point, involving somewhat more mathematical preparation than has been provided or assumed. As in general a decision procedure can be replaced by one based on a sufficient statistic, so in estimating a parameter an estimator can be replaced by a function of a sufficient statistic without deterioration of the risk. In particular, given an unbiased estimate U of the parameter $h(\theta)$, an unbiased estimate based on the sufficient statistic T can be constructed whose variance is not greater than that of U. In some instances the method yields an unbiased estimate of *minimum* variance.

Given the statistic U, then, consider the function

$$g(t) = E(U \mid T = t).$$

If T is sufficient, the conditional distribution of X, and therefore that of the statistic U, are independent of the state θ. The function $g(t)$ really depends, then, only on t, as the notation implies. It defines a statistic

$$V = g(T),$$

whose mean is the same as that of U:

$$E(V) = E[E(U \mid T)] = E(U).$$

Consequently, if U is an unbiased estimate of $h(\theta)$, so is V.

The variance of U can be expressed as follows:

$$\text{var } U = E[(U - E(V))^2]$$

$$= \text{var } V + E[(U - V)^2] + 2E[(U - V)(V - E(V))].$$

The assertion that var $U \geq$ var V will be established as soon as it is shown that the cross-product term vanishes. So, consider

$$E[(U - V)(V - E(V))] = \int_{-\infty}^{\infty} E[(U - V)(V - E(V)) \mid T = t] \, dF_T(t),$$

where $F_T(t)$ is the distribution function of T. Now,

$$E(V - U \mid T = t) = E(V \mid T = t) - E(U \mid T = t)$$

$$= g(t) - g(t) = 0,$$

and

$$E[(U - V)(V - E(V)) \mid T = t] = E[(U - V)(g(t) - h(\theta)) \mid T = t]$$
$$= [g(t) - h(\theta)]E(U - V \mid T = t) = 0.$$

Thus the above integral vanishes, and var $U \geq$ var V. The variance of V is actually smaller if U does not depend on the data through the value of T only, and so one can do better using V than using U.

Clearly, any estimator that is unbiased and has a smaller variance than does $g(T)$ would also have to be a function of the sufficient statistic T (since otherwise the preceding technique would yield a function of T that does at least as well). But if there is such a function, $k(T)$, also unbiased in estimating $h(\theta)$, then

$$Ek(T) = h(\theta) = Eg(T)$$

for all θ. Frequently the family of densities for T has the property of *completeness*, which says that if

$$\int_{-\infty}^{\infty} k(t) \, dF_T(t) = \int_{-\infty}^{\infty} g(t) \, dF_T(t)$$

for all θ, then $k(t)$ is essentially the same function as $g(t)$. In this event $g(T)$ is actually an unbiased estimate of $h(\theta)$ with minimum variance.

EXAMPLE 5–19. Consider a random sample $(X_1, \ldots, X_n)$ from a normal population with mean μ and known variance v. The statistic $T = \sum X_i$ is sufficient, and the statistic $U = X_1$ is unbiased as an estimate of μ. The conditional density of U given $T = t$ can be shown to be

$$f_{U|T=t}(u) = \frac{f(u, t)}{f_T(t)} = \frac{1}{[2\pi v(n - 1)/n]^{1/2}} \exp\left\{-\frac{(u - t/n)^2}{2v(n - 1)/n}\right\}.$$

The expected value of this normal density is clearly t/n, so the statistic $g(T) = T/n = \bar{X}$ is an unbiased estimate with smaller variance than that of X_1 (which was known at the outset). The family of densities here can be shown to be complete, which would imply that $\bar{X}$ has minimum variance among unbiased estimators.

Although maximum likelihood estimates are known to be consistent, asymptotically efficient, and asymptotically normal, there are usually other estimates that have these properties and which would then appear to serve just as well for large samples. (They might even be better for small samples). Such estimates are called *best asymptotically normal*, or BAN, and can be obtained in various ways.

One class of BAN estimates consists of certain "minimum chi-square" estimates, defined as follows: Consider a sample $X_1, \ldots, X_n$ from a vector-valued population X with mean vector $\mu(\theta)$ and covariance matrix $M(\theta)$, θ being the parameter to be estimated (it could be multidimensional). The quadratic expression

$$\chi^2 = \frac{1}{n}(\overline{X} - \mu(\theta))'[M(\theta)]^{-1}(\overline{X} - \mu(\theta))$$

(where the prime means transpose) is minimized as a function of θ for given $X_1, \ldots, X_n$. The minimizing value $\theta(X_1, \ldots, X_n)$ is called the *minimum chi-square estimate* of θ. It is known to be BAN when X has a distribution belonging to the exponential family. Various modifications of the minimum chi-square method also yield BAN estimates.

EXAMPLE 5–20. Let X have the negative exponential distribution with mean $1/\theta$ and variance $1/\theta^2$. Given a random sample $X_1, \ldots, X_n$,

$$\chi^2 = \frac{1}{n}\left(\overline{X} - \frac{1}{\theta}\right)\theta^2\left(X - \frac{1}{\theta}\right) = \frac{1}{n}(\theta\overline{X} - 1)^2.$$

This is minimized for $\theta = 1/\overline{X}$, which is then the minimum chi-square estimate of θ.

In minimizing χ^2 or in maximizing the likelihood function, one may be confronted with equations that are not readily solvable, say,

$$G'(\theta) = 0,$$

where G denotes either the likelihood or χ^2. Newton's method of solving such an equation approximately is to make a guess θ_0 and then obtain an improved guess by solving the linear approximation

$$G'(\theta) \doteq G'(\theta_0) + G''(\theta_0)(\theta - \theta_0) = 0,$$

to obtain

$$\theta_1 = \theta_0 - \frac{G'(\theta_0)}{G''(\theta_0)}.$$

It turns out that if θ_0 is taken to be any consistent estimate of θ such that $\sqrt{n}(\theta_0 - \theta)$ is asymptotically normal when θ is the true state, then the first approximation θ_1 is BAN.[4]

5.3 Interval Estimates

In presenting an estimate of a population parameter (giving the value of $\overline{X}$, for example, as an estimate of the population mean), no indication of the re-

---

[4] These matters are discussed more fully by T. S. Ferguson, "A method of generating best asymptotically normal estimates . . .," *Ann. Math. Stat.* **29**, 1046–1062 (1958).

liability of the estimate is found in the bare announcement of the estimated value. Giving the size of the sample used along with the estimate would be helpful but would assume that everyone who is to interpret the result is equipped to interpret sample size in terms of the "accuracy" of the estimate. Such is not ordinarily the case, and a more direct indication is desirable.

The standard error of estimate, given in Section 5.1.2, is one device used for indicating the reliability or precision of an estimation process. What is wanted, perhaps, is really a range of values within which the population parameter being estimated is almost sure to lie, in some sense. The notion of *confidence interval* for a parameter is commonly used to serve this purpose, and will be introduced by means of an example.

EXAMPLE 5–21.   Consider a sample of n from a normal population with unit variance. The interval from $\bar{X} - 2/\sqrt{n}$ to $\bar{X} + 2/\sqrt{n}$ is four standard deviations wide and ought to trap the actual population mean within it, one feels. What *can* be said is that the random interval from $\bar{X} - 2/\sqrt{n}$ to $\bar{X} + 2/\sqrt{n}$ has the property that

$$P\left(-\frac{2}{\sqrt{n}} < \bar{X} - \mu < +\frac{2}{\sqrt{n}}\right) = P\left(\bar{X} - \frac{2}{\sqrt{n}} < \mu < \bar{X} + \frac{2}{\sqrt{n}}\right) \doteq .95.$$

That is, an interval computed in this way will happen to cover the actual population mean 95 per cent of the time. Such a random interval is called a (95 per cent) *confidence interval* for the population mean.

In general, a confidence interval for a parameter θ is constructed from a statistic T whose distribution depends on θ, in the following way: Determine two numbers depending on θ, $t_1(\theta)$, and $t_2(\theta)$, such that for a given *confidence coefficient η*,

$$P(t_1(\theta) < T < t_2(\theta)) = \eta.$$

Then invert the inequalities here: solve for θ, to obtain an equivalent inequality of the form $g(T) < \theta < h(T)$. This has the same probability η, and the statistics $g(T)$ and $h(T)$ are called *confidence limits* for θ. These limits are random (they vary from sample to sample); some of the time they do include the actual value of θ, and some of the time they don't.

EXAMPLE 5–22.   The approximate normality of $\bar{X}$, the relative frequency of "success" in a sequence of independent trials of a Bernoulli experiment with $p = P(\text{success})$, can be used to obtain approximate confidence limits for p. Since $E\bar{X} = p$ and var $\bar{X} = p(1 - p)/n$, it follows that if the fraction γ of the standard normal distribution is included between $+k$ and $-k$, then

$$P\{|\bar{X} - p| < k[p(1 - p)/n]^{1/2}\} = \gamma.$$

The inequality in parentheses is equivalent to, and therefore has the same probability as what is obtained upon squaring both sides:

$$(\bar{X} - p)^2 < k^2(p - p^2)/n.$$

Transposing everything to the left yields a quadratic inequality in p. Because a quadratic function with positive leading coefficient is negative between the points where it is zero, the roots of the equation

$$(1 + k^2/n)\, p^2 - 2p[\bar{X} + k^2/(2n)] + \bar{X}^2 = 0$$

are the desired *confidence limits* for p:

$$\frac{1}{1 + k^2/n}\left\{\bar{X} + \frac{k^2}{2n} \pm k\left[\frac{\bar{X}(1 - \bar{X})}{n} + \frac{k^2}{4n^2}\right]^{1/2}\right\}.$$

The probability that these define an interval between them, the confidence interval for p, which snares the actual p on its interior is approximately γ, the *confidence coefficient*. A further simplification of the above confidence limits can be achieved if n is quite large by dropping the terms involving k^2/n and k^2/n^2. (The sample size should run in the hundreds for this to be successful.) The simplified limits are then

$$\bar{X} \pm k[\bar{X}(1 - \bar{X})/n]^{1/2},$$

which are of the form $\bar{X}$ plus or minus k times the standard error of estimate.

Notice the effect of sample size—the larger the sample, the narrower the confidence interval. Also, a smaller confidence coefficient would mean a smaller k and a narrower confidence interval: one can make a more precise claim about p with a lower degree of confidence.

Unfortunately, giving a confidence interval in an actual problem with actual numbers sounds like something different from what is really meant. Stating that a 90 per cent confidence interval for θ is (9.1, 9.6), for instance, would suggest that θ is a random variable that, with probability 0.90, lies between 9.1 and 9.6. In the analysis leading to a confidence interval, however, it is assumed that θ is a *constant* that, although not known, remains fixed throughout the sampling process. Nevertheless, a user of statistics (who is not a statistician) is likely to interpret a confidence interval statement as giving a probability for the "random variable" θ; in other words, as coming from a posterior distribution for θ. That in certain instances this point of view has some basis is seen in the following example.

EXAMPLE 5–23. If the mean of a random sample of size 100 from a normal population with unit variance is $\bar{X} = 20$, the 95 per cent confidence interval for μ, as obtained in Example 5–21, is defined by the limits $20 \pm 2/\sqrt{100}$, or 19.8 and 20.2.

Assuming a uniform prior weighting for μ, the absolute distribution of $\bar{X}$ has the density function

$$f_{\bar{X}}(y) = \sqrt{\frac{n}{2\pi}} \int_{-\infty}^{\infty} \exp\left[\frac{-n(y-\mu)^2}{2}\right] d\mu = 1,$$

and the posterior distribution for μ is then defined by the density

$$h(\mu \mid \bar{X} = y) = \frac{f_{\bar{X}}(y;\mu)g(\mu)}{f_{\bar{X}}(y)} = \sqrt{\frac{n}{2\pi}} \exp\left[-\frac{1}{2}n(y-\mu)^2\right]$$

and then (with $y = 20$)

$$P_h(19.8 < \mu < 20.2) = \sqrt{\frac{n}{2\pi}} \int_{19.8}^{20.2} \exp\left[\frac{-n(20-\mu)^2}{2}\right] d\mu = .95,$$

so the confidence interval has the interpretation of a 95 per cent probability interval for μ in the posterior distribution, assuming a uniform prior weighting. For other prior weightings this is not necessarily true.

Problems

5–29. It is known from long experience that the reliability of a certain chemical measurement is indicated by a standard deviation $\sigma = .005$ gm/ml. Determine a sample size n such that a 99 per cent confidence interval for μ has a width of .001 gm/ml. (Is it necessary to assume that the measurements are normal in order that the normal table be used?)

5–30. A series of measurements of a certain dimension of twenty-five parts has a mean 2.3 and a standard deviation .1. Construct an approximate confidence interval for the population mean assuming that the sample size is large enough to make a normal approximation to the distribution of the sample mean, and large enough so that using the sample standard deviation in place of the population standard deviation does not introduce much error. Use a 99 per cent confidence coefficient and then repeat with a 95 per cent confidence coefficient.

5–31. Construct a confidence interval for the mean of the population given the sample mean and variance of the preceding problem, but assuming a sample size of 400.

5–32. Compare the 95 per cent confidence limits for p using the crude and the more precise formulas in Example 5–22, given that 40 trials result in 22 successes.

5–33. Construct the large sample confidence interval for the mean θ, of a negative exponential density $(1/\theta)e^{-x/\theta}$, $x > 0$, in terms of the sample mean, using a 95 per cent confidence coefficient.

5–34. A sample of 60 observations from a Poisson population has a mean of 2.1. Construct the corresponding 90 per cent confidence interval for the population mean (using a normal approximation).

CHAPTER 6

TESTING HYPOTHESES

Statistical decision problems in which there are just two possible actions constitute an important class called (in traditional terminology) *hypothesis-testing* problems. The possible states of nature are called *hypotheses* about nature; each individual state is termed a *simple* hypothesis. A simple hypothesis, then, is a complete specification of a probability distribution—the distribution of the population on which observations are obtained for inference. The "hypothesis" is that this particular distribution is the correct one. A set of several states of nature, or the "hypothesis" that the actual state of nature is one of those in the set, is called a *composite hypothesis*.

EXAMPLE 6–1. The statement that X is normally distributed is a composite statistical hypothesis, since the property of normality does not completely define the distribution of X, the state of nature. This hypothesis includes such simple hypotheses as this one: X is normal with mean 2 and variance 9.

The hypothesis that X has mean 2 and variance 9 is in general composite, since the mean and variance do not alone define a distribution.

Let the two actions open to the decision maker be denoted A and B. The analysis will be given in terms of the regret function; this has the property that for each state of nature, one action (at least) has zero regret. This action is correct for that state of nature. The set of all states of nature is therefore divided into two subsets, the set of all states for which A is the correct action—called H_0, and the complementary set including all states for which B is the correct action—called H_1. Thus, if the decision is made to take action A, the hypothesis H_0 is said to be *accepted* (and H_1 *rejected*). If the decision is made to take action B, then H_0 is *rejected* (and H_1 is *accepted*). The decision problem is often described by saying that one is "testing the hypothesis H_0 against the alternative H_1." The asymmetry in this language reflects an asymmetry in attitude in the early development (and even in current practice) of the subject, as will be discussed later.

6.1 Basic Concepts

With θ used to index the states of nature, and A and B denoting the two available actions, the regret function will be assumed to have the following form:

$$r(\theta, A) = \begin{cases} 0, & \text{if } \theta \text{ is in } H_0, \\ b(\theta), & \text{if } \theta \text{ is in } H_1, \end{cases}$$

$$r(\theta, B) = \begin{cases} a(\theta), & \text{if } \theta \text{ is in } H_0, \\ 0, & \text{if } \theta \text{ is in } H_1, \end{cases}$$

where (as above) H_0 is the name of the set of states for which A is the better action, and H_1 the name of the set for which B is the better action. Choosing action A when θ is actually in the set H_1 is an error, called the *error of type II*; choosing action B when θ is actually in H_0 is an *error of type I*. Although the designation is arbitrary, it stems from situations in which one kind of error is the more serious—and so called type I—namely, that of rejecting H_0 when H_0 is true. (The designation of H_0 and H_1 can be arranged so that the type I error is the more serious.)

It is assumed further that a sample X from the population whose possible distributions are the states of nature is at hand. Often (from considerations of sufficiency, for example) it is agreed at the outset that only procedures based on some statistic $T = t(X)$ will be considered. Whether the sample space is considered to be the space of vector values of X or the space of values of T is immaterial.

A decision function or statistical procedure will assign to each possible sample X (or, to each value of some test statistic T) one of the two actions, A or B. The procedure or decision rule is called a *statistical test* or a test of H_0 against H_1. It is carried out by obtaining a particular sample and then taking action A or action B according to what is assigned by the rule to that particular point. A given test partitions the sample space (of values x or values t) into two sets, those assigned action A, and those assigned action B. The set of sample points assigned action B, equivalent to rejecting H_0, is called the *critical region* of the test. Thus, a test is characterized by a corresponding critical region—if the sample X falls in the critical region, reject H_0 (that is, act as though H_1 were true); if X falls on the complement of the critical region, accept H_0 (act as though H_0 were true).

The risk function for a given test is computed as the expected value of the loss function. For the test with critical region C it is

$$R(\theta, C) = \begin{cases} a(\theta)P(C \mid \theta) + 0 \cdot P(C^c \mid \theta), & \text{for } \theta \text{ in } H_0, \\ 0 \cdot P(C \mid \theta) + b(\theta)P(C^c \mid \theta), & \text{for } \theta \text{ in } H_1. \end{cases}$$

Notice that this risk is computable from the functions $a(\theta)$ and $b(\theta)$ together with the function

$$\pi(\theta) = P(C \mid \theta),$$

called the *power function* of the test C.

6.1.1 Simple H_0 and Simple H_1

The simplest hypothesis-testing problem is that in which there are only two states of nature, θ_0 and θ_1—that is, in which both H_0 and H_1 are simple hypotheses. In this case the "functions" $a(\theta)$ and $b(\theta)$ are really just constants, being defined for only one θ, and will be denoted by a and b, respectively. (The regret is then surely monotone.) For this case the risk function of a test with critical region C is

$$R(\theta, C) = \begin{cases} a\alpha, & \text{if } H_0 \text{ is true } (\theta = \theta_0), \\ b\beta, & \text{if } H_1 \text{ is true } (\theta = \theta_1), \end{cases}$$

where

$$\alpha = P(C \mid H_0) = P(\text{test rejects } H_0 \mid H_0)$$

and

$$\beta = P(C^c \mid H_1) = P(\text{test accepts } H_0 \mid H_1),$$

called, respectively, the *size* of the type I error and the size of the type II error. For this case of simple H_0 and simple H_1 and for given losses a and b, the constants α and β determine the risk function and so serve to describe the performance of the test.

EXAMPLE 6–2. Let X denote a random sample of size 25 from a normal population with variance $\sigma^2 = 4$, whose mean is known to be either $\mu = 0$ or $\mu = 1$. The problem is to test

$$H_0: \quad X \text{ is normal } (0, 4)$$

against

$$H_1: \quad X \text{ is normal } (1, 4).$$

The sample mean $\bar{X}$ is sufficient for this problem; moreover, the family of distributions of X has a monotone likelihood ratio in terms of $\bar{X}$. A monotone procedure then divides the space of values of $\bar{X}$ into $\bar{X} < K$ and $\bar{X} > K$ for some choice of "critical value" K, action A (accepting the smaller mean $\mu = 0$) being taken if $\bar{X} < K$ and action B (rejecting $\mu = 0$) if $\bar{X} > K$. The critical region defined by such a procedure is given by $\bar{X} > K$, the set of values of $\bar{X}$ calling for rejection of H_0; and the sizes of the type I and type II errors are as follows:

$$\alpha = P(\bar{X} > K \mid \mu = 0) = 1 - \Phi\left(\frac{K - 0}{2/\sqrt{25}}\right)$$

$$\beta = P(\bar{X} < K \mid \mu = 1) = \Phi\left(\frac{K - 1}{2/\sqrt{25}}\right).$$

Figure 6–1 shows the density functions of the test statistic $\bar{X}$ under the two states of nature, and exhibits areas equal to the error sizes corresponding to the particular test in which $K = .4$, that is, calling for rejection of H_0 if $\bar{X} > .4$. The

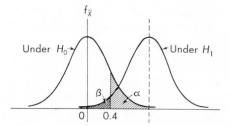

Figure 6–1. Error sizes for Example 6–2.

values are $\alpha = .1587$ and $\beta = .0668$. It can be seen from the graph, by imagining the critical value K at different points along the horizontal scale, that increasing K decreases α but increases β, and that decreasing it increases α and decreases β. This "struggle" between α and β is also evident in a plot of the relation between α and β, given by the parametric equations above (expressing them in terms of the "parameter" K). This curve is shown in Figure 6–2 for the case $n = 4$, and the case $n = 25$, along with the corresponding curve for a different kind of critical region, $\bar{X} < K$. Notice the disastrous effect of using this latter, nonmonotone (and certainly nonintuitive) type of procedure. Notice also the effect of the larger sample size—the error sizes are generally smaller, and the curve is pulled in toward (0, 0).

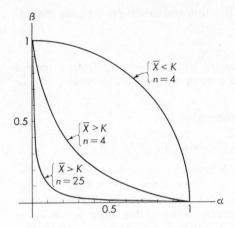

Figure 6–2. Plot of β vs. α for Example 6–2.

Having determined the risk function and expressed it in terms of the error sizes α and β, one is still faced with the problem of selecting a test that will involve as little risk as possible without knowing the state of nature, on which the risk depends. Because the problem of testing a simple hypothesis against a simple alternative involves just two possible states of nature, the graphical analysis introduced in Section 4.2 can be applied. For a given test with critical region C, define

$$\begin{cases} L_0 = R(\theta_0, C) = a\alpha, \\ L_1 = R(\theta_1, C) = b\beta, \end{cases}$$

and consider the test as represented by the point (L_0, L_1) in the plane. The minimax procedure is chosen among the set of all possible tests as the one first encountered by a wedge moving up towards the set of points representing all tests from beneath, with vertex along the line $L_0 = L_1$. A Bayes test is one corresponding to that point (in the set of points representing all tests), first encountered in moving a line up parallel to a direction defined by given prior probabilities g_0 for H_0 and g_1 for H_1, with slope $-g_0/g_1$. Another procedure that might be considered is one corresponding to the point closest to the origin, which then minimizes $L_0{}^2 + L_1{}^2$.

EXAMPLE 6–3.   Consider again the problem of the preceding example—testing between $\mu = 0$ and $\mu = 1$ in a normal population with $\sigma^2 = 4$, but now based on a random sample of size $n = 4$. The plot of (L_0, L_1) for tests of the form $\bar{X} > K$ is shown in Figure 6–3, assuming losses $b = 1$ and $a = 3$. Also indicated on the graph are the tests of this family of monotone tests that are obtained by (a) applying the minimax procedure; (b) applying the Bayes procedure with prior probabilities $g_0 = .2$ and $g_1 = .8$; and (c) minimizing $L_0{}^2 + L_1{}^2$. (The minimax test is given by $K = .98$, with $3\alpha = \beta = .49$, and the Bayes test is given by $K = .213$, with $\alpha = .416$ and $\beta = .216$.)

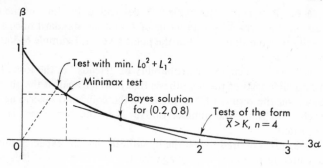

Figure 6–3.

Problems

6–1. Determine in each case whether the hypothesis given is simple or composite:

(a) A pair of dice is "straight."
(b) A pair of dice is "crooked."
(c) $E(X) = 3$.
(d) X is negative exponential with mean 3.
(e) X is uniformly distributed.
(f) A coin is biased.
(g) The distribution function of X is $1 - e^{-x}, x > 0$.
(h) The distribution function of X is not $1 - e^{-x}, x > 0$.

6–2. A bag contains five beads, some white and the others not white. Consider testing

$$\begin{cases} H_0: \text{At most one bead is white,} \\ H_1: \text{At least two beads are white,} \end{cases}$$

on the basis of a sample of two drawn without replacement from the bag.

(a) List all possible tests based on the sample of two—sensible or not.
(b) Determine the probability of a type I error for each simple hypothesis in H_0 and the probability of a type II error for each simple hypothesis in H_1, for the test that rejects H_0 if and only if any white beads are drawn.
(c) Is there a test with smaller type II error sizes than the test in (b)?

6–3. Determine the minimax test, among those of the type $\bar{X} > K$, for $\mu = 0$ against $\mu = 1$ in a normal population with variance 4, based on a sample of size 4 and given losses $a = 2$ and $b = 1$.

6–4. Referring to Example 6–2, compute the error sizes for the test that accepts H_0 if $0 < \bar{X} < 1$ but otherwise rejects H_0. (Notice where the point (α, β) falls in the plot of Figure 6–2.)

6–5. In testing $\mu = 0$ against $\mu = 1$ in a normal population with variance 4, express the error sizes in terms of n and K (cf. Example 6–3). Determine n and K

(a) so that $\alpha = \beta = .01$,
(b) so that $\alpha = .01$ and $\beta = .10$.

6–6. Referring to Example 6–3, determine the slope of the curve representing tests of the form $\bar{X} > K$ in terms of K and the standard normal density function. Verify that the slope is $-\frac{1}{4}$ at the point given in Example 6–3 as the Bayes test for $g_0 = .2, g_1 = .8$.

6–7. Let p denote the probability of "Heads" in the toss of a coin. Construct all possible tests of the hypothesis that $p = 1/2$ against the alternative that $p = 1$, based on the results of two tosses of the coin, and determine the error sizes for each test. (Since the number of Heads in the two tosses is sufficient, use this statistic.)

6–8. It is desired to test the hypothesis that the expected number of arrivals in a 1-minute period is $m = 1$ against the alternative that it is $m = 1.5$, assuming Poisson arrivals, and using Y, the number of arrivals in a 10-minute period. Determine α and β for the test with critical region $Y > 12$.

6.1.2 Composite Hypotheses

Since risk depends upon the state θ, it is not uniquely defined for H_0 if H_0 is composite, and not uniquely defined for H_1 if H_1 is composite.

The simplest form of loss function for the case of composite H_0 or H_1 (or both) is that in which the losses are constant on H_0 and constant on H_1:

$$\ell(\theta, A) = \begin{cases} 0, & \text{for } \theta \text{ in } H_0, \\ b, & \text{for } \theta \text{ in } H_1, \end{cases}$$

$$\ell(\theta, B) = \begin{cases} a, & \text{for } \theta \text{ in } H_0, \\ 0, & \text{for } \theta \text{ in } H_1. \end{cases}$$

It must be admitted that this loss function is usually not very realistic, but nevertheless it is the one that will be used in the discussion to follow. In practice, losses are not easy to determine with great precision, and it therefore seems reasonable to develop the theory of testing in terms of a loss function that is as simple as possible. The theory could not be so well developed if a more general loss were used, and it is questionable that such theory would be any more appropriate in view of the difficulties in measuring loss.

In terms of the simple loss function given above, then, the risk function for a statistical test with critical region C becomes

$$R(\theta, C) = \begin{cases} aP_\theta(C), & \text{for } \theta \text{ in } H_0, \\ b[1 - P_\theta(C)], & \text{for } \theta \text{ in } H_1. \end{cases}$$

Again observe that the risk is completely determined, given a and b, by the *power function* of the test used:

$$\pi_C(\theta) = P(C \mid \theta) = P(\text{test rejects } H_0 \mid \theta),$$

or alternatively, by the *operating characteristic function*:

$$OC(\theta) = 1 - \pi(\theta) = P(C^c \mid \theta) = P(\text{test accepts } H_0 \mid \theta).$$

Which of these complementary functions is used is a matter of taste. In some applications it is the operating characteristic that is tabulated, but in theoretical work the language of power is more common. The term *power* refers to the ability of a test to detect that H_0 is false when such is the case.

The risk function would be zero if the power function were the following *ideal power function*:

$$\pi(\theta) = \begin{cases} 0, & \text{for } \theta \text{ in } H_0, \\ 1, & \text{for } \theta \text{ in } H_1. \end{cases}$$

Actual power functions, based on a finite amount of data, will ordinarily not be ideal, but to the extent that the information in the sample permits, will tend to be small on H_0 and large on H_1—at least, for "good" tests.

EXAMPLE 6–4.   Consider a Bernoulli experiment—success with probability p and failure with probability $1 - p$, and the following composite hypotheses:

$$\begin{cases} H_0: & 0 \leq p \leq .5, \\ H_1: & .5 < p \leq 1. \end{cases}$$

Consider the particular test based on three observations that rejects H_0 if three successes occur. The power function for this test is as follows:

$$\pi(p) = P_p(3 \text{ successes in 3 trials}) = p^3.$$

For the test that rejects H_0 when either two or three successes occur in three trials, the power function is

$$\pi(p) = P_p(2 \text{ or 3 successes in 3 trials}) = 3p^2(1 - p) + p^3.$$

These two power functions are plotted on the same axes in Figure 6–4.

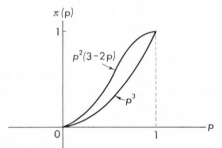

Figure 6–4.   Power curves for Example 6–4.

Notice that the division of $[0, 1]$ into H_0 and H_1 does not enter the computation of $\pi(p)$, but of course it will enter in deciding whether a power function is acceptable or not. The power function for the second test is higher than that for the first test, not only on H_1 (which is desirable) but also on H_0 (which is not so desirable).

The problem of Example 6–4 is actually a monotone problem, in which the states in H_0 all lie to one side of those in H_1—the alternative is said to be *one-sided*. The procedures considered in that example are monotone procedures, and it will be shown in Section 6.3.3 that the monotoneity of the power function is no accident. The following considers a monotone procedure for another monotone problem.

EXAMPLE 6–5.   Consider a normal population with variance 9; it is desired to test

$$H_0: \mu \leq 1 \qquad \text{against} \qquad H_1: \mu > 1,$$

using a critical region of the form $\bar{X} > K$, based on a random sample of size n from the population. The power function is

$$\pi(\mu) = P_\mu(X \text{ in } C)$$

$$= P_\mu(\bar{X} > K) = 1 - \Phi\left(\frac{K - \mu}{3/\sqrt{n}}\right) = \Phi\left(\frac{\mu - K}{3/\sqrt{n}}\right).$$

This function of μ looks like a cumulative normal distribution; it is shown in Figure 6–5 for $K = 1$, $n = 36$, and for $K = 1$, $n = 144$. Both functions are high

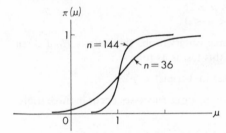

Figure 6–5.   Power curves for Example 6–5.

on H_1 and not so high on H_0. The center of symmetry of the graphs is at $\mu = 1$, and it is clear from the computations above that a change in the boundary of the critical region from $K = 1$ to, say, $K = 2$ would shift the curve laterally so that the center of symmetry would be $\mu = 2$.

Although the probability of rejecting H_0 when H_0 is true is not uniquely defined (depending as it does on the state θ), one might define a "size" for type I errors as the maximum (or supremum, if the maximum does not exist) of such probabilities:

$$\alpha = \max_{\theta \text{ in } H_0} P_\theta(\text{reject } H_0) = \max_{\theta \text{ in } H_0} \pi(\theta).$$

This is sometimes called the *significance level* of the test. The size for type II errors could similarly be taken to be

$$\beta = \max_{\theta \text{ in } H_1} [1 - \pi(\theta)].$$

In problems in which θ is a real parameter or a vector of real parameters and where $\pi(\theta)$ does not jump at the boundary between the region H_0 and the region H_1, the sizes defined in this way will add up to 1. They could not *both* be made small, no matter how closely the power function approximates the ideal function for θ not on the boundary. A typical situation might be that in Figure 6–6. Increasing the sample size, which might steepen the power curve, as in Example 6–5, could not reduce both α and β to acceptably small levels.

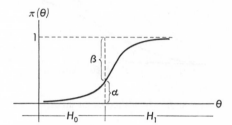

Figure 6–6.

In such situations, where the division between H_0 and H_1 is a boundary point of each, a finite sampling experiment could not really be expected to discriminate well between H_0 and H_1 if the actual state is near that boundary point. Sometimes an "indifference zone" or "no man's land" including the boundary is defined, say, from θ' to θ'', in which one is indifferent to the action taken. This amounts to a revision of the loss function to be zero in this indifference zone for both actions, and the ideal power function (to produce zero risk) is unrestricted there, as in Figure 6–7, for the monotone case.

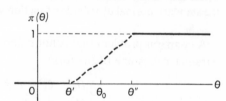

Figure 6–7.

With such a modification the error sizes could be defined to be

$$\alpha = \max_{H_0-I} \pi(\theta) \quad \text{and} \quad \beta = \max_{H_1-I} [1 - \pi(\theta)],$$

where I denotes the set of values of θ in the indifference zone. These are shown in Figure 6–8, for a montone problem with a monotone power function.

Actually, the modification of a monotone testing problem in this way amounts to replacing the given hypotheses with the simple hypotheses $\theta = \theta'$ and $\theta = \theta''$, the error sizes then being those defined for this simpler problem. With the sample size and the critical boundary at one's disposal, one can select them to produce the specified α and β. However, having used this method as a practical means of constructing a test, one should realize that the test cannot be characterized by the two numbers α and β; the whole power function should be examined to see what protection is afforded at other values of θ.

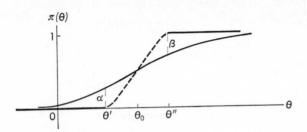

Figure 6-8. Modified error sizes.

EXAMPLE 6-6. Let X be normal with variance 9. It is decided that the probability of rejecting $\mu \leq 1$ when $\mu = .8$ should not exceed .05, and the probability of accepting $\mu \leq 1$ when $\mu = 1.2$ should not exceed .10. If the test used is $\bar{X} > K$, then

$$.05 = P_{\mu=.8}(\bar{X} > K) = 1 - \Phi\left(\frac{K - .8}{3/\sqrt{n}}\right)$$

and

$$.10 = P_{\mu=1.2}(\bar{X} < K) = \Phi\left(\frac{K - 1.2}{3/\sqrt{n}}\right).$$

These are readily solved with the aid of Table I (Appendix), giving the values of the standard normal distribution function $\Phi(z)$, to obtain $n = 481$ and $K = 1.025$.

A common problem that is not monotone, although involving a single real parameter θ, is one of the form

$$\begin{cases} H_0: & \theta_1 \leq \theta \leq \theta_2 \\ H_1: & \theta > \theta_2 \quad \text{or} \quad \theta < \theta_1. \end{cases}$$

This is often simplified to the form

$$\begin{cases} H_0: & \theta = \theta_0, \\ H_1: & \theta \neq \theta_0. \end{cases}$$

One says that such problems are *two-sided*, or involve two-sided alternatives. (Sometimes a problem is cast in this form when it is really a three-action problem—different actions being called for, when H_0 is not true, depending on whether θ is on one side or the other of H_0.) For such problems, if the likelihood ratio is monotone in terms of a statistic T, the type of critical region usually used (and intuitively plausible) is two-sided, excessively large or excessively small values of T both calling for rejection of H_0.

EXAMPLE 6–7.   Let X have a Bernoulli distribution with unknown p, and let $S = X_1 + \cdots + X_5$ denote the number of successes in five independent trials. To test $p = .5$ against $p \neq .5$, it would seem reasonable to reject $p = .5$ for values of S that are either too small or too large. The test with critical region $S = 0, 1, 4,$ or 5 has the power function

$$\pi(p) = P_p[S = 0, 1, 4, \text{ or } 5]$$

$$= 1 - \binom{5}{2} p^2(1 - p)^3 - \binom{5}{3} p^3(1 - p)^2$$

$$= \tfrac{3}{8} + 5(p - .5)^2 - 10(p - .5)^4,$$

as shown in Figure 6–9. It is symmetrical about $p = .5$ and has a minimum at that value of p. Since H_0 is a simple hypothesis, α is uniquely defined as $\pi(.5) = 3/8$.

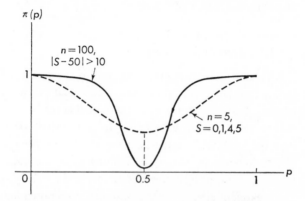

Figure 6–9.   Power curves for Example 6–7.

To see the effect of an increase in sample size, consider also the test under which H_0 is rejected if more than 60 or fewer than 40 successes occur in 100 independent trials. With this sample size, the sample sum S is approximately normal:

$$\pi(p) = P_p(|S - 50| > 10) \doteq 1 - \Phi\left(\frac{60.5 - 100p}{\sqrt{100pq}}\right) + \Phi\left(\frac{39.5 - 100p}{\sqrt{100pq}}\right).$$

The graph of this function is shown in Figure 6–9. α is $\pi(.5) = .036$.

Problems

6–9.   Determine and sketch the power function of the test that calls for action B when no successes or three successes occur in three independent trials of a Bernoulli experiment.

6–10.   Consider a test with critical region $\bar{X} > K$, where $\bar{X}$ is the mean of a random sample from a normal population with standard deviation 10. Select K and the sample size n so that the probability of the critical region is .05 when $\mu = 100$ and .98 when $\mu = 110$. Sketch the power function of the test. For what H_0 and H_1 is the test suited?

6–11.   A lot contains ten articles. To choose between accepting and rejecting the lot, a sample of four is drawn (without replacement). If more than one defective is found, the lot is rejected, but otherwise it is accepted. Determine the operating characteristic function of the test.

6–12. A test concerning the variance of a normal population has the critical region $s_x{}^2 > K$, where $s_x{}^2$ is the variance of a random sample of size 100. Use the asymptotic normality of the sample variance to determine K and the power function given that the power is .98 at $\sigma^2 = .05$.

6–13. Determine the power function of the test with critical region $|\bar{X} - 1| > K$, where $\bar{X}$ is the mean of a random sample of size 25 from a normal population with variance 1, and K is determined so that in testing $\mu = 1$ against $\mu \neq 1$, the size of the type I error (which is uniquely defined) is .05.

6–14. Determine the size of the type I error of the test of $\theta = \theta_0$ against $\theta \neq \theta_0$ that calls for rejection of $\theta = \theta_0$ if the 95 per cent confidence interval (based on some given statistic) includes θ_0 on its interior. Show that the test in the preceding problem is of this type.

6.1.3   Tests of Significance

A type of inference closely related to the testing of hypotheses is that of *testing significance*. A typical situation is that in which, say, a physical theory suggests that a certain probability model is the "correct" one; an experiment is then conducted in an attempt to substantiate or contradict the assertion that the proposed model is correct. The proposed model is ordinarily a simple hypothesis; it may be defined by a particular value for some parameter: $\theta = \theta_0$, or by a completely specified c.d.f. $F_0(x)$, or by a hypothesis of "no treatment effect" (so that samples from potentially different populations are considered to be from the same population). In any case, the specific model to be tested is called the *null* hypothesis, a terminology possibly stemming from that context in which the hypothesis is one of "no difference."

To *test* the null hypothesis, one determines (from a sample) the value of some test statistic T. (In the case of testing $\theta = \theta_0$ this statistic would be an estimator of θ.) Knowing what to "expect," in view of the probability distribution of T as determined by and computed from the null distribution in the sample space of the experiment, one determines whether the computed value of T is "significantly far" from what it is expected to be by specifying (intuitively) a "critical region" C of significant values. When T falls in this critical region, the phenomenon is thought to be "significant" and is taken as "evidence" that the null hypothesis being tested is not correct and should therefore be rejected.

On the other hand, if T turns out to have a value that is not one of those deemed significant, no conclusion is drawn. A nonsignificant value of T is *not* taken as evidence that the null hypothesis is correct because there would be many other states of nature that might equally well account for this value of T that is held to be nonsignificant for H_0. Thus, a significance test *can* lead to rejecting H_0 but *cannot* lead to accepting H_0. Indeed, any particular model is almost sure to be wrong (except perhaps when the possible states are finite in number or even countable), because it is usually impossible even to specify a particular state accurately enough, let alone guess the true state with infinite precision.

The decision to reject H_0 can be incorrect—the test can lead to rejecting H_0 even when H_0 is true, since randomness will occasionally lead to a value of the test statistic T that is more suggestive of the falsity than the truth of H_0. The probability, when H_0 is true, that a given test (i.e., a given critical region) leads to the rejection of H_0 is called the *significance level* of the test and denoted by α, as before.

Specification of a significance level clearly involves some arbitrariness. Perhaps for this reason the results of a significance test are sometimes reported by giving not just the decision "significant" or "not significant" at some specified level, but by stating the level at which the data would yield a T-value just on the boundary between "significant" and "not significant." Equivalently, one can report the value of T as a certain percentile of the distribution of T, and let the consumer of the statistical analysis perform his own test—that is, adopt his own significance level.

If the determination of a significance level involves arbitrariness, even more so does the choice of a critical region. In simple problems there is sometimes a certain type of critical region that seems to suggest itself, especially after the decision is made as to what statistic T is appropriate. But more generally, the choice of statistic and the choice of critical region can be made intuitively only with some awareness and analysis (perhaps subconcious) of the kinds of alternatives to H_0 that are lurking in the background. And this puts the problem back into the domain of hypothesis-testing problems.

When the problem is one of testing a value θ_0 of a real-valued parameter (i.e., number) θ, the alternatives are pretty clear; indeed, one almost has to be protecting against either $\theta \neq \theta_0$ or against θ on one side of θ_0. And if an estimator T is available that is closely linked to θ, the proper type of critical region practically announces itself—and there is not really much room for serious debate as to what "proper" might mean. But if the parameter space is multidimensional, a good choice of statistic and critical region can hardly be made without a careful consideration of the types of alternatives that the test is supposed to detect.

EXAMPLE 6–8.   A coin is presumed to be a fair coin, with $p = P(\text{Heads}) = 1/2$. But it is desired, possibly because of suspicion of the tossing mechanism, or of the coin's balance properties, to test this null hypothesis that $p = 1/2$. The coin is tossed 100 times. If it is fair, the number of Heads in these 100 tosses will be approximately normally distributed with mean 50 and standard deviation 5. Intuition suggests that a number of Heads that is either too large or too small might be reason to doubt that the coin is fair. A significance level of .05 defines a two-sided test that rejects $p = .5$ if the number of Heads differs from 50 by more than 10 on either side (approximately). Thus, if the tosses result in 65 Heads, this is said to be significant at the five per cent level. Indeed, being three standard deviations above the mean, if p were really 1/2, it would be significant at any level down to about .0026. On the other hand, it would not be considered significant at the .1 per cent level; it is within the bounds of reasonableness for a fair coin, with this measure of what is reasonable.

A test that would call 50 Heads in 100 tosses unreasonable or "significant" and any other number of Heads not significant has a significance level of about .08 (which is the probability of 50 Heads in 100 tosses of a fair coin). But without consideration of the type II error it is not clear (except from intuition) whether this kind of significance test is worse than that using extreme values as significant.

The attitude of being willing (or even anxious!) to reject H_0 but unwilling to accept it is used by some expositors in connection with their discussions of hypothesis testing. In this book it is assumed that a problem is one of hypothesis testing when one is willing to take one of two actions—that is, he will either act as though H_0 were true, or act as though H_1 were true, without necessarily being convinced one way or the other. If the problem is really not a two-action problem, but more like what has been termed above a problem of significance testing, there is some question as to the effective meaning of the level α. For, in practice, if one obtains a nonsignificant result, his action is likely to be to obtain more data and conduct another significance test. But if he keeps this up, sooner or later he will be led to reject H_0—because of chance, and not because H_0 is necessarily false.

Treating a problem as one of significance testing seems to be related to the asymmetry inherent in the competition of a simple hypothesis against a highly composite or vaguely specified alternative. Posing a problem in this way may often be a considerable oversimplification. Thus, the hypothesis that $\theta = \theta_0$ may simply serve to represent a band of θ-values about θ_0, the same action or conclusion being appropriate if θ is almost equal to θ_0 as when θ is exactly equal to θ_0.

Admittedly, asking an experimenter to consider alternatives to H_0 is asking him to impose on the problem a certain type of mathematical structure that may be overly restrictive. It is not always clear that the alternative is even a probability distribution, let alone a specific class of probability distributions. At any rate, the significance tester regards the decision theorist as overly demanding and restrictive in his interrogation of Nature, feeling as he usually does that null distributions are injury enough without the added insult of alternative distributions.

6.1.4 Mixed Strategies

In a problem of testing hypotheses, a mixed strategy can be constructed by

assigning a probability distribution to the set of possible critical regions—an
extraneous experiment of chance which is not simple to define and not simple
to carry out. A mixed strategy can also be given by assigning a Bernoulli experiment of chance to each sample point. That is, if the sample result is $X = x$,
an additional experiment is performed, the toss of a "coin," with probability
$\phi(x)$ for Heads and $1 - \phi(x)$ for Tails. The mixed or randomized decision
rule is then defined by a function $\phi(x)$, with $0 \le \phi(x) \le 1$; it is carried out by
obtaining the sample $X = x$ and tossing the coin assigned to x, rejecting H_0 if
it lands Heads and accepting H_0 if it lands Tails.

This class of randomized tests *includes* the "pure" tests defined earlier, as
special cases. For, the test with critical region C is defined also by the function

$$\phi(x) = \begin{cases} 0, & \text{if } x \text{ is in } C^c, \\ 1, & \text{if } x \text{ is in } C, \end{cases}$$

in other words, the indicator function of C. If X falls in C, the coin tossed has
two Heads and leads automatically to rejecting H_0, whereas if X falls in C^c,
the coin tossed has two Tails, and H_0 is accepted.

An important kind of randomized test is one in which the extra randomization really occurs only on the boundary of some region. The way in which this
kind of test might be used to achieve a specified significance level in a problem
in which the test statistic has a discrete distribution is illustrated in the following example.

EXAMPLE 6–9.   Consider the problem of testing between $\lambda_0 = .1$ and $\lambda_1 = .2$
in a Poisson distribution for the number of events in an interval of 1 minute, using
tests with critical regions of the form $\sum X_i > K$, where X_i is the number of events
in the ith minute in a series of 1-minute intervals. Using ten such intervals (that is,
a sample of size ten), one finds the type I error sizes to be as follows:

Test	$\sum X_i > 0$	$\sum X_i > 1$	$\sum X_i > 2$	$\sum X_i > 3$
α	.6321	.2642	.0803	.0190

None of these gives exactly, say, .05. If a most powerful test with $\alpha = .05$ is
desired, it must be a randomized test. Consider then the randomized test that re-
jects λ_0 if $\sum X_i > 3$, accepts λ_0 if $\sum X_i < 3$, and rejects λ_0 with probability p if
$\sum X_i = 3$. The α for this test is

$$\begin{aligned} P_{\lambda_0}(\text{reject } \lambda_0) &= P(\text{rej. } \lambda_0 \mid \sum X_i > 3)P_{\lambda_0}(\sum X_i > 3) \\ &\quad + P(\text{rej. } \lambda_0 \mid \sum X_i = 3)P_{\lambda_0}(\sum X_i = 3) \\ &\quad + P(\text{rej. } \lambda_0 \mid \sum X_i < 3)P_{\lambda_0}(\sum X_i < 3) \\ &= 1 \times .0190 + p \times .0613 + 0 \times .9197. \end{aligned}$$

This can be made equal to .05 by taking $p = .506$.

The power function of a test defined by $\phi(x)$ is (as with a pure test) the probability that the test calls for rejection, as a function of the state of nature. Since

$$P(H_0 \text{ is rejected} \mid X = x) = \phi(x),$$

it follows (upon averaging out the X) that

$$\pi_\phi(\theta) = P(H_0 \text{ is rejected} \mid \theta) = E_\theta[\phi(X)],$$

where E_θ denotes an averaging with respect to the distribution of X defined by the state θ. This formula for the power function will be found to be quite convenient in some of the theory to follow, making it even simpler to establish certain results for the broad class of randomized tests which then automatically hold for the smaller class of pure tests.

Problems

6-15. Determine and sketch the power function for the test that rejects H_0 if 100 tosses yield 50 Heads, given in Example 6–8, and comment on its appropriateness for the various alternatives to $p = .5$.

6-16. In testing hypotheses about the mean of a normal population with unit variance, the mean of a sample of size 100 is found to be 2.15. In testing $\mu = 2$ against $\mu > 2$, what is the level at which this result would just be significant?

6-17. A test based on a statistic T calls for rejecting H_0 when $T < 2$, accepting H_0 when $T > 2$, and tossing a (fair) coin when $T = 2$.

(a) Give the function $\phi(t)$ that defines this test.

(b) If T is discrete and H_0 is simple, with $P(T = t \mid H_0) = f_0(t)$, express α in terms of $f_0(t)$.

6-18. Determine a randomized test of level .10 for the problem of Example 6–9.

6-19. Express in terms of $\phi(x)$ the type I and type II error sizes of the randomized test defined by $\phi(x)$.

6.2 Theory for the Two-State Problem

Although somewhat unrealistic, in terms of actual practice, the testing problem in which both H_0 and H_1 are simple hypotheses is worth considering because of the rather definitive "solution" that can be given, namely, a way of determining a complete class of tests. It will be convenient to denote the density (or probability) function of the sample by $f_0(x)$, when H_0 is true (and A is the better action) and by $f_1(x)$ when H_1 is true (and B is the better action). It was shown in Problem 4–90 that the likelihood ratio $f_0(X)/f_1(X)$ is minimal sufficient, and the admissible tests will be defined in terms of this statistic.

6.2.1 Most Powerful Tests

If two tests of simple H_0 against simple H_1 have the same α, the one with the smaller β dominates the other and is the preferred test of the two. It is said to be more *powerful*.

Definition. A test is said to be *most powerful* if among the class of tests whose α's are not greater, none has a β which is smaller.

The quantity $1 - \beta$ is referred to as *power* (the "power" of a test to detect the alternative hypothesis); it is the probability of taking action B when action B should be taken (H_1 is true). Even though a given test is most powerful, there may be tests with greater power achieved by sacrificing the size of the type I error.

The notion of "greatest power for given α" stems from situations in which one type of error is far more serious than the other; by proper labeling of hypotheses, this can be made the type I error. In such cases the risk can be controlled by controlling the size of the type I error, and so α is fixed at some acceptable level, the test that does as well as possible with respect to β being the preferred test.

When H_0 and H_1 are both simple, a most powerful test can always be constructed. The following reasoning suggests the way to construct this test: Let the sample observations have joint density $f_0(x)$ under H_0 and $f_1(x)$ under H_1. These functions attach numbers or measures to each point in the space of observation vectors x. Imagine that f_0 assigns to each x a certain "cost" and that f_1 assigns a "return." Choosing a critical region C so as to have a certain size α amounts to putting into C enough points x so that the total "cost" of C is α:

$$\alpha = \int_C f_0(x) \, dx = \text{total "cost" of } C.$$

Then, among those regions having the same total cost, look for one that has the smallest β or largest $1 - \beta$:

$$1 - \beta = \int_C f_1(x) \, dx = \text{total "return" from } C.$$

It is now clear that the way to make this selection is to construct C by putting into it those points x having the largest "return" per unit "cost": $f_1(x)/f_0(x)$. That is, points x are lined up according to the value of this ratio, and the points with the largest such values are put into C. The best critical region would then appear to be defined by

$$f_0(x)/f_1(x) < \text{constant},$$

where the "constant" is chosen to make the size of C equal to α.

Neyman–Pearson Lemma. In testing simple H_0 against simple H_1, using samples of a given size n, the test defined by the critical region containing those points x for which

$$\frac{f_0(x_1, \ldots, x_n)}{f_1(x_1, \ldots, x_n)} < K$$

is most powerful, where $f_0(x)$ and $f_1(x)$ denote the joint density (or probability) functions of the sample X under H_0 and H_1, respectively.

Although the discussion above was intended to make this seem correct, a more precise argument will now be given, which shows that the given critical region is not only most powerful among critical regions of the same or smaller size but also among the set of *mixed* strategies having the same or smaller α's. Thus consider an arbitrary mixed strategy defined by $\phi(x)$, with

$$\alpha(\phi) = E_{H_0}[\phi(x)]$$

no larger than the α of the pure strategy defined by C:

$$\alpha(C) = E_{H_0}[\phi_C(x)],$$

where

$$\phi_C(x) = \begin{cases} 1, & \text{if } x \text{ is in } C, \\ 0, & \text{if } x \text{ is in } C^c. \end{cases}$$

The difference in β's for $\phi(x)$ and $\phi_C(x)$ is

$$\beta(\phi) - \beta(C) = E_{H_1}[1 - \phi(X)] - E_{H_1}[1 - \phi_C(X)]$$

$$= E_{H_1}[\phi_C(X) - \phi(X)]$$

$$= \int_C [\phi_C(x) - \phi(x)] f_1(x) \, dx + \int_{C^c} [\phi_C(x) - \phi(x)] f_1(x) \, dx.$$

Now, on C,

$$[\phi_C(x) - \phi(x)] = 1 - \phi(x) \geqq 0,$$

and on C^c,

$$[\phi_C(x) - \phi(x)] = -\phi(x) \leqq 0.$$

Also, for x in C (by definition of C), $f_1(x) \geq K' f_0(x)$; while on C^c, $f_1(x) \leq K' f_0(x)$. Therefore,

$$\int_C [\phi_C(x) - \phi(x)] f_1(x) \, dx \geq K' \int_C [\phi_C(x) - \phi(x)] f_0(x) \, dx$$

and

$$\int_{C^c} [\phi_C(x) - \phi(x)] f_1(x) \, dx \geq K' \int_{C^c} [\phi_C(x) - \phi(x)] f_0(x) \, dx.$$

Finally, then,

$$\beta(\phi) - \beta(C) \geq K'E_{H_0}[\phi_C(X) - \phi(X)] = K'[\alpha(C) - \alpha(\phi)] \geq 0.$$

EXAMPLE 6–10.   Let X be normally distributed with variance 4 and consider testing $H_0:\mu = 0$ against $H_1:\mu = 1$, using a sample of size n. The joint density of X is, under H_0,

$$f_0(x) = \frac{1}{(8\pi)^{n/2}} \exp\left[-\frac{1}{8}\sum x_i^2\right],$$

and under H_1,

$$f_1(x) = \frac{1}{(8\pi)^{n/2}} \exp\left[-\frac{1}{8}\sum (x_i - 1)^2\right].$$

The crucial ratio is then

$$\frac{f_0(x)}{f_1(x)} = \exp\left[-\sum \frac{x_i^2}{8} + \frac{1}{8}\sum (x_i - 1)^2\right]$$

$$= \exp\left[-\sum \frac{2x_i - 1}{8}\right].$$

This does not exceed K, provided

$$\bar{x} > \frac{1}{2} - \frac{4 \log K}{n} = K'.$$

Therefore a critical region of the type $\bar{X} > K'$ is best among those having a given α. The value of K' would be determined by that α. For example, if $\alpha = .1$ and $n = 25$,

$$.1 = P_{\mu=0}(\bar{X} > K) = 1 - \Phi\left(\frac{K - 0}{2/\sqrt{25}}\right).$$

so that

$$\frac{5K}{2} = 1.28 \quad \text{or} \quad K = .512.$$

As in this last example, the method used to determine a best critical region in the space of possible sample points frequently introduces a natural test statistic that is easier to work with than the likelihood ratio or than X itself. The critical region is then defined in terms of this statistic. If the likelihood ratio $f_0(X)/f_1(X)$ is a monotone increasing function of a statistic T, then the Neyman–Pearson test is equivalent to a critical region of the form $T < K'$. In particular, if the hypotheses being tested are defined by values θ_0 and θ_1 of a real parameter θ, and the family $\{f(x; \theta)\}$ has a monotone likelihood ratio with respect to the statistic T, then the Neyman–Pearson test is equivalent to the critical region $T < K'$, when $\theta_0 < \theta_1$.

If X has a distribution in the general exponential family with one parameter θ:

$$f(x; \theta) = B(\theta)e^{Q(\theta)S(x)}h(x),$$

and H_0 and H_1 are defined by $\theta = \theta_0$ and $\theta = \theta_1$, respectively, then the likelihood ratio is a monotone increasing function of $S(X)$ if $Q(\theta_0) > Q(\theta_1)$, and the Neyman–Pearson test is of the form $S(X) < K$. If $Q(\theta_0) < Q(\theta_1)$, it is of the form $S(X) > K$. If (as in Example 6–10) the states θ_0 and θ_1 are particular values of a real parameter θ and the density $f(x; \theta)$ is in the exponential family with a monotone increasing $Q(\theta)$, then the test $S(X) > K$ is most powerful for any θ_0 against any θ_1 that is larger than θ_0.

6.2.2 Other Properties of Neyman–Pearson Tests

The tests given in the Neyman–Pearson lemma, to be referred to as "Neyman–Pearson tests," are asserted in that lemma to be most powerful for a given α. It is immediate, because of the symmetry of the problem, that they also have the smallest α among tests with no larger β. Thus, in the plot of R_0 vs. R_1 (the risks under H_0 and H_1, respectively, for a given test) one finds no points (that is, no tests) directly below a point representing a Neyman–Pearson test, and no points directly to the left. This suggests that the Neyman–Pearson tests are admissible, but does not prove it. For, if the likelihood ratio has a discrete distribution, not all values of α are assumed by likelihood ratio tests. In such cases the Neyman–Pearson lemma can be extended to provide a most powerful test for a specified α, a randomized test that will reject H_0 if $f_0(x)/f_1(x) < K$ and reject H_0 according to a random device if the ratio equals K. This means that there are no tests represented by points below or to the left of the curve representing this extended family of Neyman–Pearson tests.

The likelihood ratio procedure guaranteed by the Neyman–Pearson lemma to be most powerful for simple H_0 and H_1, can be shown to be a modified maximum likelihood procedure. According to the maximum likelihood principle given in Section 4.4.4, the action to take is that which would be appropriate if the state of nature were the θ that maximizes the likelihood function $f(X; \theta)$. In the present context, with only two states, the principle would call for rejecting H_0 if $f(X; H_0) < f(X; H_1)$, or in the above notation, if

$$\frac{f_0(X)}{f_1(X)} < 1.$$

The reverse inequality would call for accepting H_0.

EXAMPLE 6–11. In testing between $\mu = 0$ and $\mu = 1$ in a normal population with $\sigma^2 = 4$, the critical region defined by $f_0(x) < f_1(x)$ is (using the calculations of Example 6–10) equivalent to

$$\exp\left[-\sum(2X_i - 1)/8\right] < 1,$$

or

$$\bar{X} > \tfrac{1}{2}.$$

The corresponding error sizes are equal: $\alpha = \beta$.

As seen in Example 6–11, the maximum likelihood procedure clearly does not take into account the different regrets that might be associated with the two types of error. A *modified maximum likelihood* procedure calls for acting as though the state of nature were the θ that maximizes $w(\theta)L(\theta) = w(\theta)f(X; \theta)$, where $w(\theta)$ is a weighting function indicating a gain in utility for a correct decision when θ is the state relative to zero gain for an incorrect decision. In the case at hand, H_1 is accepted (H_0 rejected) if the sample X is such that

$$w(H_0)f_0(X) < w(H_1)f_1(X),$$

or

$$\frac{f_0(X)}{f_1(X)} < \frac{w(H_1)}{w(H_0)} = \text{constant}.$$

This is a Neyman–Pearson test and therefore is most powerful.

It is also of interest to know that in the simple two-state case being considered, a Bayes solution is most powerful. To see this, consider prior probabilities g_0 for H_0 and g_1 for H_1 and the corresponding posterior probability function:

$$h(\theta \mid X = x) = \begin{cases} \dfrac{g_0 f_0(x)}{g_0 f_0(x) + g_1 f_1(x)}, & \text{if } \theta = H_0, \\[3mm] \dfrac{g_1 f_1(x)}{g_0 f_0(x) + g_1 f_1(x)}, & \text{if } \theta = H_1. \end{cases}$$

The posterior expected losses are

$$\begin{cases} E_h[\ell(\theta, A)] = \dfrac{b g_1 f_1(x)}{f(x)}, \\[3mm] E_h[\ell(\theta, B)] = \dfrac{a g_0 f_0(x)}{f(x)}, \end{cases}$$

where $f(x) = g_0 f_0(x) + g_1 f_1(x)$. The Bayes procedure is then to take action A or B according to which of these posterior expected losses is the smaller, taking action B (rejecting H_0) if

$$a g_0 f_0(x) < b g_1 f_1(x),$$

or

$$\frac{f_0(x)}{f_1(x)} < \frac{b g_1}{a g_0} = \text{constant},$$

again a Neyman–Pearson test.

Problems

6–20. Let m denote the parameter of a Poisson distribution, and suppose it is desired to test $H_0: m = m_0$ against $H_1: m = m_1$, where $m_1 > m_0$.

(a) Determine the nature of the best test based on a sample $(X_1, \ldots, X_n)$, and the α and β for the test with critical region $\sum X_i > 4$, when $n = 3$, $m_0 = 1$, $m_1 = 2$.

(b) Assuming that the sample size turns out to be large enough for a normal approximation, determine approximately the sample size and critical boundary corresponding to $\alpha = \beta = .01$ for the best test.

6–21. Determine the best type of critical region for testing θ_0 against θ_1, where $\theta_1 > \theta_0$, in the negative exponential density: $\theta \exp(-\theta x)$, $x > 0$.

6–22. Consider testing $\sigma = \sigma_0$ against $\sigma = \sigma_1$ in a normal population with given mean μ. Obtain the most powerful test, given $\sigma_1 > \sigma_0$, and determine the sample size and critical boundary corresponding to $\alpha = \beta = .01$ and $\sigma_0 = 2$, $\sigma_1 = 3$.

6–23. Obtain the most powerful test for θ_0 against θ based on a random sample from $f(x; \theta) = B(\theta) \exp[Q(\theta)R(x)] h(x)$.

6–24. In Problem 4–94 there was obtained a statistic T in terms of which the likelihood ratio, given the following table of probabilities, is monotone:

	z_1	z_2	z_3	z_4	z_5
H_0	.2	.3	.1	.3	.1
H_1	.3	.1	.3	.2	.1

(a) Determine the most powerful tests (i) in terms of T, (ii) in terms of values of Z, the data whose distribution is given in the above table.

(b) Determine a most powerful test of size $\alpha = .3$, and compare the β of this test with the β of the test with critical region $\{z_4\}$.

6–25. Let X have the Cauchy density:

$$f(x; \theta) = \frac{1/\pi}{1 + (x - \theta)^2}.$$

(a) Determine the critical region in terms of X for the most powerful test of $H_0: \theta = 0$ against $H_1: \theta = 2$, defined by $\Lambda = f(X; 0)/f(X; 2) < 5$. Calculate the error sizes for this test.

(b) Repeat (a) for the test that rejects $\theta = 0$ if $\Lambda < 17/37$.

(c) Are the procedures obtained in (a) and (b) monotone? (Why could you not anticipate a monotone procedure for every α as most powerful for that α?) Are there any most powerful monotone procedures? (*Hint*: Try $\Lambda < 1$.)

6–26. Show that the relation between α and β for the family of Neyman–Pearson tests is monotone nonincreasing. (That is, "the larger the α, the smaller the β.")

6–27. Show that if the statistic $\Lambda = f_0(X)/f_1(X)$ has a continuous distribution then there is a Neyman–Pearson test for each α on the interval $0 \le \alpha \le 1$.

6.3   Theory for the General Case

The risk function for a test was seen in Section 6.1 to depend (given constant losses a, b) on the *power function* of the test:

$$\pi(\theta) = P(\text{test rejects } H_0 \mid \theta).$$

For a test defined by a critical region C, the power function is

$$\pi_C(\theta) = P(C \mid \theta),$$

and for a test defined by a function $\phi(x)$, the probability of rejecting H_0 when $X = x$, it is

$$\pi_\phi(\theta) = E_\theta[\phi(X)].$$

That any test can be viewed as a randomized test based on a sufficient statistic can be seen as follows. Let $T = t(X)$ be sufficient for the family $\{f(x; \theta)\}$, and consider an arbitrary test $\phi(X)$. The conditional expectation of any function of the observations, given $T = t$, is independent of θ; and so a function of t is defined by

$$h(t) = E(\phi(X) \mid T = t).$$

This defines a randomized test, namely, reject H_0 with probability $h(t)$ if $T = t$ is observed. The power function of this test is

$$\pi_h(\theta) = E_\theta[h(T)] = E_\theta\{E[\phi(X) \mid T]\}$$

$$= E\{E_\theta[\phi(X) \mid T]\} = E_\theta[\phi(X)] = \pi_\phi(\theta),$$

precisely the same as the power function of the given test $\phi(x)$.

6.3.1   Test Properties in Terms of Power

A procedure was called *consistent* if, as the sample size tends to infinity, the expected regret tends to zero. This will occur if the power function tends to 0 for θ in H_0 and tends to 1 for θ in H_1; in other words, if it tends to the ideal power function at each θ.

A procedure d was said to *dominate* a procedure d' if $R(\theta, d) \leq R(\theta, d')$ for all θ. In terms of power, then, a test ϕ will dominate ϕ' if

$$\begin{cases} \pi_\phi(\theta) \leq \pi_{\phi'}(\theta), & \text{for } \theta \text{ on } H_0, \\ \pi_\phi(\theta) \geq \pi_{\phi'}(\theta), & \text{for } \theta \text{ on } H_1. \end{cases}$$

Figure 6–10 shows power curves for tests ϕ and ϕ' such that ϕ dominates ϕ'.

A procedure d was called *unbiased* if for all θ and θ',

$$E_\theta[\ell(\theta', d(X))] \geq E_\theta[\ell(\theta, d(X))].$$

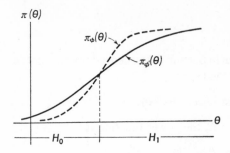

Figure 6–10.

In the present context this would imply that if θ is in H_0, and θ' is in H_0,

$$E_\theta[\ell(\theta', d(X))] = a\pi(\theta) \geq E_\theta[\ell(\theta, d(X))] = a\pi(\theta).$$

For θ in H_0 and θ' in H_1, it implies that

$$E_\theta[\ell(\theta', d(X))] = b[1 - \pi(\theta)] \geq E_\theta[\ell(\theta, d(X))] = a\pi(\theta).$$

The first of these conditions is not a restriction, and so for θ in H_0,

$$b[1 - \pi(\theta)] \geq a\pi(\theta).$$

Similarly, for θ in H_1, unbiasedness requires that

$$a\pi(\theta) \geq b[1 - \pi(\theta)].$$

That is, it must be that

$$\begin{cases} \pi(\theta) \leq \dfrac{b}{a + b}, & \text{for } \theta \text{ in } H_0, \\[2mm] \pi(\theta) \geq \dfrac{b}{a + b}, & \text{for } \theta \text{ in } H_1. \end{cases}$$

The power function must therefore be smaller for any θ in H_0 than for any θ in H_1. This last condition is usually taken as the definition of an unbiased test; if it is fulfilled, then there are losses a and b such that $b/(a + b)$ is an upper bound for $\pi(\theta)$ on H_0 and a lower bound for $\pi(\theta)$ on H_1, in which case the general definition of an unbiased procedure is fulfilled.

6.3.2 *Uniformly Most Powerful Tests*

In the case of simple H_0 and H_1, a test was called most powerful among the class of tests having no larger α's if it had maximum power for H_1. When H_1 is composite, the power for H_1 depends on which state of H_1 is true; consequently a test that is most powerful for certain states of H_1 may not be so for others. A test that is most powerful for each simple hypothesis in H_1 (for a given α) is called *uniformly most powerful* for simple H_0 against composite H_1.

EXAMPLE 6–12.   In testing $\mu = \mu_0$ against $\mu > \mu_0$ in a normal population with given variance, it was seen in Example 6–10 that against any single μ which exceeds μ_0, the test $\bar{X} > K$ is most powerful, K being determined so that the level of the test is α:

$$P_{\mu_0}(\bar{X} > K) = \alpha.$$

But then for each $\mu > \mu_0$,

$$P_\mu(\bar{X} > K) \geq P_\mu(C^*),$$

where C^* is any other test of level not exceeding α. Hence, $\bar{X} > K$ is uniformly most powerful against the composite $\mu > \mu_0$.

Next suppose that H_0 and H_1 are both composite. Let the critical region C have size

$$\alpha = \sup_{H_0} \pi_C(\theta).$$

The test defined by C is said to be *uniformly most powerful* with respect to the class of tests $\phi(X)$ with no larger levels:

$$\sup_{H_0} \pi_\phi(\theta) \leq \alpha,$$

provided

$$\pi_\phi(\theta) \leq \pi_C(\theta), \qquad \text{for all } \theta \text{ in } H_1.$$

A uniformly most powerful test can sometimes be found by locating a θ_0 such that for the simple hypothesis $\theta = \theta_0$, a region C is uniformly most powerful on H_1, and such that the power function of C at any other θ in H_0 is less than or equal to the power at θ_0.

EXAMPLE 6–13.   As in Example 6–12, consider testing $\mu \leq \mu_0$ against $\mu > \mu_0$ in a normal population with given variance. The power function of the test $\bar{X} > K$ is

$$\pi(\mu) = P(\bar{X} > K) = \Phi\left(\frac{\mu - K}{\sigma/\sqrt{n}}\right) \leq \Phi\left(\frac{\mu_0 - K}{\sigma/\sqrt{n}}\right) = \alpha,$$

for any $\mu \leq \mu_0$. Then, since $\bar{X} > K$ is uniformly most powerful among all tests whose type I error at μ_0 does not exceed α, it is automatically uniformly most powerful among the smaller class of tests whose power is no larger than

$$\sup_{H_0} \pi(\mu) = \pi(\mu_0) = \alpha,$$

at *every* μ in H_0.

A uniformly most powerful test is necessarily an unbiased test. For, given a uniformly most powerful test of level α, the randomized test defined by $\phi(X) \equiv \alpha$ for all X has level α and has power α at each θ in H_1. The UMP test must therefore have power at least α at each θ in H_1, and so is unbiased.

A uniformly most powerful test need not always exist. Perhaps the most common situation of this kind is that of testing $\theta_1 \le \theta \le \theta_2$ against the alternative: $\theta > \theta_2$ or $\theta < \theta_1$. The possibility that a uniformly most powerful test may not exist in the case of a simple H_0 and a two-sided alternative can be seen as follows: A UMP test is unbiased, and its power function therefore has a minimum at $H_0 : \theta = \theta_0$. On the other hand, a most powerful test of θ_0 against θ_1 where $\theta_1 > \theta_0$ would have a power function that in general would be increasing as θ passes through θ_0. For some θ's just to the right of θ_0, it would exceed the power function with a minimum at θ_0. This excess power on one side of θ_0 is paid for in considerably less power on the other. The following example illustrates this point.

EXAMPLE 6–14. Referring to Example 6–7 consider also the randomized test that calls for rejection of $p = .5$ when $S = 4$ or 5, and for rejection of $p = .5$ with probability .6 when $S = 3$, the statistic S again denoting the number of successes in five trials. The power function here is

$$\pi(p) = 5p^4(1 - p) + p^5 + (.6)\,10p^3(1 - p)^2$$
$$= p^3(p - 2)(2p - 3).$$

The graph of this power function is shown in Figure 6–11 along with the power function corresponding to the rejection region $S = 0, 1, 4,$ or 5. The randomiza-

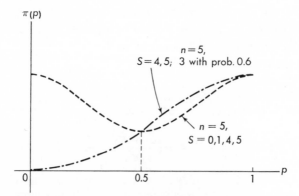

Figure 6–11. Power curves for Example 6–14.

tion here was fixed up so that these two tests have the same α, but this one-sided test is more powerful than the symmetric one for $p > .5$. This extra power is achieved by sacrificing power on $p < .5$. At any rate, it is clear that the symmetric test is *not* UMP, although it is unbiased.

6.3.3 Monotone Problems

In a problem in which the states of nature are indexed by a single real parameter θ, the regret function is monotone only if the states in H_0 all lie to one side of those in H_1. Moreover, the losses $a(\theta)$ and $b(\theta)$ must be nondecreasing as θ moves away from H_1 and H_0, respectively, a condition that is fulfilled in case $a(\theta) \equiv a$ and $b(\theta) \equiv b$. One approach in testing in such a case is to represent H_0 by a single state θ_0 in H_0 and H_1 by a single state θ_1 in H_1, to construct the Neyman–Pearson test for θ_0 against θ_1, and then to study the performance of this test in the original problem. This technique actually produces a uniformly most powerful test if the likelihood ratio is monotone.

Suppose, then, that $\{f(x; \theta)\}$ has a monotone likelihood ratio in terms of the statistic $T = t(X)$, and let C be the critical region of a Neyman–Pearson test for $\theta = \theta_0$ against $\theta = \theta_1$, where $\theta_0 < \theta_1$. It will now be shown that the power function of the test C is a monotone increasing function of θ. For this purpose, consider arbitrary θ' and θ'' with $\theta' < \theta''$. Because C is equivalent to $T < K$, which in turn is equivalent to $f(X; \theta')/f(X; \theta'') < K'$ (by the monotoneity of the likelihood ratio), it follows that C is also a Neyman–Pearson test for θ' against θ'' and so is most powerful for θ' against θ''. But this means that for *any* test $\phi(X)$ with the same power at θ', and in particular for the test $\phi(X) \equiv \gamma$, where $\gamma = \pi_C(\theta')$, the region C has greater power at θ'':

$$\pi_C(\theta'') \geq \pi_\phi(\theta'') = E_{\theta''}[\phi(X)] = E_{\theta''}[\gamma] = \gamma = \pi_C(\theta').$$

Since θ' and θ'' were arbitrary, with $\theta' < \theta''$, this last inequality shows that $\pi_C(\theta)$ is monotone nondecreasing.

The fact that the power function is monotone can be exploited, as in Example 6–13 to show that the Neyman–Pearson test for θ_0 against θ_1, a number greater than θ_0, is actually uniformly most powerful for testing $\theta \leq \theta^*$ against $\theta > \theta^*$. In particular, if the sample X has a distribution in the exponential family, with

$$f(x; \theta) = B(\theta)e^{Q(\theta)S(x)}h(x),$$

and if $Q(\theta)$ is monotone increasing, then the critical region $S(X) > K$ is uniformly most powerful for $\theta \leq \theta^*$ against $\theta > \theta^*$. (Obvious modifications of this statement hold if Q is monotone decreasing, or if H_0 is of the form $\theta \geq \theta^*$.)

EXAMPLE 6–15.   It is desired to test $\tau \leq 2$ against $\tau > 2$, where τ is the mean life of a system whose time to failure has the negative exponential distribution, with density $(1/\tau) \exp(-x/\tau)$, $x > 0$. The joint density of a random sample X is

$$f(x; \tau) = \frac{1}{\tau^n} \exp\left[-\frac{1}{\tau}\sum x_i\right], \qquad x_i > 0.$$

Since $-1/\tau$ is a monotone increasing function of τ, the critical region $\sum X_i >$ constant is UMP for $\tau \leq 2$ against $\tau > 2$.

Problems

6–28. Show that in a monotone problem the Neyman–Pearson test for θ_0 against θ_1, with $\theta_0 < \theta_1$, is unbiased for testing H_0 against H_1 if H_0 is to the left of H_1.

6–29. Show that the test in Problem 6–13 is unbiased and consistent.

6–30. Consider a normal population with mean 0 and unknown variance v. For $H_0 : v \le 1$ against $H_1 : v > 1$ determine a uniformly most powerful test based on a random sample of 25 observations, such that $\alpha = .05$. (Show that the population belongs to the exponential family, so that the UMP test can be deduced from that for the exponential family.)

6–31. Referring to Example 6–7, determine a test based on 100 observations with the same α as in that example but which is UMP against $p > .5$. Compare the power function of this test with that of the two-sided test in Example 6–7.

6–32. A "sampling plan" calls for accepting a lot of N articles, each of which can be classed as "good" or "defective," if a sample of n articles taken (without replacement) from the lot contains no more than c defectives. (The number c is called the "acceptance number" of the plan.) Show that the operating characteristic of such a plan is a monotone decreasing function of the number of defectives in the lot.

6–33. Construct the uniformly most powerful test of $m \le 2$ in a Poisson population, having the property that the probability of accepting $m \le 2$ when $m = 2.2$ and the probability of accepting $m > 2$ when $m = 1.8$ are each .01. (That is, determine the sample size and critical boundary.)

6.3.4 Likelihood Ratio Tests

In the case of simple H_0 and H_1 a likelihood ratio test (or modified maximum likelihood procedure) is most powerful. In the more general case of composite hypotheses, the maximum likelihood method does not guarantee a good test. (Indeed, examples have been constructed of maximum likelihood tests that are worse than acting in ignorance of the data.) Nevertheless, in many standard problems the method does give tests that have good characteristics, and it pays to consider the method.

As discussed in Section 6.2.2, the generalized maximum likelihood method consists in choosing the θ that maximizes the weighted likelihood function $w(\theta)L(\theta)$ and taking the action that would be correct if the maximizing θ were the true state of nature. This procedure applied to the testing of hypotheses is equivalent to determining the θ in H_0 that maximizes $w(\theta)L(\theta)$, determining the θ in H_1 that maximizes $w(\theta)L(\theta)$, and then acting as though that θ were true which gives the greater maximum. It is now assumed that the gain $w(\theta)$ is w_0 (a constant) for all θ in H_0 and w_1 (another constant) for all θ in H_1. With this assumption a critical region is defined to be the set of X such that

$$\sup_{\theta \text{ in } H_0} w_0 L(\theta) < \sup_{\theta \text{ in } H_1} w_1 L(\theta),$$

or

$$\Lambda^* \equiv \frac{\sup_{H_0} L(\theta)}{\sup_{H_1} L(\theta)} < \text{constant}.$$

(The "sup" or smallest upper bound is used here because it will exist when the "max" does not; whereas if the maximum exists, it is equal to the "sup.")

The numerator in Λ^* is thought of as the best "explanation" in H_0 of the observed result, and the denominator as the best explanation in H_1. If the ratio is large, a better explanation is found in H_0 than in H_1, and action A is taken; if the ratio is small, a better explanation is found in H_1, and action B is taken. Fixing the "constant" (deciding how large is "large") is again a matter of weighing the importance of the two types of errors.

In many instances it is convenient to alter the method slightly. Instead of Λ^* one considers

$$\Lambda = \frac{\sup_{H_0} L(\theta)}{\sup_{H_0 + H_1} L(\theta)} < \text{constant}.$$

Observe that if $\Lambda^* < 1$, then $\Lambda = \Lambda^*$, but if $\Lambda^* \geq 1$, then $\Lambda = 1$. The rejection region defined by $\Lambda < K$ is exactly the same as that defined by $\Lambda^* < K$, provided $K < 1$. In the problems in which we shall use the method, the least upper bound over $H_0 + H_1$ will be the same as the least upper bound over H_1, so that $\Lambda = \Lambda^*$.

For random samples it is again convenient to work with the logarithm of the likelihood function and to use $-\log \Lambda$, for which the critical region becomes $-\log \Lambda > \text{constant}$.

If a test is to be based on the statistic Λ (or on $-\log \Lambda$), it is necessary to know the distribution of Λ. This is ordinarily very complicated, and it is useful to know that the asymptotic distribution of $-2 \log \Lambda$ is of the chi-square type (Table II, Appendix), discussed in detail in Chapter 3. The parameter of this chi-square distribution is the difference[1] in the dimension of $H_0 + H_1$ and the dimension of H_0.

Often the likelihood ratio test can be shown equivalent to a test involving a more natural or convenient statistic, whose distribution is known or readily derived. This is illustrated in the following example.

EXAMPLE 6–16.   Consider testing $H_0: \mu = \mu_0$ against $H_1: \mu \neq \mu_0$ in a normal population with given variance v. The likelihood function is

$$L(\mu) = (2\pi v)^{-n/2} \exp\left[\frac{-1}{2v} \sum (X_i - \mu)^2\right].$$

---

[1] See Lehmann, E. [13], Section 7.13.

This is a maximum over all μ for $\hat{\mu} = \bar{X}$, the maximum likelihood estimate of μ, and so the denominator of Λ is $L(\bar{X})$. The numerator is just $L(\mu_0)$, since H_0 consists of the single point μ_0. The ratio Λ is then $L(\mu_0)/L(\bar{X})$, and

$$\log \Lambda = \log L(\mu_0) - \log L(\bar{X})$$

$$= -\frac{1}{2v} \{\sum (X_i - \mu_0)^2 - \sum (X_i - \bar{X})^2\}$$

$$= -\frac{n}{2v} [\bar{X} - \mu_0]^2.$$

The critical region $\log \Lambda <$ constant is therefore equivalent to

$$|\bar{X} - \mu_0| > \text{constant},$$

which is intuitively very appealing. (Incidentally, under H_0, $-2 \log \Lambda$ is not only *asymptotically* of the chi-square type, it *is* the square of a standard normal variable, and therefore exactly of the chi-square type with one "degree of freedom.")

Problems

6-34. Consider the problem of testing $v = v_0$ against $v \neq v_0$ in a normal population with *given* mean μ and unknown variance v. Discuss the nature of the likelihood ratio test in terms of the m.l.e. of $\hat{v}$.

6-35. Construct the likelihood ratio test for $\theta = \theta_0$ against $\theta \neq \theta_0$ in the density $\theta \exp(-\theta x)$, $x > 0$, obtaining as the critical region: $\bar{X} \exp(-\theta_0 \bar{X}) <$ constant. Sketch the graph of this function of $\bar{X}$ and indicate the corresponding critical region in terms of $\bar{X}$. Is this symmetrical about the population mean corresponding to θ_0? (In practice, one would probably take symmetrical tails for the rejection region, even though the right and left boundaries would correspond to different values of Λ, using the likelihood ratio notion only to justify the selection of a two-tailed critical region.)

6-36. Consider testing $p = .5$ against $p \neq .5$, using three independent observations on a Bernoulli variable. Construct the probability distribution of the statistic Λ under H_0.

6-37. Determine the likelihood ratio test of $v = v_0$ against $v = v_1$, where v is the variance of a sample from a normal population with unknown mean μ and variance v. Obtain also the power function of the test.

6-38. Obtain the form of the likelihood ratio test of $\mu = \mu_0$ against $\mu \neq \mu_0$, where μ is the mean of a normal population with unknown variance v, in terms of the sample mean and sample variance.

6-39. An observation Z takes on one of four values according to one of the three distributions or states of nature as shown in the following table of probabilities:

	z_1	z_2	z_3	z_4
θ_1	.2	.3	.1	.4
θ_2	.5	.1	.2	.2
θ_3	.3	0	.4	.3

(a) Determine the critical regions of all likelihood ratio tests for $\theta = \theta_1$ against $\theta = \theta_2$ or θ_3, and the significance level of each test.
(b) Determine the statistic $T = t(Z)$ that is the maximum likelihood estimate of θ.

6.4   Fitting and Comparing Distributions

Goodness of fit tests are used to test the hypothesis that nature is in a certain specified state when the alternative hypothesis is the general one that nature is not in that state, or that nature is in one of a family of states when the alternative is that the state of nature is not one of that family.

In the case of a discrete random variable X with a finite number of possible values $x_1, \ldots, x_k$ with corresponding probabilities $p_1, \ldots, p_k$, the null hypothesis is

$$H_0: \quad p_1 = \pi_1, \ldots, \quad \text{and} \quad p_k = \pi_k,$$

where $\pi_1, \ldots, \pi_k$ are specified numbers on the interval $[0, 1]$ whose sum is 1. The basis for testing H_0 is a random sample of n observations on X, usually presented in a tabulation such as this:

Value	x_1	x_2	$\cdots$	x_k
Frequency	f_1	f_2	$\cdots$	f_k

The statistic $(f_1, \ldots, f_k)$ is sufficient, inasmuch as the joint probability function of a random sample is

$$f(x; p) = p_1^{f_1} p_2^{f_2} \cdots p_k^{f_k},$$

which depends on the observations $(X_1, \ldots, X_n)$ only through the frequencies $f_1, \ldots, f_k$.

A likelihood ratio test for $p = \pi$ against $p \neq \pi$ is constructed as follows: The likelihood function is the above joint probability function, considered as a function of p for given f's:

$$L(p) = p_1^{f_1} \cdots p_k^{f_k}.$$

Its maximum on the simple hypothesis $p = \pi$ is just $L(\pi)$. Its maximum on $H_0 + H_1$ was found in Example 5–16 to be achieved for $p = \hat{p}$, where $\hat{p}_i = f_i/n$. Therefore,

$$\Lambda = \frac{L(\pi)}{L(\hat{p})} = \frac{\pi_1^{f_1} \cdots \pi_k^{f_k}}{(f_1/n)^{f_1} \cdots (f_k/n)^{f_k}} = n^n \prod_{i=1}^{k} \left(\frac{\pi_i}{f_i}\right)^{f_i}.$$

The likelihood ratio test is then to reject H_0 for $\Lambda <$ constant. The value of the constant to use is determined by an assignment of an α from the distribution of Λ under H_0. Problem 6–36 illustrates the fact that even for small samples, the calculation of the distribution of Λ under H_0 may not be trivial. Thus the large sample distribution of $-2 \log \Lambda$ is useful. Here, $-2 \log \Lambda$ is asymptotically chi-square with $k - 1$ degrees of freedom, and the rejection limit is simply the $100(1 - \alpha)$th percentile of that distribution. (The numerator of Λ is a maximum over a space of dimension 0; the denominator is a maximum over a space of dimension $k - 1$, since the k parameters $p_1, \ldots, p_k$ are restricted by the condition that $p_1 + \cdots + p_k = 1$.)

EXAMPLE 6–17.   To test the equal likelihood of the six faces of a die, the die is cast 120 times with the following results:

Face	1	2	3	4	5	6
Frequency	18	23	16	21	18	24

The quantity $-2 \log \Lambda$ is computed to be

$$-2[120 \log 120 + 120 \log (\tfrac{1}{6}) - 18 \log 18 - 23 \log 23 - \cdots - 24 \log 24] \doteq 2.9.$$

The 5 per cent rejection limit is 11.1 (the ninety-fifth percentile of the chi-square distribution with five degrees of freedom), and so at the 5 per cent level, the null hypothesis of equal likelihood of the faces is accepted.

It should be pointed out that in this discrete problem and in the test, there is no need for a numerical coding of the possible outcomes, and that if there is one inherent in the problem, this is not used.

The null hypothesis that a population distribution is given by a certain density function $f_0(x)$ can be tested approximately by discretizing the population and applying the above procedure. The range of possible values of X can be divided into a finite number of "class intervals" or "cells" $S_1, \ldots, S_k$. Each cell has a certain probability under the assumption that the state is $f(x)$:

$$p_i = P(X \text{ in } S_i) = \int_{S_i} f(x)\, dx,$$

and the test for $p = \pi$ [with $\pi_i = P_{H_0}(X \text{ in } S_i)$] is an approximate test of $f(x) = f_0(x)$ against $f(x) \neq f_0(x)$. The designation of the cells is not unique. Further, the distribution of a random variable involves a definite ordering of its values, which does not enter at all into this kind of test.

Another approach to the problem of testing $f(x) = f_0(x)$ against $f(x) \neq f_0(x)$ is to consider the discrepancy between the observed sample distribution function and the distribution function corresponding to $f_0(x)$. The ordering of the values is brought in, and no classification into cells is required in using such an approach. Various tests result from the different ways in which the "discrepancy" can be measured. This approach is taken up in Sections 6.4.2 and 6.4.3.

A goodness-of-fit test is usually employed when the alternative is not very well defined, so that the notion of power is not especially helpful in selecting a test. When the alternative *is* rather clear cut, it is usually the case that other tests are more powerful. For instance, a goodness-of-fit test can be used to test $\mu = \mu_0$ in a normal population with given variance; but if the alternative is that $\mu = \mu_1 > \mu_0$, a test of the form $\bar{X} > K$ is most powerful.

A somewhat disconcerting aspect of goodness-of-fit tests (shared by tests in other cases in which H_0 is simple and the composite H_1 includes states that are arbitrarily close in some sense to H_0) is that if these tests are consistent, a sufficiently large sample would almost surely call for rejection of H_0. That is, the actual state of nature is almost certainly not precisely the one set up as H_0, even though it may be practically close enough so that one would really want to accept H_0 (act as though H_0 were true). The point is that, usually, testing a simple hypothesis against a highly composite alternative is not exactly the problem that should be posed.

6.4.1 The Classical Chi-Square Test

It is natural to consider the differences $(f_i - n\pi_i)$ as related to the goodness of fit of the observed frequencies f_i to the expected frequencies $n\pi_i$. If these differences are larger than sampling fluctuations would ordinarily produce, there would be reason to reject the π's as the true cell probabilities. Pearson introduced in 1900 the following measure, which is large when the differences $(f_i - n\pi_i)$ are large:

$$\chi^2 = \sum_{i=1}^{k} \frac{(f_i - n\pi_i)^2}{n\pi_i}.$$

Aside from intuitive arguments that can be and have been proposed for this statistic, one of its virtues is that its asymptotic distribution is known under H_0. This asymptotic distribution, in fact, is identical with that of $-2 \log \Lambda$, namely, the chi-square distribution with $k - 1$ degrees of freedom.[1]

The asymptotic distribution of χ^2 is suggested intuitively by the following reasoning (suggested by R. A. Fisher). The joint distribution of the frequencies $(f_1, \ldots, f_k)$ is multinomial:

$$P(f_1 = v_1, \ldots, f_k = v_k) = \frac{n!}{f_1! \cdots f_k!} p_1^{v_1} \cdots p_k^{v_k}.$$

[1] A derivation of this fact is found, for instance, in Reference [4], p. 417 ff.

But these probabilities also give the conditional distribution of k independent Poisson variables $Y_1, \ldots, Y_k$ with parameters $np_1, \ldots, np_k$ (where $p_1 + \cdots + p_k = 1$), given that $Y_1 + \cdots + Y_k = n$. The standardized variables $Z_i = (Y_i - np_i)/(np_i)$ are then asymptotically normally (and independently) distributed, so that $\sum (Y_i - np_i)^2/(np_i)$ is asymptotically the sum of k squares of standard normal variables. It will be shown in Problem 7–20 that the *conditional* distribution of such a sum, given $Z_1 + \cdots + Z_k = 0$, is the chi-square distribution with $k - 1$ degrees of freedom. The linear restriction reduces the number of degrees of freedom by one.

EXAMPLE 6–18.   Given the problem and data of Example 6–17:

Face	1	2	3	4	5	6
Frequency	18	23	16	21	18	24

The statistic χ^2 is computed as follows:

$$\chi^2 = \tfrac{1}{20}[(18 - 20)^2 + (23 - 20)^2 + \cdots + (24 - 20)^2] \doteq 2.5.$$

The value of $-2 \log \Lambda$ was given in Example 6–17 as 2.9.

In order that the asymptotic distribution apply with reasonable accuracy, it would seem necessary that the expected frequencies (which are the Poisson parameters in the above intuitive argument) should be large. Experience has suggested that when there are several classes, a few of them can have relatively small expected frequencies, even below 1. But generally the classes should be chosen so that not all expected frequencies are that small and should be, say, five or more.[2]

A modification of the chi-square test can be used to test a distribution in which the class expected frequencies depend on unknown parameters. The statistic used is

$$\chi^2 = \sum_{i=1}^{k} \frac{[f_i - np_i(\hat{\theta})]^2}{np_i(\hat{\theta})}.$$

where $p_i(\theta) = P_\theta(X = x_i)$ and $\hat{\theta}$ is an estimate of θ based on the sample. It can be shown[3] that if $\hat{\theta}$ is a BAN estimate of θ, the limiting distribution of the test statistic is again of the chi-square type, but now with $k - 1 - r$ degrees of freedom, where r is the dimension of θ (that is, the number of real parameters being estimated). Reduction of the number of degrees of freedom pulls in the critical boundary so that χ^2 has to be smaller for acceptance at a given level.

[2] A detailed discussion of the selection of class intervals is found in the expository article by W. G. Cochran, "The χ^2 test of goodness and fit," *Ann. Math. Stat.* 23, 315–345 (1952).

[3] See Cramer, H. [4], p. 424 ff.

This should not be unexpected, inasmuch as the fit is bound to be better when values from the sample are used for the parameters. Indeed, a *perfect* fit ($\chi^2 = 0$) can be achieved by estimating each cell probability (as a population "parameter") with the corresponding sample relative frequency; this would mean that $r = k - 1$, and no degrees of freedom would be left to test goodness of fit. But as long as there are at least two more cells than unknown parameters, there is residual information in the sample with which to test goodness of fit, after estimation of the parameters.

EXAMPLE 6–19.   Five "coins" with identical but unknown values of $p = P(\text{Heads})$ are tossed together 100 times to test the hypothesis that the number of Heads per toss follows a binomial distribution. (Perhaps some kind of dependence is introduced in the tossing process.) The results are given as follows:

Number of heads	0	1	2	3	4	5
Frequency	3	16	36	32	11	2

The maximum likelihood estimate of p is the mean number of Heads per five coins divided by five, which turns out to be 0.476. Using this to calculate the cell probabilities by the binomial formula, one obtains the following expected frequencies:

$$4.0, \quad 17.9, \quad 32.6, \quad 29.6, \quad 13.5, \quad 2.4.$$

The value of χ^2 is then found to be

$$\chi^2 = \frac{(3 - 4)^2}{4} + \cdots + \frac{(2 - 2.4)^2}{2.4} \doteq 1.53.$$

The 5 per cent rejection limit would be the ninety-fifth percentile of the chi-square distribution with $6 - 1 - 1 = 4$ degrees of freedom, which is 9.49. Since $1.53 < 9.49$, the null hypothesis is accepted.

There is a point that should be mentioned in connection with using a chi-square test of a continuous distribution with an unknown parameter. For instance, one might want to test the null hypothesis that a population is normal. The mean and variance must then be estimated from the sample, and the natural inclination is to use the sample mean and sample variance, since these are joint maximum likelihood estimates. Then the question arises: Should one use the sample mean and variance as computed from the original data, or from the frequency tabulation after regrouping? The answer is that neither of these procedures will guarantee an asymptotic chi-square distribution for χ^2, and that what is required is to use the maximum likelihood estimates based on the likelihood function

$$L(\mu, \sigma^2) = [p_1(\mu, \sigma^2)]^{f_1} \cdots [p_k(\mu, \sigma^2)]^{f_k}.$$

The maximizing μ and σ^2 are, to say the least, somewhat awkward to obtain, yet if one uses one of the naive estimates in this normal case, he may be operating at a significance level appreciably higher than intended. In some cases, including the Poisson, the error is not serious.

Problems

6-40. (a) Use the chi-square test for the hypothesis that $P(\text{Heads}) = 0.5$ on the basis of 640 tosses of a coin, of which 339 turn out to be Heads.

(b) Show that the chi-square test for a particular Bernoulli model is equivalent to a two-sided test based on the number of Heads in a random sample.

6-41. Test the hypothesis that X has a binomial distribution with $n = 4$ on the basis of these results:

x_i	0	1	2	3	4
f_i	6	38	58	47	11

6-42. Given the following data, test the hypothesis that the distribution involved is normal with mean 32 and variance 3.24:

Class Interval	Frequency
26.75–28.25	2
28.25–29.75	1
29.75–31.25	16
31.25–32.75	27
32.75–34.25	19
34.25–35.75	11
35.75–37.25	4

6-43. Test the hypothesis that the population is normal, using the data in Problem 6–42.

6-44. Mistakes in the first printing of a certain book were found in the following distribution. Test the hypothesis that the distribution is Poisson.

Number of mistakes on a page	0	1	2	4
Number of pages	221	34	11	1

---

[4] See H. Chernoff and E. L. Lehmann, "The use of the maximum likelihood estimates in χ^2 tests of goodness of fit," *Ann. Math. Stat.* **25**, 579 (1954).

6.4.2   The Kolmogorov–Smirnov Statistic

The sample distribution function:

$$F_n(x) = \frac{j}{n}, \qquad \text{for} \quad X_{(j)} \le x < X_{(j+1)}, \quad j = 0, \ldots, n,$$

(with $X_{(0)} = -\infty$ and $X_{(n+1)} = \infty$) will generally differ from the population distribution function. But if it differs from an assumed distribution $F(x)$ by "too much," this may serve as grounds to reject the hypothesis that $F(x)$ is the population distribution function. That is, the amount of the difference between the empirical and assumed distribution functions should be a useful statistic in determining whether or not to accept the assumed distribution function as correct.

It is the actual numerical difference $|F_n(x) - F(x)|$ that is used in the Kolmogorov–Smirnov test. More precisely, since this difference depends on x, the Kolmogorov–Smirnov statistic is taken to be the least upper bound of such differences:

$$D_n = \sup_{\text{all } x} |F_n(x) - F(x)|.$$

This statistic has a distribution, under H_0, which is independent of the c.d.f. $F(x)$ that defines H_0. Such a statistic is called *distribution-free*. (The chi-square statistic of the preceding section is asymptotically distribution-free.) That D_n is distribution-free will be demonstrated in Section 8.1.4.

For a given n, a single table is required for the distribution function of D_n and can be used for any $F(x)$. This table can be computed through the use of recursion formulas, and has been computed for various sample sizes (Table VI, Appendix). Asymptotic percentiles can be computed from the limiting distribution:

$$\lim_{n \to \infty} P(D_n < z/\sqrt{n}) = 1 - 2 \sum_{j=1}^{\infty} (-1)^{j-1} \exp(-2j^2 z^2)$$

$$\doteq 1 - 2 \exp(-2z^2).$$

The statistic D_n is essentially "two-sided," involving the *absolute* difference of $F(x)$ and $F_n(x)$. The critical region $D_n > $ const. is used to test $F(x)$ against the alternative that the c.d.f. is *not* $F(x)$.

EXAMPLE 6–20.   Consider testing the hypothesis that a distribution is normal with mean 32 and variance 3.24, using the ten observations: 31.0, 31.4, 33.3, 33.4, 33.5, 33.7, 34.4, 34.9, 36.2, 37.0. The sample distribution function and the population distribution function being tested are sketched in Figure 6–12. The maximum deviation is about .56.

According to Table VI, Appendix, the ninety-fifth percentile of the distribution of

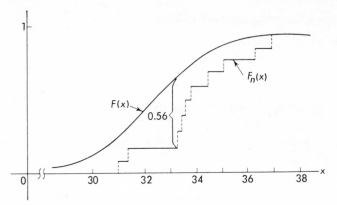

Figure 6–12.

D_{10} is .409. Since .56 > .409, the distribution being tested is rejected at the 5 per cent level.

It is not possible to talk about a power "function," since the alternatives are too numerous to be indexed by even a finite number of parameters. One known result concerning the power of the *K–S* test is shown in Figure 6–13.

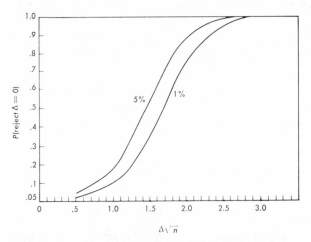

Figure 6–13. Reproduced from "The Kolmogorov-Smirnov Test for Goodness of Fit" by F. J. Massey, Jr., *Journal of the American Statistical Association*, 46 (1951). 68–78.

For each value of Δ, there is given a lower bound on the power among the class of alternatives $F_1(x)$ for which

$$\Delta = \sup_{\text{all } x} |F_1(x) - F_0(x)|.$$

One curve gives this bound for the test $D_n > K$ where K is chosen so that

$\alpha = .05$, and the other curve corresponds to $\alpha = .01$. Experiments de-scribed in the article from which the curves are taken indicate that the lower bounds given are usually quite conservative. It is also shown in that article that the K–S test is consistent and biased.

It has been assumed so far that the populations in question are continuous. However, it happens that in the case of a population that is not of the con-tinuous type, the probability of rejecting H_0 is no larger (under H_0) than that given in the table constructed for use in the continuous case. That is, using Table VI, Appendix, to determine the rejection limit for a given α results in a test with an α that is no larger than that given.

EXAMPLE 6–21.   Four coins are tossed 160 times, with results given in the tabu-lation below. Also shown in this tabulation are the values of the binomial dis-tribution function with $n = 4$ and $p = .5$ multiplied by 160, and the sample cumulative frequency function. Examination of the differences, also shown in the table, yields the value of D_n: $7/160 \doteq .044$.

Number of heads	0	1	2	3	4
Frequency	10	33	61	43	13
Sample cum. frequency	10	43	104	147	160
Cum. frequency under H_0	10	50	110	150	160
Differences	0	7	6	3	0

The 20 per cent rejection limit for a continuous population is

$$\frac{1.07}{\sqrt{160}} \doteq .085.$$

The test $D_n > .085$ in the present problem has then an α that does not exceed .20. Thus, at a level not exceeding .20, the null hypothesis is accepted, since D_n turned out to be .044, which does not exceed the rejection limit .085.

Since D_n is based on the notion of a distribution function, the values of the random variable X and their ordering play an essential role, as opposed to the circumstances of a chi-square test, in which any ordering of outcomes is not taken into account. In order to apply the K–S test to an experiment in which the outcomes are not inherently numerical, one would first have to set up an arbitrary coding of outcomes with numbers. This coding is not unique, and maximum deviations D_n can be different for different codings, as seen in the following example. This phenomenon suggests that the K–S test should not be used in such cases.

EXAMPLE 6–22.   To test the equal likelihood of the six faces of a die, it is cast 120 times, with the following resulting frequencies of the six faces: 18, 23, 16, 21,

18, 24. The sample distribution function has step heights proportional to 0, 18, 41, 57, 78, 96, 120, as compared with the step heights of the H_0 distribution, which are proportional to 0, 20, 40, 60, 80, 100, 120. The maximum discrepancy is $4/120 \doteq .033$, which is smaller than the 10 per cent rejection limit $1.22/\sqrt{120} = .111$. Thus, acceptance of H_0 is called for.

Suppose, however, that the following code is used: one dot $= 2$, two dots $= 5$, three dots $= 1$, four dots $= 4$, five dots $= 3$, and six dots $= 6$. Using the same sample of 120 tosses as above, we now find that the sample distribution function has step heights above the horizontal proportional to 16, 34, 52, 73, 96, 120. The maximum departure from the null distribution function is now $8/120 \doteq 0.067$, considerably closer to the rejection limit than with the original coding, even though the same experimental results have been used.

A one-sided K–S statistic is sometimes employed to test $F_0(x)$ against the one-sided alternative $F(x) \geq F_0(x)$, with $F(x) \not\equiv F_0(x)$. The statistic used is

$$D_n{}^+ = \sup_{\text{all } x} [F_n(x) - F_0(x)].$$

The distribution of this statistic under the null hypothesis is defined by[5]

$$P(D_{n+} > u) = \sum_{0 \leq k \leq n(1-u)} \binom{n}{k}\left(u + \frac{k}{n}\right)^{k-1} u\left(1 - u - \frac{k}{n}\right)^{n-k}.$$

The asymptotic formula

$$P\left(D_n{}^+ < \frac{x}{\sqrt{n}}\right) \doteq 1 - \exp(-2x^2)$$

was obtained by Smirnov.

An exposition of Kolmogorov–Smirnov tests and of the Cramér–von Mises tests to be considered in the next section is given in a paper by Darling.[6] This includes a consideration of what is and is not known concerning the relative power of such tests. For some kinds of alternatives the K–S test has a power advantage over the chi-square test. For testing a specific normal population against the alternative of a mean shifted to one side, the power of K–S does not compare favorably with that of the usual uniformly most powerful test. Chapman[7] considers the relative powers of various one-sided tests including that based on $D_n{}^+$.

No general treatment of a K–S type of test for the composite hypothesis $F_0(x; \theta)$ with θ unknown is available. However, it has been shown[8] that the

[5] See Birnbaum, Z. W., and Tingey, F. H. "One-sided confidence contours for distribution functions," in *Ann. Math. Stat*. **22**, 592 (1951).

[6] Darling, D. A. "The Kolmogorov–Smirnov, Cramér–von Mises tests," *Ann. Math. Stat*. **28**, 823 (1957).

[7] Chapman, D. G., "A comparative study of several one-sided goodness-of-fit tests," *Ann. Math. Stat*. **29**, 655 (1959).

[8] Kac, M., Kieffer, J., and Wolfowitz, J., "On tests of normality and other tests of fit based on distance methods," *Ann. Math. Stat*., **25**, 189 (1955).

K–S statistic, with (μ, σ^2) estimated by $(\bar{X}, s_x^2)$, yields a test for normality which is more powerful than the chi-square test. Of course, even in general, if one used the rejection limit for D_n, a value of D_n in excess of that limit should certainly call for rejection when estimates of parameters based on the sample are used in its computation, since adjusting the theoretical distribution on the basis of the sample would tend to improve the fit.

6.4.3   Other Tests

Other measures of discrepancy between two distribution functions lead to corresponding statistics for testing goodness of fit. Given a nonnegative weight function $G(y)$, the statistic

$$n \int_{-\infty}^{\infty} [F_n(x) - F(x)]^2 G[F(x)]\, dF(x),$$

like the K–S statistic, is distribution-free—its distribution does not depend on $F(x)$. Using such a statistic was proposed by Cramér and by von Mises; the particular form with weighting function $G \equiv 1$ was proposed by Smirnov, who then also obtained an expression for its limiting distribution. With $G \equiv 1$, the statistic reduces to

$$n\omega_n^2 = n \int_{-\infty}^{\infty} [F_n(x) - F(x)]^2\, dF(x) = n \int_0^1 [F_n^*(y) - y]^2\, dy.$$

Some of the percentiles of its asymptotic distribution are as follows[9]:

$P(n\omega_n^2 \le x)$	.80	.85	.90	.95	.98	.99
x	.241	.284	.347	.461	.620	.743

For computations in samples that are not too large, the following formula is useful (it is obtained by carrying out the integration indicated in $n\omega_n^2$):

$$n\omega_n^2 = \frac{1}{12n} + \sum_{j=1}^{n} \left\{ \frac{2j-1}{2n} - F(X_{(j)}) \right\}^2,$$

where $X_{(1)}, \ldots, X_{(n)}$ are the ordered observations and $F(x)$ the distribution function of the null hypothesis.

EXAMPLE 6–23.   Consider the ten observations of Example 6–20 for use in

---

[9] These entries come from an article by Anderson and Darling, "Asymptotic theory of certain 'goodness of fit' criteria based on stochastic processes," *Ann. Math. Stat.* **23**, 193 (1952). Computations by A. W. Marshall (*Ann. Math. Stat.*, **29**, 307 (1958)) indicate that the convergence to the asymptotic distribution is very rapid, the asymptotic expressions being useful even for n as small as three or four.

testing (as in that example) a normal distribution with mean 32 and standard deviation 1.8. For $X_{(1)}$,

$$F(X_{(1)}) = F(31) = \Phi\left(\frac{31 - 32}{1.8}\right) \doteq .29,$$

and

$$\left\{\frac{2 - 1}{20} - .29\right\}^2 \doteq .057.$$

Proceeding in this fashion, one finds $n\omega_n{}^2$ to be about 0.88, whereas for $\alpha = .05$, the rejection limit is .461 (from the table of the asymptotic distribution given above). The null hypothesis that the distribution is normal with mean 32 and standard deviation 1.8 is rejected at the 5 per cent level.

A test of the Cramér–von Mises type for the null hypothesis $F(x; \theta)$, where θ is an unknown parameter and estimated from the sample, has been constructed by Darling.[10] The test statistic is again $n\omega_n{}^2$ except that the value of θ used is a sample estimate of θ. If this estimate is properly chosen, the asymptotic distribution of the test statistic can be determined under H_0 and for certain problems is distribution-free.

The effect of grouping data in K–S and C–vM tests has been studied in a series of Russian papers.[11]

A somewhat different measure of discrepancy between theoretical and empirical distribution functions has been proposed by Sherman[12]:

$$\sum_{i=1}^{n+1}\left| F(X_{(i)}) - F(X_{(i-1)}) - \frac{1}{n+1}\right|,$$

where $X_{(0)} = -\infty$ and $X_{(n+1)} = \infty$. This statistic is suggested by the fact that the expected area under the population density curve between a pair of successive ordered observations is $1/(n + 1)$, as shown in Section 8.1.4. The exact distribution is given by Sherman, who also shows that it is asymptotically normal.

Another type of goodness of fit statistic for testing normality has been proposed by Shapiro and Wilk[13]; the statistic is approximately

$$W = r_{Y,m}{}^2,$$

where $Y_i = X_{(i)}$, X is the random sample being used for the test, m_i is[14] the

---

[10] Darling, D. A., "The Cramér–Smirnov test in the parametric case," *Ann. Math. Stat.* **26**, 1 (1955).

[11] Cf. the survey paper by D. A. Darling referred to in Section 6.4.2 (footnote, p. 332) for references.

[12] Sherman, B., "A random variable related to the spacing of sample values," *Ann. Math. Stat.* **21**, 339 (1950).

[13] Shapiro, S., and Wilk, M., "An analysis of variance test for normality," *Biometrika* **52** (1965), 591–611.

[14] The statistic actually proposed involves a set of constants *a* for which *2m* is an approximation.

expected value of the ith order statistic corresponding to a random sample from a standard normal population, and $r_{Y,m}$ is the correlation of the vectors Y and m. (Observe that because the correlation coefficient is unchanged by a linear transformation of either X or Z, the statistic W has to do only with normality, and not with a particular normal population.) The critical region used is of the form $W < K$. A table of critical values for sample sizes up to 20 is given in the referenced paper, as well as the results of an empirical study of power characteristics for various alternatives—results suggesting that this W-test will outperform the K–S test and the chi-square test. The adaptability of the basic idea to testing other distribution types (than normal) is under study.

6.4.4   Comparison of Distributions

Different populations have different distribution functions, and it is expected that samples from these different populations will have sample distribution functions that differ. Of course random sampling fluctuations can introduce a difference in sample distribution functions even though the samples be from the same population, but a very large discrepancy between sample distribution functions might reasonably serve as the basis for an inference that the populations are different.

Tests based on the discrepancy between sample distribution functions are ordinarily employed when the alternatives to the null hypothesis of identical populations include all ways in which the populations can differ, as opposed to problems in which the alternatives are that one population has simply "shifted" away from the other. Different ways of measuring discrepancies between sample distribution functions lead to different tests. The two-sample Kolmogorov–Smirnov test (or the Smirnov test) is based on the statistic D, defined as follows:

$$D = \sup_{\text{all } x} |F_m(x) - G_n(x)|,$$

where $F_m(x)$ is the sample distribution function of a sample of size m from X and $G_n(x)$ is the sample distribution function of a sample of size n from Y. Smirnov has shown that for large samples of sizes m and n:

$$P_{H_0}\left[D > z\left(\frac{1}{m} + \frac{1}{n}\right)^{1/2}\right] \doteq 2 \sum_{k=1}^{\infty} (-1)^{k-1} \exp[-2k^2 z^2],$$

the same function appearing on the right as showed up in the one-sample K–S test. Again the first-term approximation is very good and on the safe side. Using this, the above probability is seen to be approximately α if

$z = [-(\log \alpha/2)/2]^{1/2}$, and so a test with level α is obtained by rejecting H_0 for

$$D > \left[-\frac{1}{2}\left(\frac{1}{m} + \frac{1}{n}\right) \log \frac{\alpha}{2} \right]^{1/2}.$$

Values of this asymptotic rejection limit for $\alpha = .05$ and $\alpha = .01$ are given in Table VII, Appendix, along with small-sample rejection limits for these two levels.

EXAMPLE 6–24.   Consider the two samples of size 60 given in the accompanying frequency tabulations. The maximum absolute difference in cumulative relative frequencies is .1 and the 5 per cent rejection limit from Table VII (see Appendix) is about .25. The null hypothesis of identical distributions is accepted.

x_i	Frequencies		Cumulative Frequencies	
	Sample 1	Sample 2	Sample 1	Sample 2
0	5	6	5	6
1	9	2	14	8
2	4	5	18	13
3	5	7	23	20
4	7	8	30	28
5	2	4	32	32
6	8	4	40	36
7	4	9	44	45
8	9	6	53	51
9	7	9	60	60

The test just described is two-sided, since either positive or negative differences are counted. A one-sided test is provided by the one-sided statistic

$$D^+ = \sup_{\text{all } x} [F_m(x) - G_n(x)],$$

which would intuitively be appropriate for a one-sided class of alternatives, say, $F_Y(\lambda) < F_X(\lambda)$. The large sample distribution of D^+ was shown by Smirnov to be defined by

$$P\left[D^+ > z\left(\frac{1}{m} + \frac{1}{n}\right)^{1/2} \right] = \exp(-2z^2), \qquad z \geq 0.$$

From this it is evident that the large sample distribution of

$$\frac{4(D^+)^2 mn}{m + n}$$

is given by

$$P\left[\frac{4(D^+)^2 mn}{m + n} < u \right] = 1 - \exp(-u/2), \qquad u \geq 0,$$

which is of the negative exponential type and happens also to be the chi-square distribution function with two degrees of freedom.

EXAMPLE 6–25.   Had the data been gathered as in Example 6–24, but to test instead the hypothesis that the population distributions are identical against the alternative that population 2 is shifted to the right, the one-sided D^+ should be used. Since for the data obtained all the differences between the sample distribution functions are positive, $D^+ = D = .1$. Then, since

$$\frac{4(D^+)^2 mn}{m + n} = 1.2 < 5.99,$$

where 5.99 is the ninety-fifth percentile of the chi-square distribution with two degrees of freedom, the null hypothesis would be accepted at the 5 per cent level.

Problems

6–45.   Use the Kolmogorov–Smirnov statistic to test the hypothesis that X has a binomial distribution with $n = 4$ and $p = \frac{1}{2}$ on the basis of the following results:

x_i	0	1	2	3	4
f_i	6	38	58	47	11

6–46.   Use the Kolmogorov–Smirnov statistic to test the hypothesis that the data in Example 6–20 were obtained from a normal population with mean 34 and variance 3.24.

6–47.   Compute the power of the test $|\bar{X} - \mu_0| > K$, with K chosen so that $\alpha = .05$ and $n = 25$, at the alternative $\mu = \mu_0 + .6$ in a problem involving normal populations with known variance $\sigma^2 = 1$. Compare this with the lower bound (given by the curve in Figure 6–13) for the power of the K–S test.

6–48.   Discuss the construction of a confidence band about $F_n(x)$ based on the distribution of the K–S statistic. [A confidence band at level α would be defined by a pair of functions $A(x)$ and $B(x)$ such that $P[A(x) < F(x) < B(x)] = 1 - \alpha$, where A and B are determined by $F_n(x)$.]

6–49.   Carry out the details in Example 6–23.

6–50.   Determine a five per cent critical region in terms of $D_N{}^+$ for testing $F(x) = F_0(x)$ against the hypothesis $F(x) \geq F_0(x)$ for a sample of size 25. (Use the Smirnov asymptotic formula.)

6–51.   (a) Discuss the first-term approximation and the statement that it is on the safe side, for the distribution of D in Section 6.4.4.

(b) Verify the claim in Section 6.4.4 concerning the large sample distribution of $4(D^+)^2 mn/(m + n)$.

(c) Measurements of viscosity for a certain substance were made with the following results:

First day	37.0,	31.4,	34.4,	33.3,	34.9
	36.2,	31.0,	33.5,	33.7,	33.4
	34.8,	30.8,	32.9,	34.3,	33.3

Second day   28.4,   31.3,   28.7,   32.1,   31.9
                      32.8,   30.2,   30.2,   32.4,   30.7

Would you say the population has changed from one day to the next?

6.5   Sequential Tests

In testing a simple hypothesis against a simple alternative, the most powerful test was found to be given by a critical region of the form

$$\Lambda_n = \frac{f_0(X_1, \ldots, X_n)}{f_1(X_1, \ldots, X_n)} < K,$$

where $f_0(x)$ and $f_1(x)$ are the joint density functions of the observations (or
probability functions in the discrete case) corresponding to H_0 and H_1, respectively. Given any two of the four quantities α, β, n, and K, the other two
are determined by the relations

$$\alpha = P_{H_0}(\Lambda_n < K), \qquad \beta = P_{H_1}(\Lambda_n \geq K).$$

In carrying out such a test, one picks, say, α and β, and determines from them
values of n and K. He then gathers the data, using that n as the size of the
sample, computes Λ_n, and accepts or rejects H_0 according as $\Lambda_n \geq K$ or
$\Lambda_n < K$. No provision is made to fulfill the natural desire to obtain more
data when the nature of the sample is not sufficiently suggestive either of H_0
or of H_1 as to be really convincing. Nor, on the other hand, is there oppor-
tunity to cut the sampling short if a conclusion becomes obvious early in the
process of obtaining the sample. Of course nothing really *prevents* one from
doing these things—gathering, according to how things go, more or less data
than dictated by the choice of α and β; but it must be recognized that doing
them alters the test and makes the given error sizes meaningless.

A procedure of "double sampling" would be somewhat more satisfying.
For such a plan there is chosen a preliminary sample size m with corresponding constants C and D, and a second sample size $n - m$ with corresponding
constant K. The procedure is then to draw a sample of size m, compute Λ_m,
and

$$\begin{cases} \text{Accept } H_0, & \text{if } \Lambda_m \geq D, \\ \text{Reject } H_0, & \text{if } \Lambda_m \leq C, \\ \text{Draw a sample of size } n - m, & \text{if } C < \Lambda_m < D. \end{cases}$$

If the second sample is called for, it is drawn, Λ_n computed, and

$$\begin{cases} H_0 \text{ accepted}, & \text{if } \Lambda_n \geq K, \\ H_0 \text{ rejected}, & \text{if } \Lambda_n < K. \end{cases}$$

This idea can clearly be extended to plans with more than two stages at each of which a decision is made to reject, to accept, or (at stages prior to the last one) to continue sampling. The hope is that with such schemes one can get away with less sampling than would be necessary using a sample of fixed size, and such is usually the case. Of course, comparisons of sample sizes must be made on a probability basis, or on the average; for, the sample size in sequential plans is usually a random variable, since the decision to stop or to continue depends on the observations at hand.

In situations in which unknown parameters other than those of interest—"nuisance parameters"—make planning difficult, an adaptive scheme of sampling in stages might be considered, in which results in the early stages furnish a guide to more intelligent planning of the future stages.

The only sequential procedure to be studied here is the *sequential probability ratio test* of Wald. An extensive treatment is given by Wald [20], and its optimality properties are considered in a decision theoretic framework in the book by Blackwell and Girshick [2].

6.5.1 The Sequential Likelihood Ratio Test

Wald [20] first presented—and systematically studied—the following sequential test of a simple hypothesis against a simple alternative. Let H_0 denote the hypothesis that the population density (or probability function) is $f_0(x)$, and H_1 the hypothesis that it is $f_1(x)$. Numbers A and B are chosen, with $A < B$, and after each observation in a sequence the corresponding likelihood ratio is computed:

$$\Lambda_n = \frac{f_0(X_1, \ldots, X_n)}{f_1(X_1, \ldots, X_n)},$$

where the f_0 and f_1 denote the joint distributions of $X_1, \ldots, X_n$ under H_0 and H_1, respectively. The procedure is then as follows: Reject H_0 if $\Lambda_n \leq A$, accept H_0 if $\Lambda_n \geq B$, and obtain another observation if $A < \Lambda_n < B$. It is conceivable that such a procedure might never terminate, but this contingency will be shown to have probability zero, in Section 6.5.2.

If the observations in the sequence $X_1, X_2, \ldots$ are independent random variables, the likelihood ratio is a product:

$$\Lambda_n = \prod_{i=1}^{n} f_0(X_i)/f_1(X_i),$$

and in such a case the logarithm is often easier to work with:

$$\log \Lambda_n = \sum_{i=1}^{n} \log \left[f_0(X_i)/f_1(X_i) \right] = Z_1 + \cdots + Z_n,$$

where

$$Z_i = \log \left[f_0(X_i)/f_1(X_i) \right].$$

The sequence of Z's is again a sequence of independent random variables, if the X's are independent. The inequality for continuing sampling can be written in the form

$$\log A < \log \Lambda_n < \log B,$$

where usually $\log A < 0$ and $\log B > 0$. Figure 6–14 shows a plot of $(n, \log \Lambda_n)$ in a typical case, the points being connected by straight lines for

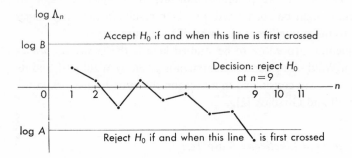

Figure 6–14.

ease in following the progress of the test. A decision is reached when the path first crosses a boundary; if that boundary is the upper one, H_0 is accepted, and if it is the lower one, H_0 is rejected. In either case, the sampling stops at that point.

In an actual situation the plot made would usually be neither Λ_n nor $\log \Lambda_n$, but some simpler statistic that arises naturally in the likelihood ratio. For instance, if the population distributions are in the exponential family, the log of the likelihood ratio for $\theta = \theta_0$ against $\theta = \theta_1$ is

$$\log \Lambda_n = n \log \left[B(\theta_0)/B(\theta_1) \right] + \left[Q(\theta_0) - Q(\theta_1) \right] \sum_{i=1}^{n} R(X_i),$$

and the inequality for continuing the sampling can be expressed in the form

$$C_1 + Dn < \sum_{i=1}^{n} R(X_i) < C_2 + Dn$$

where the constants C_1, C_2, and D depend on θ_0 and θ_1. Thus, one can plot two parallel lines, corresponding to the linear functions of n in the extremes of this last inequality, and simply cumulate the $R(X_i)$ graphically as the sampling proceeds.

EXAMPLE 6–26.   Consider testing $\theta = \theta_0$ against $\theta = \theta_1$, where $\theta_1 > \theta_0$, in a population with density $f(x; \theta) = (1/\theta) \exp(-x/\theta)$. The log of the likelihood ratio for a single observation is

$$Z = \log \frac{f(X; \theta_0)}{f(X; \theta_1)} = \log(\theta_0/\theta_1) - (\theta_0 - \theta_1)X,$$

and so

$$\log \Lambda_n = Z_1 + \cdots + Z_n = n \log(\theta_0/\theta_1) - (\theta_0 - \theta_1) \sum X_i.$$

The inequality for continuing sampling after the nth observation is then

$$\frac{1}{\theta_0 - \theta_1} [\log A + n \log(\theta_1/\theta_0)] < \sum X_i < \frac{1}{\theta_1 - \theta_0} [\log B + n \log(\theta_1/\theta_0)].$$

Error sizes for the sequential likelihood ratio test are easily expressed, formally, in terms of the numbers A and B which define the test:

$$\begin{cases} \alpha = P_{H_0}(\Lambda_1 \le A) + P_{H_0}(A < \Lambda_1 < B \text{ and } \Lambda_2 \le A) + \cdots; \\ \beta = P_{H_1}(\Lambda_1 \ge B) + P_{H_1}(A < \Lambda_1 < B \text{ and } \Lambda_2 \ge B) + \cdots. \end{cases}$$

Although easy to write down, these expressions are by no means easily computed. Moreover, one could not hope to *solve* these equations for A and B in terms of given α and β, despite the desirability of being able to do so in setting up a test to meet specified protection. Another approach is fortunately more fruitful.

The probability in terms of which α and β are defined is actually a probability on a sample space of infinite sequences, and in this probability measure, the set of sequences leading to a decision at a finite stage has been asserted to have probability 1. Moreover, the probability of a set of sequences leading to rejection, say, at stage k is really a marginal distribution in the space of values of the first k observations, $X = (X_1, \ldots, X_k)$, inasmuch as the decision to terminate the sampling comes from those observations. Thus, if E_k denotes the set of $(x_1, \ldots, x_k)$ that call for termination at stage k with a decision to reject H_0, and F_k the set calling for accepting H_0 at that stage, then

$$\alpha = P_{H_0}(\text{reject } H_0) = \sum P_{H_0}(E_k)$$

and

$$1 - \beta = P_{H_1}(\text{reject } H_0) = \sum P_{H_1}(E_k).$$

But according to the rule that determines the decision, the inequality $f_0(x) \le A f_1(x)$ holds at each point of E_k, so that

$$P_{H_0}(E_k) = \int_{E_k} f_0(x)\,dx \le A \int_{E_k} f_1(x)\,dx = A P_{H_1}(E_k).$$

Summing on k yields

$$\alpha = \sum P_{H_0}(E_k) \le A(1 - \beta).$$

A similar argument results in the inequality

$$\beta \le (1 - \alpha)/B.$$

Dividing these inequalities by, respectively, $1 - \beta$ and $1 - \alpha$ (which, for practical purposes can be assumed positive, since $\alpha = 1$ implies $\beta = 0$ and $\beta = 1$ implies $\alpha = 0$) one obtains

$$\frac{\alpha}{1 - \beta} \ge A \quad \text{and} \quad \frac{\beta}{1 - \alpha} \ge \frac{1}{B}.$$

These relations satisfied by the α and the β of the test defined by a given A and B do not exactly yield α and β,—but they almost do.

Since *in*equalities are obtained in this derivation simply because Λ_n does not usually attain *exactly* the value A or the value B, the inequalities are almost equalities. Indeed, in practice, A and B are taken to be *equal* to $\alpha/(1 - \beta)$ and $(1 - \alpha)/\beta$, respectively. Doing so, of course, means that the test actually carried out has error sizes somewhat different from those specified. Let α' and β' denote the actual sizes of the type I and type II errors of the test defined by the limits $A = \alpha/(1 - \beta)$ and $B = (1 - \alpha)/\beta$. According to the above inequalities, then,

$$\frac{\beta'}{1 - \alpha'} \le \frac{1}{B} = \frac{\beta}{1 - \alpha} \quad \text{and} \quad \frac{\alpha'}{1 - \beta'} \le A = \frac{\alpha}{1 - \beta}.$$

Multiplying these through to eliminate denominators and adding the results, one obtains

$$\alpha' + \beta' \le \alpha + \beta.$$

It could not be, therefore, that *both* $\alpha' > \alpha$ and $\beta' > \beta$; so, at most one of the error sizes will be larger than specified when using the approximate formulas for A and B. Further, it follows from the inequalities obtained that for small α and β,

$$\alpha' \le \frac{\alpha'}{1 - \beta'} \le \frac{\alpha}{1 - \beta} \doteq \alpha(1 + \beta),$$

and

$$\beta' \le \frac{\beta'}{1 - \alpha'} \le \frac{\beta}{1 - \alpha} \doteq \beta(1 + \alpha).$$

Thus the one error size that does increase does not increase by more than a factor of about $(1 + \alpha)$ or $(1 + \beta)$. For example, if both α and β are .05, the α' and β' actually achieved by using A and B as specified above are bounded by about .0525.

Although using the approximate values of A and B results in error sizes that are not appreciably larger than specified, it is possible that they are *smaller* than specified. This would only be disturbing in the sense that the statistician could get away with less sampling and still be within the desired α and β. This effect should be as slight as is the increase in α and β, since both are caused by the discontinuity of the sample number necessary to reach a decision. If one could imagine a continuous sample number, the formulas for A and B would be correct. Wald shows [20] (pp. 65–69) that the change in sample size is at most slight; in certain common cases it amounts to at most one or two in small samples and around 1 or 2 per cent in larger samples.

EXAMPLE 6–27. It is desired to test $H_0: p = .5$ against $H_1: p = .2$ in a Bernoulli population, using a sequential test with $\alpha = .1$ and $\beta = .2$. The likelihood ratio after n independent observations is

$$\Lambda_n = \frac{(.5)^f (.5)^{n-f}}{(.2)^f (.8)^{n-f}},$$

where f is the number of successes in n independent trials. Thus,

$$\Lambda_{n+1} = \begin{cases} (5/2)\Lambda_n, & \text{if success occurs in the } (n+1)\text{st trial,} \\ (5/8)\Lambda_n, & \text{if failure occurs in the } (n+1)\text{st trial.} \end{cases}$$

A success raises the value of Λ_n, and a failure lowers it. If Λ_n falls below the value $A = .1/(1 - .2) = 1/8$, H_0 is rejected in favor of the lower value $p = .2$. If Λ_n reaches $B = (1 - .1)/.2 = 9/2$, H_0 is accepted. Otherwise sampling is continued.

If a sequence of observations turns out to be $T, H, H, T, H, T, H, H, T, T, \ldots$, the corresponding Λ_n's are

.625, 1.56, 3.91, 2.44, 6.10, 3.82, 9.53, 23.8, 14.9, 9.30, ...

At the fifth observation H_0 is accepted and the sampling stopped (despite the return at the sixth observation to the region between A and B, since this observation would not have been obtained in practice).

6.5.2 Finite Termination of the Test

It will be demonstrated here that although one might obtain a sequence of observations that called for continuing the sampling at each stage, with no decision reached, the probability of such an occurrence is zero. As before, let the hypothesis being tested be that the population density (or probability) function is $f_0(x)$, and the alternative that it is $f_1(x)$. The logarithm of the likelihood ratio for any single observation:

$$Z = \log [f_0(X)/f_1(X)],$$

will be zero if and only if f_0 and f_1 agree at that point. If they are to define essentially different distributions, then the set of points at which Z is zero would have to have probability 0 under any possible state of nature. Assuming then that $P(Z = 0) < 1$, it must follow that there is a $d > 0$ and a $q > 0$ so that either $P(Z > d) \geq q$ or $P(Z < -d) \geq q$. In the former case, choose an integer r such that $rd > \log (B/A)$, and break up the sum of Z's that gives Λ_n for $n = kr$ into k sections of length r:

$$Z_1 + \cdots + Z_n = (Z_1 + \cdots + Z_r) + \cdots + (Z_{k-r+1} + \cdots + Z_{kr}).$$

For the first group of terms,

$$P\left\{ \left| \sum_1^r Z_i \right| > \log \frac{B}{A} \right\} \geq P\left(\sum_1^r Z_i > \log \frac{B}{A} \right) \geq P(\sum_1^r Z_i > rd)$$

$$\geq P(Z_i > d, \quad i = 1, \ldots, r) \geq q^r > 0.$$

If, on the other hand, $P(Z < -d) = q$, the integer r is chosen such that $-rd < -\log (B/A)$, with the same result, namely

$$P[|\sum_1^r Z_j| > \log (B/A)] \geq q^r.$$

Moreover, the same result would be true for each group of r Z's in the sum of kr Z's, since the Z's are identically distributed.

Now let N denote the (random) sample size necessary to reach a decision. The events $\{N > n\}$ form a descending sequence whose intersection is the event that N is not finite, and then

$$P(N \text{ not finite}) = \lim_{n \to \infty} P(N > n) = \lim_{k \to \infty} P(N > kr),$$

where r is the positive integer defined before. The last equality follows from the fact that the sequence of probabilities $P(N > n)$ is monotone, bounded below, and so has a limit; this limit is also the limit of any subsequence— such as the sequence consisting of every rth element. But if $N > kr$, then no decision is reached through stage kr, so that

$$\log A < \log \Lambda_n < \log B, \qquad \text{for } n \leq kr,$$

which means that none of the groups of Z's can exceed $\log (B/A)$:

$$|Z_{(j-1)r+1} + \cdots + Z_{jr}| < \log (B/A), \qquad j = 1, 2, \ldots, k$$

(for otherwise $\log \Lambda_n$ could not remain between $\log A$ and $\log B$ for $n \leq kr$). Hence,

$$P(N > kr) \leq P\left\{ |Z_{(j-1)r+1} + \cdots + Z_{jr}| < \log \frac{B}{A}, j = 1, 2, \ldots, k \right\}$$

$$= \left\{ P\left(|Z_1 + \cdots + Z_r| < \log \frac{B}{A} \right) \right\}^k \leq (1 - q^r)^k.$$

Taking the limit as k becomes infinite one finds

$$P(N \text{ not finite}) \leq \lim_{k \to \infty} (1 - q^r)^k = 0,$$

because $q > 0$, and therefore $1 - q^r < 1$.

Problems

6-52. Construct and carry out a sequential test for $p = \frac{1}{2}$ against the alternative $p = \frac{1}{3}$, with $\alpha = .1$ and $\beta = .2$, using an ordinary coin.

6-53. Construct the sequential likelihood ratio test for $\mu = \mu_0$ against $\mu = \mu_1$ in a normal population with given variance σ^2. Express the inequality for continuing sampling in terms of the sample sum, and determine the nature of the curves bounding the region in which this inequality is satisfied. Sketch these curves for the particular values $\mu_0 = 4$, $\mu_1 = 6$, $\alpha = \beta = .05$, and $\sigma^2 = 9$. Observe the change in the curves corresponding to a change in error sizes to $\alpha = .1$ and $\beta = .2$, and also corresponding to a change in μ_1 to 10. What are the curves like if one considers the sample *mean* instead of the sample sum?

6-54. Obtain the sequential test, in terms of the sum of a sequence of observations, of $m = m_0$ against $m = m_1$ with $m_1 > m_0$, where m is the mean of a Poisson distribution. Use $\alpha = \beta = .05$.

6-55. Fill in the details showing the asserted inequality, in Section 6.5.2, in the case $P(Z < -d) \geq q$.

6.5.3   The Operating Characteristic

The operating characteristic (probability of accepting H_0) of a sequential likelihood ratio test can be obtained, somewhat indirectly, as follows: Consider a test defined by given constants A and B, with $A < 1 < B$, to test $H_0 : f_0(x)$ against $H_1 : f_1(x)$. If one considered f_0 and f_1 to be the only possible states of nature, there would be little point to an "operating characteristic." However, the population is frequently one of a family $f(x; \theta)$, with $f_1(x) = f(x; \theta_1)$ and $f_0(x) = f(x; \theta_1)$ used as convenient states for defining the test, the interest lying in distinguishing $\theta \leq \theta^*$ from $\theta > \theta^*$. In such a case one *is* interested in the operating characteristic as a function of all possible values of θ.

Let θ be fixed and determine as a function of that θ a value of h other than 0 for which

$$E_\theta\left(\left\{\frac{f(x; \theta_0)}{f(x; \theta_1)}\right\}^h\right) = 1.$$

This expectation is 1 when $h = 0$, but there is often just one other value of h for which it is also 1. Observe in particular that $h = 1$ does the trick if $\theta = \theta_1$ and that $h = -1$ works for $\theta = \theta_0$.

From the integral expression for the above-expected value:

$$\int_{-\infty}^{\infty} \left\{\frac{f(x; \theta_0)}{f(x; \theta_1)}\right\}^h f(x; \theta) \, dx = 1,$$

it follows that the integrand function can be thought of as a density function:

$$f^*(x; \theta) = \left\{\frac{f(x; \theta_0)}{f(x; \theta_1)}\right\}^h f(x; \theta).$$

Consider now the auxiliary problem of testing

$$H^*: f^*(x; \theta) \qquad \text{against} \qquad H: f(x; \theta),$$

which are simple hypotheses for fixed h and θ. Using the constants A^h and B^h in the inequality for continuing sampling in testing H^* against H:

$$A^h < \prod \frac{f^*(X_i; \theta)}{f(X_i; \theta)} = \prod \left\{\frac{f(X_i; \theta_0)}{f(X_i; \theta_1)}\right\}^h < B^h,$$

one finds, upon taking the $1/h$ power (assume $h > 0$), the same inequality as that used for continuing sampling in testing H_0 against H_1. (If $h < 0$, the lower boundary could have been taken as B^h and the upper one as A^h, with the same net result.) Consequently,

$$P_\theta(\text{accept } H_0) = P_\theta(\text{accept } H^*) = P_H(\text{accept } H^*) = \beta^*,$$

where β^* is the size of the type II error for the auxiliary problem. This can be expressed in terms of the cease-sampling limits for the *auxiliary* problem:

$$OC(\theta) = P_\theta(\text{accept } H_0) = \beta^* \doteq \frac{1 - A^h}{B^h - A^h}.$$

Thus the operating characteristic is expressed in terms of h. But θ, too, depends on h, and these two relations define the operating characteristic curve $OC(\theta)$ parametrically: Each choice of h determines a θ and a value of $P(\text{accept } H_0)$, that is, a point on the OC curve.

The expression relating h and θ does not define θ for $h = 0$, since it is automatically satisfied for any θ; however, the point on the operating characteristic curve corresponding to $h = 0$ can be determined by passing to the limit as $h \to 0$. Similarly, the expression for $OC(\theta)$ is indeterminate for $h = 0$, but it can be evaluated by means of l'Hospital's rule, with the result

$$OC(\theta) \big|_{h=0} = \frac{-\log A}{\log B - \log A}.$$

The values $h = 1$ and $h = -1$ have been seen to correspond to $\theta = \theta_1$ and $\theta = \theta_0$, respectively, and of course $OC(\theta_1) = \beta$, and $OC(\theta_0) = 1 - \alpha$. As $h \to \infty$, the operating characteristic clearly tends to 0, and as $h \to -\infty$, it tends to 1. Thus there are five convenient points, which frequently suffice to furnish an adequate sketch of the OC curve:

h	$-\infty$	-1	0	1	∞
θ		θ_0		θ_1	
OC	1	$1 - \alpha$	$\dfrac{-\log A}{\log B - \log A}$	β	0

EXAMPLE 6–28.   Consider testing $p = p_0$ against $p = p_1 > p_0$ in a Bernoulli population. Here $f(x; p) = p^x(1 - p)^{1-x}$, $x = 0, 1$, so that

$$E_p\left\{\left[\frac{f(X; p_0)}{f(X; p_1)}\right]^h\right\} = \left[\frac{1 - p_0}{1 - p_1}\right]^h (1 - p) + \left(\frac{p_0}{p_1}\right)^h p.$$

Upon setting this equal to 1 and solving for p, the expression for p as a function of h is found to be

$$p = \frac{1 - [(1 - p_0)/(1 - p_1)]^h}{(p_0/p_1)^h - [(1 - p_0)/(1 - p_1)]^h}.$$

As $h \to 0$, this becomes

$$\frac{-\log [(1 - p_0)/(1 - p_1)]}{\log (p_0/p_1) - \log [(1 - p_0)/(1 - p_1)]}.$$

Taking the particular values $p_0 = .5$, $p_1 = .9$, $\alpha = \beta = .05$, one obtains these points on the operating characteristic curve, shown in Figure 6–15.

h	$-\infty$	-1	0	1	∞
p	0	$.5$	$.733$	$.9$	1
OC	1	$.95$	$.5$	$.05$	0

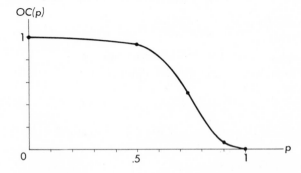

Figure 6–15.

6.5.4 *Required Sample Size*

The number of observations required to reach a decision, in a given sequential likelihood ratio test, is a random variable. Let it be denoted by N. Its distribution depends on the state of nature that obtains during the sampling process. In Section 6.5.2 it was seen that $N < \infty$ with probability 1, so that N has values $1, 2, 3, \ldots$ with probabilities $p_1, p_2, \ldots$ where $\sum p_i = 1$.

The moments of N are not easily computed, but can be shown to be finite. With an integer r chosen as in Section 6.5.2, consider the terms defining $E(N^i)$ grouped in bunches of r:

$$E(N^i) = [1^i p_1 + \cdots + r^i p_r] + [(r+1)^i p_{r+1} + \cdots + (2r)^i p_{2r}] + \cdots$$

$$\leq r^i(p_1 + \cdots + p_r) + (2r)^i(p_{r+1} + \cdots + p_{2r}) + \cdots.$$

Use of the inequalities

$$p_1 + \cdots + p_r \leq 1, \qquad p_{r+1} + \cdots + p_{2r} \leq 1 - q^r,$$

$$p_{2r+1} + \cdots + p_{3r} \leq (1 - q^r)^2, \qquad \text{etc.}$$

which follow from Section 6.5.2, yields

$$E(N^i) \leq r^i + (2r)^i(1 - q^r) + (3r)^i(1 - q^r)^2 + \cdots$$

$$= r^i[1 + 2^i(1 - q^r) + 3^i(1 - q^r)^2 + \cdots].$$

The series in brackets can be shown to be finite by the standard ratio test, given (as is the case) that $0 < q \leq 1$.

Suppose for the moment that $Z, Z_1, Z_2, \ldots$ are independent, identically distributed random variables, and that n is a random variable with values $1, 2, \ldots$ such that the event $\{N \geq i\}$ is independent of any events involving $Z_i, Z_{i+1}, \ldots$. Let Y_i be 0 if $N < i$ and 1 if $N \geq i$. Then

$$E(Z_1 + \cdots + Z_N) = E\left\{ \sum_{i=1}^{\infty} Y_i Z_i \right\} = \sum_{i=1}^{\infty} E(Y_i Z_i) = E(Z) \sum_{i=1}^{\infty} E(Y_i).$$

provided one can interchange summation and expectation. Now

$$\sum_{i=1}^{\infty} E(Y_i) = \sum_{i=1}^{\infty} P(N \geq i) = \sum_{i=1}^{\infty} \sum_{j=i}^{\infty} P(N = j) = \sum_{j=1}^{\infty} \sum_{i=1}^{j} P(N = j) = E(N),$$

which gives the desired expression for $E(\log \lambda_N)$, namely, $E(Z)E(N)$. The interchange employed is valid if the following series is convergent:

$$\sum_{i=1}^{\infty} |E(Y_i Z_i)| \leq \sum_{i=1}^{\infty} E(|Y_i|) E(|Z_i|) = E(|Z|) E(N).$$

It will be convergent if $E(|Z|)$ is finite and $E(N)$ is finite.

Application of this last result to the sequence $Z_i = \log [f_0(X_i)/f_1(X_i)]$ provides an expression for the value of $E(N)$:

$$E(N) = E(\log \Lambda_N)/E(Z),$$

which can be computed approximately. For, the random variable Λ_N is approximately a Bernoulli variable, with the value $\log A$ if the decision reached is to reject H_0 and the value $\log B$ if the decision reached is to accept H_0:

$$E_\theta(\log \Lambda_N) \doteq (\log A)\pi(\theta) + (\log B)[1 - \pi(\theta)],$$

where $\pi(\theta)$ is the power function or probability that the given test rejects H_0 when the state is actually θ. In particular, then,

$$E(N \mid H_0) = \frac{1}{E(Z \mid H_0)} [\alpha \log A + (1 - \alpha) \log B],$$

and

$$E(N \mid H_1) = \frac{1}{E(Z \mid H_1)} [(1 - \beta) \log A + \beta \log B].$$

EXAMPLE 6–29.   To test $\mu = 0$ against $\mu = 1$ in a normal population with unit variance with $\alpha = \beta = .01$, one uses constants $A = 1/99$ and $B = 99$. Then $\log A = -\log 99 = -\log B = -4.595$, and

$$E_{H_0}(\log \Lambda_N) = \alpha \log A + (1 - \alpha) \log B = (1 - 2\alpha) \log 99$$

$$= 4.5031.$$

The log of the likelihood ratio is

$$Z = \log [f_0(X)/f_1(X)] = \log\left\{\frac{\exp [-X^2/2]}{\exp [-(X - 1)^2/2]}\right\} = 1/2 - X.$$

and then $E(Z) = E(1/2 - X) = 1/2 - \mu$. If $\mu = 0$,

$$E(N) = \frac{E(\log \Lambda_N)}{E(Z)} = \frac{4.5031}{1/2 - 0} \doteq 9.$$

Similarly, if $\mu = 1$,

$$E(N) = \frac{(1 - \beta) \log A + \beta \log B}{1/2 - 1} \doteq 9.$$

In a likelihood ratio test of fixed sample size, the conditions

$$.01 = \alpha = P(\bar{X} > k \mid \mu = 0)$$

$$.01 = \beta = P(\bar{X} < k \mid \mu = 1)$$

lead to $n \doteq 22$, much larger than the expected sample size in the sequential test.

The expected sample size can be computed for other states than the two used to define the test, if H_0 and H_1 correspond to particular values θ_0 and θ_1 of a parameter θ:

$$E(N \mid \theta) = \frac{1}{E(Z \mid \theta)} \{(\log A) \pi(\theta) + (\log B)[1 - \pi(\theta)]\}.$$

(Notice that logs are to the base e if the log in Z is to that base.)

The expected value of N is usually a function of θ. One annoying feature of the sequential likelihood ratio test, when it is used to test a one-sided situation such as $H_0: \theta \le \theta'$ against $H_1: \theta > \theta'$ is the following: The test would be set up by choosing θ_0 in H_0 (that is, $\theta_0 < \theta'$) and θ_1 in H_1 ($\theta_1 > \theta'$), the zone between θ_0 and θ_1 being an "indifference zone." And yet, if the actual population is described by a θ in this indifference zone (that is, near θ'), $E(N)$ tends to be largest. Thus the test tends to take longer to reach a decision when θ is near the point θ' where there is perhaps little concern as to which way the test turns out. It is certainly intuitively reasonable that it should not take so long to discover that a population is violently of one kind or the other as it does to discover which kind it is when it is near the borderline. What is annoying, then, is that in the borderline case, wrong decisions are likely not to be very costly anyway, and it seems a shame to invest the effort or cost in the large sample required to reach a decision. Ways of altering the sequential testing procedure have been proposed, but these are not taken up here.

EXAMPLE 6–30.   In testing p_0 against p_1, possible values of a Bernoulli parameter p, it was found in Example 6–28 that

$$p = \frac{1 - (q_0/q_1)^h}{(p_0/p_1)^h - (q_0/q_1)^h}$$

where $q_i = 1 - p_i$ and h is such that $E(e^{hZ}) = 1$. The power in terms of h is

$$\pi[p(h)] = \frac{B^h - 1}{B^h - A^h}.$$

Now, using again $p_0 = .5$, $q_0 = .9$, and $\alpha = \beta = .05$, one obtains

$$E(Z) = p \log \frac{p_0 q_1}{q_0 p_1} + \log \frac{q_0}{q_1} = -p \log 9 + \log 5.$$

At $h = 0$ both EZ and $E(\log \Lambda_N)$ are zero, but their ratio can be evaluated by computing its limit as $h \to 0$, the result given in the following table.

h	$-\infty$	-1	0	1	∞
p	0	.5	.733	.9	1
$E(N \mid p)$	1.83	5.19	9.17	7.2	5.01

The entry for $h = 0$ involves evaluation of an indeterminate form. This is perhaps most easily accomplished by using series expansions. For instance, since $B^h = \exp[h \log B]$,

$$B^h - A^h = e^{h \log B} - e^{h \log A} = h(\log B - \log A) + \frac{h^2}{2}(\log^2 B - \log^2 A) + \cdots.$$

Similar expansions for other ingredients of $E(N)$ yield

$$E(N)\big|_{h=0} = \frac{\log A \log B}{\log 5 \log (5/9)} = 9.17.$$

Although finite, the required N can be very large in any single experiment—much larger than one might want to tolerate. In practice, one establishes a bound n_0 beyond which he refuses to go; if no decision is reached by the (n_0)th stage, sampling is stopped anyway, with H_0 accepted if $\lambda_{n_0} > 1$ and rejected if $\lambda_{n_0} < 1$. The effect of such a modification, which surely alters the error sizes of the test, has been studied in Reference [20], and is slight if n_0 is large.

Graphically, the stopping rule just described amounts to altering the decision lines from those shown in Figure 6–14 to those shown in Figure 6–16.

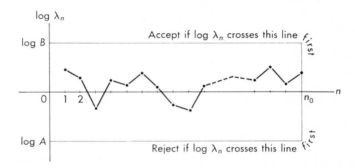

Figure 6–16.

Problems

6–56. Determine the relation between μ and h in a sequential test for $\mu = 0$ against $\mu = 1$ in a normal population with unit variance. Plot the power function of the test with $\alpha = \beta = .01$.

6–57. Use the result of Problem 6–56 to sketch (using 5 points) the graph of the expected sample size for the test of that problem.

6–58. Show that in testing $m = m_0$ against $m = m_1$ in a Poisson population, the relation between m and h is

$$m = \frac{(m_1 - m_0)^h}{1 - (m_0/m_1)^h}.$$

6–59. Obtain the graphs of $OC(\theta)$ and $E(N \mid \theta)$ in a sequential test of the density $\theta_0 e^{-\theta_0 x}$ against $\theta_1 e^{-\theta_1 x}$ $(x > 0)$ using $\theta_0 = 2$ and $\theta_1 = 1$, $\alpha = .05$, $\beta = .10$. Observe that for one of the five points used, $E(N) = 0$. In view of the fact that $N \geq 1$ this result must be wrong. Explain.

CHAPTER *7*

NORMAL POPULATIONS

Both the techniques of inference and the distribution theory that gives those techniques a mathematical basis have been most highly developed in the case of a normal population. This is partly because the form of the normal density makes it particularly amenable to such a development, partly because—although perhaps never *exactly* the right model—the normal model is often sufficiently close to correct for practical purposes, partly because the very scope of the methods and theory of the normal model provide a prototype for such development, and partly because the methods developed for normal populations often turn out to work reasonably well when the population is moderately different from normal.

7.1 Distribution Theory

A treatment of inference for even a univariate normal population requires, for completeness, an understanding of the multivariate normal distribution.

This, then, is the opening topic—first the case of two variates, and then any finite number. Distributions of statistics encountered in methods of inference for univariate normal populations are discussed in the latter parts of this section.

7.1.1 Bivariate Transformations

A review of certain aspects of transformations in one dimension will perhaps serve to point up the similarities between transformations in one dimension and transformations in several dimensions and make the latter seem more natural. Consider then a transformation defined by the continuously differentiable function $y = g(x)$, which maps the region R of x-values into the region S of y-values. If the derivative is continuous and does not vanish in R:

$$\frac{dy}{dx} = g'(x) \neq 0, \qquad \text{all } x \text{ in } R,$$

the transformation is monotonic. The graph of $y = g(x)$ is then steadily increasing or steadily decreasing. For each y in S there is a unique x in R, called $g^{-1}(y)$, such that $g[g^{-1}(y)] = y$. The function $g^{-1}(y)$ is the *inverse* function, and this is differentiable with derivative

$$\frac{dg^{-1}(y)}{dy} = \frac{dx}{dy} = \frac{1}{dy/dx} = \frac{1}{g'(x)}.$$

The differential coefficient dy/dx provides a change-in-length factor from dx to $dy = (dy/dx)\,dx$, and dx/dy similarly provides the change factor in going from dy to $dx = (dx/dy)\,dy$. A definite integral is transformed as follows:

$$\int_R h(x)\,dx = \int_S h(g^{-1}(y))\,\frac{dx}{dy}\,dy,$$

in which, of course, dx/dy represents the function of y obtained by differentiating $g^{-1}(y)$. If X is a random variable with density function $f_X(x)$, the random variable $Y = g(X)$ has the density function

$$f_Y(y) = f_X(g^{-1}(y))\left|\frac{dx}{dy}\right|.$$

In two dimensions a transformation

$$\begin{cases} u = g(x, y) \\ v = h(x, y) \end{cases}$$

maps a region R of points in the xy plane into a region S of points in the uv plane. It is assumed that g and h are continuously differentiable. The quantity that plays the role of the derivative is now the *Jacobian* of the transformation:

$$\frac{\partial(u, v)}{\partial(x, y)} = \begin{vmatrix} \dfrac{\partial u}{\partial x} & \dfrac{\partial u}{\partial y} \\[2mm] \dfrac{\partial v}{\partial x} & \dfrac{\partial v}{\partial y} \end{vmatrix}.$$

If this is not zero over R, there is a unique inverse transformation

$$\begin{cases} x = G(u, v) \\ y = H(u, v) \end{cases}$$

which takes each point (u, v) of S into a unique point (x, y) in R such that

$$\begin{cases} g[G(u, v), H(u, v)] = u \\ h[G(u, v), H(u, v)] = v, \end{cases}$$

these being identities in (u, v). Further, the Jacobian of the inverse transformation is the reciprocal of the Jacobian of the direct one:

$$\frac{\partial(x, y)}{\partial(u, v)} = \left(\frac{\partial(u, v)}{\partial(x, y)}\right)^{-1}.$$

The Jacobian is the factor needed for conversion of area elements, and the change of variables in a double integral is accomplished as follows.

$$\iint\limits_{R} f(x, y)\, dx\, dy = \iint\limits_{S} f(G(u, v), H(u, v)) \left|\frac{\partial(x, y)}{\partial(u, v)}\right| du\, dv.$$

where S is the image of the region R under the transformation.

If (x, y) is a possible value of the random vector (X, Y), the transformation being considered defines the new random vector (U, V) with

$$\begin{cases} U = g(X, Y) \\ V = h(X, Y). \end{cases}$$

This transformation induces a probability distribution in the uv plane as follows: If S is a set in the uv plane and R is the set of all points in the xy plane that have "images" in S under the transformation, then

$$P[(U, V) \text{ in } S] = P[(X, Y) \text{ in } R].$$

If the distribution of (X, Y) is of the continuous type, the probability of S can be expressed as an integral over R:

$$P[(U, V) \text{ in } S] = \iint\limits_{R} f_{X,Y}(x, y)\, dx\, dy$$

$$= \iint\limits_{S} f_{X,Y}(G(u, v), H(u, v)) \left|\frac{\partial(x, y)}{\partial(u, v)}\right| du\, dv,$$

where $f_{X,Y}(x, y)$ is the joint density function of (X, Y). Since this relation holds for each event S in the uv plane, the density of (U, V) is the integrand function of the uv-integral:

$$f_{U,V}(u, v) = f_{X,Y}(G(u, v), H(u, v)) \left| \frac{\partial(x, y)}{\partial(u, v)} \right|.$$

That is, to obtain the density of (U, V), solve the transformation equations for x and y in terms of u and v, substitute for x and y in the joint density of X and Y, and multiply by the absolute value of the Jacobian of (x, y) with respect to (u, v). And then, similarly, the density of (X, Y) as obtained from that of (U, V) is

$$f_{X,Y}(x, y) = f_{U,V}(g(x, y), h(x, y)) \left| \frac{\partial(u, v)}{\partial(x, y)} \right|.$$

EXAMPLE 7–1.   Let R denote the rectangular region in the plane of (λ, μ) defined by the inequalities $0 < \lambda < \pi/2$, $0 \le \mu < 2\pi$, and consider the transformation to the (x, y) plane defined by

$$x = \sin \lambda \cos \mu, \qquad y = \sin \lambda \sin \mu.$$

The region R is mapped into the interior of the unit circle in the xy plane, which is then the region S shown in Figure 7–1. The random vector (θ, ϕ) defined on R with

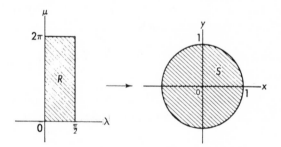

Figure 7–1.

density $(\sin \lambda)/2\pi$ (as discussed in Example 2–21) is transformed into (X, Y), where

$$X = \sin \theta \cos \phi, \qquad Y = \sin \theta \sin \phi.$$

The density function of (X, Y) is easily written down, using the inverse transformation,

$$\begin{cases} \lambda = \arcsin (x^2 + y^2)^{1/2} \\ \mu = \arctan (y/x). \end{cases}$$

It is

$$f_{X,Y}(x, y) = f_{\theta,\phi}[\arcsin (x^2 + y^2)^{1/2}, \arctan (y/x)] \frac{1}{\sin \lambda \cos \lambda}$$

$$= \frac{1/2\pi}{[1 - (x^2 + y^2)]^{1/2}},$$

which holds for $x^2 + y^2 < 1$, or in S. The factor $[\sin \lambda \cos \lambda]^{-1}$ is the Jacobian of (λ, μ) with respect to (x, y), or the reciprocal of

$$\frac{\partial(x, y)}{\partial(\lambda, \mu)} = \begin{vmatrix} \cos \lambda \cos \mu & -\sin \lambda \sin \mu \\ \cos \lambda \sin \mu & \sin \lambda \cos \mu \end{vmatrix}.$$

The results discussed above will now be specialized to the particular type of transformation called *linear*:

$$\begin{cases} x = au + bv, \\ y = cu + dv. \end{cases}$$

The Jacobian of this transformation is just the determinant of the coefficients:

$$\frac{\partial(x, y)}{\partial(u, v)} = \begin{vmatrix} a & b \\ c & d \end{vmatrix} = ad - bc \equiv \Delta.$$

If Δ vanishes, the coefficients a and b are proportional to c and d, so that y is a multiple of x. This degenerate case is ruled out by the assumption that the Jacobian of the transformation does not vanish, in which case there is a unique inverse:

$$\begin{cases} u = Ax + By, \\ v = Cx + Dy, \end{cases}$$

where $A = d/\Delta$, $B = -b/\Delta$, $C = -c/\Delta$, and $D = a/\Delta$. The Jacobian of the inverse transformation is

$$\frac{\partial(u, v)}{\partial(x, y)} = \begin{vmatrix} A & B \\ C & D \end{vmatrix} = AD - BC = 1/\Delta.$$

Suppose now that the transformation is applied to define a random vector (X, Y) from a given random vector (U, V):

$$\begin{cases} X = aU + bV, \\ Y = cU + dV. \end{cases}$$

If (U, V) has a continuous distribution with joint density function $f_{U,V}(u, v)$, the random vector (X, Y) has the joint density

$$f_{X,Y}(x, y) = \frac{1}{|\Delta|} f_{U,V}(Ax + By, Cx + Dy),$$

in the nonsingular case ($\Delta \neq 0$).

EXAMPLE 7–2. Let U and V have independent negative exponential distributions with mean 1, and define

$$\begin{cases} X = U + V, \\ Y = U - V. \end{cases}$$

The joint density of (U, V) is the product of the marginal densities:

$$f_{U,V}(u, v) = e^{-u-v}, \qquad u > 0 \qquad \text{and} \qquad v > 0.$$

The Jacobian of the transformation is

$$\frac{\partial(x, y)}{\partial(u, v)} = \begin{vmatrix} 1 & 1 \\ 1 & -1 \end{vmatrix} = \Delta = -2,$$

and the inverse transformation is readily seen (upon solving for U and V) to be

$$\begin{cases} U = \tfrac{1}{2}(X + Y), \\ V = \tfrac{1}{2}(X - Y). \end{cases}$$

The first quadrant of the uv-plane, which carries the distribution of (U, V), is mapped into the region X between $x = y$ and $x = -y$ as shown in Figure 7–2. The joint density function of (X, Y) is

$$f_{X,Y}(x, y) = \tfrac{1}{2}f_{U,V}(\tfrac{1}{2}[x + y], \tfrac{1}{2}[x - y]) = \tfrac{1}{2}e^{-x}, \qquad \text{for } (x, y) \text{ in } S.$$

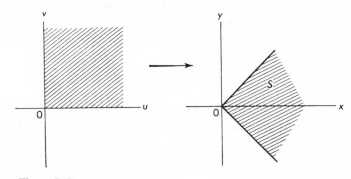

Figure 7–2.

From this, incidentally, one can determine the density of the sum $U + V$ as the marginal density of X, by integrating out the y:

$$f_{U+V}(x) = f_X(x) = \int_{-\infty}^{\infty} f_{X,Y}(x, y)\, dy$$

$$= \tfrac{1}{2}\int_{-x}^{x} e^{-x}\, dy = xe^{-x}, \qquad x > 0.$$

7.1.2   The Bivariate Normal Distribution

A random vector (X, Y) is said to have a *bivariate normal* distribution if X and Y can each be expressed linearly in terms of two independent, standard normal variables U and V:

$$\begin{cases} X = aU + bV + h \\ Y = cU + dV + k. \end{cases}$$

The moments of (X, Y) can be expressed in terms of the constants in this transformation, as follows:

$$\mu_X = E(X) = h, \qquad \mu_Y = E(Y) = k$$
$$\sigma_X^2 = \text{var } X = \text{var } (aU + bV) = a^2 + b^2,$$
$$\sigma_Y^2 = \text{var } Y = \text{var } (cU + dV) = c^2 + d^2,$$
$$\sigma_{XY} = \text{cov } (X, Y) = \text{cov } (aU + bV, cU + dV) = ac + bd.$$

Further,

$$\Delta^2 = (ad - bc)^2 = (a^2 + b^2)(c^2 + d^2) - (ac + bd)^2$$
$$= \sigma_X^2 \sigma_Y^2 (1 - \rho^2),$$

where ρ denotes the correlation coefficient of (X, Y), defined in Section 2.3.3.

If $\Delta = 0$, or $ad = bc$, then $\rho = \pm 1$ and X and Y are linearly related (with probability 1). In this case the distribution is *singular*, all the probability being concentrated on the line representing the linear relation; the density does not exist. The distribution is essentially univariate rather than bivariate.

In the strictly bivariate case, with $ad \neq bc$, there is a density function, which will now be derived from the joint density function of (U, V), the product of two standard normal densities:

$$f_{U,V}(u, v) = (1/2\pi) \exp \left[-\tfrac{1}{2}(u^2 + v^2) \right].$$

Since $X - h$ and $Y - k$ are given by a linear transformation on (U, V), their joint density is written down as a special case of the general formula obtained earlier:

$$f_{X-h, Y-k}(r, s) = \frac{1}{2\pi|ad - bc|} \exp \left\{ -\tfrac{1}{2}[(Ar + Bs)^2 + (Cr + Ds)^2] \right\},$$

where, as before, $A = d/\Delta$, $B = -b/\Delta$, $C = -c/\Delta$, $D = a/\Delta$, and $\Delta = ad - bc$. The quantity in brackets in the exponent of the above density functions can then be written

$$\frac{1}{\Delta^2} [(d^2 + c^2)r^2 - 2(db + ca)rs + (b^2 + a^2)s^2]$$

$$= \frac{1}{1 - \rho^2} \left\{ \frac{r^2}{\sigma_X^2} - 2\rho \frac{rs}{\sigma_X \sigma_Y} + \frac{s^2}{\sigma_Y^2} \right\}.$$

Finally, then (using the result of Problem 7–2):

$$f_{X,Y}(x, y) = \frac{1}{2\pi \sigma_X \sigma_Y \sqrt{1 - \rho^2}} \exp \left(-\tfrac{1}{2}Q \right),$$

where

$$Q = \frac{1}{1 - \rho^2} \left\{ \frac{(x - h)^2}{\sigma_X^2} - 2\rho \frac{(x - h)(y - k)}{\sigma_X \sigma_Y} + \frac{(y - k)^2}{\sigma_Y^2} \right\}.$$

It is instructive to introduce the second moment matrix M:

$$M = \begin{pmatrix} \sigma_X{}^2 & \sigma_{XY} \\ \sigma_{XY} & \sigma_Y{}^2 \end{pmatrix},$$

and compute the inverse:

$$M^{-1} = \frac{1}{1 - \rho^2} \begin{pmatrix} 1/\sigma_X{}^2 & -\rho/(\sigma_X\sigma_Y) \\ -\rho/(\sigma_X\sigma_Y) & 1/\sigma_Y{}^2 \end{pmatrix}.$$

The quantity Q in the density function of (X, Y) can be written in terms of M^{-1}:

$$Q = (x - h \quad y - k)M^{-1} \begin{pmatrix} x - h \\ y - k \end{pmatrix}.$$

EXAMPLE 7–3.   Let X and Y have means 0 and 2 and variances 10 and 4, respectively, and let cov $(X, Y) = 6$. The second-moment matrix M is then

$$M = \begin{pmatrix} 10 & 6 \\ 6 & 4 \end{pmatrix},$$

with determinant det $M = 40 - 36 = 4$. The inverse is

$$M^{-1} = \frac{1}{4} \begin{pmatrix} 4 & -6 \\ -6 & 10 \end{pmatrix},$$

and now the density function can be written out:

$$f(x, y) = \frac{1}{2\pi\sqrt{4}} \exp\left\{ -\frac{1}{2}\left[x^2 - 3x(y - 2) + \frac{5}{2}(y - 2)^2 \right] \right\}.$$

A function of the form

$$f(x, y) = (\text{const.}) \exp\left[-\tfrac{1}{2}(\alpha x^2 + 2\beta xy + \gamma y^2) \right]$$

defines a bivariate density provided $\alpha > 0$ and $\alpha\gamma > \beta^2$, that is, provided the matrix of the quadratic form in the exponent is positive definite (see Problem 7–5). For, the substitution

$$\begin{cases} x = (\cos \theta)u - (\sin \theta)v, \\ y = (\sin \theta)u + (\cos \theta)v, \end{cases}$$

where θ is an angle such that $\cot 2\theta = \dfrac{a - c}{2b}$, transforms the exponent into

$$-\tfrac{1}{2}(\alpha' u^2 + \gamma' v^2)$$

where

$$\begin{cases} \alpha' = \alpha \cos^2 \theta + 2\beta \cos \theta \sin \theta + \gamma \sin^2 \theta, \\ \beta' = \alpha \sin^2 \theta - 2\beta \cos \theta \sin \theta + \gamma \cos^2 \theta, \end{cases}$$

which are positive if $\alpha > 0$ and the discriminant $\beta^2 - \alpha\gamma$ is negative. That is, with (U, V) defined by

$$\begin{cases} X = (\cos\theta)U - (\sin\theta)V, \\ Y = (\sin\theta)U + (\cos\theta)V, \end{cases}$$

where (X, Y) has the joint density function $f(x, y)$, the joint density of (U, V) is

$$f_{U,V}(u, v) = (\text{const.}) \exp\left[-\tfrac{1}{2}(\alpha'u^2 + \gamma'v^2)\right].$$

This (with the proper choice of multiplying constant) is the joint density of independent normal variates. With simple changes of scale these become *standard* normal, so that (X, Y) is obtained by a linear transformation on independent, standard normal variables—and so has a bivariate normal distribution.

EXAMPLE 7-4.   Consider the function

$$f(x, y) = (\text{const.}) \exp\left[-x^2/2 + xy + y^2 - x - 2y\right].$$

The linear terms in the exponent can be eliminated by a translation, since the above is equivalent to

$$f(x, y) = K\exp\left\{-\tfrac{1}{2}[x^2 + 2x(y - 1) + 2(y + 1)^2]\right\}.$$

The quadratic form in brackets has the matrix

$$M^{-1} = \begin{pmatrix} 1 & 1 \\ 1 & 2 \end{pmatrix},$$

which is positive definite, with inverse

$$M = \begin{pmatrix} 2 & -1 \\ -1 & 1 \end{pmatrix} = \begin{pmatrix} \sigma_X^2 & \sigma_{XY} \\ \sigma_{XY} & \sigma_Y^2 \end{pmatrix}.$$

Thus, $f(x, y)$ is a multivariate normal density if the constant K is properly chosen:

$$K = \frac{1}{2\pi\sigma_X\sigma_Y\sqrt{1 - \rho^2}} = \frac{1}{2\pi}.$$

An expression for (X, Y) in terms of independent, standard normal (U, V) could be obtained by a rotation (through θ as defined above), followed by scale changes. But in this case it is easily achieved by completing the square:

$$K\exp\left\{-\tfrac{1}{2}[x^2 + 2x(y - 1) + (y - 1)^2] - (y + 1)^2\right\}$$
$$= K\exp\left\{-\tfrac{1}{2}[x + (y - 1)]^2 - (y + 1)^2\right\}.$$

Clearly, with

$$\begin{cases} U = X + Y - 1 \\ V = 2(Y + 1) \end{cases}$$

the density reduces to that of independent, standard normal variates.

Problems

7–1.   Show that the transformation $u = x$, $v = x - y$ has a unique inverse, by solving for x and y. Determine the Jacobian of the transformation and of the inverse. Determine the image of the first quadrant of the xy plane under this transformation. Determine the inverse images of the u-axis and the v-axis.

7–2.   Discuss the geometric significance of the transformation $x' = x + h$, $y' = y + k$, for given constants h and k. Determine the joint density function of (X', Y') induced by this transformation on the variables (X, Y) with joint density $f(x, y)$.

7–3.   Let X and Y be independent, standard, normal random variables. Let $U = X$ and $V = X/Y$, and determine the joint density of (U, V). From this obtain the density of $X/Y = V$.

7–4.   The "product" of two-by-two matrices is defined as follows:

$$\begin{pmatrix} a & b \\ c & d \end{pmatrix} \begin{pmatrix} e & f \\ g & h \end{pmatrix} = \begin{pmatrix} ae + bg & af + bh \\ ce + dg & cf + dh \end{pmatrix},$$

with analogous definitions for products involving one-by-two and two-by-one matrices. Given

$$x = \begin{pmatrix} x_1 \\ x_2 \end{pmatrix}, \qquad x' = (x_1 \quad x_2),$$

$$A = \begin{pmatrix} 3 & 2 \\ -1 & 1 \end{pmatrix}, \qquad B = \begin{pmatrix} 2 \\ 5 \end{pmatrix},$$

(a) Determine a matrix A^{-1} with the property $AA^{-1} = I = A^{-1}A$, where

$$I = \begin{pmatrix} 1 & 0 \\ 0 & 1 \end{pmatrix},$$

and equality of two matrices means that they agree element by element.
(b) Show that $IC = CI = C$ for any two-by-two matrix C.
(c) Compute the matrices Ax, $x'A$, AB, $x'Ax$, $A^{-1}B$.
(d) Write out the equations $Ax = B$ and show that $x = A^{-1}B$ is a solution.

7–5.   Show that the quadratic form $Q(x_1, x_2) = ax_1{}^2 + 2bx_1x_2 + cx_2{}^2$ can be written as

$$Q(x_1, x_2) = x' \begin{pmatrix} a & b \\ b & c \end{pmatrix} x.$$

Show also that $Q(x_1, x_2) > 0$ for all $x \neq 0$ if and only if $a > 0$ and $ac - b^2 > 0$. (Such a Q is called *positive definite*.)

7–6.   Write out the density function of the normally distributed (X, Y) with means $(0, 4)$ and moment matrix

$$M = \begin{pmatrix} 1 & 2 \\ 2 & 9 \end{pmatrix}.$$

7–7.   A certain bivariate normal density is given by

$$f(x, y) = (\text{constant}) \exp{(-x^2 + xy - 2y^2)}.$$

Determine the first and second moments and the proper constant multiplier.

7-8. Curves in the xy-plane defined by $f(x, y) = $ constant are called level curves of $f(x, y)$ (see Section 1.1.6). Determine the nature of the level curves of a bivariate normal distribution, with special note of the impact of independence on these level curves.

7-9. Determine the characteristic function $E[\exp{(isX + itY)}]$ of normal (X, Y) by expressing X and Y in terms of independent, standard, normal (U, V). Show that it can be expressed in the form $\exp{(-\frac{1}{2}Q)}$, where Q is a quadratic form in (s, t) with matrix M (the matrix of second moments).

7-10. Show that if (X, Y) is bivariate normal, then

(a) any (Z, W) linearly related to (X, Y) is also bivariate normal.

(b) The marginal distributions of any bivariate normal distribution are normal.

(c) A linear function $AX + BY + C$ is normal.

7.1.3   Multivariate Transformations

Given the outcome $(x_1, \ldots, x_n)$, one may wish to define the related quantities:

$$\begin{cases} u_1 = g_1(x_1, \ldots, x_n) \\ \vdots \qquad \vdots \\ u_n = g_n(x_1, \ldots, x_n), \end{cases}$$

for given functions $g_1, \ldots, g_n$. For inverses and integral transformations, the crucial quantity is again the *Jacobian* of the transformation:

$$\frac{\partial(u_1, \ldots, u_n)}{\partial(x_1, \ldots, x_n)} = \begin{vmatrix} \dfrac{\partial u_1}{\partial x_1} & \cdots & \dfrac{\partial u_n}{\partial x_1} \\ \vdots & & \vdots \\ \dfrac{\partial u_1}{\partial x_n} & \cdots & \dfrac{\partial u_n}{\partial x_n} \end{vmatrix}$$

If this does not vanish in a region R, there exists an inverse transformation defined on the image of R:

$$\begin{cases} x_1 = G_1(u_1, \ldots, u_n) \\ \vdots \qquad \vdots \\ x_n = G_n(u_1, \ldots, u_n), \end{cases}$$

whose Jacobian is the reciprocal of that of the forward transformation. Making the transformation from x to u in a multiple integral over R is accomplished by substituting x from the inverse transformation and transforming the volume element as follows:

$$dx_1 \cdots dx_n \rightarrow \left| \frac{\partial(x_1, \ldots, x_n)}{\partial(u_1, \ldots, u_n)} \right| du_1 \cdots du_n,$$

the integral in u then extending over the image of R.

If $(x_1, \ldots, x_n)$ is a possible value of the random vector $(X_1, \ldots, X_n)$, the transformation from x to u defines a random vector U with components

$$\begin{cases} U_1 = g_1(X_1, \ldots, X_n) \\ \vdots \quad \vdots \\ U_n = g_n(X_1, \ldots, X_n). \end{cases}$$

If S denotes a set of points $(u_1, \ldots, u_n)$ and R the set of all points $(x_1, \ldots, x_n)$ having images in S, then

$$P[(U_1, \ldots, U_n) \text{ in } S] = P[(g_1(X_1, \ldots, X_n), \ldots, g_n(X_1, \ldots, X_n)) \text{ in } S]$$

$$= P[(X_1, \ldots, X_n) \text{ in } R].$$

In the continuous case, and if it is assumed that the transformation has a non-vanishing Jacobian in R, this last probability can be expressed as an integral of the joint density function of the X's:

$$P(S) = \int_R \cdots \int f(x_1, \ldots, x_n)\, dx_1 \cdots dx_n$$

$$= \int_S \cdots \int f(G_1(u_1, \ldots, u_n), \ldots, G_n(u_1, \ldots, u_n)) \left| \frac{\partial(x_1, \ldots, x_n)}{\partial(u_1, \ldots, u_n)} \right| du_1 \cdots du_n$$

The integrand of this u-integral is then the joint density functions of the U's.

So far the transformed variable has been assumed to be of the same dimension as the X's, but it is possible that one may be interested in a smaller number of U's than X's:

$$\begin{cases} U_1 = g_1(X_1, \ldots, X_n) \\ \vdots \quad \vdots \\ U_m = g_m(X_1, \ldots, X_n), \end{cases}$$

where $m \leq n$. (If m were greater than n, the U's would be "overdetermined," and if not incompatible, then not all necessary.) One could supply $n - m$ additional compatible relations and then determine the distribution of the m U's of interest as a marginal distribution of that of the n U's. However, the transformation to $(U_1, \ldots, U_m)$ and the distribution in the X space determine a probability distribution directly in the m-dimensional U space, in the usual way:

$$P[(U_1, \ldots, U_m) \text{ in } T] = \int_R \cdots \int f(x_1, \ldots, x_n)\, dx_1 \cdots dx_n,$$

where R is the set of $(x_1, \ldots, x_n)$ with image points in T. Taking T to be a semi-infinite rectangle and differentiating yields, as usual, the density function of $(U_1, \ldots, U_m)$.

364

In considering the particular important case of a linear transformation, it is convenient to use matrix notation. The vectors $(x_1, \ldots, x_n)$ and $(u_1, \ldots, u_m)$ are written as column matrices:

$$x = \begin{pmatrix} x_1 \\ \vdots \\ x_n \end{pmatrix}, \qquad u = \begin{pmatrix} u_1 \\ \vdots \\ u_m \end{pmatrix}.$$

The linear transformation from x to u defined by the equations

$$\begin{cases} u_1 = a_{11}x_1 + \cdots + a_{1n}x_n \\ \vdots \qquad \vdots \qquad \qquad \vdots \\ u_m = a_{m1}x_1 + \cdots + a_{mn}x_n \end{cases}$$

is then written

$$u = Ax,$$

where A is the matrix of the transformation:

$$A = (a_{ij}) = \begin{pmatrix} a_{11} & \cdots & a_{1n} \\ \vdots & & \\ a_{m1} & \cdots & a_{mn} \end{pmatrix}.$$

[Again a matrix equality means equality element by element; matrix multiplication is defined in general much as it was for the two-by-two case (see Problem 7–12).]

If $m = n$ and if the Jacobian of the transformation, which is then the determinant of the square matrix A (written det A) does not vanish, the inverse transformation exists. It is given by

$$x = A^{-1}u,$$

with

$$A^{-1} = \frac{1}{\det A} \begin{pmatrix} A_{11} & \cdots & A_{n1} \\ \vdots & & \\ A_{1n} & \cdots & A_{nn} \end{pmatrix},$$

where A_{ij} is $(-1)^{i+j}$ times the determinant of order $n - 1$ obtained by striking from det A the row and column containing a_{ij}. (This reduced determinant associated with a_{ij} is its "minor," and A_{ij} is its "cofactor.") The inverse matrix A^{-1} has the property that $AA^{-1} = A^{-1}A = I$, the "identity matrix" of order n, which has zeros in every position except along the diagonal where $i = j$, and ones along that diagonal.

Let V denote an m by n matrix whose elements are random variables V_{ij}. Define

$$E(V) = \begin{pmatrix} E(V_{11}) & \cdots & E(V_{1n}) \\ \vdots & & \vdots \\ E(V_{m1}) & \cdots & E(V_{mn}) \end{pmatrix}$$

and observe that for any constant matrices A and B (of dimensions such that the products are defined):

$$E(AVB) = AE(V)B.$$

Consider now the random vector $(X_1, \ldots, X_n)$ written as a column matrix X. The column matrix of mean values is

$$\mu = E(X) = \begin{pmatrix} E(X_1) \\ \vdots \\ E(X_n) \end{pmatrix},$$

and the *covariance matrix* M, defined to be the matrix of second moments, about the means, is

$$M = E[(X - \mu)(X - \mu)'],$$

where the prime denotes transposition or interchange of rows and columns. The element in the ith row and jth column of M is m_{ij}, the covariance of X_i and X_j. Clearly M is *symmetric*: $M = M'$, since $m_{ij} = m_{ji}$. If $(X_1, \ldots, X_n)$ are independent, the covariance matrix is diagonal (nonzero elements occur only on the diagonal $i = j$), all covariances being zero for $i \neq j$.

A covariance matrix is *nonnegative definite*. This means that it is symmetric and that for any constants $(c_1, \ldots, c_n)$ the quadratic form

$$c'Mc = \sum_{i=1}^{n} \sum_{j=1}^{n} c_i c_j m_{ij}$$

is nonnegative. This is seen as follows:

$$c'Mc = c'E[(X - \mu)(X - \mu)']c = E[c'(X - \mu)(X - \mu)'c]$$
$$= E([c'(X - \mu)]^2) \geq 0.$$

Moreover, if at least one c_i is not zero, the vanishing of $c'Mc$ would imply that the linear combination $c'(X - \mu)$ is zero with probability one and that $X_i - \mu_i$ is a linear combination of the other X's with probability one. This would mean that the distribution of X is singular; therefore, if the distribution of X is *not* singular, the quadratic form $c'Mc$ is actually positive unless $c_1 = \cdots = c_n = 0$. In this case M is said to be *positive definite*.

The joint characteristic function of $(X_1, \ldots, X_n)$ is conveniently expressed in matrix notation:

$$\phi_X(t) = E[\exp(it_1 X_1 + \cdots + it_n X_n)] = E(e^{it'X}),$$

where $\phi_X(t)$ is short for $\phi_{X_1, \ldots, X_n}(t_1, \ldots, t_n)$.

Suppose now that Y is an m-dimensional random vector (written as a column matrix) defined by a linear transformation on X:

$$Y = AX,$$

where $m \leq n$. Then

$$\mu_Y = E(Y) = E(AX) = AE(X) = A\mu_X,$$

and the matrix of second moments of Y is

$$M_Y = E[(Y - \mu_Y)(Y - \mu_Y)'] = E[A(X - \mu_X)(X - \mu_X)'A']$$

$$= AE[(X - \mu_X)(X - \mu_X)']A' = AM_XA'.$$

The characteristic function of Y is also easily obtained in terms of the characteristic function of X:

$$\phi_Y(t) = E(e^{it'Y}) = E(e^{it'AX}) = E(e^{i[A't]'X}) = \phi_X(A't).$$

If Y is n-dimensional, so that A is square, and if A is nonsingular (that is, if $\det A \neq 0$), there is an inverse transformation, $X = A^{-1}Y$. If X has the density function $f_X(x)$, the corresponding density function for Y is

$$f_Y(y) = \frac{1}{|\det A|} f_X(A^{-1}y).$$

The assumption of nonsingularity of A simply means that the random variables Y are really n distinct random variables; that is, one is not just a linear combination of the others, in which case the distribution of Y would be singular (concentrated in the hyperplane of the linear relation).

7.1.4 Multivariate Normal Distributions

The random vector $X = (X_1, \ldots, X_p)$, written in matrix form as a column matrix:

$$X = \begin{pmatrix} X_1 \\ \vdots \\ X_p \end{pmatrix},$$

is said to have a p-variate normal distribution if it is of the form

$$X = AY + b,$$

where A is a $p \times p$ matrix of constants, b is a column matrix of constants, and $Y_1, \ldots, Y_p$ are independent, standard normal random variables (having zero means and unit variances).

The joint distribution of the standard normal Y's has a density obtained by multiplying together the univariate densities:

$$f_Y(y_1, \ldots, y_p) = \frac{1}{(2\pi)^{p/2}} \exp\left[-\tfrac{1}{2}(y_1^2 + \cdots + y_p^2)\right]$$

$$= \frac{1}{(2\pi)^{p/2}} \exp\left[-\tfrac{1}{2}y'y\right].$$

The characteristic function of the Y's is obtained by multiplying together their univariate characteristic functions:

$$\phi_Y(s) = \prod_{k=1}^{p} \phi_{Y_k}(s_k) = \exp\left[-\tfrac{1}{2}(s_1^2 + \cdots + s_p^2)\right]$$

$$= \exp\left[-\tfrac{1}{2}s's\right].$$

The mean vector of Y is a column of zeros; and the covariance matrix has zeros off the main diagonal, since the Y's are pairwise uncorrelated, and 1's on the main diagonal, since their variances are 1:

$$M_Y = E(YY') = I.$$

The nature of the distribution of $X = AY + b$ can now be determined from the distribution of Y. The expectation of X is

$$\mu = E(X) = E(AY + b) = AE(Y) + b = b,$$

and the covariance matrix,

$$M_X = AM_YA' = AA'.$$

The characteristic function is

$$\phi_X(t) = E\{\exp[it'(AY + b)]\} = e^{it'b}\phi_Y(A't)$$

$$= \exp[it'b - \tfrac{1}{2}(A't)'(A't)] = \exp[it'\mu - \tfrac{1}{2}t'Mt],$$

in which the subscript on M has been dropped: $M = M_X$. Observe that this reduces to the univariate normal characteristic function with $p = 1$ and $M = \sigma^2$.

It is important to know that if M is a nonnegative definite symmetric matrix, a distribution with characteristic function $\exp[it'\mu - \tfrac{1}{2}t'Mt]$ is multivariate normal. Surely, if $M = AA'$ for some matrix A, an X with this characteristic function is multivariate normal, since the distribution of $AY + \mu$ would have the same characteristic function, which uniquely determines the distribution. The fact that any nonnegative definite symmetric M

can be expressed in the form AA' will not be proved here.[1] It is a consequence of a "diagonalization theorem" that will be used in Section 7.7.1.

It is now immediate that any marginal distribution of a multivariate normal distribution is multivariate normal. For, the characteristic function of a marginal distribution is obtained by putting 0's for the t's corresponding to the dropped variables, and the resulting expression is again of the same type, with a nonnegative definite submatrix of M.

If M is positive definite, a distribution with characteristic function $\exp [it'\mu - \frac{1}{2}t'Mt]$ has a nonsingular p-variate normal distribution, the matrix A in the factorization $M = AA'$ being nonsingular ($\det A \neq 0$). In this case the distribution has a density function, which can be obtained from the density of the independent standard normal Y's:

$$f_X(x_1, \ldots, x_p) = \frac{1}{|\det A|} f_Y(A^{-1}[x - b])$$

$$= \frac{1}{(2\pi)^{p/2}|\det A|} \exp [-\frac{1}{2}(x - \mu)'(A^{-1})'A^{-1}(x - \mu)].$$

Now, since $ABB^{-1}A^{-1} = AIA^{-1} = I$, the inverse of AB is $(AB)^{-1} = B^{-1}A^{-1}$, and therefore

$$M^{-1} = (AA')^{-1} = (A')^{-1}A^{-1} = (A^{-1})'A^{-1}.$$

Also, it can be shown that $\det (AB) = (\det A)(\det B)$, and so

$$\det M = (\det A)(\det A') = (\det A)^2.$$

Consequently the density of X can be rewritten in terms of μ and M:

$$f_X(x) = \frac{1}{(2\pi)^{p/2}\sqrt{\det M}} \exp[-\frac{1}{2}(x - \mu)'M^{-1}(x - \mu)],$$

which again in the univariate case ($p = 1$) reduces to the univariate normal distribution of Section 3.3.

EXAMPLE 7–5. Let Y_1, Y_2, and Y_3 be independent, standard normal random variables. Consider X defined by

$$\begin{cases} X_1 = 2Y_1 - Y_2 + Y_3 \\ X_2 = Y_1 - 3Y_2, \end{cases}$$

or

$$X = \begin{pmatrix} 2 & -1 & 1 \\ 1 & -3 & 0 \end{pmatrix} Y.$$

[1] See Hohn, F. E., *Elementary Matrix Algebra*, 2nd ed., New York: Macmillan, 1964.

The covariance matrix X is

$$M = \begin{pmatrix} 2 & -1 & 1 \\ 1 & -3 & 0 \end{pmatrix} \begin{pmatrix} 2 & 1 \\ -1 & -3 \\ 1 & 0 \end{pmatrix} = \begin{pmatrix} 6 & 5 \\ 5 & 10 \end{pmatrix},$$

with det $M = 35$ and

$$M^{-1} = \frac{1}{35} \begin{pmatrix} 10 & -5 \\ -5 & 6 \end{pmatrix}.$$

With these one can write out the characteristic function of X:

$$\exp\left[-\tfrac{1}{2}(6t_1{}^2 + 10t_1 t_2 + 10t_2{}^2)\right];$$

and the density function:

$$\frac{1}{2\pi\sqrt{35}} \exp\left[-\tfrac{1}{70}(10x_1{}^2 - 10x_1 x_2 + 6x_2{}^2)\right].$$

Given X with a multivariate normal distribution, let Z be a linear function of X,

$$Z = CX + d,$$

with no restriction on the number of components of Z. The characteristic function of Z is

$$\phi_Z(u) = e^{iu'd}\phi_X(C'u)$$
$$= \exp\left[iu'(C\mu + d) - \tfrac{1}{2}u'CMC'u\right].$$

It is concluded from the form of this characteristic function that Z has a multivariate normal distribution with mean $C\mu + d$ and covariance matrix CMC'. Thus any set of linear combinations of normal X's is normal; in particular, any single linear combination of normal variables is normal.

EXAMPLE 7–6.   Given the normal X of Example 7–5, let Z be obtained from X as follows:

$$Z = \begin{pmatrix} 1 & -1 \\ 2 & 1 \\ 1 & 2 \end{pmatrix} X.$$

The distribution of Z must be singular, since there are more Z's than X's; indeed, $Z_3 = Z_2 - Z_1$, so the distribution of Z is concentrated in the plane $z_1 - z_2 + z_3 = 0$. The covariance matrix of Z is

$$M_Z = \begin{pmatrix} 1 & -1 \\ 2 & 1 \\ 1 & 2 \end{pmatrix} \begin{pmatrix} 6 & 5 \\ 5 & 10 \end{pmatrix} \begin{pmatrix} 1 & 2 & 1 \\ -1 & 1 & 2 \end{pmatrix} = \begin{pmatrix} 6 & -3 & -9 \\ -3 & 54 & 57 \\ -9 & 57 & 66 \end{pmatrix},$$

which is singular.

Problems

7-11. Let $(U_1, \ldots, U_n)$ have the density function

$$f_U(u) = \begin{cases} n!, & \text{for } 0 < u_1 < u_2 < \cdots < u_n < 1 \\ 0, & \text{elsewhere.} \end{cases}$$

Let $X_1 = U_1$, $X_2 = U_2 - U_1, \ldots, X_n = U_n - U_{n-1}$, and determine the joint density function of $(X_1, \ldots, X_n)$.

7-12. Given matrices A with elements a_{ij} and B with elements b_{ij}, the product AB is defined, if the number of columns of A equals the number of rows of B, as a matrix in which the element of the ith row and jth column is

$$\sum_k a_{ik}b_{kj}.$$

(a) Show that $(AB)C = A(BC)$.

(b) If the transpose A' of A is defined as a matrix whose rows are the columns of A and whose columns are the rows of A, show that $(AB)' = B'A'$.

(c) Show that the identity matrix I has the property that $IA = A$ and $BI = B$ (where in each case the order of I is that which makes the multiplication possible).

7-13. Let X have a multivariate normal distribution with mean and covariance matrices

$$\mu = \begin{pmatrix} 3 \\ 3 \\ 0 \\ 0 \end{pmatrix}, \quad M = \begin{pmatrix} 2 & 0 & 2 & 0 \\ 0 & 1 & 1 & 0 \\ 2 & 1 & 5 & 1 \\ 0 & 0 & 1 & 1 \end{pmatrix}.$$

(a) Show that M is nonsingular.

(b) Compute the correlation between X_1 and X_3.

(c) Let $Y = CX + d$, with

$$C = \begin{pmatrix} 1 & 1 & 1 & -1 \\ 1 & -1 & 1 & 1 \\ 1 & 0 & 1 & 0 \end{pmatrix}, \quad d = \begin{pmatrix} 2 \\ 0 \\ -1 \end{pmatrix}.$$

Compute the mean and covariance matrices of Y.

(d) Obtain the characteristic function and density function of Y_1 and Y_2 in (c).

(e) Determine the mean and variance of Y_3 directly, using $E(\cdot)$ computations.

7-14. Use the result about a linear transformation of a multivariate normal distribution to show that any subset of $(X_1, \ldots, X_n)$ with a multivariate normal distribution is also multivariate normal.

7.1.5 Gamma and Beta Functions

In evaluating certain constants, it will be convenient to have the notation

$$\Gamma(t) = \int_0^\infty e^{-x}x^{t-1}\, dx.$$

The value of this definite integral, when it converges, depends on the parameter t. As a function of this parameter the integral is called the *gamma function*. This integral is an improper integral—the range of integration is infinite, and the integrand is discontinuous at $x = 0$ if $t < 1$. It can be verified, however, that the integral is convergent for $t > 0$. (The domain of definition of the gamma function is sometimes extended to other values of t but not by means of the above integral; this extension will not be required here.)

One interesting property of the gamma function is that it can be considered as a "factorial" function—its value at a positive integer is a factorial. To see how this comes about, integrate by parts (recalling that t is a positive real number):

$$\Gamma(t) = \int_0^\infty e^{-x}x^{t-1}\,dx = (e^{-x}x^t/t)\big|_0^\infty + \int_0^\infty (x^t/t)e^{-x}\,dx$$

$$= 0 + (1/t)\Gamma(t+1),$$

or

$$\Gamma(t+1) = t\Gamma(t).$$

By carrying out the integration for $t = 1$, it is easily seen that $\Gamma(1) = 1$, and then for any positive integer n:

$$\Gamma(n+1) = n\Gamma(n) = n(n-1)\Gamma(n-1)$$

$$= \cdots = n(n-1)\cdots 3\cdot 2\cdot 1\cdot\Gamma(1) = n!$$

Other integral formulas involving $\Gamma(t)$ are obtained by change of variable in the integral. In particular, these will be useful:

$$\int_0^\infty e^{-ax}x^{t-1}\,dx = \frac{1}{a^t}\Gamma(t), \qquad a > 0,$$

and

$$\int_0^\infty x^{2t-1}\exp(-x^2/2)\,dx = 2^{t-1}\Gamma(t).$$

EXAMPLE 7–7.   Even-order moments of a normal distribution can be expressed in terms of gamma functions. For, if X has the standard normal distribution,

$$E(X^{2k}) = \frac{1}{\sqrt{2\pi}}\int_{-\infty}^\infty x^{2k}\exp(-x^2/2)\,dx$$

$$= \sqrt{\frac{2}{\pi}}\int_0^\infty x^{2k}\exp(-x^2/2)\,dx = \frac{2^k}{\sqrt{\pi}}\Gamma\left(k+\frac{1}{2}\right),$$

the last expression obtained either from a substitution $x^2/2 = u$ or from the formula given above. In particular, with $k = 0$:

$$1 = E(X^0) = \frac{1}{\sqrt{\pi}}\Gamma\left(\frac{1}{2}\right) \qquad \text{or} \qquad \Gamma\left(\frac{1}{2}\right) = \sqrt{\pi}.$$

From this, by successive application of $\Gamma(t + 1) = t\Gamma(t)$, it follows that

$$\Gamma\left(k + \frac{1}{2}\right) = (2k - 1)(2k - 3) \cdots 5 \cdot 3 \cdot 1 \frac{\sqrt{\pi}}{2^k}.$$

whence

$$E(X^{2k}) = (2k - 1)(2k - 3) \cdots 5 \cdot 3 \cdot 1.$$

EXAMPLE 7–8. The following density function defines the *gamma distributions*:

$$f(x) = \frac{\lambda^\alpha}{\Gamma(\alpha)} x^{\alpha-1} e^{-\lambda x}, \qquad \text{for } x > 0,$$

where α and λ are positive parameters. The characteristic function corresponding to this density is

$$\phi(t) = \frac{\lambda^\alpha}{\Gamma(\alpha)} \int_0^\infty e^{-x(\lambda - it)} x^{\alpha - 1} \, dx$$

$$= \left(1 - \frac{it}{\lambda}\right)^{-\alpha}.$$

Substitution of $t = 0$ shows, incidentally, that the proper multiplying constant was chosen in $f(x)$; its integral is 1. A special case already treated earlier, the negative exponential distribution, is obtained by setting $\alpha = 1$.

The "beta function" arises in considering the product of two gamma functions [using the form involving $\exp(-\frac{1}{2}x^2)$]:

$$\Gamma(s)\Gamma(t) = \int_0^\infty \int_0^\infty \left(\frac{u^2}{2}\right)^{s-1} \left(\frac{v^2}{2}\right)^{t-1} \exp\left[-\tfrac{1}{2}(u^2 + v^2)\right] uv \, du \, dv$$

$$= \int_0^{\pi/2} \int_0^\infty \left(\frac{r^2}{2}\right)^{s+t-1} 2(\cos\theta)^{2s-1}(\sin\theta)^{2t-1} \exp(-\tfrac{1}{2}r^2) r \, dr \, d\theta$$

$$= \int_0^\infty w^{s+t-1} e^{-w} \, dw \int_0^{\pi/2} 2(\cos\theta)^{2s-1}(\sin\theta)^{2t-1} \, d\theta$$

$$= \Gamma(s + t)\, B(s, t),$$

where, then,

$$B(s, t) = 2\int_0^{\pi/2} \cos^{2s-1}\theta \sin^{2t-1}\theta \, d\theta = \frac{\Gamma(s)\Gamma(t)}{\Gamma(s + t)}$$

$$= \int_0^1 x^{s-1}(1 - x)^{t-1} \, dx = \int_0^1 (1 - y)^{s-1} y^{t-1} \, dy = B(t, s).$$

This symmetric function of s and t is called the *beta function* (the B is a capital "beta").

EXAMPLE 7–9. The derivation of $B(s, t)$ given above is along the same lines as the calculation of the integral of the normal density, and the latter is a special case of the present formula, with $s = t = \frac{1}{2}$:

$$\Gamma(\tfrac{1}{2})\Gamma(\tfrac{1}{2}) = B(\tfrac{1}{2}, \tfrac{1}{2})\Gamma(1)$$

$$= 2 \int_0^{\pi/2} \cos^0 \theta \sin^0 \theta \, d\theta = \pi.$$

EXAMPLE 7–10.   The family of *beta distributions* is defined by the density

$$f(x) = \frac{1}{B(r, s)} x^{r-1}(1 - x)^{s-1}, \qquad \text{for } 0 < x < 1,$$

where r and s are positive parameters. The kth moment about zero is readily computed:

$$\frac{1}{B(r, s)} \int_0^1 x^k x^{r-1}(1 - x)^{s-1} \, dx = \frac{B(r + k, s)}{B(r, s)}.$$

In particular, the expected value is obtained by setting $k = 1$:

$$\frac{B(r + 1, s)}{B(r, s)} = \frac{r}{r + s},$$

7.1.6   *The Chi-Square Distribution*

The chi-square distribution was defined in Section 3.3.4 as the distribution of a sum of squares of independent, standard normal random variables. The number of terms in the sum is called the number of *degrees of freedom*. The characteristic function of the chi-square distribution with k degrees of freedom was seen to be

$$\phi(t) = (1 - 2it)^{-k/2}.$$

This is the characteristic function of a gamma distribution (cf. Section 7.1.5) with $\alpha = k/2$ and $\gamma = \frac{1}{2}$, and so the density function of the distribution is

$$f(x) = \frac{1}{2^{k/2}\Gamma(k/2)} x^{k/2-1} e^{-x/2}, \qquad x > 0.$$

The chi-square distribution is often encountered in large sample theory as an asymptotic distribution of a statistic used in inference. For example, it has been given as the asymptotic distribution of $-2 \log \Lambda$ in Section 6.3.4, as well as the asymptotic distribution of the Pearson test for goodness-of-fit in Section 6.4.1. In small sample theory the chi-square distribution will be seen to be (except for a constant) the distribution of the variance of a sample from a normal population, and also of certain variance estimates in the analysis of various experimental designs. The following example gives an instance, not terribly practical, in which a variance estimate involves the chi-square distribution.

EXAMPLE 7–11.   Let X have a normal distribution whose mean μ is known. The maximum likelihood estimate of the variance σ^2 is

$$s^2 = \frac{1}{n} \sum (X_i - \mu)^2.$$

Observe, then, that

$$\frac{ns^2}{\sigma^2} = \sum \left(\frac{X_i - \mu}{\sigma} \right)^2,$$

a sum of squares of n-independent, standard normal variables. Therefore, ns^2/σ^2 has the chi-square distribution with n degrees of freedom.

The chi-square distribution (according to Problem 3–68) has the property that a sum of independent chi-square variates has again the chi-square distribution, the number of degrees of freedom of the sum being the sum of the numbers of degrees of freedom of the summands. This property will give the distribution of variance estimates obtained by pooling estimates of variance from independent samples.

Problems

7–15.   Compute the following:

(a) $\Gamma(6)$;

(b) $\Gamma(11/2)$;

(c) $B(2, 3/2)$;

(d) $\int_0^1 (-\log_e u)^{5/2} u \, du$ (Let $u = e^{-x}$);

(e) $\int_0^\infty e^{-3x} x^4 \, dx$;

(f) $\int_0^1 x^5 (1 - x)^9 \, dx$;

(g) $\int_0^{\pi/2} \cos^4 \theta \sin^6 \theta \, d\theta$.

7–16.   Suppose that Y/σ^2 has a chi-square distribution with ten degrees of freedom. (a) Determine a 90 per cent confidence interval for σ^2 based on a single observation on Y.

(b) Determine the power function of the test with critical region $Y > 40$, where Y has the distribution of the Y in the preceding problem.

7–17.   Show that the gamma distributions (and hence chi-square distributions) belong to the exponential family, and also that Y in Problem 7–16 has a distribution in this family.

7–18.   Show that the beta distributions belong to the exponential family.

7–19.   Show that if X is multivariate normal with mean vector $(0, \ldots, 0)$ and covariance matrix M, the quantity $X'M^{-1}X$ has a chi-square distribution with n degrees of freedom. (Use the fact that X can be written as AY, where Y has independent, standard normal components.)

7-20. Show that if $X_1, \ldots, X_k$ are independent, standard, normal variables, the conditional distribution of $X_1^2 + \cdots + X_k^2$, given $X_1 + \cdots + X_k = 0$, is chi-square with $k - 1$ degrees of freedom. (*Hint*: Let $U = AX$, where A is orthogonal and $a_{1i} = 1/\sqrt{k}$. Apply Cochran's theorem to conclude that $X_1^2 + \cdots + X_k^2 - U_1^2$ is chi-square with $k - 1$ degrees of freedom and is independent of U_1.)

7.1.7 A Partitioning Theorem

A kind of converse of the addition theorem for chi-square distributions given in Problem 3–68 will now be taken up. It is basically a theorem of algebra, and so it is not out of order to do some algebra first.

Consider the linear transformation from $(u_1, \ldots, u_n)$ to $(L_1, \ldots, L_m)$ defined by the matrix A:

$$\begin{cases} L_1 = a_{11}u_1 + \cdots + a_{1n}u_n \\ \;\vdots \qquad\qquad\quad \vdots \\ L_m = a_{m1}u_1 + \cdots + a_{mn}u_n \end{cases}$$

Let Q denote the sum of squares of these linear combinations of u's:

$$Q = L_1^2 + \cdots + L_m^2.$$

Let r denote the *rank* of the matrix A (that is, the number of rows in the largest nonsingular square submatrix of A). This number will be called the *number of degrees of freedom* of Q, and indicates the largest number of L's among which there is no linear relation. If it is assumed that the nonsingular matrix of rank r comes from the first r rows of A (which can be arranged by renumbering, if necessary), the quantities $L_{r+1}, \ldots, L_m$ can each be expressed as linear combinations of the first r L's in the sum of squares Q, resulting in a quadratic expression involving just the first r L's:

$$Q = \sum_{j=1}^{r} \sum_{i=1}^{r} b_{ij} L_i L_j = L'BL,$$

where L is the column matrix with entries $L_1, \ldots, L_r$, and B is the symmetric matrix of b_{ij}'s. Since Q is clearly positive definite (as a quadratic form in the L's), B is nonsingular.

Now, the crux of the whole argument is that Q is expressible as a sum of exactly r squares of linear combinations of the u's, and this fact is obtained as follows: As in the two-dimensional case in which a rotation of axes eliminates the cross-product term, so in the n-dimensional case there is an orthogonal transformation of coordinates that will eliminate the cross-product terms in a quadratic form, leaving only the squared terms. The matrix of the new form is diagonal and can be written as $P'BP$, where B is the original matrix and P is the transformation matrix. After elimination of the cross-product terms, a further change of scale along the various axes will give each squared term a coefficient 1, so that the matrix of the new form is the identity matrix. By combining the two transformations, then, it is possible to find a (nonsingular) matrix P with the property that $P'BP$ is the identity matrix.[2]

With the matrix P determined in this way, so that $P'BP = I$, let $v = P^{-1}L$, or $L = Pv$, and substitute this in Q:

$$Q = L'BL = v'P'BPv = v'v = v_1{}^2 + \cdots + v_r{}^2,$$

which represents Q as the sum of r linear combinations of u's, as was claimed to be possible. That is, the v's, being linear combinations of L's, are then linear combinations of the u's.

This result will now be applied. Suppose that $U_1, \ldots, U_n$ are independent, standard, normal random variables, and that

$$\sum_{i=1}^{n} U_i{}^2 = Q_1 + Q_2 + \cdots + Q_k,$$

where *each* Q_i is a sum of squares of linear combinations of the U's. Let r_i denote the number of degrees of freedom (rank), as defined for Q above, of the term Q_i. It is now known that Q_i is expressible as the sum of exactly r_i squares of linear combinations of U's:

$$\begin{cases} Q_1 = W_1{}^2 + \cdots + W_{r_1}{}^2 \\ Q_2 = W_{r_1+1}{}^2 + \cdots + W_{r_1+r_2}{}^2 \\ \vdots \end{cases}$$

where there are, all-in-all, $r_1 + r_2 + \cdots + r_k$ W's or linear combinations of U's involved. If, then, this sum of the ranks is n, one has

$$\sum_{i=1}^{n} U_i{}^2 = U'U = W_1{}^2 + \cdots + W_n{}^2 = W'W.$$

But, since each W_i is a linear combination of U's, $W = CU$; and

$$U'U = (CU)'(CU) = U'C'CU.$$

Clearly, $C'C = I$, and since C is square and $C^{-1} = C'$, then also $CC' = I$. But, if U is multivariate normal with mean vector $(0, 0, \ldots, 0)$ and covariance matrix I, $W = CU$ is multivariate normal, with mean vector $(0, 0, \ldots, 0)$ and covariance matrix $CIC' = I$. That is, $W_1, W_2, \ldots$, and W_n are independent, standard, normal variables, which means that $Q_1, \ldots, Q_k$ are independent

---

[2] Hohn, F., *Elementary Matrix Algebra*, 2nd ed., New York: Macmillan, 1964.

chi-square variables, with $r_1 \ldots, r_k$ degrees of freedom, respectively. In summary, then, we have "Cochran's theorem"[3]:

Let $U_1, \ldots, U_n$ be independent and normally distributed with means zero and unit standard deviations. Let

$$\sum_{i=1}^{n} U_i{}^2 = Q_1 + \cdots + Q_k,$$

where each Q_i is a sum of squares of linear combinations of $U_1, \ldots, U_n$, with r_i "degrees of freedom." Then, if

$$r_1 + \cdots + r_k = n,$$

the quantities $Q_1, \ldots, Q_k$ are independent chi-square variables with $r_1, \ldots, r_k$ degrees of freedom, respectively.

This result will be applied to situations in which $X_1, \ldots, X_n$ are independent, normal variables with $E(X_i) = \mu$ and var $X_i = \sigma^2$, and

$$\sum_{i=1}^{n} \left(\frac{X_i - \mu}{\sigma} \right)^2 = Q_1 + \cdots + Q_k,$$

each Q being a sum of squares of linear combinations of X's. Of course a linear combination

$$L_i = a_{i1} X_1 + \cdots + a_{in} X_n$$

is automatically a linear function of U's, with $U_i = (X_i - \mu)/\sigma$:

$$L_i = \sigma(a_{i1} U_1 + \cdots + a_{in} U_n) + c_i$$

and is homogeneous if $c_i = 0$. But since $E(L_i) = c_i$, it is only necessary to verify that $E(L_i) = 0$ and examine the rank in the linear dependence of the L's on the X's.

For each Q the rank of the corresponding matrix A can be determined by looking for the determinant of highest order that does not vanish, or more simply in many instances as follows: If there are j linear relations among the m L's, the rank of A is at most $m - j$. Then the fact that the rank of a sum of quadratic forms is no larger than the sum of the ranks (a theorem from matrix theory)[4] can often be exploited to conclude that the rank of A is exactly $m - j$. This point will be illustrated in the following example.

---

[3] Cochran's theorem is frequently given in a slightly different but equivalent form in which each Q is simply assumed to be a quadratic form in the U's: $Q = U'BU$, rather than a sum of squares of linear combinations. In the version given here the B is $A'A$, and it can be shown that the rank of A is the same as that of $A'A$. Therefore the rank condition can be investigated for either A or B. In the applications to be made in this book the Q will arise as a sum of squares of linear combinations; hence the given version seems simpler to use.

[4] Hohn, *op. cit.*, p. 240.

EXAMPLE 7–12.   Let $X_1, \ldots, X_n$ be independent and normally distributed with common mean μ and common variance σ^2. Since for each i the variable $(X_i - \mu)/\sigma$ is standard normal, the following sum of squares has a chi-square distribution with n degrees of freedom:

$$\sum \left(\frac{X_i - \mu}{\sigma}\right)^2 = \sum \left(\frac{X_i - \bar{X}}{\sigma}\right)^2 + n\left(\frac{\bar{X} - \mu}{\sigma}\right)^2$$

$$= Q_1 + Q_2,$$

where the partitioning into the two Q's is essentially the parallel axis theorem. The term Q_2 is a square of a single linear combination of the standard normal variables $(X_i - \mu)/\sigma$, and the rank is just 1. The term Q_1 is the sum of squares of $L_1, \ldots, L_n$, where

$$L_i = \frac{X_i - \bar{X}}{\sigma} = \frac{X_i - \mu}{\sigma} - \frac{1}{n}\sum \frac{X_j - \mu}{\sigma}.$$

That is, $L = AU$, where $U_i = (X_i - \mu)/\sigma$. and

$$A = \begin{pmatrix} 1 - 1/n & -1/n & -1/n & \cdots & -1/n \\ -1/n & 1 - 1/n & -1/n & \cdots & -1/n \\ \vdots & \vdots & \vdots & \vdots & \vdots \\ -1/n & -1/n & -1/n & \cdots & 1 - 1/n \end{pmatrix}$$

Since the sum of the L's is zero (a linear relation among them), the rank of A does not exceed $n - 1$. The rank of the sum is n; thus $n \leq \text{rank } A + 1$, or rank $A \geq n - 1$. But then if the rank of A is neither greater than nor less than $n - 1$, it must be $n - 1$. Consequently the ranks of the Q's do add up to n, and Cochran's theorem applies: The Q's have independent chi-square distributions with $n - 1$ degrees of freedom for Q_1 and 1 degree of freedom for Q_2. (The distribution of Q_2 is obvious from the start; the new information is the distribution of Q_1 and the fact that Q_1 and Q_2 are independent random variables.)

Problems

7–21.   Let $L = AU$, where

$$L = \begin{pmatrix} L_1 \\ L_2 \\ L_3 \end{pmatrix}, \qquad U = \begin{pmatrix} U_1 \\ U_2 \\ U_3 \\ U_4 \end{pmatrix}, \qquad A = \begin{pmatrix} 3 & 4 & 1 & 5 \\ 2 & 2 & 0 & 3 \\ 1 & 2 & 1 & 2 \end{pmatrix}.$$

(a) Show that the rank of A is 2, and express the third row of A as a linear combination of its first two rows. (That is, express L_3 as a linear combination of L_1 and L_2.)

(b) Rewrite $L_1^2 + L_2^2 + L_3^2$ as a quadratic form in L_1 and L_2, and give the matrix B of this form.

(c) Show that $P'BP = I$, where

$$P = \begin{pmatrix} 1/\sqrt{6} & 1/\sqrt{2} \\ -1/\sqrt{6} & 1/\sqrt{2} \end{pmatrix}.$$

(d) Show that if

$$\begin{pmatrix} L_1 \\ L_2 \end{pmatrix} = P \begin{pmatrix} V_1 \\ V_2 \end{pmatrix},$$

then

$$L_1{}^2 + L_2{}^2 + L_3{}^2 = V_1{}^2 + V_2{}^2.$$

(Verify this on two levels: by expressing the V's in terms of the L's, and then by expressing both V's and L's in terms of the U's.)

7-22. Let X_{ij}, $i = 1, \ldots, m$ and $j = 1, \ldots, n$, be independent and normally distributed, each with mean μ and variance σ^2. Let

$$\bar{X}_{i\cdot} = \frac{1}{n} \sum_{j=1}^{n} X_{ij}, \qquad \bar{X} = \frac{1}{mn} \sum_{i=1}^{m} \sum_{j=1}^{n} X_{ij}.$$

(a) Show that

$$\sum_i \sum_j (X_{ij} - \bar{X})^2 = \sum_i \sum_j (X_{ij} - \bar{X}_{i\cdot})^2 + n \sum_i (\bar{X}_{i\cdot} - \bar{X})^2.$$

(b) What is the distribution of the left-hand side of the equation in (a)?

(c) Determine the ranks of the quadratic forms in the right-hand side of the equation in (a) and draw a conclusion concerning the distributions of those forms.

7-23. Referring to Problem 7–22, and thinking of $\bar{X}_{1\cdot}, \ldots, \bar{X}_{m\cdot}$ as a random sample of size m from a normal population with mean μ and variance σ^2/n, show (without Cochran's theorem) that the second term on the right of the equation in (a), when divided by σ^2, has a chi-square distribution. What additional information is given by Cochran's theorem?

7.1.8   F and t Distributions

In the problem of comparing normal populations with respect to their variances, as well as in a variety of other problems, it will be necessary to know the distribution of the ratio of two chi-square random variables.

Let U and V denote independent chi-square variables with, respectively, m and n degrees of freedom. The joint distribution of U and V is defined by the joint density, which is obtained by multiplying together the densities of U and V:

$$f_{U,V}(u, v) = \frac{2^{-(m+n)/2}}{\Gamma(\tfrac{1}{2}m)\Gamma(\tfrac{1}{2}n)} u^{m/2 - 1} v^{n/2 - 1} e^{-(u+v)/2},$$

which holds for $u > 0$ and $v > 0$. Consider then the ratio $W = U/V$: This random variable has the distribution function (for $w > 0$)

$$F_W(w) = P(W < w) = P(U/V < w)$$

$$= \iint\limits_{u/v < w, u > 0} f_{U,V}(u, v) \, du \, dv$$

$$= \int_0^\infty \int_0^{vw} f_{U,V}(u, v) \, du \, dv$$

$$= \frac{2^{-(m+n)/2}}{\Gamma(\tfrac{1}{2}m)\Gamma(\tfrac{1}{2}n)} \int_0^\infty e^{-v/2} v^{n/2-1} \int_0^{vw} e^{-u/2} u^{m/2-1} \, du \, dv.$$

The density function is then

$$f_W(w) = \frac{d}{dw} F_W(w) = \frac{2^{-(m+n)/2} w^{m/2-1}}{\Gamma(\tfrac{1}{2}m)\Gamma(\tfrac{1}{2}n)} \int_0^\infty e^{-(v+vw)/2} v^{n/2+m/2-1} \, dv$$

$$= \frac{\Gamma(\tfrac{1}{2}[m+n])}{\Gamma(\tfrac{1}{2}m)\Gamma(\tfrac{1}{2}n)} w^{m/2-1}(1+w)^{-(m+n)/2},$$

for $w > 0$. The fact that the integral of this density over $(0, \infty)$ must be 1 provides a convenient integration formula, one that could be put in the form of a beta function by means of the change of variable $w = u/(1-u)$.

The F distribution is now defined as the distribution of the ratio of two independent chi-square variables, each divided by the corresponding number of degrees of freedom:

$$F = \frac{U/m}{V/n} = \frac{n}{m} W.$$

The density function of F is obtained at once from the density of W:

$$f_F(x) = \frac{m}{n} f_W\left(\frac{m}{n} x\right).$$

The expected value of W is readily obtained by using the integration formula mentioned in the preceding paragraph:

$$E(W) = \int_0^\infty w f_W(w) \, dw = \frac{\Gamma(\tfrac{1}{2}m + 1)\Gamma(\tfrac{1}{2}n - 1)}{\Gamma(\tfrac{1}{2}m)\Gamma(\tfrac{1}{2}n)} = \frac{m}{n-2},$$

and from this one obtains

$$E(F) = E\left(\frac{nW}{m}\right) = \frac{nE(W)}{m} = \frac{n}{(n-2)}.$$

The variance of F is obtainable in much the same fashion.

The percentiles of the F distribution are available in tables (see Table IV, Appendix), but it is customary to give only the lower or the higher percentiles, not both. For instance, if $F_{.05}$ is given, then $F_{.95}$ need not be listed because it is contained elsewhere in the table of fifth percentiles. For,

$$.05 = P(F < F_{.05}) = 1 - P(F > F_{.05})$$

$$= 1 - P\left(\frac{1}{F} < \frac{1}{F_{.05}}\right).$$

and therefore $1/F_{.05}$ is the ninety-fifth percentile of the distribution of $1/F$. But $1/F$ is again a random variable with an F distribution, n degrees of freedom in the numerator, and m in the denominator (if F itself has m degrees of freedom in the numerator and n in the denominator).

The t *distribution* with n degrees of freedom can be defined as that of a random variable symmetrically distributed about 0 whose square has the F distribution with 1 and n degrees of freedom in numerator and denominator, respectively. Let T denote such a random variable, so that T^2 has the F density

$$f_{T^2}(x) = \frac{\Gamma(\frac{1}{2}[1+n])}{\Gamma(\frac{1}{2})\Gamma(\frac{1}{2}n)n} \left(\frac{x}{n}\right)^{1/2-1} \left(1 + \frac{x}{n}\right)^{-(1+n)/2}, \qquad x > 0.$$

Then, for $x > 0$,

$$f_{|T|}(x) = \frac{d}{dx} P(|T| < x) = \frac{d}{dx} P(T^2 < x^2) = 2x f_{T^2}(x^2).$$

But since T is symmetrically distributed, its distribution density is obtained from that of $|T|$ as follows:

$$f_T(\pm x) = \tfrac{1}{2} f_{|T|}(|x|) = |x| f_{T^2}(x^2)$$

$$= \frac{\Gamma(\frac{1}{2}[n+1])}{\sqrt{n\pi}\,\Gamma(\frac{1}{2}n)} \left(1 + \frac{x^2}{n}\right)^{-(n+1)/2}.$$

This is the desired density function of a t distribution.

The symmetry of the t distribution about $x = 0$ implies that the mean value of T, if it exists, must be 0. The integral defining the mean is clearly absolutely convergent for $n > 1$, and so for those values of n, $E(T) = 0$. For $n = 1$, the density of T reduces to what has been called the *Cauchy density*, having no absolute moments of any integral order. For $n > 2$, the integral defining $E(T^2)$ is absolutely convergent, and so for those values of n, var $T = E(T^2) = n/(n-2)$, as derived above for the F distribution.

As $n \to \infty$, the density function of T approaches that of a standard normal variate. For,

$$\left(1 + \frac{x^2}{n}\right)^{-(n+1)/2} = \left\{\left(1 + \frac{x^2}{n}\right)^{n/x^2}\right\}^{-x^2/2} \left(1 + \frac{x^2}{n}\right)^{-1/2} \to \exp\left(-x^2/2\right).$$

Moreover, the constant factor tends to $1/\sqrt{2\pi}$. This can be seen using "Stirling's formula"[5]

$$\Gamma(p) \sim \sqrt{\frac{2\pi}{p}} \left(\frac{p}{e}\right)^p \qquad \text{(large } p\text{)},$$

[5] See Cramer, H. [4], p. 128.

which implies that

$$\frac{\Gamma(p + h)}{\Gamma(p)} \sim p^h \quad \text{(large } p\text{)}.$$

This approach to normality accounts for the fact that in t tables (such as Table III, Appendix), there is often a sequence of entries for $n = \infty$, which are simply the corresponding points on a standard normal distribution.

7.1.9 Noncentral Chi-Square Distribution

A sum of squares of independent, normal variables, each having unit variance but with possibly nonzero means is said to have a *noncentral chi-square* distribution. That is, if $Z_1, \ldots, Z_k$ are independent, and $Z_i \stackrel{d}{=} \mathcal{N}(\mu_i, 1)$, then

$$\chi'^2 = Z_1^2 + \cdots + Z_k^2$$

has the noncentral chi-square distribution with k degrees of freedom. This distribution would seem to depend on the k parameters $\mu_1, \ldots, \mu_k$, but the following development[6] will show that the dependence is only through the value of the *noncentrality parameter*:

$$\lambda \equiv \tfrac{1}{2}(\mu_1^2 + \cdots + \mu_k^2).$$

The moment generating function of the noncentral χ'^2 is computed as follows. If Z is a normal variate with unit variance and mean μ, then

$$\psi_{Z^2}(t) = \frac{1}{\sqrt{2\pi}} \int_{-\infty}^{\infty} \exp\left[tz^2 - (z - \mu)^2/2\right] dz$$

$$= (1 - 2t)^{-1/2} \exp\left[\mu^2 t/(1 - 2t)\right]$$

The moment generating function of χ'^2 can then be obtained as a product of such functions:

$$\psi_{\chi'^2}(t) = \prod \psi_{Z_i^2}(t) = \prod \frac{1}{(1 - 2t)^{-k/2}} \exp\left[\mu_i^2 t/(1 - 2t)\right]$$

$$= (1 - 2t)^{-k/2} \exp\left[2\lambda t/(1 - 2t)\right].$$

It is evident from this that the distribution depends on the μ_i's through the value of λ. It is also clear that with $\lambda = 0$ (or $\mu_i = 0$ for all i) the distribution becomes the *central* chi-square, or ordinary chi-square distribution defined earlier.

The corresponding noncentral chi-square density function does not have a

---

[6] Taken from van der Vaart, H. R., "A note on the derivation of the noncentral chi-square density function," *Statistica Neerlandica* **21**, 99 (1967).

"closed" form but can be expressed in terms of a power series. To obtain this, write

$$\frac{2t}{1 - 2t} = -1 + \frac{1}{1 - 2t}.$$

and expand $\exp [\lambda/(1 - 2t)]$ in its Maclaurin series:

$$\psi_{\chi'^2}(t) = (1 - 2t)^{-k/2} e^{-\lambda} \sum_0^\infty \frac{1}{h!} \left(\frac{\lambda}{1 - 2t}\right)^h$$

$$= \sum_{h=0}^\infty \frac{e^{-\lambda} \lambda^h}{h!} (1 - 2t)^{-(k + 2h)/2}.$$

From this it follows (the m.g.f. being a *linear* operation on density functions) that the density of χ'^2 is

$$f_{\chi'^2}(u) = \sum_{h=0}^\infty \frac{e^{-\lambda} \lambda^h}{h!} f_{\chi^2(k + 2h)}(u)$$

where $f_{\chi^2(k + 2h)}(u)$ is the central chi-square density with $k + 2h$ degrees of freedom.

When $\lambda = 0$ (that is, when $\mu_1 = \cdots = \mu_k = 0$), this reduces to the ordinary "central" chi-square density with k degrees of freedom. (Incidentally, the final formula is also valid for $k = 1$, even though it was implicit in the derivation that $k > 1$.)

It is perhaps worth noting explicitly that although the variables that make up χ'^2 involve k parameters, the distribution of the sum of squares depends only on the single noncentrality parameter λ.

The expression finally obtained above for the noncentral chi-square density is still not especially pleasant to behold or to work with. However, various tables are available.[7]

"Noncentral" F and t distributions are required for power functions of certain tests concerning normal populations. A ratio of chi-square variates, each divided by the corresponding number of degrees of freedom, has a noncentral F distribution if the numerator has a noncentral chi-square distribution that is independent of the central chi-square distribution in the denominator. The noncentral t-distribution is the distribution of the ratio of a normal random variable with mean μ and variance 1 to the square root of a central chi-square variable divided by its number of degrees of freedom.[8]

---

[7] For example, Fix, E., "Tables of Noncentral χ^2," *Univ. Calif. Publ. Statistics* **1**, 15–19 (1949).

[8] Tables of these distributions are available: Lieberman, G., and Resnikoff, G., *Tables of the Non-central t-distribution*. Stanford, California: Stanford Univ. Press, 1957; see also Fox, M., "Charts of the power of the F-test," *Ann. Math. Stat.* **27**, 484–497 (1956).

Problems

7–24. Carry out the computation of the variance of the F distribution.

7–25. Show that the F distribution becomes a beta distribution under a suitable transformation.

7–26. Show that the t distribution with one degree of freedom is a Cauchy distribution.

7–27. Determine the first percentile of an F distribution with 15 and 8 degrees of freedom, respectively, in numerator and denominator.

7–28. Determine which columns in the F tables are squares of which columns in the t table.

7–29. Show that the distribution of the ratio of the variances of two independent samples from normal populations with the same population variances is obtainable from the F distribution.

7.2 Univariate Normal Inference

The joint density functions of the observations in a random sample X from a normal population is

$$f(x; \mu, \sigma^2) = (2\pi\sigma^2)^{-n/2} \exp \left\{ - \sum \frac{(x_i - \mu)^2}{2\sigma^2} \right\}.$$

A minimal sufficient statistic for this family (which is included in the two-parameter exponential family) is given by the sum and the sum of squares of the observations: $(\sum X_i, \sum X_i^2)$, or equivalently, by the sample mean and sample variance (see Example 4–41). The sample mean and sample variance are joint maximum likelihood estimates of the population mean and population variance, and they are jointly asymptotically efficient (an extension to the two-parameter case of the notion of asymptotic efficiency of Chapter 5[9]).

7.2.1 The Variance

If the mean of the population is known, the maximum likelihood estimate of the population variance is the statistic

$$s^2 = \frac{1}{n} \sum_{i=1}^{n} (X_i - \mu)^2.$$

This is unbiased, consistent, and efficient. The normal family with given mean belongs to the one-parameter exponential family, with $Q(\sigma^2) = -1/(2\sigma^2)$, which is monotone increasing. Thus, s^2 is minimal sufficient, and the test $s^2 >$ constant is UMP for $\sigma^2 \leq \sigma_0^2$ against $\sigma^2 > \sigma_0^2$. The distribution of s^2 is obtainable from the chi-square distribution; specifically, ns^2/σ^2 has the chi-

---

[9] See Cramér, H. [4], p. 495.

square distribution with n degrees of freedom, being the sum of n squares of independent standard normal variables.

The usual situation, though, is that the population mean is not known, and second moments that are to provide information about variability must be moments about some sample quantity. As pointed out above, $(\bar{X}, s_x^2)$ is minimal sufficient, and so the pertinent second moment is that about the sample mean.

The sample variance s_x^2 has a distribution depending only on the population variance. To be specific, ns_x^2/σ^2 has a chi-square distribution with $n - 1$ degrees of freedom. Consequently the mean of s_x^2 is $[(n - 1)/n]\sigma^2$ and the variance is $2(n - 1)\sigma^4/n^2$. As an estimate of σ^2 the sample variance s_x^2 is consistent. Since it is biased, its efficiency for a finite sample size is not defined, but as mentioned above, it is with $\bar{X}$ jointly asymptotically efficient.

Other estimates based on the sample sum of squares and the sample mean are used. The unbiased form $\sum (X_i - \bar{X})^2/(n - 1)$ is preferred by some, but the best multiple of $\sum (X_i - \bar{X})^2$ uses a constant multiplier $1/(n + 1)$, if by "best" is meant having minimum mean squared deviation about σ^2 (which is an appropriate criterion if a quadratic regret is used) (see Problem 7–32).

In estimating the standard deviation σ, the statistic s_x suggests itself. The distribution of s_x can easily be derived from that of s_x^2, and in particular the rth moment is obtained as follows:

$$E(s_x^r) = E\left[\left(\frac{ns_x^2}{\sigma^2}\right)^{r/2}\right] \frac{\sigma^r}{n^{r/2}}$$

$$= \frac{\sigma^r}{n^{r/2}2^{(n-1)/2}\Gamma[\tfrac{1}{2}(n - 1)]} \int_0^\infty x^{r/2}x^{(n-3)/2}e^{-x/2}\,dx$$

$$= \frac{\Gamma[\tfrac{1}{2}(n + r - 1)]}{\Gamma[\tfrac{1}{2}(n - 1)]}\left(\frac{2}{n}\right)^{r/2}\sigma^r.$$

Putting $r = 1$ and $r = 2$, one obtains

$$E(s_x) = \alpha_n\sigma, \qquad \text{var } s_x = \beta_n^2\sigma^2,$$

where

$$\alpha_n = \sqrt{\frac{2}{n}}\,\frac{\Gamma(\tfrac{1}{2}n)}{\Gamma[\tfrac{1}{2}(n - 1)]}, \qquad \beta_n^2 = 1 - \frac{1}{n} - \alpha_n^2.$$

The statistic s_x/α_n is unbiased and has variance

$$\text{var } (s_x/\alpha_n) = \left[\frac{n - 1}{n}\,\alpha_n^{-2} - 1\right]\sigma^2.$$

Since as n becomes infinite α_n tends to 1, s_x/α_n is a consistent estimate of σ (as is s_x, for that matter).

A somewhat less efficient but useful estimate of σ is provided by the sample range R. In Example 8–4 it will be seen that the distribution of R/σ is independent of (μ, σ^2). This distribution, its mean a_n and variance b_n^2 are tabulated for various small sample sizes in Table V (Appendix). The statistic R/a_n is an unbiased estimate of σ with variance:

$$\text{var}\left(\frac{R}{a_n}\right) = \left(\frac{b_n}{a_n}\right)^2 \sigma^2.$$

Table V provides percentiles w_p of $W = R/\sigma$ from which confidence limits for σ can be computed. For, since

$$P\left(w_{\alpha/2} < \frac{R}{\sigma} < w_{1-\alpha/2}\right) = 1 - \alpha,$$

the confidence limits at level α for the parameter σ (as obtained by solving the inequality for σ) are given by

$$\frac{R}{w_{1-\alpha/2}} < \sigma < \frac{R}{w_{\alpha/2}}.$$

EXAMPLE 7–13. The efficiency of the unbiased estimate R/a_n relative to the unbiased estimate s_x/α_n is the ratio of the variance of the latter to the variance of the former. For $n = 10$, the computation is as follows: $\alpha_n = .925$, $\alpha_n^2 = .853$, $\beta_n^2 = 1 - .1 - .853 = .047$. From Table V one obtains $a_{10} = 3.078$ and $b_{10} = .797$. Then

$$\text{var}\left(\frac{s_x}{\alpha_n}\right) = \frac{\beta_n^2 \sigma^2}{\alpha_n^2} = \frac{.047}{.853}\sigma^2 = .0508\sigma^2,$$

$$\text{var}\left(\frac{R}{a_n}\right) = \frac{b_n^2 \sigma^2}{a_n^2} = \left(\frac{.797}{3.078}\right)^2 \sigma^2 = .067\sigma^2,$$

and the efficiency is then

$$\frac{\text{var}(s_x/\alpha_n)}{\text{var}(R/a_n)} = \frac{.0508}{.067} = .76.$$

EXAMPLE 7–14. Consider the following nine readings of inlet oil temperature, assumed to be normally distributed: 99, 93, 99, 97, 90, 96, 93, 88, 89. The range is $R = 11$ and the standard deviation is 3.97. The range divided by $a_9 = 2.97$ yields an estimate of 3.71 for σ. The standard deviation divided by $\alpha_9 = .913$ yields 4.35. The confidence interval based on R is obtained by dividing 11 by $w_{.025} = 1.55$ and by $w_{.975} = 4.70$ to obtain: (2.34, 7.10).

Testing between two specific values of σ^2, say, v_0 and $v_1 > v_0$, is *not* a problem with two states of nature and a corresponding most powerful test, since specification of the variance does not determine completely a normal population. A likelihood ratio test can be constructed:

$$\Lambda^* = \frac{L(\bar{X}, v_0)}{L(\bar{X}, v_1)} = \left(\frac{v_1}{v_0}\right)^{n/2} \exp\left[\frac{-ns_x^2}{2}(1/v_0 - 1/v_1)\right] < \text{constant}.$$

This is equivalent to $s_x^2 > \text{constant}$. The power function of this test is obtained by using the fact that ns_x^2/σ^2 has a chi-square distribution with $n - 1$ degrees of freedom:

$$\pi(\sigma^2) = P(s_x^2 > c) = P\left(\frac{ns_x^2}{\sigma^2} > \frac{nc}{\sigma^2}\right)$$

$$= 1 - F\left(\frac{nc}{\sigma^2}\right),$$

where F denotes the chi-square distribution function with $n - 1$ degrees of freedom. This is clearly an increasing function of σ^2, and so the test is at least unbiased for a problem in which the σ^2 in H_0 are to the left of those in H_1.

A corresponding test based on sample range is given by the critical region $R > c$. The power function for this test is

$$\pi(\sigma) = P_\sigma(R > c) = 1 - F_W(c/\sigma),$$

where $W = R/\sigma$, and F_W is given in Table V, Appendix.

EXAMPLE 7–15.   In Figure 7–3 are plotted power functions for the test $s_x^2 > 4.32$ and for the test $R > 7.66$, based on a sample size 15. These were constructed to have the same power of .30 at $\sigma^2 = 4$. (If H_0 were $\sigma^2 \leq 4$, these tests would have the same $\alpha = .30$. Notice that the test based on s_x is slightly more powerful than

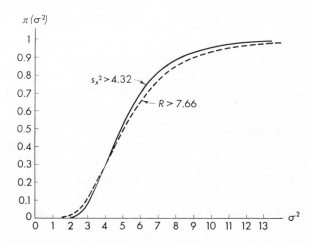

Figure 7–3.

that based on R. Indeed, the former strictly dominates the latter, but the degree of dominance is not overwhelming.)

Problems

7-30. Outside diameters of 70 supposedly identical parts are given in the following frequency table:

Diameter (inches)	Frequency
1.0950	2
1.0945	2
1.0940	9
1.0935	15
1.0930	26
1.0925	10
1.0920	6

Construct a 90 per cent confidence interval for the population variance, assuming normality.

7-31. Sketch the power function of the test whose critical region is $s_x^2 > 7$, based on a sample of size 30 from a normal population.

7-32. Determine the value of A that minimizes the risk (with quadratic regret), using the estimator $A \sum (X_i - \bar{X})^2$ for the variance of a normal population.

7-33. Compute the efficiency as in Example 7–13 but for various other sample sizes—say, $n = 2, 5, 8, 15$. Is the result for $n = 2$ to be expected?

7-34. In Example 7–15, what rejection limits would be used if the tests based on s_x^2 and on R are to have the same power of .2 at $\sigma^2 = 10$?

7.2.2 The Mean

In estimating the mean of a normal population, the sample mean $\bar{X}$ appears to be the best estimator from many points of view. Assuming a quadratic regret, the sample mean is the best multiple of the sample sum in the sense of minimizing the risk among the class of such multiples. It is the maximum likelihood estimate of μ, when σ^2 is known; and it is the maximum likelihood of μ, jointly with s_x^2 for σ^2, when σ^2 is unknown. It is unbiased and consistent. If σ^2 is known, $\bar{X}$ is an efficient estimate of μ; if σ^2 is unknown, it is asymptotically efficient for μ, jointly with s_x^2 for σ^2.

The distribution of $\bar{X}$ is readily available, being normal with parameters $(\mu, \sigma^2/n)$, but the dependence of its variance on the population variance complicates matters. The reliability of $\bar{X}$ in representing the population mean depends on an unrelated parameter, σ^2.

The sample median can also be used to estimate the mean of a normal population. It can be shown[10] that the sample $100p$th percentile is asymptotically normally distributed with parameters

$$\left(\zeta_p, \frac{p(1-p)}{nf^2(\zeta_p)}\right),$$

where ζ_p is the $100p$th population percentile, and $f(x)$ is the population density function. In particular, then, the median of a sample from a normal population is asymptotically normal $(\mu, \pi\sigma^2/2n)$. It is therefore consistent and has an asymptotic efficiency of $2/\pi$, or about 64 per cent, relative to the sample mean.

Another location statistic, which can be useful because of the simplicity of its computation, is the average of the largest and smallest observations: $A = [X_{(1)} + X_{(n)}]/2$. The distribution of this random variable is derived in Section 8.1.2 in terms of an arbitrary population distribution. In the normal case, one obtains (by means of a pair of substitutions of the form $s = \sigma t + \mu$):

$$f_B(z) = \frac{n(n-1)}{\pi} \int_{-\infty}^{z} \left\{\int_{t}^{2z-t} \frac{\exp(-v^2/2)}{2\pi} dv\right\}^{n-2} \exp\left[\frac{-t^2}{2} - \frac{(2z-t)^2}{2}\right] dt,$$

where $B = (A - \mu)/\sigma$. Since B is symmetrically distributed about 0, it follows that $E(A) = \mu$, and so A is an unbiased estimate of μ. Its efficiency relative to the sample mean would be var $\bar{X}/$var A or $1/(n$ var $B)$.

A likelihood ratio test can be constructed for testing the hypothesis $\mu = \mu_0$ against the two-sided alternative $\mu \neq \mu_0$. The numerator of the likelihood ratio Λ is the maximum of $L(\mu, \sigma^2)$ over σ^2 holding $\mu = \mu_0$, achieved when σ^2 is $\sum(X_i - \mu_0)^2/n$. The denominator is $L(\bar{X}, s_x^2)$, the maximum when both μ and σ^2 are allowed to vary; and therefore the likelihood ratio is

$$\Lambda = \frac{L\left(\mu_0, \frac{1}{n}\sum(X_i - \mu_0)^2\right)}{L(\bar{X}, s_x^2)} = \left\{1 + \left(\frac{\bar{X} - \mu_0}{s_x}\right)^2\right\}^{-n/2}$$

The critical region $\Lambda <$ constant is clearly equivalent to

$$T^2 = \frac{(n-1)(\bar{X} - \mu_0)^2}{s_x^2} > \text{constant}.$$

The quantity T^2 can be written in the form

$$T^2 = \frac{\left(\dfrac{\bar{X} - \mu_0}{\sigma/\sqrt{n}}\right)^2}{\dfrac{ns_x^2}{\sigma^2(n-1)}},$$

in which the numerator is a chi-square variable with one degree of freedom,

[10] See Cramér, H. [4], p. 367ff.

under H_0, and the denominator is a chi-square variable with $n - 1$ degrees of freedom (under any state in $H_0 + H_1$) divided by that number of degrees of freedom. Since numerator and denominator are independent, T^2 has under H_0 the F distribution with parameters $(1, n - 1)$. Under H_1 the numerator is no longer a central chi-square variable but, for $E(X) = \mu$, has a noncentral chi-square distribution with noncentrality parameter $[n(\mu - \mu_0)^2]/2\sigma^2$. The power function of the test can therefore be obtained from the noncentral F distribution.

A two-sided confidence interval for μ can be constructed using T^2, with μ_0 replaced by a general μ. For instance, a 95 per cent confidence interval is obtained from the F-distribution with $(1, n - 1)$ degrees of freedom:

$$P(T^2 < F_{.95}) = .95,$$

or

$$P\left\{-\sqrt{F_{.95}} < \sqrt{n - 1}\,\frac{\bar{X} - \mu}{s_x} < +\sqrt{F_{.95}}\right\} = .95.$$

Since $\sqrt{F_{.95}} = t_{.975}$ and $-\sqrt{F_{.95}} = t_{.025}$ (percentiles of the t distribution with $n - 1$ degrees of freedom), the confidence interval can be written in the form

$$\bar{X} - t_{.975}\frac{s_x}{\sqrt{n - 1}} < \mu < \bar{X} + t_{.975}\frac{s_x}{\sqrt{n - 1}}.$$

The symmetrically distributed square root of T^2 (using $\mu = \mu_0$),

$$T = \frac{\sqrt{n - 1}(\bar{X} - \mu_0)}{s_x},$$

can be used as the basis for a test for the one-sided hypothesis $\mu \leq \mu_0$ against $\mu > \mu_0$. The power function of the test $T > K$ is

$$\pi(\mu) = P_\mu(T > K) = P_\mu\left[\sqrt{n - 1}\,\frac{\bar{X} - \mu_0}{s_x} > K\right],$$

which can be computed from the noncentral t distribution.

7.2.3 Confidence Regions for Mean and Variance

A region of (μ, σ^2) values can be constructed from the $(\bar{X}, s_x^2)$ of a given sample, which with a specified probability will cover the actual (μ, σ^2), as follows: Let z_p and χ_p^2 denote percentiles of the standard normal distribution and of the chi-square distribution with $n - 1$ degrees of freedom, respectively. Given a confidence level α, choose δ and ϵ such that $1 - \alpha = (1 - 2\delta)(1 - 2\epsilon)$.

Then

$$P\left\{\left(\frac{\bar{X}-\mu}{\sigma/\sqrt{n}}\right)^2 < z_{1-\delta}^2 \quad \text{and} \quad \chi_\epsilon^2 < \frac{ns_x^2}{\sigma^2} < \chi_{1-\epsilon}^2\right\}$$

$$= P\left\{\left(\frac{\bar{X}-\mu}{\sigma/\sqrt{n}}\right)^2 < z_{1-\delta}^2\right\} P\left\{\chi_\epsilon^2 < \frac{ns_x^2}{\sigma^2} < \chi_{1-\epsilon}^2\right\}$$

$$= (1 - 2\delta)(1 - 2\epsilon) = 1 - \alpha.$$

The inequalities whose probability is given here define a region of the (μ, σ^2) plane, depending on $(\bar{X}, s_x^2)$, which is the desired confidence region.

This confidence region is not just the rectangle defined by the confidence intervals constructed for μ alone and for σ alone. Strictly speaking, these confidence intervals could not be combined by intersection to obtain a confidence rectangle whose level is the product of the individual levels, since the statistics t and s_x^2 on which the intervals are based are not independent. The figure in the following example shows, however, that the rectangular region would be a reasonable approximation for the actual confidence region.

EXAMPLE 7–16.   Suppose that it is desired to construct a 90 per cent confidence region on the basis of a sample of size 20, in which $\bar{X} = 11.2$ and $s_x^2 = 6.8$. Since $.90 \doteq .95 \times .95$, let $2\delta = 2\epsilon = .05$. The inequalities defining the confidence region are then

$$(11.2 - \mu)^2 < (1.96)^2(\sigma^2/20) \quad \text{and} \quad 8.91 < 136/\sigma^2 < 32.9.$$

The boundaries of this region are the curves defined by making the inequalities into equalities, and are the parabola and horizontal lines shown in Figure 7–4. Also shown in that figure are the 95 per cent confidence intervals for μ and σ^2 alone.

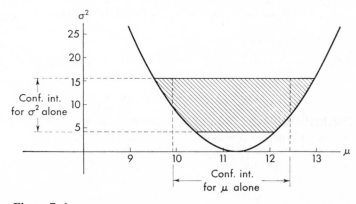

Figure 7–4.

Problems

7–35. Given these observations from a normal population:

$$4.28, \quad 4.32, \quad 4.32, \quad 4.29, \quad 4.31, \quad 4.35, \quad 4.29$$
$$4.32, \quad 4.33, \quad 4.28, \quad 4.37, \quad 4.38, \quad 4.28, \quad 4.32,$$

construct 90 per cent confidence intervals for μ and for σ^2 and an 80 per cent confidence region for (μ, σ^2).

7–36. Assuming σ^2 to be known, determine (in terms of K, σ^2, and n) the large sample power function $\pi(\mu)$ of the test having as a critical region $m > K$, where m is the sample median.

7–37. Construct the likelihood ratio Λ^* for testing $\mu = \mu_0$ against $\mu = \mu_1$. Show that the test $\Lambda^* < 1$ is equivalent to $\bar{X} > (\mu_0 + \mu_1)/2$, if $\mu_1 > \mu_0$. Does $(\Lambda^*)^{2/n}$ have a distribution which is familiar? Obtain an expression for the power function of the test $\Lambda^* < 1$.

7.3 Comparisons

When the populations from which two samples are drawn are both normal, a natural way to compare them is with respect to the parameters. Usually the problem calls for a comparison with respect to just one of the parameters— either with respect to means (or location parameters) or with respect to variances (or scale parameters). The latter is the simpler problem (as in the case of single sample problems), since the distributions of the variances of the samples do not involve the population means.

The notation to be used in this section is as follows:

Population	Mean	Variance	Sample Size	Sample Mean	Sample Variance
X	μ	σ^2	m	$\bar{X}$	s^2
Y	ν	τ^2	n	$\bar{Y}$	t^2

7.3.1   *Variances*

Consider first the following two-sided problem of hypothesis-testing:

H_0: X and Y are independent and normal, with $\sigma^2 = \tau^2$,
H_1: X and Y are independent and normal, with $\sigma^2 \neq \tau^2$.

The likelihood ratio test for this problem is constructed as follows: The likelihood function (for random samples) has the logarithm

$$\log L(\mu, \nu; \sigma^2, \tau^2) = -\frac{m+n}{2} \log 2\pi - \frac{m}{2} \log \sigma^2 - \frac{n}{2} \log \tau^2$$

$$-\frac{1}{2\sigma^2} \sum_{i=1}^{m} (X_i - \mu)^2 - \frac{1}{2\tau^2} \sum_{j=1}^{n} (Y_j - \nu)^2.$$

Allowing all four parameters to vary, differentiating with respect to each one in turn, and setting the derivatives equal to zero, one obtains the following solutions, which are then the joint maximum likelihood estimates:

$$\hat{\mu} = \bar{X}, \qquad \hat{v} = \bar{Y}, \qquad \hat{\sigma}^2 = s^2, \qquad \hat{\tau}^2 = t^2.$$

(It is readily seen that $(\bar{X}, \bar{Y}, s^2, t^2)$ is sufficient for the problem.)

The numerator of the likelihood ratio is the maximum of the likelihood function with the restriction of H_0, namely, that $\sigma^2 = \tau^2$. Holding these equal to the value v, allowing v, μ, and v to vary, setting the derivatives with respect to v, μ, and v equal to zero, and solving simultaneously the resulting equations, one obtains

$$\hat{\mu} = \bar{X}, \qquad \hat{v} = \bar{Y}, \qquad \hat{v} = \frac{1}{m+n}(ms^2 + nt^2).$$

The estimate $\hat{v}$ is a "pooled variance," the average sum of squared deviations of the observations each about the mean of the sample to which it belongs:

$$\hat{v} = \frac{1}{m+n}\left\{ \sum_{i=1}^{m}(X_i - \bar{X})^2 + \sum_{j=1}^{n}(Y_j - \bar{Y})^2 \right\}.$$

The likelihood ratio is now obtained by dividing the maximum of the likelihood function subject to H_0 by its maximum without restriction. These maxima are, respectively,

$$L(\bar{X}, \bar{Y}; \hat{v}, \hat{v}) = (2\pi)^{-(m+n)/2}\left(\frac{m+n}{ms^2 + nt^2}\right)^{(m+n)/2} \exp\left[-\tfrac{1}{2}(m+n)\right],$$

and

$$L(\bar{X}, \bar{Y}; s^2, t^2) = (2\pi)^{-(m+n)/2}s^{-m}t^{-n}\exp\left[-\tfrac{1}{2}(m+n)\right].$$

The likelihood ratio is then

$$\Lambda = \frac{L(\bar{X}, \bar{Y}; \hat{v}, \hat{v})}{L(\bar{X}, \bar{Y}; s^2, t^2)} = (m+n)^{(m+n)/2} \cdot \frac{(s^2)^{m/2}(t^2)^{n/2}}{(ms^2 + nt^2)^{(m+n)/2}}$$

$$= \frac{(m+n)^{(m+n)/2}}{m^{m/2}n^{n/2}} \cdot \frac{Z^{m/2}}{(1+Z)^{(m+n)/2}},$$

where

$$Z = \frac{ms^2}{nt^2} = \frac{\sum(X_i - \bar{X})^2}{\sum(Y_j - \bar{Y})^2}.$$

The critical region $\Lambda <$ constant defines a critical region for Z which calls for rejecting equality of variances if Z is either too large or too small. This is seen in Figure 7–5, in which the distribution of Z is sketched (schematically) beneath the sketch of the functional relationship between Λ and Z. The two

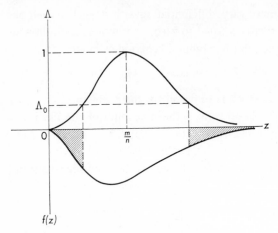

Figure 7–5.

shaded regions, whose total area is the probability of rejecting H_0 with the test $\Lambda < \Lambda_0$, are not necessarily of equal area, but it is convenient to choose modified limits for Z such that they would be of equal area. Such a modification yields a test that is not the same as the likelihood ratio test—but which is not radically different. In practice, it is the ratio of the unbiased variance estimates,

$$F \equiv \frac{n-1}{m-1} Z = \frac{\sum (X_i - \bar{X})^2/(m-1)}{\sum (Y_j - \bar{X})^2/(n-1)} = \frac{\tilde{s}^2}{\tilde{t}^2},$$

which is used in place of Z. This ratio has the F distribution with parameters $(m-1, n-1)$, independent of the values of the population means. (Indeed the cogent reason for using F in place of Z is that the F tables are available and can be used directly.)

EXAMPLE 7–17. To test $\sigma^2 = \tau^2$ against the alternative of unequal variances, samples of sizes $m = 25$ and $n = 20$ are obtained, respectively, from X and Y. If the significance level is to be $\alpha = .10$, the test used calls for accepting equality of variances if the ratio of the unbiased sample variances falls between the fifth and ninety-fifth percentiles of the F distribution with parameters $(24, 19)$. From the F table (Table IV, Appendix), it is found that

$$F_{.95}(24, 19) = 2.11 \quad \text{and} \quad F_{.05}(24, 19) = \frac{1}{F_{.95}(19, 24)} = .485.$$

If $\tilde{s}^2/\tilde{t}^2$ exceeds 2.11 or is less than .485, equality of variances is rejected.

For testing the one-sided hypothesis $\sigma^2 \leq \tau^2$ against $\sigma^2 > \tau^2$, it would seem reasonable to adopt the test with critical region $F >$ constant. The power function of this test is a function of the ratio τ^2/σ^2:

$$P(F > k) = 1 - P(F < k)$$

$$= 1 - P\left(\frac{\tilde{s}^2/\sigma^2}{\tilde{t}^2/\tau^2} < \frac{\tau^2}{\sigma^2}k\right) = 1 - F\left(\frac{\tau^2}{\sigma^2}k\right),$$

where $F(\lambda)$ is the distribution function of the random variable F. Since this distribution function is monotone increasing, the power function is a monotone decreasing function of the ratio τ^2/σ^2, and the test is at least unbiased. It can be shown that there is no uniformly most powerful test for even this one-sided problem.[11]

7.3.2   Means

Comparison of the means of two normal populations is a simpler problem when the variances (if unknown) can be assumed to be equal than it is when they are not equal. The case of *equal variances* will therefore be considered first.

Using the notation established above, the maximum likelihood estimates of the means μ and ν and of the common variance σ^2 are (as shown in Section 7.3.1)

$$\hat{\mu} = \bar{X}, \qquad \hat{\nu} = \bar{Y}, \qquad \hat{\sigma}^2 = \frac{1}{m+n}(ms^2 + nt^2),$$

which happen to be minimal sufficient for the normal family considered. Using these estimates in the likelihood function, one obtains the maximum over all states:

$$L(\bar{X}, \bar{Y}, \hat{\sigma}^2) = (2\pi\hat{\sigma}^2)^{-(m+n)/2} \exp\left[-\tfrac{1}{2}(m+n)\right].$$

For a likelihood ratio test of $\mu = \nu$ against the two-sided alternative $\mu \neq \nu$, the maximum of the likelihood function subject to the restriction $\mu = \nu$ is required. The maximizing values of $\mu = \nu$ and σ^2 are found to be

$$\tilde{\mu} = \frac{m\bar{X} + n\bar{Y}}{m+n}, \qquad \tilde{\sigma}^2 = \frac{1}{m+n}\left\{\sum(X_i - \tilde{\mu})^2 + \sum(Y_j - \tilde{\mu})^2\right\}.$$

Substitution in the likelihood function again produces $-(m+n)/2$ in the exponent, and the likelihood ratio becomes

$$\Lambda = \left(\frac{\hat{\sigma}^2}{\tilde{\sigma}^2}\right)^{(m+n)/2}$$

[11] See Lehmann, E. [13], p. 117.

Then

$$(1/\Lambda)^{2/(m+n)} = \tilde{\sigma}^2/\hat{\sigma}^2$$

$$= \frac{\sum(X_i - \bar{X})^2 + \sum(Y_j - \bar{Y})^2 + m(\bar{X} - \tilde{\mu})^2 + n(\bar{Y} - \tilde{\mu})^2}{\sum(X_i - \bar{X})^2 + \sum(Y_j - \bar{Y})^2}$$

$$= 1 + \frac{1}{m+n-2}T^2,$$

where

$$T^2 = mn\left(\frac{m+n-2}{m+n}\right)\frac{(\bar{X} - \bar{Y})^2}{ms^2 + nt^2} = \frac{Z^2}{Q/(m+n-2)}$$

and

$$Z^2 = \frac{(\bar{X} - \bar{Y})^2}{\sigma^2(1/m + 1/n)}, \qquad Q = \frac{ms^2 + nt^2}{\sigma^2}.$$

Under H_0 the quantity Z^2 has a chi-square distribution with one degree of freedom, and Q has a chi-square distribution with $m + n - 2$ degrees of freedom. Further, they are independent, and so under H_0 the ratio T^2 has the F distribution with parameters $(1, m + n - 2)$, independent of the value of the common variance σ^2. The value of the constant would be determined by specification of α, using Table IV, or equivalently from the table of the t distribution, since the symmetrically distributed square root T of T^2 has the t distribution.

EXAMPLE 7–18.   Consider the following data, taken from independent normal populations with equal (but unknown) variances: $s^2 = .4$, $t^2 = .3$, $\bar{X} = 2.3$, $\bar{Y} = 2.8$, and $m = n = 10$. Then

$$T^2 = 100 \cdot \frac{18}{20} \cdot \frac{(.5)^2}{4+3} = 3.2,$$

and from Table IVa one finds $F_{.95}(1, 18) = 4.41$.   Since $3.2 < 4.41$, equality of means would be accepted at the 5 per cent level.

When it is not assumed that $\mu = \nu$, the distribution of T^2 is noncentral F, the numerator Z^2 being then noncentral chi-square with noncentrality parameter

$$\frac{(\mu - \nu)^2}{2\sigma^2\left(\dfrac{1}{m} + \dfrac{1}{n}\right)}.$$

Thus the power of the test $T^2 > k$ can be expressed as a function of $(\mu - \nu)/\sigma$:

$$\pi\left(\frac{\mu - \nu}{\sigma}\right) = P(T^2 > k) = 1 - F(k),$$

where $F(\cdot)$ denotes the noncentral F distribution function.

A two-sided confidence interval is readily constructed by using the fact that

$$T^2 = \frac{[\bar{X} - \bar{Y} - (\mu - \nu)]^2}{(m + n)(ms^2 + nt^2)} \, mn(m + n - 2)$$

has the F distribution with parameters $(1, m + n - 2)$.

A test of $\mu \leq \nu$ against $\mu > \nu$ is provided by the critical region $T >$ constant, where

$$T \doteq (\bar{X} - \bar{Y}) \left[\frac{mn(m + n - 2)}{(m + n)(ms^2 + nt^2)} \right]^{1/2}.$$

The power function of this test would involve the noncentral t distribution.

Next consider the case of *unequal variances*. The problem of comparing means of two normal populations when the variances are unknown and possibly unequal is called the *Behrens-Fisher problem*. It has an extensive history of controversy, and there are still unsettled aspects of the problem. The difficulty lies in the fact that the ratio T^2 used above for the case of equal variances no longer has a distribution under H_0 which is independent of population parameters.

Considerations of invariance have served to suggest that the critical region of a test ought to be of the form (for the one-sided case):

$$\frac{\bar{Y} - \bar{X}}{ms^2 + nt^2} \geq h \left(\frac{nt^2}{ms^2} \right).$$

for a suitably chosen function h. It is not known whether there is an h such that the probability of the critical region is a given α under H_0, for all values of the common mean and for all values of τ/σ, although a test with approximately this property is available.[12]

Given here is a test proposed by Scheffé.[13] It is assumed for definiteness that $m < n$. The statistic used is

$$S = \frac{\bar{X} - \bar{Y}}{\sqrt{Q}} \, [m(m - 1)]^{1/2},$$

where

$$Q = \sum_{i=1}^{m} (U_i - \bar{U})^2, \qquad U_i = X_i - \sqrt{\frac{m}{n}} \, Y_i, \qquad i = 1, \ldots, m.$$

Under the null hypothesis that $\mu = \nu$, the statistic S has a t distribution with

[12] See Welch, B. L., "The generalization of Student's problem when several different population variances are involved," *Biometrika* **34**, 28–35 (1947).

[13] "On solutions of the Behrens–Fisher problem, based on the *t*-distribution," *Ann. Math. Stat.* **14**, 35–44 (1943).

$m - 1$ degrees of freedom, independent of the population variances. To see why this is so, put

$$d_i = X_i - \sqrt{\frac{m}{n}}\, Y_i + \sum_{i=1}^{m} \frac{Y_i}{\sqrt{mn}} - \bar{Y}, \qquad i = 1, \ldots, m.$$

Being linear combinations of the normally distributed observations, the d's have a multivariate normal distribution, with means

$$E(d_i) = E(X_i) - \sqrt{\frac{m}{n}}\, E(Y_i) + \frac{mE(Y)}{\sqrt{mn}} - E(Y) = \mu - \nu,$$

and covariances

$$\mathrm{cov}\,(d_i, d_j) = \begin{cases} 0, & \text{if } i \neq j, \\ \sigma^2 + (m/n)\tau^2, & \text{if } i = j, \end{cases}$$

That is, the d's may be thought of as making up a random sample of size m from a normal population with mean $\mu - \nu$ and variance $\sigma^2 + (m/n)\tau^2$. The mean of this sample, $\bar{d} = \bar{X} - \bar{Y}$, is then normally distributed; further, it is independent of the variance of the sample consisting of the d's, and the following ratio has the t distribution with $m - 1$ degrees of freedom:

$$S^* = [m(m - 1)]^{1/2} \frac{\bar{d} - (\mu - \nu)}{\sqrt{Q}},$$

where again

$$Q = \sum_{i=1}^{m} (U_i - \bar{U})^2 = \sum_{i=1}^{m} (d_i - \bar{d})^2.$$

Then, under H_0 the variable S^* is S, which has the distribution claimed.

EXAMPLE 7–19.   Consider the following data from two normal populations:

From X: 17, 21, 19, 23, 18, 22;
From Y: 21, 19, 23, 26, 20, 22, 24, 21.

Here $m = 6$, $n = 8$, $\sqrt{m/n} = .866$, $\bar{X} = 20$, and $\bar{Y} = 22$. The U's are as follows: $-1.2, 4.5, -.9, .5, .7, 2.9$. From these are obtained $\bar{U} = 1.083$ and $Q = 24.63$; and then

$$S = \sqrt{6 \times 5}\, \frac{(20 - 22)}{\sqrt{24.63}} = -2.21.$$

Since this is less than -2.01, the fifth percentile of the t distribution with $m - 1 = 5$ degrees of freedom, the hypothesis of equal population means would be rejected in favor of unequal means at the 10 per cent level. A two-sided 90 per cent confidence interval would be given as follows:

$$-2 - 2.01 \sqrt{24.63/30} < \mu - \nu < -2 + 2.01 \sqrt{24.63/30},$$

or $(-3.82, -.18)$, which does not contain 0.

This test of Scheffé has certain desirable properties. It is based on the readily accessible t tables; the distribution of the test statistic under the null hypothesis is independent of the population variances; and (as shown by Scheffé) the confidence interval that results has a property of minimum length among the class of procedures based on linear combinations of the observations. However, the test statistic is *not* independent of the ordering of the observations— it is not symmetric in the X's and in the Y's. Indeed, if the original ordering is lost, the test must be applied to a randomly selected one of the possible orderings of the observations in the order statistic. It is also noted that if the population variances *are* equal, the t test discussed first would apply and is based on $n + m - 2$ degrees of freedom; the fact that only $m - 1$ degrees of freedom are available in using the Scheffé procedure suggests that the latter is not so good as might be hoped for.

Problems

7–38.   Show that $(\bar{X}, \bar{Y}, s^2, t^2)$ is minimal sufficient for problems involving two independent normal populations with unknown parameters.

7–39.   If the data of Example 7–18 has been obtained to test equality of variances, what conclusion would be drawn?

7–40.   Determine the power function of the test defined in Example 7–17 (as a function of the ratio of population variances).

7–41.   Would equality of means be accepted on the basis of the data in Example 7–19 if it could be assumed that the population variances are equal? Construct a confidence interval for $\mu - \nu$ under this assumption.

7–42.   Verify the computation of cov (d_i, d_j) in the development of the Scheffé test.

7–43.   Compute the value of the Scheffé statistic for the data of Example 7–19, but using a different ordering of the Y values (for instance, let $Y_i \rightarrow Y_{i+1}$, and $Y_8 \rightarrow Y_1$).

CHAPTER **8**

NONPARAMETRIC STATISTICS

When the class of distributions or states of nature that are admitted in a given statistical problem is defined by a density function or a probability function depending on a finite number of real parameters, say by $f(x; \theta)$, the problem is said to be *parametric*. Most of the problems considered so far are of this type. In other cases the problem is said to be *nonparametric*. The goodness-of-fit problem is such a case, and could have been treated logically under the present heading.

It is often both desirable and possible to use *distribution-free* procedures—procedures involving a statistic whose distribution (at least under the null hypothesis) does not depend on the particular form of the population distribution. The Kolgmogorov–Smirnov test for goodness-of-fit, discussed in Chapter 6, is of this type, and the classical chi-square test for goodness-of-fit is asymptotically distribution-free. In each case, a single table suffices no matter what the null population distribution function.

Some of the problems to be considered will involve, for instance, location as measured by the median. And although the median is in a sense a "parameter" of the population distribution, as opposed to being a statistic computed from a sample, it is generally not a parameter in the sense of being a real variable θ that indexes a family of distributions with a density $f(x; \theta)$. So inference concerning population medians comes under the heading of "nonparametric."

8.1   Order Statistics and Related Distributions

The joint distribution of the ordered observations in a random sample from a continuous population with density $f(x)$ will now be derived.

Let ν denote one of the $n!$ possible permutations of the integers $1, 2, \ldots, n$:

$$\nu = (\nu_1, \nu_2, \ldots, \nu_n).$$

Each of these permutations defines a region of sample points x:

$$R_\nu = \{\text{set of } x \text{ such that } x_{\nu_1} < x_{\nu_2} < \cdots < x_{\nu_n}\}.$$

Let R denote the region R_ν in which ν is the particular permutation $(1, 2, \ldots, n)$:

$$R = \{\text{set of } x \text{ such that } x_1 < x_2 < \cdots < x_n\}.$$

The $n!$ sets $\{R_\nu\}$ together make up the space of sample points x, except for the boundaries, which have probability zero under the assumption of a continuous population.

Each permutation ν defines a linear transformation $y = T_\nu x$, where $y_k = x_{\nu_k}$. Such a transformation has the property that $\det T_\nu = \pm 1$, and the inverse is just another permutation transformation. Under such a transformation the region R_ν of points x such that $x_{\nu_1} < \cdots < x_{\nu_n}$ is carried into the region R of points y such that $y_1 < \cdots < y_n$. Further, since the joint density of the random sample X is a *symmetric* function of the coordinates of x, it is unchanged by $y = T_\nu x$:

$$f(x) \equiv \prod f(x_k) = \prod f(x_{\nu_k}) = \prod f(y_k) = f(y).$$

Therefore,

$$P(R_\nu) = \int_{R_\nu} f(x)\, dx = \int_R f(y)\, dy = P(R),$$

which means that each R_ν has the probability $1/n!$.

Consider now the order statistic

$$Y = t(X_1, \ldots, X_n) = (X_{(1)}, \ldots, X_{(n)})$$

This function $t(x)$ carries each x into a point in R, and so induces a measure in R which is the probability distribution of the ordered observations. This distribution has zero density outside R, but for any set A in R, the probability that Y is in A can be computed. Let A_ν denote the set of those points in R_ν whose coordinates when ordered yield a point in A. Then

$$P(Y \text{ in } A) = P\left(X \text{ in } \sum_\nu A_\nu\right) = \sum_\nu P(X \text{ in } A_\nu) = \sum_\nu \int_{A_\nu} f(x)\, dx$$

$$= \sum_\nu \int_A f(y)\, dy = n! P(X \text{ in } A).$$

Therefore,

$$f_Y(y) = \begin{cases} n!\, f(y), & \text{if } y \text{ is in } R, \\ 0, & \text{otherwise.} \end{cases}$$

That is, the joint density is essentially unchanged in R, being only multiplied by $n!$ to take into account the requirement that the total probability be 1.

EXAMPLE 8–1.   It is perhaps helpful to write out some of these relations for the simple case $n = 2$. There are just two permutations of $(1, 2)$; call them **0**: $(1, 2)$, and **1**: $(2, 1)$. The regions $R_0 = R$ and R_1 are the half-planes in which $x_1 < x_2$ and $x_2 < x_1$, respectively, as shown in Figure 8–1. Shown also is a set A of points

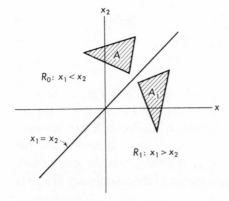

Figure 8–1.

in R and the set A_1 of points in R_1 which are carried into A under the transformation $y_1 = x_2$, $y_2 = x_1$. The order statistic $(X_{(1)}, X_{(2)})$ has "values" only in R and takes each point (where $x_1 \neq x_2$) into a point in R. For instance, both $(4, 1)$ and $(1, 4)$ would be carried into $(1, 4)$, which is in R; and

$$P[(X_{(1)}, X_{(2)}) \text{ in } A] = P(X \text{ in } A_0) + P(X \text{ in } A_1)$$

$$= 2P(X \text{ in } A_0) = \int_{A_0} 2f(x_1)f(x_2)\, dx_1\, dx_2.$$

The joint density of $X_{(1)}$ and $X_{(2)}$ is zero at any point in R_1 and is just twice the joint density of X_1 and X_2 in R_0.

8.1.1   Conditional Distribution Given the Order Statistic

The order statistic determined from a random sample X is easily seen to be sufficient for any family of distributions by the factorization criterion. For the joint density at $(x_1, \ldots, x_n)$ is just

$$f_X(x) = \prod f(x_i) = h(y),$$

where $f(x)$ is the population density and $y = (x_{(1)}, \ldots, x_{(n)})$ is the order statistic value corresponding to x. That is, given the ordered coordinates $x_{(1)}, \ldots, x_{(n)}$ one can determine $f_X(x)$, which is then a function (h) of the ordered coordinates.

The sufficiency can also be seen by computing the conditional distribution of X given the order statistic, which turns out to be independent of the population distribution. This conditional distribution is of interest in itself, so (even though the sufficiency has been quickly established above) it will now be derived. Specifically, it will be shown that this conditional distribution assigns probability $1/n!$ to each of the $n!$ sample points whose coordinates are permutations of a given point in R.

Consider a set B of sample points and a set A of possible "values" of the order statistic Y; that is, A lies in R, the set of x such that $x_1 < \cdots < x_n$. Then

$$P(Y \text{ in } A \text{ and } X \text{ in } B) = P(X \text{ in } \tilde{A}B)$$

$$= \int_{\tilde{A}} \phi_B(x)f(x)\,dx,$$

where $\tilde{A}$ denotes the union of all A_v as defined earlier, and $\phi_B(x)$ is the "indicator function" of B, the function that is 1 for x in B and 0 for x in B^c. Since a permutation transformation T_v would not alter the set $\tilde{A}$ (which already contains all permutations of any point in it), such a change of variable in the integral above yields

$$P(Y \text{ in } A \text{ and } X \text{ in } B) = \int_{\tilde{A}} \phi_B(T_v x)f(x)\,dx.$$

Since this is the same for each permutation v, it is the same as the average over all such permutations:

$$P(Y \text{ in } A \text{ and } X \text{ in } B) = \int_{\tilde{A}} \frac{1}{n!} \sum_v \phi_B(T_v x)f(x)\,dx.$$

Now the integrand has the same values in any A_v as in A, and therefore this integral over $\tilde{A}$ can be written as $n!$ times the integral over A:

$$P(Y \text{ in } A \text{ and } X \text{ in } B) = \int_A \left[\frac{1}{n!} \sum_v \phi_B(T_v y)\right] n! f(y)\,dy.$$

This can be interpreted as the integral with respect ot the distribution of Y of the conditional probability of X given $Y = y$. That is,

$$P(X \text{ in } B \mid Y = y) = \frac{1}{n!} \sum_{v} \phi_B(T_v y).$$

Since $\phi_B(x) = 1$ for x in B and zero otherwise, the sum here is just the number of permutations of y that are in B. In particular, if B is a single point that is one of the permutations of y in R, the conditional probability is $1/n!$, as claimed. That is, the various permutations that could have led to a given order statistic are equally likely to have been the original sample point.

8.1.2 Distributions of the Components of the Order Statistic

It is possible to derive (in principle) the distribution of the individual components of the order statistic or the joint distribution of several of them from the distribution of the complete order statistic. Consider instead the following more elementary approach. The distribution function of the kth smallest observation is

$$P[X_{(k)} \le y] = P(k \text{ or more of the } n \text{ observations are } \le y)$$

$$= \sum_{j=k}^{n} \binom{n}{j} [F(y)]^j [1 - F(y)]^{n-j},$$

the individual terms in this sum being probabilities that in n independent trials precisely j result in an observation that does not exceed y. [The individual trials are of the Bernoulli type with $p = F(y)$.]

The density function of $X_{(k)}$ can be obtained from the above distribution function by differentiating with respect to y:

$$f_{X_{(k)}}(y) = \sum_{j=k}^{n} \binom{n}{j} j[F(y)]^{j-1} f(y)[1 - F(y)]^{n-j}$$

$$+ \sum_{j=k}^{n} \binom{n}{j} (n-j)[F(y)]^j [1 - F(y)]^{n-j-1}[-f(y)]$$

$$= nf(y) \left\{ \sum_{j=k}^{n} \binom{n-1}{j-1} [F(y)]^{j-1}[1 - F(y)]^{n-j} \right.$$

$$\left. - \sum_{j=k}^{n-1} \binom{n-1}{j} [F(y)]^j [1 - F(y)]^{n-j-1} \right\}.$$

Letting $j = m - 1$ in the second sum results in terms identical with those in the first sum, but from $m = k + 1$ to n. These then cancel except for the term $j = k$ in the first sum:

$$f_{X_{(k)}}(y) = nf(y) \binom{n-1}{k-1} [F(y)]^{k-1}[1 - F(y)]^{n-k}.$$

Putting $k = n$, one obtains the distribution and density functions for the largest observation $X_{(n)}$:

$$F_{X_{(n)}}(y) = [F(y)]^n, \qquad f_{X_{(n)}}(y) = n[F(y)]^{n-1}f(y),$$

and putting $k = 1$, the distribution and density functions of $X_{(1)}$:

$$F_{X_{(1)}}(y) = 1 - [1 - F(y)]^n, \qquad f_{X_{(1)}}(y) = n[1 - F(y)]^{n-1}f(y).$$

With a little more work one can obtain the joint distribution of any *pair* of the ordered observations. The extra work is perhaps a minimum in the case of the smallest and largest observations, whose joint distribution function is

$$F_{X_{(1)}, X_{(n)}}(u, v) = P[X_{(1)} \leq u \text{ and } X_{(n)} \leq v].$$

To evaluate this, first observe that

$$\{X_{(n)} \leq v\} = \{X_{(1)} \leq u \text{ and } X_{(n)} \leq v\} + \{X_{(1)} > u \text{ and } X_{(n)} \leq v\}.$$

The events on the right are disjoint, so the probability of the sum is the sum of the probabilities; transposing the second term, then, one obtains

$$F_{X_{(1)}, X_{(n)}}(u, v) = P[X_{(n)} \leq v] - P[X_{(1)} > u \text{ and } X_{(n)} \leq v]$$

$$= [F(v)]^n - P(\text{all } X_i \text{ lie between } u \text{ and } v)$$

$$= \begin{cases} [F(v)]^n - [F(v) - F(u)]^n, & \text{if } u \leq v, \\ [F(v)]^n, & \text{if } u > v. \end{cases}$$

The joint density is found by differentiation:

$$f_{X_{(1)}, X_{(n)}}(u, v) = \begin{cases} n(n - 1)[F(v) - F(u)]^{n-2}f(u)f(v), & \text{if } u \leq v, \\ 0, & \text{if } u > v. \end{cases}$$

The distributions of statistics based on the smallest and largest observations can be obtained by using this joint density function. For instance, the average

$$A = \tfrac{1}{2}[X_{(1)} + X_{(n)}]$$

is sometimes useful in location problems. Its distribution function is

$$F_A(x) = P(A \leq x) = P[X_{(1)} + X_{(n)} \leq 2x] = \int\int_R f(u, v) \, du \, dv,$$

where R denotes the region (Figure 8–2) in the uv plane defined by the inequalities $u + v \leq 2x$ and $u \leq v$, and $f(u, v)$ denotes the joint density of $X_{(1)}$ and $X_{(n)}$. Making the change of variable $u = s$ and $v = t - s$, one obtains

$$F_A(x) = \int_{-\infty}^{2x} \int_{-\infty}^{t/2} f(s, t - s) \, ds \, dt.$$

The derivative with respect to x, which appears only in the upper limit of the

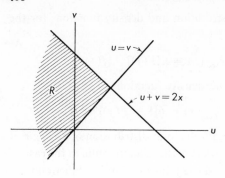

Figure 8–2.

outer integral, is the inner integral evaluated at $t = 2x$ times the derivative of $2x$ with respect to x:

$$f_A(x) = 2 \int_{-\infty}^{x} f(s, 2x - s)\, ds,$$

$$= 2n(n - 1) \int_{-\infty}^{x} [F(2x - s) - F(s)]^{n-2} f(s) f(2x - s)\, ds.$$

EXAMPLE 8–2.   Let X be uniform on $[0, 1]$. For $x < 0$ the $f(s)$ in the above integral formula for $f_A(x)$ vanishes, since $s < x < 0$. For $x > 1$, $2x - s > x > 1$ (for $s < x$), and therefore the factor $f(2x - s)$ vanishes. For $0 < x < 1$, it is quickly discovered that different calculations are required in the left and right halves of the interval.

For $0 < x < \frac{1}{2}$, one has $0 < s < x < \frac{1}{2}$ and also $0 < x < 2x - s < 1 - s$ < 1. Thus, both s and $2x - s$ are within $[0, 1]$, where the density of X is 1, and the c.d.f. is x. Consequently, for $0 < x < \frac{1}{2}$,

$$f_A(x) = 2n(n - 1) \int_{0}^{x} [(2x - s) - s]^{n-2}\, ds = n2^{n-1} x^{n-1}.$$

On the interval $\frac{1}{2} < x < 1$, on the other hand, one finds $2x - 1 > 0$; but then since $f(2x - s)$ is zero for $2x - s > 1$ or $2x - 1 > s$, it follows that the s-integration really starts at $2x - 1$ instead of at 0. Further, on this reduced interval $(2x - 1, x)$ over which the integral is taken, one has $1 > 2x - s > x > \frac{1}{2}$ and $0 < 2x - 1 < s < x < 1$, so that both s and $2x - s$ are on $[0, 1]$, where the density is 1 and the c.d.f. is x:

$$f_A(x) = 2n(n - 1) \int_{2x-1}^{x} [(2x - s) - s]^{n-2}\, ds = n2^{n-1}(1 - x)^{n-1}.$$

This is the reflection about $x = \frac{1}{2}$ of the earlier formula for the left half of the interval. That is, $f_A(x)$ is symmetric about $x = \frac{1}{2}$—which should certainly not offend one's intuition.

Problems

8–1.   Compute the expected values of the smallest, the largest, and the average of the smallest and largest observations in a random sample of size n from a population uniform on $[a, b]$.

8–2.   Compute the covariance of the smallest and largest observations of a random sample of size n from a uniform distribution on $[0, 1]$.

8–3.   Compute the variance of the average of the smallest and largest observations in a random sample of size n from a population uniform on $[a, b]$.

8–4.   Consider a random sample of four observations from a uniform distribution on $[0, 1]$. From the joint distribution of the ordered observations obtain the joint density function of the smallest and next smallest observations by integrating out the unwanted variables. Check to see that your result is a density function.

8–5.   Compute the expected value of the second smallest observation in Problem 8–4.

8–6.   Identical units, each with time to failure having the c.d.f. $F(x)$ and reliability function $R(x) = 1 - F(x)$ (see Example 2–11), are operated in a system so that the system fails if and only if all units fail. (The units are said to be in *parallel*.) Show that the time to failure of the system is the maximum of the times to failure of the individual units, and so obtain a formula for system reliability in terms of $R(x)$. Obtain also a corresponding formula for the case in which the individual units have possibly different life characteristics—that is, the reliability of the ith unit is $R_i(x)$.

8–7.   Paralleling Problem 8–6, study the case of units in *series*—that is, units operated in a system so that the system fails as soon as one unit fails.

8.1.3   The Sample Range

The sample range, $R = X_{(n)} - X_{(1)}$, can also be treated using the joint distribution of the smallest and largest observations. Its distribution function is

$$F_R(r) = P[X_{(n)} - X_{(1)} \le r] = \int\int_S f(u, v) \, du \, dv,$$

where $f(u, v)$ is the joint density as before, and S is the region in the uv plane defined by $0 < v - u < r$. Then

$$F_R(r) = \int_{-\infty}^{\infty} \int_u^{u+r} f(u, v) \, dv \, du,$$

and the density function is the derivative of this with respect to r:

$$f_R(r) = \int_{-\infty}^{\infty} f(u, u + r) \, du$$

$$= n(n - 1) \int_{-\infty}^{\infty} [F(u + r) - F(u)]^{n-2} f(u) f(u + r) \, du,$$

which is valid for $r > 0$. If $r < 0$, both $F_R(r)$ and $f_R(r)$ are zero.

EXAMPLE 8–3.   Consider the uniform distribution on $[a, b]$. Since the density function vanishes outside $[a, b]$, the product $f(u)f(u + r)$ vanishes outside $[a, b - r]$. On this latter interval both $f(u)$ and $f(u + r)$ are equal to $1/(b - a)$, and

$$F(u + r) - F(u) = \int_u^{u+r} \frac{1}{b - a} \, du = \frac{r}{b - a}.$$

Hence,

$$f_R(r) = \frac{n(n-1)}{(b-a)^n} r^{n-2}(b - r - a), \qquad \text{for } 0 < r < b - a.$$

EXAMPLE 8–4.   Consider a normal population with mean μ and variance σ^2. Although in general the choice of population parameter values would affect the distribution of the sample range, one might expect that in the normal case (in which the choice of population mean does not affect the dispersion) the range distribution would not depend on μ. Not only is this so, but the dependence on σ is especially simple. Instead of R, consider $W = R/\sigma$, whose density function is

$$f_W(w) = \sigma f_R(\sigma w).$$

Putting the normal density function into the expression for the density function of the sample range and making two substitutions of the type $y = (x - \mu)/\sigma$, one obtains

$$f_W(w) = \frac{n(n-1)}{(2\pi)^{n/2}} \int_{-\infty}^{\infty} \exp\{-[y^2 + (y + w)^2]/2\}\left\{\int_{y}^{y+w} \exp(-v^2/2)\, dv\right\}^{n-2} dy.$$

Since this is independent of μ and σ, a single table suffices for the distribution of W, for each sample size (Table V, Appendix).

8.1.4   The Transformation F(X)

Let X again be continuous with distribution function $F(x)$, and let x_u denote the maximum of the possible inverses $F^{-1}(u)$. Then, if $U = F(X)$ and if $0 \le u \le 1$,

$$F_U(u) = P[F(X) \le u] = P(X \le x_u) = F(x_u) = u.$$

For $u < 0$, $F_U(u) = 0$, and for $u > 1$, $F_U(u) = 1$. Thus U is uniformly distributed on $[0, 1]$.

Now let each of the ordered observations in a random sample from X be transformed in this way: $U_i = F(X_{(i)})$, yielding new random variables $(U_1, \ldots, U_n)$. The Jacobian of this transformation is

$$\frac{\partial(u_1, \ldots, u_n)}{\partial(y_1, \ldots, y_n)} = f(y_1) \cdots f(y_n),$$

and so the joint density of $(U_1, \ldots, U_n)$ is

$$f_U(u) = \begin{cases} n!, & \text{if } 0 < u_1 < u_2 < \cdots < u_n < 1 \\ 0, & \text{otherwise.} \end{cases}$$

That is, $(U_1, \ldots, U_n)$ is a set of ordered observations from a population that is uniform on $[0, 1]$.

The distribution function of the sample $(X_1, \ldots, X_n)$ is

$$F_n(x) = k/n, \qquad \text{for } X_{(k)} \le x < X_{(k+1)}.$$

But then, since $F(x)$ is monotonic,

$$F_n(F^{-1}(u)) = k/n, \quad \text{if } F(X_{(k)}) \le F(x) < F(X_{(k+1)}) \quad \text{or} \quad U_k \le u < U_{k+1}.$$

This is just the distribution function of the sample from the uniform population whose order statistic is $(U_1, \ldots, U_n)$; call this $F_n^*(u)$. This fact is useful in showing that a statistic of the form

$$\int_{-\infty}^{\infty} G[F_n(x), F(x)] \, dF(x),$$

encountered in Section 6.4.3, has a distribution independent of $F(x)$. For, making the change of variable $u = F(x)$, the integral becomes

$$\int_0^1 G[F_n^*(u), u] \, du.$$

The random variable $F(X_{(k)})$ is the area under the population density to the left of the kth smallest observation. Its distribution is just the distribution of the kth smallest observation from a population that is uniform on $[0, 1]$; the density of this distribution can be found in Section 8.1.2, putting $F(y)$ there equal to y:

$$f_{U_k}(u) = n \binom{n-1}{k-1} u^{k-1}(1-u)^{n-k},$$

for $0 < u < 1$. From this one can readily compute (see Section 7.1.5)

$$E(U_k) = \int_0^1 n \binom{n-1}{k-1} u^k(1-u)^{n-k} \, du = \frac{k}{n+1}.$$

The area between two successive ordered observations is then found to have the expected value:

$$E[F(X_{(k)}) - F(X_{(k-1)})] = E(U_k - U_{k-1}) = \frac{k}{n+1} - \frac{k-1}{n+1} = \frac{1}{n+1}.$$

That is, the expected area under the population density curve between two successive ordered observations is $1/(n+1)$; the ordered observations thus tend to divide the area under the density curve into $n + 1$ equal areas.

The quantity $Z = U_n - U_1 = F(X_{(n)}) - F(X_{(1)})$ is used in construction of "tolerance intervals." It is the area under the population density curve between the smallest and largest observations in a random sample. The joint density of (U_1, U_n) was found in Section 8.1.2 to be (writing it for a uniform population)

$$f(u, v) = n(n-1)(v-u)^{n-2}, \quad \text{for } v > u.$$

Using this, one obtains for $0 < z < 1$:

$$F_Z(z) = P(U_n - U_1 \le z)$$

$$= \iint\limits_{0 < v - u < z} n(n-1)(v-u)^{n-2} \, du \, dv$$

$$= \int_0^z \int_0^v n(n-1)(v-u)^{n-2} \, du \, dv + \int_z^1 \int_{v-z}^v n(n-1)(v-u)^{n-2} \, du \, dv.$$

The density of Z is the derivative of this, namely,

$$f_Z(z) = n(n-1)(1-z)\, z^{n-2}, \qquad \text{for } 0 < z < 1.$$

This is independent of the population distribution function $F(x)$.

EXAMPLE 8–5.   Suppose that it is desired to find a sample size n such that at least 99 per cent of a certain population, with probability .95, will lie between the smallest and largest sample observations. That is, n is to be chosen so that

$$.95 = P[F(X_{(n)}) - F(X_{(1)}) > .99]$$

$$= P(U_n - U_1 > .99) = n(n-1) \int_{.99}^1 (1-z)z^{n-2} \, dz$$

$$= 1 - (.99)^{n-1}(.01n + .99).$$

This yields an n of about 475. [Note $(.99)^{n-1} \doteq e^{-.01(n-1)}$.] In about 95 per cent of samples of size 475, the extreme values of the sample will include 99 per cent of the population, or more.

8.1.5   Sample Percentiles

Unless np is an integer, there is a unique $100p$th percentile of the sample distribution function of a sample of size n. It is, to be specific, the kth smallest observation $X_{(k)}$, where $k = [np] + 1$, the quantity $[np]$ denoting the greatest integer not exceeding np. If np is an integer, the $100p$th percentile is not uniquely defined and can be taken to be any value between $X_{(np)}$ and $X_{(np+1)}$. When the percentile is uniquely defined, it is one of the ordered observations whose density function has been given in Section 8.1.2 in terms of the population density. It can be shown[1] that the *asymptotic* distribution is normal with mean x_p, the corresponding population percentile, and variance

$$\frac{1}{[f(x_p)]^2} \frac{p(1-p)}{n},$$

where $f(x)$ is the population density function, assumed to have a continuous derivative in the neighborhood of x_p.

---

[1] See Cramér, H. [4], p. 367 ff.

EXAMPLE 8–6.   The median of a sample is the sample 50th percentile. The asymptotic normal distribution of the sample median then has $x_{.5}$, the population median, as its expected value, and the variance is $[4nf^2(x_{.5})]^{-1}$. If the population is normal (μ, σ^2), the sample median is asymptotically normal $(\mu, \pi\sigma^2/2n)$, since then

$$f(x_{.5}) = f(\mu) = \frac{1}{\sqrt{2\pi}\sigma} \exp\left[-\frac{1}{2\sigma^2}(\mu - \mu)^2\right] = \frac{1}{\sqrt{2\pi}\sigma} \cdot$$

Problems

8–8.   Compute the expected value and variance of the distribution of the range of a random sample from a uniform population.

8–9.   Carry out the changes of variable suggested in Example 8–4 to determine the density of R/σ.

8–10.   Compute the variance of U_k.

8–11.   Compute the probability that the smallest and largest observations will include between them 99 per cent of the population distribution for a sample of size two.

8–12.   Given the following joint density function of U_r and U_s, where $r < s$, $u < v$:

$$f(u, v) = \frac{n!}{(r - 1)!(s - r - 1)!(n - s)!} u^{r-1}(v - u)^{s-r-1}(1 - v)^{n-s},$$

determine the probability that at least 95 per cent of a probability distribution falls between the second smallest and second largest of 200 observations in a random sample.

8.2   Sign Tests

Certain nonparametric problems can be treated so as to be reduced to problems concerning the parameter p in a Bernoulli distribution. Because it is customary to indicate "success" by a plus sign $(+)$ and "failure" by a minus sign $(-)$, the tests are called *sign tests*. Since the number of successes (or number of $+$'s) is minimal sufficient, assuming independence of the observations, this is the statistic employed. It has a binomial distribution with parameter p.

8.2.1   The Population Median

A problem involving the location of a population can sometimes be expressed in terms of the population median, which is a measure of location. Let X be a continuous random variable, and let m denote its median:

$$P(X > m) = P(X < m) = 1/2.$$

Since the sample median is asymptotically normal with mean m and variance $[4nf^2(m)]^{-1}$, where $f(x)$ is the population density function, the sample median is at least a consistent estimate of the population median. Because the variance of the sample median depends on the unknown $f(m)$, the obvious tests based on the sample median are not readily analyzed. A sign test can be devised as follows.

Suppose that it is desired to test the hypothesis that $m = m_0$. If m_0 is actually the median, approximately half of the observations in a random sample would be expected to lie on either side of m_0. This suggests using the number of sample observations to the right of m_0 (or equivalently, the number to the left) as the test statistic. Too many or too few observations on one side of m_0 would be used as a basis for rejecting $m = m_0$.

The distribution of the number of observations to the right of m_0 is binomial with parameter

$$p = P(X > m_0).$$

Under $H_0 : m = m_0$, the value of p is 1/2, and the expected number of observations on each side is $n/2$. The power (probability of rejecting H_0) would be the same for all alternative states having a given p, and this $\pi(p)$ can be computed from the binomial distribution or from the normal distribution if n is large.

EXAMPLE 8–7. Consider a test that rejects $m = m_0$ when more than 15 or fewer than 5 of 20 observations in a random sample fall to the right of m_0. The α for this test is the probability of the critical region under $p = 1/2$:

$$\left[\binom{20}{0} + \cdots + \binom{20}{4} + \binom{20}{16} + \cdots + \binom{20}{20}\right]/2^{20} \doteq .012.$$

The power function is given approximately by

$$\pi(p) = 1 - P_p(5, 6, \ldots, \text{ or } 15 \text{ obs. to right of } m_0)$$

$$\doteq 1 - \left[\Phi\left(\frac{15.5 - 20p}{\sqrt{20pq}}\right) - \Phi\left(\frac{4.5 - 20p}{\sqrt{20pq}}\right)\right].$$

Given the following 20 observations:

37.0, 31.4, 34.4, 33.3, 34.9, 31.6, 31.3, 34.6, 32.6, 31.6,
36.2, 31.0, 33.5, 33.7, 33.4, 34.4, 32.1, 33.3, 32.7, 31.5,

to test $m = 32$ against $m \neq 32$, the following pattern of signs yields the desired statistic, $+$ indicating an observation above and $-$ an observation below the value 32:

+ − + + + − − + + −
+ − + + + + + + + −

There are 14 plus signs, not enough for rejection of $m = 32$ at the level .012.

A confidence interval for the population median can be constructed as follows. Let $X_{(1)}, \ldots, X_{(n)}$ denote the observations in a random sample arranged in numerical order. Then if $r < s$,

$$P[X_{(r)} < m < X_{(s)}] = P(\text{exactly } r, r + 1, \ldots, \text{or } s - 1 \text{ observations} < m)$$

$$= \sum_{k=r}^{s-1} \binom{n}{k} \left(\frac{1}{2}\right)^n.$$

The random interval from the rth smallest to the sth smallest observation is therefore a confidence interval for m with confidence coefficient given by the above sum of binomial probabilities.

EXAMPLE 8–8.   In the case of 20 observations, the interval from the fourth smallest to the sixteenth smallest observation will include m with probability .993, according to the calculation of Example 8–7. For the 20 observations in that example, the fourth and sixteenth observations (in order of size) are 31.5 and 34.6. These are then 99.3 per cent confidence limits.

8.2.2   Comparing Locations

A sign test can be used to test the null hypothesis that two populations have the same distributions against the alternative that one is shifted away from the other—that they differ in location.

The observations in a random sample from X of size n and those in a random sample from Y of the same size n are paired according to the order of observation: (X_i, Y_i), $i = 1, \ldots, n$. For each pair a plus sign $(+)$ or a minus sign $(-)$ is recorded according as the Y exceeds or is exceeded by the X. Assume for the present that the distribution of (X, Y) is continuous so that ties have probability zero. If the probability that Y exceeds X is called p: $p = P(Y > X)$, the null hypothesis that X and Y are identically distributed yields the value $p = \frac{1}{2}$. Of course p can be $\frac{1}{2}$ even though X and Y are not identically distributed, and it is really the hypothesis $p = \frac{1}{2}$ that the sign test is designed for.

The test statistic used is the number of $+$ signs or the number of pairs of observations in which Y exceeds X. Considering each pair (X_i, Y_i) as a trial of a Bernoulli experiment, the statistic is simply the number of successes in n independent trials, which has been seen to be minimal sufficient for problems involving p. The statistic has the binomial distribution with parameters (n, p).

Pairing the observations makes the two-sample problem into a one-sample problem—indeed, into a parametric one-sample problem, which has already been studied. The potential disadvantage in the requirement of equal sample sizes is offset by the fact that X and Y do not have to be independent; the test can be used in comparing twins, or right- and left-hand characteristics in individuals, or two sides of a tire, etc. In fact, all that is required is that the probability $P(Y_i > X_i)$ remain fixed.

Even though the populations be assumed continuous, ties *do* occur in practice owing to round-off. Rather than make half of the ties + and half −, or to assign + and − by the toss of a coin, the best procedure[2] for handling ties appears to be to ignore them. That is, the test is applied, using only those pairs in which there is not a tie. Using this procedure results in a significance level that is at most as large as that used in determining the critical region based on the assumption of continuous populations. For, with the critical region C determined for each m so that under the null hypothesis

$$P(C \mid m \text{ nonzero differences}) \leq \alpha,$$

it follows that

$$P_{H_0}(C) = \sum_{m=0}^{n} P_{H_0}(C \mid m \text{ nonzero differences}) P_{H_0} (m \text{ nonzero differences})$$

$$\leq \sum_{m=0}^{n} \alpha P_{H_0} (m \text{ nonzero differences}) = \alpha.$$

Of course, with an agreement as to how to handle ties, the sign test can be used even if the populations are discrete. The null hypothesis in this case would be that $P(X < Y) = P(X > Y)$, or that $P(X < Y \mid X \neq Y) = \frac{1}{2}$.

It would appear intuitively that since the sign test does not exploit the magnitudes of the observations except in a crude way, there might be more efficient methods of comparison. In a sense this is so in some cases, but to what extent depends on the nature of the populations. Pitman[3] has introduced the notion of asymptotic efficiency of one test relative to another in the case of a parametric family of alternatives. For comparisons, with $m = n$, the asymptotic efficiency of a procedure d relative to a procedure d^* is the limit of the ratio n^*/n, where n and n^* are the sample sizes under d and d^* required to achieve the same power β for the same alternative, if this ratio has a limit independent of α and β as $n \to \infty$. Pitman showed that the relative asymptotic efficiency of the sign test with respect to the t test is $8\sigma^2 f^2(0)$, in the case of shift alternatives: $F_X(\lambda) = F_Y(\lambda - \theta)$, where f denotes the density of $F_{X-Y}(\lambda)$ and $X - Y$ is symmetrical about 0. This relative asymptotic efficiency does not have a positive lower bound; for normal alternatives it reduces to $2/\pi \doteq$ .63. (For small samples the efficiency is greater than this.)

---

[2] See Lehmann, E. [13], Section 4.7, and J. Hemelryk, "A theorem on the sign test when ties are present," Proc. Kon. Ned. Akad. Sect. of Sciences A55, p. 322.
[3] Columbia lecture notes, 1949.

The sign test has the feature of being applicable to situations in which comparisons are qualitative; for these, tests like the t test, which depend on numerical comparisons, cannot be applied.

EXAMPLE 8–9.   Pipes of two different alloys are to be compared as to corrosion resistance. To avoid the influencing of results by differences in composition of the earth, $2n$ pipes are buried in pairs; the extraneous factors are different from pair to pair but the same for each pair. The null hypothesis of no difference in alloys would be equivalent to the hypothesis that the probability is one-half that one pipe in a given pair will outlast the other. If corrosion is indicated by a numerical measure which is, say, normally distributed, the null hypothesis would be that the means for the two alloys are equal, or that their difference is zero. The sample would then be considered a sample of size n from a normal population with mean zero. The observations would be the n differences for the n pairs, and a t test with $n - 1$ degrees of freedom could be used.

If the numerical measure cannot be considered to be normally distributed, or if (as is more likely the case) the comparisons are made qualitatively, the problem should be treated nonparametrically, and the sign test is one technique for handling it. Suppose that there are altogether four dozen pipes, and that when they are compared in pairs, there are six ties, and pipes of alloy A fared better than those of alloy B in 13 of the remaining 18 pairs. The probability of five or fewer minuses or five or fewer pluses among 18 observations is about .096 under the hypothesis of no difference in alloys, or $p = \frac{1}{2}$. A two-sided test at the level .096 therefore calls for rejection of equal corrosion resistance of the two alloys. (Here is a situation in which a three-action problem would better represent actual practice. No doubt different action would be called for if $p < \frac{1}{2}$ than if $p > \frac{1}{2}$.)

Problems

8–13.   In a table of "random normal numbers" taken from a population with expectation 2 and variance 1, 88 out of 150 entries are found to be larger than 2. Would you accept $\mu = 2$ on this basis?

8–14.   In testing $H_0 : m = 20$ against $H_1 : m > 20$, consider the rule that if more than 8 out of 10 observations exceed 20, H_0 is rejected. Compute α, and also the probability that if $P(X > 20) = \frac{2}{3}$, H_0 is accepted.

8–15.   Determine the probability that m is included between the fortieth and sixtieth observations (in numerical order) of a random sample of 100 observations from a continuous population.

8–16.   One puppy is fed diet A and another diet B in each of 30 pairs of puppies, each pair taken from a single litter. If diet A puppies fare better (according to some specified mode of comparison) in 16 of the 30 pairs and fare worse in 10 pairs, is this sufficient evidence to assert that diet A is superior?

8–17.   Test the hypothesis of no change using a two-sided critical region with $\alpha = .10$ on the basis of the following data from populations A and B:

A. $+4, +1, +6, -1, -1, -1, -2, +3, -4, +4, -1, 0, +6, 0, -2, 0, +5,$
   $-2, 0, -3, -3, -1, -3, 0, -2, 0, -2, -7, -4, -1, -2, +1, +3, +3,$
   $+1, +1, -5, +6, +2, +1$

B. $+2, -3, +1, 0, -2, -10, +2, +1, 0, -4, +6, 0, -10, -1, +1, -5,$
$-3, -3, -3, 0, +1, -1, -5, +3, 0, -1, +3, 0, +4, +5, -2, 0, -1,$
$+4, -2, +1, -9, +1, +4, +1$

8–18.   Determine the power function (as a function of p, the probability that $Y > X$) for the test that rejects identical distributions if fewer than three or more than eight of ten comparisons result in $+$.

8.3   Randomness

A random sample was defined in Chapter 4 as a sequence of identically distributed, independent random variables—a sequence of independent observations on a certain "population." If there is any reason to suspect that the process of obtaining a "random sample" might *not* fit the mathematical model of a random sample, it would be in order to test the hypothesis

$$H_0: F(x_1, \ldots, x_n) = F(x_1) \cdots F(x_n),$$

where $F(x_1, \ldots, x_n)$ is the joint distribution function of the sample observations $(X_1, \ldots, X_n)$ and $F(x)$ is a fixed (but unknown) univariate distribution function, namely, the population distribution function.

The statistical problem is not completely posed until there is specified an alternative to H_0, and herein lies one of the major obstacles to an adequate treatment of this problem of "randomness." The most inclusive alternative hypothesis would be that the observations are *not* independent replicas of a population variable—in other words, that H_0 is not true. This class of alternatives is rather unwieldy. For instance, given *any* test with a critical region of specified size under H_0, there would be many states not in H_0 for which the power of that test is zero. (Any multivariate distribution with zero mass on the critical region and dependent marginals would serve as such a state.) Thus, it is better to consider a more restricted class of alternative states which are especially feared, and then to look for a test which has reasonably high power for this restricted class, not worrying about *all* conceivable alternatives to randomness.

One way to restrict the class of alternatives is to keep the assumption of independence of the observations, allowing the distribution function to vary from observation to observation. In particular, a *trend* alternative is one in which the joint distribution function of the observations is assumed to be of the form

$$F(x_1, \ldots, x_n) = \prod_{i=1}^{n} F[x_i - g(i)].$$

With this assumption the distributions for the various observations are identical in shape but shifted in location, as would be the case if the mean of a normal population were gradually changing as the observations were taken, for example.

The principles sometimes used to derive procedures (minimax, likelihood, Bayes) appear to be especially difficult to apply in the problem of randomness, even when the class of alternatives is restricted. For one thing, costs would ordinarily be rather difficult to assess when tests of randomness are used to decide whether or not to proceed with a method of collecting data in another statistical test. The tests to be discussed here are proposed on an intuitive basis, and the discussion will include at most the derivation of the distribution of the test statistic under the null hypothesis, in the spirit of "significance testing."

8.3.1 Run Tests

A *run* in a sequence of symbols is a group of consecutive symbols of one kind preceded and followed by (if anything) symbols of another kind. For example, in the sequence

$$+ + + - + + - - - - - + + - -$$

the runs can be exhibited by putting vertical bars at the changes of symbol:

$$+ + + \mid - \mid + + \mid - - - - \mid + + \mid - -$$

Here there are a run of three $+$'s, a run of one $-$, a run of two $+$'s, and so on. There are altogether six runs, three runs of $+$'s and three of $-$'s.

Consider now a sequence of observations from a continuous population, and let each observation be assigned the letter "a" if it is above the median of the observations and the letter "b" if it is below. The sample sequence then defines a sequence of a's and b's. If, to simplify the discussion, it is agreed to ignore the median observation when the number of observations is odd, the sequence of a's and b's will have an even number of terms—say, $2m$ terms, of which then m are a's and m are b's. In this sequence there will be a certain number of runs of a's and a certain number of runs of b's; let these numbers be denoted by r_a and r_b, respectively, and let $r = r_a + r_b$ denote the total number of runs. Run tests are then based on the intuitive notion that an unusually large or an unusually small value of r would suggest lack of randomness.

For instance, if a downward trend is present, the a's will tend to come at the beginning and the b's at the end of the sequence of a's and b's, resulting in a relatively small number of runs. Also, one could imagine certain kinds of dependences among the observations which would result in a systematic bouncing back and forth from one side of the median to the other, producing an unusually large number of runs.

The distributions of r, r_a, and r_b can be readily computed under the null hypothesis of randomness. Under this hypothesis the $(2m)!$ arrangements of the observations are equally likely to have produced a given order statistic (see Section 8.1.2). Each arrangement leads to a sequence of a's and b's, and the distinct arrangements of m a's and m b's are then also equally likely since each one comes from $(m!)^2$ arrangements of the observations. So the probability of a given run configuration can be computed as the ratio of the number of the arrangements of a's and b's having that configuration to the total number $\binom{2m}{m}$.

To compute the joint probability that $r_a = x$ and $r_b = y$, then, it is only necessary to count the number of arrangements of a's and b's having this property and divide by $\binom{2m}{m}$. In counting arrangements for the numerator there are three cases to be considered: either (i) $x = y + 1$, (ii) $x = y - 1$, or (iii) $x = y$. The probability that r_a differs from r_b by *more* than 1 is zero, so all possibilities are covered in these three cases.

In case (i) the sequence of a's and b's begins with an a and ends with an a. To divide the a's into x separated groups, slots for the b's are inserted in $x - 1$ places selected from the $m - 1$ spaces between the m a's. This can be done in $\binom{m-1}{x-1}$ ways. Having decided where to put the b's one partitions them into y (or $x-1$) groups, just as the a's were partitioned, in one of $\binom{m-1}{y-1}$ ways, and puts the groups of b's into the prepared slots. The arrangement then has x runs of a's and y runs of b's and could have been accomplished in $\binom{m-1}{x-1}\binom{m-1}{y-1}$ ways.

Case (ii) is exactly analogous to case (i), and the number of arrangements is the same. In case (iii), in which $x = y$, the sequences begin with a and end with b, or else they begin with b and end with a. In either instance the number of ways, computed as for case (i), is again $\binom{m-1}{x-1}\binom{m-1}{y-1}$; the total for case (iii) is twice that number. Finally, then, given the order statistic one has

$$P(r_a = x \text{ and } r_b = y) = \begin{cases} 2\binom{m-1}{x-1}\binom{m-1}{y-1}\Big/\binom{2m}{m}, & \text{if } x = y \\ \binom{m-1}{x-1}\binom{m-1}{y-1}\Big/\binom{2m}{m}, & \text{if } x = y \pm 1, \\ 0, & \text{if } |x - y| > 1. \end{cases}$$

Since this is the same for any order statistic it is also the absolute probability of $r_a = x$ and $r_b = y$, and the condition has been omitted from the notation.

The probability function for the total number of runs can be computed from the above joint probability function as follows:

$$P(r = z) = \sum_{x+y=z} P(r_a = x \quad \text{and} \quad r_b = y).$$

If z is an even number, $z = 2k$, the sum has only one term—that in which $x = y = k$. If z is odd, $z = 2k + 1$, there are two terms in the sum, one in which $x = k$ and $y = k + 1$ and one in which $x = k + 1$ and $y = k$. Hence,

$$P(r = z) = \begin{cases} 2\binom{m-1}{k-1}\binom{m-1}{k-1}\Big/\binom{2m}{m}, & \text{if } z = 2k, \\ 2\binom{m-1}{k}\binom{m-1}{k-1}\Big/\binom{2m}{m}, & \text{if } z = 2k+1, \end{cases}$$

for $z = 2, 3, \ldots, 2m$. The corresponding cumulative distribution function is readily computed from this and is available in tables.[4]

EXAMPLE 8–10.   In samples of size six from a continuous population there will be three observations above and three observations below the sample median. That is, $m = 3$. The number of runs can vary from two to six, and the distribution function of this number r is as follows (computed from the formulas given above):

z	2	3	4	5	6
$F_r(z)$	.1	.3	.7	.9	1.0

It is evident that a test which calls for rejecting randomness when fewer than three runs occur has a significance level

$$\alpha = P_{H_0}(\text{reject } H_0) = P_{H_0}(2 \text{ runs}) = .1.$$

It can be shown that the mean and variance of the distribution of r are

$$E(r) = m + 1, \qquad \text{var } r = \frac{m(m-1)}{2m-1},$$

and that for large samples r is approximately normally distributed.[5] Using a continuity correction and the approximation

$$\text{var } r \doteq \tfrac{1}{4}(2m - 1)$$

---

[4] Swed, F., and Eisenhart, C., "Tables for testing randomness of grouping in a sequence of alternatives," *Annals of Math. Stat.* **14**, 66–87 (1943).
[5] For these results see Mood, A. M., "The distribution theory of runs," *Annals of Math. Stat.* **11**, 367–92 (1940).

one finds the percentiles of r to be obtained from those of the standard normal distribution as follows:

$$r_p = \tfrac{1}{2}(2m + 1 + z_p \sqrt{2m - 1}),$$

where r_p and z_p denote, respectively, the $100p$ percentiles of the distribution of r and of a standard normal variate.

Another type of run test employs the signs of the differences of successive observations. If the population mean has a rising trend, for instance, there would be a tendency for observations to increase from one observation to the next, and $+$'s would more often occur in groups than with no trend. A given sequence of n observations defines a sequence of $n - 1$ signs of differences of successive pairs of observations; let s denote the total number or runs of $+$'s and $-$'s in such a sequence. Various aspects of the distribution of s under the null hypothesis of randomness have been studied.[6] The mean and variance of s are

$$E(s) = \frac{2n - 1}{3}, \qquad \text{var } s = \frac{16n - 29}{90},$$

and the large sample distribution of s is known to be approximately normal.

EXAMPLE 8–11. In samples of size fifty the mean and variance of the total number of runs up and down, under H_0, are

$$E(s) = 33 \qquad \text{and} \qquad \text{var } s \doteq 8.57.$$

The fifth percentile of the distribution of s under H_0 is then

$$s_{.05} \doteq 33 - 1.64\sqrt{8.57} \doteq 27.2.$$

Thus, twenty-seven or fewer runs would be considered significant in testing against the presence of a trend, at the 5 per cent level, and would call for rejection of randomness.

Problems

8–19. Compute $P(r = z)$, $z = 2, \ldots, 6$, for samples of size six, and verify the tabulation of the distribution function of r given in Example 8–10. Verify also the formulas for $E(r)$ and var r in this case.

8–20. Write out the twenty distinct arrangements of three a's and three b's, determine the number of runs in each, and thereby verify directly the probabilities computed in Problem 8–19. Given the order statistic (4, 5, 6, 7, 8, 9), write out some of the thirty-six sample sequences which lead to a specific sequence of a's, and b's—say, to the sequence (a, a, b, a, b, b).

[6] See Wolfowitz, J., and Levene, H., *Ann. Math. Stat.* **15,** 58, 153 (1944).

8-21. The following thirty observations are taken from a table of "random sampling numbers" (which should exhibit randomness, if anything should):

15, 77, 01, 64, 69, 69, 58, 40, 81, 16, 60, 20, 00, 84, 22
28, 26, 46, 66, 36, 86, 66, 17, 34, 49, 85, 40, 51, 40, 10.

Would you accept randomness on the basis of the number of runs above and below the median? On the basis of runs up and down?

8.3.2   Mean Square Successive Difference

Another test[7] for randomness is based on the statistic

$$r = \frac{d^2}{s^2},$$

where d^2 denotes the mean square successive difference:

$$d^2 = \frac{1}{2(n-1)} \sum_{i=1}^{n-1} (X_{i+1} - X_i)^2,$$

and s^2 is the sample variance (unbiased version). For each i the difference $X_{i+1} - X_i$ has mean zero and variance $2\sigma^2$ under the null hypothesis that $(X_1, \ldots, X_n)$ is a random sample from a population with variance σ^2. The expected value of d^2 is then σ^2 under H_0. If a trend is present d^2 is not altered nearly so much as the variance estimate s^2, which increases greatly. Thus, the critical region $r < $ constant is employed in testing against the alternative of a trend.

In order to use this test, of course, it is necessary to know the distribution of r. It can be shown that in the case of a *normal* population

$$E(r) = 1 \qquad \text{and} \qquad \operatorname{var} r = \frac{1}{n+1}\left(1 - \frac{1}{n-1}\right),$$

and that r is approximately normal for large samples (say, $n > 20$).

EXAMPLE 8-12.   Consider the following observations from a normal population:

39 42 38 53 51 30 40 40 28 43 46 53 55 29 24
34 53 66 43 42 38 34 57 26 33,

listed in the order of observation. From these can be computed the values $d^2 \doteq 97$ and $s^2 \doteq 111.5$, so that $r \doteq .87$. The fifth percentile of r (for $n = 25$) is approximately

$$\mu_r - 1.64\sigma_r \doteq 1 - 1.64\left[\frac{1}{26}\left(1 - \frac{1}{24}\right)\right]^{1/2} \doteq .685,$$

and randomness would be accepted at the 5 per cent level, since $.87 > .685$.

---

[7] See Hart, B. I., "Significance levels for the ratio of the mean square successive difference to the variance," *Annals of Math. Stat.* **13**, 445–7 (1942), and references given there.

8.3.3   Other Tests

Whereas the test based on the mean square successive difference requires a knowledge of the population distribution under H_0 even to evaluate the significance level, a "randomization" technique (due to R. A. Fisher) provides a test whose level is independent of the distribution which is assumed to be common to the observations under H_0. A test based on this technique is called a *permutation test*, and is constructed as follows in the problem at hand.

If $(X_1, \ldots, X_n)$ is a random sample from a population with distribution function $F(x)$, the conditional probabilities of the $n!$ permutations of the observations, given the order statistic, are each $1/n!$. Then, if for each order statistic there is defined a critical region consisting of k of the $n!$ permutations, one has

$$\alpha = P_{H_0}(\text{reject randomness}) = k/n!.$$

To decide which permutations to put into the critical region one computes the value of some pertinent statistic T for each permutation, assuming that this permutation gives the order in which the observations occurred, and orders the permutations according to their T-values. The k permutations having the most "extreme" T-values make up the critical region, where the specification of what is "extreme" depends on the alternatives to randomness.

For instance, one might compute the mean square successive difference d^2 for each permutation and use this for ordering them, putting permutations with the smallest values of d^2 into the critical region when testing against trend. More generally (see Problem 8–25), one might use a "serial correlation" of the form

$$R_h = \sum_{i=1}^{n-h} X_i X_{i+h}$$

for some fixed h. Again the critical values of R_h and now also the value of h would be chosen (perhaps intuitively) in light of the alternatives to randomness.

Certain other tests for randomness are based on a consideration of *ranks* of the observations. The rank t_i of the observation X_i is its position in the order statistic (that is, one more than the number of observations less than X_i in the sample). In the case of a continuous population each sample $(X_1, \ldots, X_n)$ defines a sequence of ranks $(t_1, \ldots, t_n)$ which is one of the $n!$ permutations of the integers $(1, 2, \ldots, n)$. Under the null hypothesis of randomness these are equally likely, and again a critical region is constructed by putting into it rank sequences ordered according to some function of the ranks,

$T(t_1, \ldots, t_n)$. Two of the many rank-order statistics[8] which have been proposed are

$$\sum_{i=1}^{n} it_i, \quad \text{and} \quad \sum_{i=1}^{n} E[Z_{(i)}]t_i,$$

where $Z_{(i)}$ denotes the ith smallest among n observations from a standard normal population.

Another test for randomness[9] is based on the number of inequalities $X_j < X_k$ for $j < k$ (for downward trend alternatives). This shares with the run, permutation, and rank tests the property of being "distribution free," the distribution of the statistic under the null hypothesis being independent of the population distribution.

EXAMPLE 8–13.   Supose that in a sample of five from a continuous population the results are (1, 3, 9, 4, 7). There are 5! or 120 permutations of these numbers. Some of them, together with values of $T = \sum_{i=1}^{n-1} (X_{i+1} - X_i)^2$, the corresponding rank sequence, and the values of $\sum it_i$ are listed below. (Of course for each entry listed the permutation with numbers reversed would have the same T-value; for instance, $T(9, 7, 4, 3, 1) = 18$.)

Permutation					T	Ranks					$\sum it_i$
1	3	4	7	9	18	1	2	3	4	5	55
3	1	4	7	9	26	2	1	3	4	5	54
1	4	3	7	9	30	1	3	2	4	5	54
4	1	3	7	9	33	3	1	2	4	5	52
1	3	4	9	7	34	1	2	3	5	4	54
3	1	4	9	7	42	2	1	3	5	4	53
4	3	1	7	9	45	3	2	1	4	5	51
1	3	7	9	4	49	1	2	4	5	3	52
3	4	1	7	9	50	2	3	1	4	5	52
1	4	3	9	7	50	1	3	2	5	4	53
1	3	9	7	4	53	1	2	5	4	3	51
4	1	3	9	7	53	3	1	2	5	4	51
1	3	7	4	9	54	1	2	4	3	5	54
1	4	9	7	3	54	1	3	5	4	2	48

These are listed in order of increasing T-values, but observe that they would be ordered differently using the rank statistic $\sum it_i$. For a test based on T with $\alpha = .1$

---

[8] Such statistics are studied by A. Stuart, "The asymptotic relative efficiences of distribution-free tests of randomness against normal alternatives," *J. Amer. Stat. Assn.* **49**, 147–57 (1954); see also I. R. Savage, "Contributions to the theory of rank order statistics —the 'trend' case," *Annals of Math. Stat.* **28**, 968–77 (1957); and in Reference [13], p. 258.

[9] Mann, H. B., "Nonparametric tests against trend," *Econometrica* **13**, 245 (1945).

the twelve permutations with smallest T-values would make up the critical region; that is, randomness would be rejected for $T \leq 42$. The sequence given at the outset as the list of observations in the sample has a T-value of 74, and would therefore call for acceptance of randomness.

Problems

8–22. Test the data of Problem 8–21 for randomness using d^2/s^2.

8–23. Add k to the $(k + 1)$st observation, $k = 1, \ldots, 25$, in Example 8–12 and test the resulting sequence of numbers for randomness using the number of runs above and below the median; using the number of runs up and down; and using d^2/s^2.

8–24. Given var $d^2 = (3n - 4)\sigma^4/(n - 1)^2$ in the case of a normal population (no trend), determine the efficiency of d^2 relative to s^2 as an estimate of the variance σ^2.

8–25. Show that using the statistic d^2 is almost equivalent to using the serial correlation R_h with $h = 1$, when ordering permutations of the numbers in the order statistic. Compute R_1 for the permutations of Example 8–13.

8–26. Compute the value of the statistic $\sum t_i E[Z_{(i)}]$ for the permutations of Example 8–13.

8.4 Contingency Tables

The classification of observations each according to two schemes is referred to as a contingency table. If one scheme involves r possible categories and the other s categories, the table is said to be an "r by s" table.[10]

EXAMPLE 8–14. Persons drawn at random from a certain population are classed as married or single, and as being educated at the graduate level (G), college level (C), high school level (H), or elementary school level (E). Each person is thus counted in one cell of a two by four contingency table:

	G	C	H	E	
M	n_{11}	n_{12}	n_{13}	n_{14}	$n_{1.}$
S	n_{21}	n_{22}	n_{23}	n_{24}	$n_{2.}$
	$n_{.1}$	$n_{.2}$	$n_{.3}$	$n_{.4}$	n

The marginal totals are indicated in the table, the notation being that a dot implies that a summation has been performed over the corresponding index.

If one is attempting to study the relationship between marital status and extent of education, he might pick the n persons completely at random so that the

[10] A fuller discussion of this topic is found in Kendall, M. G., and Stuart, A. [12], Vol. II.

marginal totals are random. If he is thinking of education as a "treatment," administered at various levels, and studying the effect of the treatment on marital status, he might pick a specified number of persons from each educational group at random from that group, and determine the marital status as a "response." In this case, the one set of marginal totals at the bottom are fixed, and the problem is called that of testing homogeneity—in this case, homogeneity (or lack of it) of the populations corresponding to the different educational treatments, More rarely, cases occur in which both sets of marginal totals are fixed; one such will arise in the median test of Section 8.4.3.

Distributions for the various possible results in a contingency table and corresponding tests of hypotheses will be considered here principally for 2 by 2 tables. Exact distributions for small samples as well as asymptotic distributions for large samples will be given.

8.4.1   Independence

Consider n independent observations categorized according to two schemes, with two categories in each scheme, the data being summarized in the following two by two table:

	B_1	B_2	
A_1	n_{11}	n_{12}	$n_1.$
A_2	n_{21}	n_{22}	$n_2.$
	$n._1$	$n._2$	n

Let p_{ij} denote the probability that an observation is classified as A_i in the A-scheme and as B_j in the B-scheme, as in the following table:

	B_1	B_2	
A_1	p_{11}	p_{12}	$p_1.$
A_2	p_{21}	p_{22}	$p_2.$
	$p._1$	$p._2$	p

It is easy to obtain the maximum likelihood estimates, $\hat{p}_{ij} = n_{ij}/n$, whence (for instance) $\hat{p}._2 = n._2/n$.

Under the null hypotheses that the two schemes of classification are independent, the probabilities in the body of the 2 by 2 table are products of the marginal totals:

$$H_0: \quad p_{ij} = p_i.p._j, \qquad i, j = 1, 2.$$

There are two parameters unspecified under this hypothesis, say, $p_1.$ and $p._1$

(since the sums of the marginal probabilities must be 1). The problem can be considered as a goodness of fit problem, and tested by the chi-square test in the form in which there are unknown parameters to be estimated from the sample. The chi-square statistic is

$$\chi^2 = \sum_{i,j=1}^{2} \frac{(n_{ij} - n\hat{p}_{i\cdot}\hat{p}_{\cdot j})^2}{n\hat{p}_{i\cdot}\hat{p}_{\cdot j}},$$

which has (under the null hypothesis of independence) approximately the chi-square distribution with $4 - 1 - 2 = 1$ degree of freedom. (This is $k - 1 - r$, where k is the number of cells and r the number of parameters being estimated from the sample.) The critical region would be of the form $\chi^2 > $ const.

A conditional test based on the exact distribution can be constructed for use with small samples, as follows. Suppose that for each possible set of marginal totals, the various tables having these totals are divided into one set calling for rejection and one set calling for acceptance, in such a way that the probability (conditional, given the marginal totals) of obtaining a table in the rejection set does not exceed, under H_0, a specified α. The test is then carried out by obtaining data in the form of the two by two table, noting the marginal entries, and rejecting the null hypothesis if the table is in the critical set for the particular marginal entries actually observed. (In practice, of course, one need not bother to prepare the rejection set in advance for each set of marginal entries, but simply to determine the rejection set for the marginal entries actually obtained.) The size of the type I error for this test does not exceed α:

$$P_{H_0}(\text{reject } H_0) = E[P_{H_0}(\text{reject } H_0 \mid \text{marginal entries})] \le E[\alpha] = \alpha.$$

To carry out this scheme it is necessary to know the conditional distribution given the marginal entries, under the null hypothesis of independence. This can be derived from the fact that the table entries are multinomial, and that the marginal entries $n_{1\cdot}$ and $n_{\cdot 1}$ are independent binomials, as follows:

$$P(n_{11} = i \mid n_{\cdot 1} = j, \; n_{1\cdot} = k)$$

$$= \frac{P(n_{11} = i, \; n_{12} = k - i, \; n_{21} = j - i, \; n_{22} = n - j - k + i)}{P(n_{\cdot 1} = j, \; n_{1\cdot} = k)}$$

$$= \frac{\dfrac{n!}{i!(j-i)!(k-i)!(n-j-k+i)!} \; p_{11}{}^i p_{21}{}^{j-i} p_{12}{}^{k-i} p_{22}{}^{n-j-k+i}}{\dbinom{n}{j}\dbinom{n}{k}(p_{1\cdot})^k(p_{\cdot 1})^j(p_{2\cdot})^{n-k}(p_{\cdot 2})^{n-j}}$$

$$= \frac{\dbinom{k}{i}\dbinom{n-k}{j-i}}{\dbinom{n}{j}}.$$

where the last simplification exploits the factorization assumed under H_0, namely, $p_{ij} = p_{i\cdot}p_{\cdot j}$ $(i, j = 1, 2)$. Thus, the desired conditional distribution is hypergeometric. Extreme values of n_{11} (which determines the other n_{ij} when the margins are fixed) are used as a basis of rejection of H_0.

EXAMPLE 8–15. Persons taken at random from a certain population are classified as either male (M) or female (F), and also classified as either blue-eyed (B), or not blue-eyed (N). The results for a sample of 12 are given in the following fourfold (or two by two) table:

	M	F	
B	1	2	3
N	4	5	9
	5	7	12

The number of blue-eyed males determines the table, given the marginals as shown; this random variable takes on the values 0, 1, 2, 3 with hypergeometric probabilities

$$P(n_{11} = i) = \frac{\binom{3}{i}\binom{9}{5-i}}{\binom{12}{5}},$$

or as shown in the following table:

n_{11}	0	1	2	3
Prob.	126/792	378/792	252/792	36/792

The test that rejects independence for $n_{11} = 0$ or 3 would have an α of $126/792 + 36/792$, or $9/44$. With this test the given table would lead to accepting independence.

8.4.2 Homogeneity

The problem of homogeneity is that of testing the hypothesis that categorical data from potentially different populations can be considered to have all come from the same population. In general, there would be r populations (corresponding to r treatments) and s categories. The case to be considered here is that in which $r = s = 2$, that is, two populations and two categories. This is essentially the problem of testing the equality of two Bernoulli parameters: $p_1 = p_2$, against the alternative $p_1 \neq p_2$. Although the data are again presented in a two by two table, different notation will be used to serve as a reminder of the different context:

	"Success"	"Failure"	
Population 1	J	$m - J$	m
Population 2	K	$n - K$	n
	$J + K$	$m + n - J - K$	$m + n = N$

The parameters are p_1 and p_2, where $p_1 = P(\text{success}/\text{pop.}i)$. Observe that the entries m and n in the right margin are fixed—they are the sizes of the samples from the two populations. Observe also that the entries in the lower margin are random variables.

The two-sided problem to be considered is that of testing $H_0 : p_1 = p_2$ against $H_1 : p_1 \neq p_2$, for which problem a likelihood ratio test can be constructed. On the basis of a random sample of size m from the population with parameter p_1 and an independent random sample of size n from the population with parameter p_2, the likelihood function is

$$L(p_1, p_2) = p_1{}^J (1 - p_1)^{m-J} p_2{}^K (1 - p_2)^{n-K},$$

where J and K are the numbers of successes in the two samples. The likelihood function is maximized over H_0 by the values $p_1 = p_2 = \hat{p}$, where $\hat{p} = (J + K)/(m + n)$. Over $H_0 + H_1$ the maximum is achieved for $p_1 = J/m$ and $p_2 = K/n$. The likelihood ratio is therefore

$$\Lambda = \frac{(J + K)^{J+K}(m + n - J - K)^{m+n-J-K} m^m n^n}{J^J K^K (m - J)^{m-J} (n - K)^{n-K} (m + n)^{m+n}}.$$

The quantity $-2 \log \Lambda$ has asymptotically a chi-square distribution with one degree of freedom (H_0 is one-dimensional and $H_0 + H_1$ is two-dimensional).

EXAMPLE 8–16. Consider 50 independent trials of each of two Bernoulli experiments, with the results: 24 out of 50 successes in the first experiment and 30 out of 50 in the second. With these data,

$$\Lambda = \left(\frac{27}{24}\right)^{24} \left(\frac{27}{30}\right)^{30} \left(\frac{23}{26}\right)^{26} \left(\frac{23}{20}\right)^{20} \doteq .484.$$

The value of $-2 \log \Lambda$ is then about 1.453, which is less than the critical value of 2.71 at the 10 per cent level. Equality of p's is therefore accepted at that level.

An exact test for small samples can be constructed as a conditional test, in much the same fashion as in the preceding section. For each number s the fourfold tables with $J + K = s$ are arranged according to the value of J. A set A_S of these tables is selected whose total probability given $J + K = s$ does not exceed a specified level α, and homogeneity is rejected at that level if the observed table falls in A_S. The size of the type I error does not then exceed α, by the same type of reasoning as in the earlier situation:

$$P_{H_0} \text{ (reject } H_0) = E[P_{H_0} \text{ (reject } H_0 \mid \text{marginal entries)}] \leq \alpha.$$

Which fourfold tables are put into A_s depends on the alternatives. For testing against $p_1 < p_2$, the tables with the smallest values of J should be used in A_s. For the alternative $p_1 \neq p_2$, put into A_s first the fourfold tables for $j = 0$ and $j = m$; then, those for $j = 1$ and $j = m - 1$, and so on, until no more can be put into A_s without exceeding α.

The conditional distribution under $p_1 = p_2$, given the lower marginal entries (and with fixed right marginal entries), is again hypergeometric, as follows, with $S = J + K$ and $s = j + k$:

$$P(J = j, K = k \mid S = s) = \frac{P(J = j, K = k, \text{ and } S = s)}{P(S = s)}$$

$$= \frac{\binom{m}{j} p^j (1 - p)^{m-j} \binom{n}{k} p^k (1 - p)^{n-k}}{\binom{N}{s} p^s (1 - p)^{N-s}}$$

$$= \frac{\binom{m}{j} \binom{n}{k}}{\binom{N}{s}} = \frac{\binom{j+k}{j} \binom{N-j-k}{m-j}}{\binom{N}{m}}.$$

EXAMPLE 8–17. Suppose that in testing $p_1 \geq p_2$ against $p_1 < p_2$ one obtains the following results:

	Success	Failure	
From pop. 1	3	5	8
From pop. 2	7	5	12
	10	10	20

The fourfold tables with these same marginal totals but with fewer successes from population 1 are as follows:

2	6	8		1	7	8		0	8	8
8	4	12		9	3	12		10	2	12
10	10	20		10	10	20		10	10	20

The probabilities of these results, given 10 successes among the 20 trials of the experiments, are as follows, under H_0: .075, .0095, and .0004. A test of level .01 would call for rejection of $p_1 \geq p_2$ if either of the last two tables resulted, and a test of level .085 if any of the three most extreme tables resulted. Since the table actually obtained is not among these three most extreme cases, the null hypothesis is accepted at the 8.5 per cent level.

In large samples the asymptotic normal distribution can be used to approximate the hypergeometric probabilities. That is, the distribution of J, given $S = s$ (which is used to determine the critical region), is hypergeometric with mean and variance as follows:

$$\text{Mean: } s\frac{m}{m+n} \quad \text{Variance: } s\frac{m}{m+n}\left(1 - \frac{m}{m+n}\right)\frac{m+n-s}{m+n-1},$$

and so the following quantity has asymptotically the chi-square distribution with one degree of freedom:

$$\chi^2 \equiv \frac{\left(J - \dfrac{ms}{m+n}\right)^2}{\dfrac{ms}{m+n}\left(1 - \dfrac{m}{m+n}\right)\dfrac{m+n-s}{m+n-1}}$$

$$= \frac{(J/m - K/n)^2}{\dfrac{J+K}{m+n}\left(1 - \dfrac{J+K}{m+n}\right)\dfrac{m+n}{mn}} \cdot \frac{m+n-1}{m+n}.$$

The test that rejects H_0 for too large or too small values of J amounts, then (in large samples), to rejecting H_0 if χ^2 is too large—how large being determined from the chi-square distribution with one degree of freedom.

Notice that χ^2 has the same asymptotic distribution as $-2 \log \Lambda$; this is no accident, for it can be shown that they are asymptotically equal. The following example bears this out.

EXAMPLE 8–18. If the data of Example 8–16 (24 and 30 successes in 50 trials) are used in a computation of χ^2, the result is

$$\chi^2 = \frac{(24/50 - 30/50)^2 \cdot (50 + 50 - 1)}{(24 + 30)(100 - 54)/2500} \doteq 1.44,$$

whereas $-2 \log \Lambda \doteq 1.45$.

8.4.3 The Median Test

Again consider the null hypothesis that two populations X and Y are identical and that a test is to be based on a random sample from each—one of size m from X and one of size n from Y. It is required that X and Y be independent.

The median test is designed to detect shifts in location and is constructed as follows: The $m + n$ independent observations in the two random samples are arranged in numerical order, and the median of this combination of the two samples is determined. The test statistic is then the number of observations from X which lie to the left of this median. (Alternatively one could use the number of observations from Y or count the number to the right of the median.) Selection of this statistic is based on the intuitive notion that it will tend to be abnormally large when Y is located to the right of X and abnormally small when Y is located to the left of X. If the populations are identical (or if only they have the same median), one would expect to find close to half of the X observations and half of the Y observations on either side of the median of the combined sample.

The distribution of M_1, the number of observations from X which lie to the left of the median of the combined sample, is readily obtained under the null hypothesis. To avoid fussiness of detail, assume that $m + n = N = 2K$, where K is an integer. Then, under the null hypothesis, the combined sample is a sample of size N from the common population. Given the order statistic of this combined sample, there are $N!$ samples that could have led to it, and these are equally likely to have done so (according to Section 8.1.1). To determine the conditional probability of m_1 observations to the left of the median, given the order statistic, it is only necessary to count the sample configurations in which $M_1 = m_1$ and divide by $N!$. The number of arrangements of m X's and n Y's in which m_1 X's lie to the left of the median, is

$$\binom{m}{m_1}\binom{n}{K - m_1} K!\, K!\,,$$

and dividing this by $N!$ yields the desired probability:

$$P(M_1 = m_1 \mid \text{order statistic}) = \frac{\binom{m}{m_1}\binom{n}{K - m_1}}{\binom{N}{K}}.$$

Because this is independent of the condition, it is also the absolute probability of $m_1 X$'s to the left of the median (under H_0).

The statistic M_1 determines also the number of observations from X to the right of the median, as well as the numbers of observations from Y to the right and to the left of the median. These four numbers can be thought of in a four-fold table with fixed marginal totals:

	Number from X	Number from Y	Totals
Left of median	M_1	N_1	$N/2 = K$
Right of median	M_2	N_2	$N/2 = K$
Total	m	n	N

The probability (under H_0) of this table has been found to be hypergeometric, as it was in Section 8.4.2 where fourfold tables with fixed marginal totals arose in comparing Bernoulli populations. For a two-sided test, the quantity χ^2 defined in Section 8.4.2, which is asymptotically chi-square with one degree of freedom, can be used as the basis of the test, rejecting H_0 for large values of χ^2.

In the small sample case it is usually necessary to randomize in order to achieve a desired level α exactly, since the test statistic is discrete (cf. Section 6.1.4). It is shown by Tocher[11] that the randomized test obtained in this way is most powerful in the one-sided case.

EXAMPLE 8–19.   Wire B is to be replaced by wire A if the resistance per unit length is not significantly lower. Twenty tests on each type of wire were conducted, with the following results (in ohms):

Wire A	Wire B	Wire A	Wire B
.051	.054	.049	.057
.047	.051	.051	.051
.049	.052	.053	.054
.048	.051	.050	.051
.048	.051	.053	.052
.049	.055	.047	.052
.049	.049	.049	.050
.049	.049	.050	.052
.049	.051	.051	.052
.051	.052	.049	.048

Listing these 40 observations in a single ordered sequence, it is found that there are at least 14 observations from wire A to the left of the combined median (the

[11] Tocher, K. D.,"Extension of the Neyman–Pearson theory of tests to discontinuous variates," *Biometrika* **39**, 130–144 (1950).

ambiguity arising because of ties introduced by rounding-off). The value of χ^2 corresponding to $m_1 = 14$ is

$$\frac{20(20 \cdot 14 - 20 \cdot 6)^2(20 + 20 - 1)}{(14 + 6) \cdot 20 \cdot 20 \cdot (20 + 20 - 14 - 6)} = 6.24.$$

The 97.5 percentile of the chi-square distribution with one degree of freedom is 5.02, and so a one-sided test at the 2.5 per cent level rejects the null hypothesis of no difference.

It is shown by Mood[12] that for normal shift alternatives, the asymptotic efficiency of the median test relative to the t test is the same as that of the sign test, namely, $2/\pi$, or about .63.

Problems

8-27. Determine the value of χ^2 used to test independence in the following two by two table:

32	88	120
68	112	180
100	200	300

Would you accept independence at the 10 per cent level?

8-28. If 40 per cent of 80 patients given a placebo experience relief, and 60 per cent of 140 patients given a certain drug experience relief, would you say that the drug is effective? If the figures are 40 per cent of 10 and 60 per cent of 20, would you reach the same conclusion?

8-29. In a problem of comparing Bernoulli populations, show the minimal sufficiency of the numbers of successes (J, K) among the m trials and n trials, respectively, from the two populations.

8-30. Show that (in the notation of Section 8.4.2) $J/m - K/n$ is a consistent estimate of $p_1 - p_2$.

8-31. Construct an approximate confidence interval for $p_1 - p_2$, using the data of Example 8-16.

8-32. Apply the median test to the following data:

From X: 16, 21, 15, 18, 19, 13, 20, 22
From Y: 12, 18, 17, 14, 18, 10.

8-33. Calculate $-2 \log \Lambda$ for the table given in Problem 8-26 interpreting the columns as data from two populations, in samples of size 100 and 200, respectively. Can the populations be considered identical using $\alpha = .05$?

[12] Mood, A. M., "On the asymptotic efficiency of certain nonparametric two sample tests," *Ann. Math. Stat.* **25**, 514–522 (1954).

8-34. In testing independence, the following two by two table is observed:

X	Y	4
Z	W	8
9	3	12

Obtain the distribution (conditional on these marginal totals) for X, and give a conditional test with $\alpha \leq .30$.

8-35. Data are gathered from three Bernoulli populations, as shown in the following table:

	Population			
	1	2	3	
Frequency of 1's	30	30	40	
Frequency of 0's	50	30	20	
No. of Observations	80	60	60	200
Probability of 1	p_1	p_2	p_3	

(a) Carry out the likelihood ratio test at $\alpha = .01$ for the null hypothesis that $p_1 = p_2 = p_3$ against the alternative that the p's are not all equal.

(b) Determine the conditional distribution given the marginal totals:

$$P(I_1 = a, I_2 = b, I_3 = c \mid I_1 + I_2 + I_3 = s),$$

where I_j is the frequency of 1's in Population j.

8.5 Rank Tests for Comparisons

It is again desired to test the hypothesis that X and Y have identical distribution functions against shift alternatives, using independent random samples of size m from X and of size n from Y.

As in Section 8.3.3 it is possible to construct critical regions of given size based on the fact that the conditional distribution of probability among the various permutations of a given order statistic is uniform—all permutations are equally likely to have been the original sample. Under the null hypothesis that X and Y are identically distributed the samples can be considered to make up a single random sample; and given the order statistic corresponding to these $m + n$ observations, each permutation of the values in the order statistic has probability $1/(m + n)!$ If it is agreed, for each possible order statistic, to put a number k of the permutations leading to it into a rejection region, the resulting test has the significance level $k/(m + n)!$, as follows:

$$P_{H_0} (\text{reject } H_0) = E[P_{H_0} (\text{reject } H_0 \mid \text{order statistic})]$$

$$= E[k/(m + n)!] = k/(m + n)!$$

The selection of permutations to use in the rejection region for a given order statistic can be made according to any criterion thought to be appropriate for the alternatives against which protection is desired.

EXAMPLE 8–20.   Although the statistic $\bar{X} - \bar{Y}$ is certainly not distribution-free, it can be used to determine which permutations are appropriate for the rejection of the hypothesis of identical distributions of X and Y against shift alternatives. Actually, given the order statistic, one is also given the sum $\sum X_i + \sum Y_j$, so one could use $\sum X_i$ or $\sum Y_j$ equally well (see Problem 8–36). Moreover, since the ordering among the X's and the ordering among the Y's does not play a role in comparing values of the sum used, only the $\binom{m + n}{n}$ distinct assignments of m of the $m + n$ observations to X (the remaining n being Y's) need be considered. And these are equally likely.

To illustrate, suppose that three observations from X and two from Y yield the combined order statistic (4, 6, 7, 8, 9). Of the 120 arrangements of these numbers that might have been the combined sample $(X_1, X_2, X_3, Y_1, Y_2)$, the 10 in which the X's are (4, 6, 7) in some order and the Y's are (8, 9) all give the same value of $\sum Y_j$, namely 17. The ten selections of three of the five numbers in the order statistic for X's are shown in the following table, together with a corresponding value of $\sum Y_j$ in each case. Each has conditional probability $\frac{1}{10}$ (given the order statistic), and in devising a test at $\alpha = .2$ against the hypothesis that the Y-population is shifted to the right, the two permutations with $\sum Y_j = 17$ and $\sum Y_j = 16$ would make up the critical region. An actual sample of (4, 8, 6) from X and (9, 8) from Y would lead to rejection of H_0.

X's	Y's	$\sum Y_j$
4, 6, 7	8, 9	17
6, 4, 8	7, 9	16
4, 7, 8	6, 9	15
4, 6, 9	7, 8	15
4, 7, 9	6, 8	14
6, 7, 8	4, 9	13
4, 8, 9	6, 7	13
6, 7, 9	4, 8	12
6, 8, 9	4, 7	11
7, 8, 9	4, 6	10

In the following sections tests for comparing locations are given which are permutation tests in which the statistic used is based on the ranks of the observations in the combined order statistic. The rank of an observation is simply the index of the position it occupies in the combined order statistic. What is used is really only the set of indices of positions in the combined statistic occupied by X's, that is, the X-ranks (or alternatively and equivalently the Y-ranks). That is, one only observes which observations in the order statistic came from X and which came from Y. For instance, with four observations from X and six from Y, the Y-rank sequence $(3, 5, 6, 7, 9, 10)$ corresponds to an order statistic of the form $(X, X, Y, X, Y, Y, Y, X, Y, Y)$, in which only the source of the observation in each position is indicated. Now, each such sequence of m X's and n Y's represents (and would be obtained from) $m!\, n!$ of the $(m + n)!$ permutations giving rise to a given order statistic, and so the probability of each distinct Y-rank sequence (or of each distinct sequence of m X's and n Y's) is

$$\frac{m!\, n!}{(m + n)!} = 1 \Big/ \binom{m + n}{m}.$$

These probabilities are then used to determine how many Y-rank sequences to put into the rejection region for a given order statistic.

8.5.1   The Wilcoxon–Mann–Whitney Test

The Wilcoxon test is a permutation test based on the *sum* of the Y-ranks, motivated by the notion that a shift would suggest either an unusually high or an unusually low Y-rank sum. The Mann–Whitney test, to be introduced first, turns out to be equivalent to the Wilcoxon test, as will subsequently be demonstrated.

Consider the sequence of observations as they appear in the order statistic, noting only which population an observation comes from. For each Y observation count the number of X observations preceding it, and let U_Y denote the total of these numbers. That is, for each pair of observations X_i and Y_j define

$$Z_{ij} = \begin{cases} 1, & \text{if } X_i < Y_j, \\ 0, & \text{if } X_i > Y_j. \end{cases}$$

The sum of these Z's is the statistic U_Y:

$$U_Y = \sum_{i=1}^{m} \sum_{j=1}^{n} Z_{ij}.$$

A similar sum with 1 and 0 reversed can be used in defining U_X as the total number of X inversions; that is, the total of the numbers of Y observations preceding the X observations. Since there are mn terms in the summation of Z_{ij}, and since interchanging 0's and 1's in U_Y produces U_X, it is evident that $U_X + U_Y = mn$.

EXAMPLE 8–21. Suppose that the observations from X are 13, 17, 11, 14, and that the observations from Y are 10, 16, 15. The combined order statistic is then *10*, 11, 13, 14, *15*, *16*, 17, the italicized ones coming from Y. In terms of which populations the observations come from, the order statistic can be represented this way: Y, X, X, X, Y, Y, X. In this sequence the first X, the second X, and the third X are each preceded by one Y; the fourth X is preceded by three Y's. Therefore $U_x = 6$. Similarly, the first Y has no X's ahead of it, and the other two Y's are each preceded by three X's; so $U_Y = 6$, and $U_X + U_Y = 12 = 4 \cdot 3$.

Under the null hypothesis that the observations are independent random variables with $P(X > Y) = P(X < Y) = \frac{1}{2}$, the mean and variance of U_Y can be computed. Since $E(Z_{ij}) = \frac{1}{2}$ for all i and j,

$$E(U_Y) = E\left\{\sum_i \sum_j Z_{ij}\right\} = \sum_i \sum_j E(Z_{ij}) = \frac{mn}{2}.$$

The variance computation is not quite so simple, since the terms in the sum representing U_Y are not independent random variables:

$$\text{var } U_Y = \sum_i \sum_j \sum_h \sum_k \text{cov}(Z_{ij}, Z_{hk}).$$

Now,

$$Z_{ij}Z_{hk} = \begin{cases} 1, & \text{if } X_i < Y_j \text{ and } X_h < Y_k \\ 0, & \text{otherwise,} \end{cases}$$

so that

$$E(Z_{ij}Z_{hk}) = P(X_i < Y_j \text{ and } X_h < Y_k)$$

$$= \begin{cases} \frac{1}{2}, & i = h \text{ and } j = k, \\ \frac{1}{4}, & i \neq h \text{ and } j \neq k, \\ \frac{1}{3}, & i = h \text{ and } j \neq k \text{ or } j = k \text{ and } i \neq h. \end{cases}$$

Hence,

$$\text{cov}(Z_{ij}, Z_{hk}) = \begin{cases} 0, & i \neq h \text{ and } j \neq k, \\ 1/4, & i = h \text{ and } j = k, \\ 1/12, & i = h \text{ and } j \neq k \text{ or } j = k \text{ and } i \neq h. \end{cases}$$

To complete the computation of var U_Y, it is only necessary to count the number of terms in each case. There are mn terms in which $i = h$ and $j = k$, and m^2n terms in which $j = k$. Of the latter, however, mn have also $i = h$, leaving $m^2n - mn = mn(m - 1)$ in which $j = k$ and $i \neq h$. Similarly, there are $mn(n - 1)$ terms in which $i = h$ and $j \neq k$. Finally, then,

$$\text{var } U_Y = \tfrac{1}{4}mn + \tfrac{1}{12}[mn(m - 1) + mn(n - 1)] = \tfrac{1}{12}mn(m + n + 1).$$

For small samples, acceptance limits based on U_Y for various levels are given in Table VIII, Appendix. These values are computable from the fact that the rank sequences are equally likely (see Problem 8–44). For large samples, one uses the asymptotic distribution of U_Y which is known to be normal (even[13] when the null hypothesis is not true). That is, the standardized statistic (including a continuity correction)

$$Z = \frac{U_Y + \frac{1}{2} - \frac{1}{2}mn}{[\frac{1}{12}mn(m + n + 1)]^{1/2}}$$

has as its approximate distribution function the standard normal one.[14]

It will now be shown that the test based on U_Y is equivalent to one based on the sum of the Y-ranks. Let R_Y denote the sum of the ranks of the Y observations in the order statistic. This is simply related to U_Y:

$$R_Y = U_Y + \frac{1}{2}n(n + 1).$$

For, if the rank of the smallest Y is r_1, there are $r_1 - 1$ inversions for that Y; if the rank of the next smallest Y is r_2, there are $r_2 - 2$ corresponding inversions; and so on. Adding these numbers of inversions yields the relationship given.

Since the statistic R_Y is a constant plus the statistic U_Y, procedures based on one can be interpreted as procedures based on the other, with the same kinds of critical region. Rejection limits are tabulated in Table VIII only for U_Y. In a one-sided shift alternative,

$$F_X(\lambda) = F_Y(\lambda - \theta), \qquad \theta > 0,$$

the X's would tend to be larger than the Y's, and the value of U_Y would tend to be smaller than if $\theta = 0$. For a test against such alternatives, then, the critical region $U_Y <$ constant is used.

The asymptotic efficiency of the Wilcoxon–Mann–Whitney test relative to the t test for shift alternatives was shown by Pitman to be

$$12\sigma^2\left(\int f^2(x)\, dx\right)^2,$$

where f is the density function and σ^2 the variance. (The integral of f^2 and the variance would be the same for each alternative.) In the normal case this reduces to $3/\pi$, or about 0.96, and Hodges and Lehmann have shown that it is always at least .864.

8.5.2 The Fisher–Yates Test

The Fisher–Yates c_1 test calls for putting arrangements into the critical region according to the size of

$$c_1 = \frac{1}{n}\sum_{i=1}^{n} E(Z_{s_i}),$$

[13] Lehmann, E., "Consistency and unbiasedness of nonparametric tests," *Ann. Math. Stat.* **22**, 167 (1951).

[14] See Fix, E., and Hodges, J., "Significance probabilities of the Wilcoxon test," *Ann Math. Stat.* **26**, 301–312 (1955).

where $Z_1, \ldots, Z_N$ are the ordered observations in a random sample from a standard normal population, and $s_1, \ldots, s_n$ is the sequence of Y ranks in the combined order statistic of X's and Y's. For one-sided shift alternatives, the critical region is $c_1 >$ constant (or $c_1 <$ constant, depending on the direction of the shift), and it can be shown that this test is most powerful in the case of normal alternatives for sufficiently small shifts.[15] It is also known that in terms of the concept introduced by Pitman (Section 8.2.2), the asymptotic efficiency of the c_1 test relative to the t test is always at least 1 for shift alternatives and is equal to 1 only in the normal case.[16] Further, c_1 is asymptotically normal as m and n become infinite with a nonzero, finite limiting ratio, with mean zero and variance

$$\frac{m}{nN(N-1)} \sum_{i=1}^{N} a_{N,i}{}^2,$$

where[17] $a_{N,i} = E(Z_i)$.

EXAMPLE 8-22.   Consider the c_1 test based on samples of sizes $m = 4$ and $n = 6$. The values of $a_{10,i}$ found in Table IX are as follows: -1.539, -1.001, $-.656$, $-.376$, $-.123$, $.123$, $.376$, $.656$, 1.001, and 1.539. The sequences having largest c_1 values are then found to be those listed:

Sequence	Y Ranks	$6c_1 = \sum\limits_{i=1}^{6} a_{10, s_i}$
$X\,X\,X\,X\,Y\,Y\,Y\,Y\,Y\,Y$	5 6 7 8 9 10	3.57
$X\,X\,X\,Y\,X\,Y\,Y\,Y\,Y\,Y$	4 6 7 8 9 10	3.32
$X\,X\,X\,Y\,Y\,Y\,X\,Y\,Y\,Y$	4 5 7 8 9 10	3.07
$X\,X\,Y\,X\,X\,Y\,Y\,Y\,Y\,Y$	3 6 7 8 9 10	3.04
$X\,X\,X\,Y\,Y\,Y\,X\,Y\,Y\,Y$	4 5 6 8 9 10	2.82
$X\,X\,Y\,X\,Y\,X\,Y\,Y\,Y\,Y$	3 5 7 8 9 10	2.79
$X\,Y\,X\,X\,X\,Y\,Y\,Y\,Y\,Y$	2 6 7 8 9 10	2.69
$X\,X\,Y\,X\,Y\,Y\,X\,Y\,Y\,Y$	3 5 6 8 9 10	2.54
$X\,X\,Y\,Y\,X\,X\,Y\,Y\,Y\,Y$	3 4 7 8 9 10	2.54
$X\,X\,X\,Y\,Y\,Y\,Y\,X\,Y\,Y$	4 5 6 7 9 10	2.54
$X\,Y\,X\,X\,Y\,X\,Y\,Y\,Y\,Y$	2 5 7 8 9 10	2.45
$X\,X\,Y\,Y\,X\,Y\,X\,Y\,Y\,Y$	3 4 6 8 9 10	2.30
$X\,X\,Y\,X\,Y\,Y\,Y\,X\,Y\,Y$	3 5 6 7 9 10	2.26

For $\alpha = .05$ there would be $.05 \times \binom{10}{4} = 10.5$ points in the critical region; rather, $\theta = 0$ would be accepted for $6c_1 \leq 2.30$, rejected for $6c_1 \geq 2.54$, and re-

[15] See Lehman, E. [13], p. 236 ff.

[16] See Chernoff, H., and Savage, I. R., "Asymptotic normality and efficiency of certain nonparametric test statistics," *Ann. Math. Stat.* **29**, 972 (1958).

[17] Tables of $a_{N,i}$ are available in *Biometrika Tables for Statisticians*, Vol. 1. Cambridge, England: Cambridge Univ. Press, 1954; and in a paper by Teichrow, D., *Ann. Math. Stat.* **27**, 410 (1956). A short version appears here in Table IX, Appendix.

jected or accepted according to the toss of a suitably chosen "coin" if $6c_1 = 2.45$, the value that puts α just over the desired .05.

If the result of sampling is as follows: 22, 25, 27, 30, from X, and 24, 29, 32, 33, 35, 36, from Y, the corresponding sequence of X's and Y's in the combined order statistic is $X\ Y\ X\ X\ Y\ X\ Y\ Y\ Y\ Y$, with $6c_1 = 2.45$. This is the boundary point of the 5 per cent critical region.

It is interesting to compute the critical value of c_1 which comes from the asymptotic distribution; the approximate variance is .587, and for $\alpha = .05$ the critical value would be $1.645\sqrt{.0587} = .4$, or $6c_1 = 2.4$, which is approximately what was obtained above. Similarly, for $\alpha = .025$, $1.96\sqrt{.0587} = .475$, or $6c_1 = 2.85$. This would put the first four points into the critical region, with $\alpha = 4/\binom{10}{4}$ $= .019$. The agreement is fairly good, considering the small sample sizes.

8.5.3   The Van der Waerden Test

Van der Waerden has proposed the following test based on ranks: reject $F_X(\lambda) = F_Y(\lambda)$ in favor of a shift $F_Y(\lambda) = F_X(\lambda - \theta)$ with $\theta > 0$ if the value of

$$\mathscr{Y} = \sum_{j=1}^{n} \Psi\left(\frac{s_j}{N+1}\right)$$

is too large, where again $s_1, \ldots, s_n$ are the Y ranks, and Ψ is the inverse of the standard normal distribution function: $\Psi(\Phi(x)) = x$. The corresponding sum for X ranks $r_1, \ldots, r_m$:

$$\mathscr{X} = \sum_{i=1}^{m} \Psi\left(\frac{r_i}{N+1}\right)$$

is just equal to $-\mathscr{Y}$, since

$$\mathscr{X} + \mathscr{Y} = \sum_{k=1}^{N} \Psi\left(\frac{k}{N+1}\right) = 0.$$

[This follows from the relation $\Psi(t) = -\Psi(1-t)$.]

The mean and variance of $\mathscr{Y}$ are respectively $E(\mathscr{Y}) = 0$ and

$$\text{var } \mathscr{Y} = \frac{mn}{N(N-1)} \sum_{k=1}^{N} \Psi^2\left(\frac{k}{N+1}\right).$$

Tables of critical values and the average sum of squares needed for var $\mathscr{Y}$ are available.[18]

Again the level of the test is the ratio of the number of distinct sequences of X's and Y's in the critical region to $\binom{N}{n}$, and the test given is another scheme for deciding which points to put into the critical region first, and how many.

---

[18] See Van der Waerden, B. L., and Nievergelt, E., *Tafeln zum Vergleich zweier Stickproben mittels X-test und Zeichentest*, Springer-Verlag, 1956.

The properties of asymptotic normality and asymptotic efficiency are the same as those of the c_1 statistic of Section 8.5.2, again following from the theorem of Chernoff and Savage referred to there.

EXAMPLE 8–23.   Again consider (as in Example 8–22) the case $m = 4$ and $n = 6$. The necessary values of $\Psi(k/11)$ are as follows: -1.34, $-.91$, $-.60$, $-.35$, $-.11$, $.11$, $.35$, $.60$, $.91$, 1.34, for $k = 1, 2, \ldots, 10$, in that order. The rank sequences given in Example 10–14 are repeated below, this time with the value of $\mathscr{Y}$:

Y Ranks	$\mathscr{Y}$	
5 6 7 8 9 10	3.20	
4 6 7 8 9 10	2.96	
4 5 7 8 9 10	2.74	
3 6 7 8 9 10	2.71	
4 5 6 8 9 10	2.50	
3 5 7 8 9 10	2.49	
2 6 7 8 9 10	2.40	
3 5 6 8 9 10	2.25	
3 4 7 8 9 10	2.25	
4 5 6 7 9 10	2.25	
2 5 7 8 9 10	2.18	
3 4 6 8 9 10	2.01	
3 5 6 7 9 10	2.00	$(6c_1 = 2.26)$
4 5 6 7 8 10	1.94	$(6c_1 = 2.20)$
2 5 6 8 9 10	1.94	$(6c_1 = 2.20)$
1 6 7 8 9 10	1.97	$(6c_1 = 2.16)$

Although there are minor differences in ordering at the bottom of this list, the test for $\alpha = .05$ would be exactly the same as in the case of the c_1 test.

Problems

8–36.   Referring to Example 8–20, demonstrate the stated equivalence of ranking permutations according to the difference $\bar{X} - \bar{Y}$ and according to Y_j.

8–37.   Apply the W–M–W test to the following data:

From X: 16,   21,   15,   18,   19,   13,   20,   22
From Y: 12,   18,   17,   14,   18,   10

8–38.   Compute the sum of the ranks for the sequences listed in Example 8–20, and notice whether the Wilcoxon statistic would imply the same order of putting points into a critical region.

8–39.   Data are obtained as follows:

From X: 12.9,   12.4,   14.7,   13.8,   15.4,   11.8,   14.2,   13.3,
                12.1
From Y: 13.0,   15.1,   13.7,   16.6,   15.2,   12.3,   14.8,   15.8,
                14.3,   13.4,   14.0.

Apply Wilcoxon's test for identical distributions of X and Y against $F_Y(\lambda) = F_X(\lambda - \theta)$, for $\theta > 0$.

8-40. Compute the Pitman asymptotic efficiency of the Wilcoxon test relative to the t test for the case of shift alternatives and a basic uniform population.

8-41. Apply the c_1-test and the Van der Waerden test to the data of Example 8-21.

8-42. Apply the c_1-test to the data of Problem 8-39, using the asymptotic distribution to determine the critical region.

8-43. Derive the formula for the variance of the Van der Waerden statistic. [*Hint*: Let $a_i = \Psi(i/[N + 1])$. Then for each $j = 1, \ldots, n$, a_{s_i} is a random variable with values $a_1, \ldots, a_N$ each with probability $1/N$. Compute $E(a_{s_i})$, var a_{s_i}, $E(a_{s_i} a_{s_k})$, and then var $\mathscr{Y}$. Use the fact that $\sum a_i = 0$ and therefore $(\sum a_i)^2 = 0$ to express $\sum a_i a_j$ in terms of $\sum a_i^2$.]

8-44. Verify the entries in Table VIII (see Appendix) for $m = n = 3$ and for $m = 2, n = 5$.

8-45. Apply the permutation test based on $\bar{X} - \bar{Y}$ to the data in Example 8-22.

CHAPTER 9

LINEAR MODELS AND
ANALYSIS OF VARIANCE

The problems to be considered in this chapter are concerned with the means of several normal populations, generalizing the situation of Section 7.3.2. A null hypothesis will again be equality of means, but there are new features to be treated. In some cases it is not really expected that the means will be equal, and one is interested in determining the functional dependence of the means on a numerical index of the populations (regression problems). In other cases the means depend on several nonnumerical factors, and it is desired to test a hypothesis of no effect on the means from one factor in the presence of the other factors (analysis of variance problems). Some problems involve dependence of the mean both on a numerical index and on nonnumerical factors (analysis of covariance problems). The models to be considered in this discussion are those in which the dependence on parameters is

443

linear in the parameters—linear models. All the problems mentioned above can be treated in the framework of a general linear hypothesis model, an introduction to which will close the chapter.

The material to be presented is but an introduction to an important and highly developed field of problems to which complete books are devoted.[1] Although power functions will be touched upon, space will not permit discussion of optimality of procedures.[2]

9.1 Regression

Consider a nonrandom variable z that depends on a "controlled variable" t in some way. That is, t is an independent variable that can be preset, and z depends on $t: z = g(t)$. It is desired to measure this dependence, but the measured value of z includes a random error. Let X_t denote the *measured* value corresponding to t, and let ϵ_t be the measurement error:

$$X_t = g(t) + \epsilon_t.$$

Let n measurements be made, corresponding to preselected values of t, with the results $(t_1, X_1), \ldots, (t_n, X_n)$, where

$$X_j = X_{t_j} = g(t_j) + \epsilon_j,$$

ϵ_j denoting the measurement error ϵ_{t_j} at t_j.

It is assumed throughout that the measurement errors are all *independent* random variables, *normally* distributed; that $E(\epsilon_t) = 0$ so that $E(X_t) = g(t)$; and that there is a common variance σ^2 for all measurement errors. That is, $(\epsilon_1, \ldots, \epsilon_n)$ is assumed to have a multivariate normal distribution with mean vector $(0, 0, \ldots, 0)$ and covariance matrix $\sigma^2 I$, where I denotes the $n \times n$ identity matrix.

The main problem considered is that in which the mean function or "regression function" $g(t)$ has a known form but with certain undetermined coefficients or parameters. For instance, $g(t)$ might be: $\alpha + \beta t$, $a + bt + ct^2 + dt^3$, Ke^{at}, At^p, $A \sin \omega t$, etc. The first would be called a linear regression; the next, a cubic; and so on. In the case of linear regression, cubic regression, and indeed, any polynomial regression, the regression function is *linear in the parameters*. In the exponential, power, and trigonometric cases listed, this dependence on the parameters is not linear. However, in the exponential case one can write $\log z = \log K + at$, which is linear in the parameters a and

---

[1] See References [5], [11], and [19], to name but a few.
[2] See Lehman, E. [13], Chapter 7.

log K as well as linear in t; and in the case of At^p, $\log z = \log A + p \log t$, which is linear in the parameters $\log A$ and p.

Linear regression, with $g(t) = \alpha + \beta t$, will be the main topic of discussion. A similar development is possible whenever the regression function is linear in the parameters. Further, the linear regression case includes the exponential and power cases if the error can be assumed to be additive and normal in the logarithmic forms. Multiple regression problems, in which z is a function of more than one controlled variable, will not be treated.

9.1.1 Linear Regression

It soon becomes evident in a linear regression problem that it is advantageous to use the form $\alpha + \beta(t - \bar{t})$ for the regression function, where $\bar{t}$ is the arithmetic mean of the t-values used, and this form will be used from the beginning.

There are three unknown parameters: α, β, and σ^2, and the likelihood function is as follows, given observations $(t_1, X_1), \ldots, (t_n, X_n)$:

$$L(\alpha, \beta, \sigma^2) = (2\pi)^{-n/2}(\sigma^2)^{-n/2} \exp\left\{-\frac{1}{2\sigma^2} \sum_{i=1}^{n} [X_i - (\alpha + \beta[t_i - \bar{t}])]^2\right\}.$$

The partial derivatives of $\log L(\alpha, \beta, \sigma^2)$ with respect to α, β, and σ^2 are then

$$\frac{\partial \log L}{\partial \alpha} = -\frac{1}{2\sigma^2} \sum (-2)\{X_i - (\alpha + \beta[t_i - \bar{t}])\},$$

$$\frac{\partial \log L}{\partial \beta} = -\frac{1}{2\sigma^2} \sum (-2[t_i - \bar{t}])\{X_i - (\alpha + \beta[t_i - \bar{t}])\},$$

$$\frac{\partial \log L}{\partial \sigma^2} = -\frac{n}{2\sigma^2} + \frac{1}{2\sigma^4} \sum \{X_i - (\alpha + \beta[t_i - \bar{t}])\}^2.$$

Setting these equal to zero and solving simultaneously, one finds the maximum likelihood estimates:

$$\hat{\alpha} = \bar{X}, \quad \hat{\beta} = \frac{s_{tx}}{s_t^2}, \quad \hat{\sigma}^2 = \frac{1}{n} \sum [X_i - \hat{\alpha} - \hat{\beta}(t_i - \bar{t})]^2,$$

where

$$s_{tx} = \frac{1}{n} \sum X_i(t_i - \bar{t}) = \frac{1}{n} \sum (X_i - \bar{X})(t_i - \bar{t}),$$

and

$$s_t^2 = \frac{1}{n} \sum t_i(t_i - \bar{t}) = \frac{1}{n} \sum (t_i - \bar{t})^2.$$

(Observe that although the notation might suggest it, s_{tx} and s_t^2 are not "sample second moments" in the usual sense, since the t's are not observations but fixed values of the controlled variable t. The quantity s_t^2 is therefore not random, and in s_{tx} the randomness enters only through the X_i.)

The maximum likelihood estimates $\hat{\alpha}$, $\hat{\beta}$, and $\hat{\sigma}^2$ are readily seen to be minimal sufficient statistics (Problem 9–1). The statistics $\hat{\alpha}$ and $\hat{\beta}$ are in fact *least squares estimates* of α and β, in the sense that they are precisely the values of a and b that minimize the average of the squared deviations of the observations about the linear function $a + b(t_i - \bar{t})^2$:

$$R(a, b) = \frac{1}{n} \sum (X_i - a - b[t_i - \bar{t}])^2.$$

For, the first two of the above "likelihood equations" are just the same as the results of equating to zero the partial derivatives of $R(a, b)$ with respect to a and to b. Moreover, the minimum value $R(\hat{\alpha}, \hat{\beta})$ is the estimate $\hat{\sigma}^2$.

The "empirical regression function" $\hat{\alpha} + \hat{\beta}(t - \bar{t})$ will be shown in Section 9.1.2 to be the unbiased estimator having the smallest variance of any estimator in the class of unbiased estimators formed by taking linear combinations of the observations. For the present it is simply noted that $\hat{\alpha}$ and $\hat{\beta}$, and therefore $\hat{\alpha} + \hat{\beta}(t - \bar{t})$ are in fact unbiased in estimating α, β, and $\alpha + \beta(t - \bar{t})$, respectively. For, exploiting the linearity of the estimates in the X's and the linear nature of the averaging operation, one has

$$E(\hat{\alpha}) = E(\bar{X}) = \frac{1}{n} \sum E(X_i) = \frac{1}{n} \sum (\alpha + \beta[t_i - \bar{t}]) = \alpha,$$

and

$$E(\hat{\beta}) = \frac{1}{ns_t^2} \sum E(X_i)(t_i - \bar{t}) = \beta.$$

Hence,

$$E(\hat{\alpha} + \hat{\beta}[t - \bar{t}]) = \alpha + \beta[t - \bar{t}].$$

The fact that $\hat{\alpha}$ and $\hat{\beta}$ are *linear* combinations of the independent variables $X_1, \ldots, X_n$ permits ready computation of their variances:

$$\text{var } \hat{\alpha} = \text{var } \bar{X} = \frac{1}{n^2} \sum \text{var } X_i = \frac{\sigma^2}{n},$$

and

$$\text{var } \hat{\beta} = \frac{1}{n^2 s_t^4} \sum (t_i - \bar{t})^2 \text{ var } X_i = \frac{\sigma^2}{ns_t^2}.$$

It is seen directly from these expressions (as well as from the fact that $\hat{\alpha}$ and $\hat{\beta}$ are maximum likelihood estimates) that $\hat{\alpha}$ and $\hat{\beta}$ are consistent estimates of α and β. It is seen also from the expression for the variance of $\hat{\beta}$ that this slope estimate is most reliable when the points $t_1, \ldots, t_n$ have as much spread as possible so that s_t^2 is large. It is clear that at least two distinct values of t must be used in order to obtain an estimate of slope.

The joint distribution of $(\hat{\alpha}, \hat{\beta})$ is bivariate normal, since $\hat{\alpha}$ and $\hat{\beta}$ are linear combinations of $(X_1, \ldots, X_n)$. The covariance of $\hat{\alpha}$ and $\hat{\beta}$ is readily shown to be zero, implying independence of $\hat{\alpha}$ and $\hat{\beta}$ in their bivariate normal distribution (see Problem 9–6).

If the value of α is held fixed at α_0, the maximum of the likelihood function is found to be

$$L(\alpha_0, \hat{\beta}, \hat{\sigma}_0{}^2) = (2\pi\hat{\sigma}_0{}^2)^{-n/2} \exp\left(-\tfrac{1}{2}n\right),$$

where

$$\hat{\sigma}_0{}^2 = \frac{1}{n} \sum [X_i - \alpha_0 - \hat{\beta}(t_i - \bar{t})]^2.$$

The maximum of L over all α, β, and σ^2 is

$$L(\hat{\alpha}, \hat{\beta}, \hat{\sigma}^2) = (2\pi\hat{\sigma}^2)^{-n/2} \exp\left(-\tfrac{1}{2}n\right),$$

and so the likelihood ratio test for $\alpha = \alpha_0$ against $\alpha \neq \alpha_0$ has the critical region

$$\frac{L(\alpha_0, \hat{\beta}, \hat{\sigma}_0{}^2)}{L(\hat{\alpha}, \hat{\beta}, \hat{\sigma}^2)} = \left[\frac{\hat{\sigma}_0{}^2}{\hat{\sigma}^2}\right]^{-n/2} < \text{constant},$$

or equivalently,

$$\left(\frac{\hat{\alpha} - \alpha_0}{\hat{\sigma}/\sqrt{n}}\right)^2 > \text{constant}.$$

Similarly, the likelihood ratio critical region for $\beta = \beta_0$ against $\beta \neq \beta_0$ is given by

$$\left(\frac{\hat{\beta} - \beta_0}{\hat{\sigma}/\sqrt{ns_t{}^2}}\right)^2 > \text{constant}.$$

That is, if $\hat{\alpha}$ differs from α_0 by too much, $\alpha = \alpha_0$ is rejected—"too much" being measured with respect to the standard deviation of $\hat{\alpha}$, estimated by $\hat{\sigma}/\sqrt{n}$. How much is "too much" is determined from a prescribed size of type I error and the distribution of the statistic used.

To obtain the distributions of the statistics that have emerged, Cochran's theorem will be used. The identity

$$(X_i - \alpha - \beta[t_i - \bar{t}]) = (X_i - \hat{\alpha} - \hat{\beta}[t_i - \bar{t}]) + (\hat{\beta} - \beta)(t_i - \bar{t}) + (\hat{\alpha} - \alpha)$$

is squared, summed on i, and divided by σ^2 with the following result:

$$\sum_{i=1}^{n} \left(\frac{X_i - \alpha - \beta[t_i - \bar{t}]}{\sigma}\right)^2 = \frac{n\hat{\sigma}^2}{n^2} + \frac{(\hat{\beta} - \beta)^2}{\sigma^2/ns_t{}^2} + \frac{(\hat{\alpha} - \alpha)^2}{\sigma^2/n}.$$

In the process of squaring, three cross-product terms appear; these vanish when the summation is performed, one because the sum of $(t_i - \bar{t})$ is zero and the others because $\hat{\alpha}$ and $\hat{\beta}$ satisfy the likelihood equations (or the normal equations of the least squares process). Now, the sum on the left is a sum of squares of independent standard normal variables, a chi-square variable with n degrees of freedom. It is represented in the form $Q_1 + Q_2 + Q_3$, where the Q's are sums of squares of linear combinations of the standardized X's. In Q_1 there are n terms, but there are two linear relations among the linear combinations in that sum of squares (namely, the normal equations), which means that the rank of Q_1 is at most $n - 2$. Both Q_2 and Q_3 are of rank 1, and so the rank of Q_1 is at least $n - 2$, and therefore exactly $n - 2$. These ranks add up properly: $(n - 2) + 1 + 1 = n$; and so, according to Cochran's theorem Q_1, Q_2, and Q_3 have independent chi-square distributions with, respectively, $n - 2$, 1, and 1 degree of freedom. (The distributions of Q_2 and Q_3 were apparent without Cochran's theorem, but now it is clear that they are independent.) It should be noticed that the distribution of Q_1, and hence of $\hat{\sigma}^2$, is independent of the values of α and β.

The distributions of the statistics arising from the likelihood ratio technique can now be discussed. Except for a constant factor, they were as follows:

$$(n - 2) \frac{(\hat{\beta} - \beta_0)^2}{\hat{\sigma}^2/s_t^2} \qquad \text{and} \qquad (n - 2) \frac{(\hat{\alpha} - \alpha_0)^2}{\hat{\sigma}^2}.$$

The constants are chosen to exploit existing tables, since each of these ratios has the F distribution with $(1, n - 2)$ degrees of freedom, provided $\beta = \beta_0$ and $\alpha = \alpha_0$. If $\alpha \neq \alpha_0$, the numerator of the corresponding ratio is no longer a central chi-square variable but a noncentral one, with noncentrality parameter $n(\alpha - \alpha_0)^2/(2\sigma^2)$. The power functions of the likelihood ratio tests for $\alpha = \alpha_0$ and $\beta = \beta_0$ can therefore be obtained from the noncentral F distribution.

Confidence intervals can be constructed for α and for β. Let $-k$ denote the $100\gamma/2$ percentile of the t distribution with $n - 2$ degrees of freedom, or equivalently, $k^2 = F_{1-\gamma}(1, n - 2) = t^2_{1-\gamma/2}(n - 2)$. Then

$$P\left\{(n - 2) \frac{(\hat{\alpha} - \alpha)^2}{\hat{\sigma}^2} < k^2\right\} = 1 - \gamma,$$

or

$$P\left(\hat{\alpha} - \frac{k\hat{\sigma}}{\sqrt{n - 2}} < \alpha < \hat{\alpha} + \frac{k\hat{\sigma}}{\sqrt{n - 2}}\right) = 1 - \gamma.$$

Similarly, a confidence interval for β is found to have the limits

$$\hat{\beta} \pm \frac{k\hat{\sigma}}{\sqrt{(n - 2)s_t^2}}.$$

EXAMPLE 9–1. Suppose that calculations for a given set of 100 points (t_i, X_i) yield $s_t^2 = 9.7$, $\hat{\alpha} = 1.1$, $\hat{\beta} = .02$, and $\hat{\sigma}^2 = .0036$. The normal distribution can be used to approximate the t distribution with 98 degrees of freedom, so that for

$\gamma = .10$, $k = 1.645$. The 90 per cent confidence intervals for α and β are, respectively,

$$1.1 \pm 1.645 \times \frac{.06}{\sqrt{98}} \quad \text{or} \quad (1.0990, 1.1010),$$

and

$$.02 \pm 1.645 \times \frac{.06}{\sqrt{98 \times 9.7}} \quad \text{or} \quad (.0168, .0232).$$

The likelihood ratio test of $\beta = \beta_0$ is equivalent to the rule of rejecting β_0 if the confidence interval for β does not include it. According to this test, the value $\beta = 0$ (equality of means) would be rejected because the confidence interval obtained does not include it.

It should be pointed out that although inferences can be made concerning α without any assumptions on β, and vice versa, the statistics used for testing these two parameters are not independent, and care should be taken in making statements about α and β jointly. For instance, it cannot be asserted that both α and β lie in the corresponding 90 per cent confidence intervals with probability $.90 \times .90$. On the other hand, a *simultaneous confidence region* for (α, β) can be constructed, taking the ratio of the *sum* of the second and third terms in the chi-square partitioning to the first term; the numerator would be chi-square with 2 degrees of freedom, and the ratio would then have the F distribution with $(2, n - 2)$ degrees of freedom. Thus, given a confidence coefficient $1 - r$:

$$P\left\{ \frac{(\hat{\alpha} - \alpha)^2 + s_t^2(\hat{\beta} - \beta)^2}{2\hat{\sigma}^2/(n - 2)} < F_{1-r}(2, n - 2) \right\} = 1 - \gamma.$$

The inequality is satisfied (for given $\hat{\alpha}$, $\hat{\beta}$, and $\hat{\sigma}^2$) by the points (α, β) in an ellipse. This elliptical region, which depends on the observations and is therefore random, is the confidence region.

It is perhaps instructive to view the tests derived for α and β in the following intuitive way: The quantities

$$\frac{n\hat{\sigma}^2}{n - 2}, \quad ns_t^2(\hat{\beta} - \beta_0)^2, \quad \text{and} \quad n(\hat{\alpha} - \alpha_0)^2$$

are, under the hypothesis that $\alpha = \alpha_0$ and $\beta = \beta_0$, unbiased estimates of σ^2; the ratio of any two of these should be around 1, on the average at least. But

$$E[n(\hat{\alpha} - \alpha_0)^2] = E[n(\hat{\alpha} - \alpha)^2] + n(\alpha - \alpha_0)^2 + 2(\alpha - \alpha_0)E[n(\hat{\alpha} - \alpha)]$$

$$= \sigma^2 + n(\alpha - \alpha_0)^2,$$

so that if $\alpha \neq \alpha_0$, the estimate $n(\hat{\alpha} - \alpha_0)^2$ tends to be higher than when $\alpha = \alpha_0$. The distribution of $\hat{\sigma}^2$, on the other hand, is not affected by the value of α, and so the ratio used for tests on α tends to be higher for $\alpha \neq \alpha_0$ than for

$\alpha = \alpha_0$. The rejection rule that was derived thus appears to be intuitively quite reasonable.

Problems concerning the common variance σ^2 are handled just as in the simpler case of a sample from a single normal population, using $\hat{\sigma}^2$, except that here only $n - 2$ degrees of freedom are available, two having been "used up" in the estimation of the two parameters α and β.

Problems

9–1.   Determine the minimal sufficient statistic, given $(t_1, X_1), \ldots, (t_n, X_n)$, for the normal family of Section 9.1.1.

9–2.   Construct a 90 per cent confidence interval for σ^2, using the data in Example 9–1.

9–3.   Determine the line that best fits the following points in the least squares sense, minimizing the sum of squares of vertical deviations: $(0, 2)$, $(1, 1)$, $(4, 3)$, $(5, 2)$.

9–4.   Given the following data from a sample of size 50: $\bar{t} = 8.2$, $s_t^2 = 10.24$, $\hat{\alpha} = 6.31$, $\hat{\beta} = .092$, $\hat{\sigma}^2 = 4.6$,

    (a) Construct 95 per cent confidence intervals for α, for β, and for σ^2.
    (b) Test $\beta = 0$ at the level .01.
    (c) Construct a 90 per cent confidence region for α and β.

9–5.   Show the asserted equivalence of $[\hat{\sigma}_0^2/\hat{\sigma}^2]^{-n/2} <$ constant and $n(\hat{\alpha} - \alpha_0)^2/\hat{\sigma}^2 >$ constant.

9–6.   Compute the covariance of $\hat{\alpha}$ and $\hat{\beta}$ directly from their definitions.

9.1.2   The Minimum Variance Linear Unbiased Estimate

It was asserted in the preceding section that the maximum likelihood (least squares) estimate $\hat{\alpha} + \hat{\beta}(t - \bar{t})$ of the regression line $\alpha + \beta(t - \bar{t})$ at t is the linear unbiased estimate with smallest variance. Consider, then, any unbiased linear estimate U:

$$U = c_1 X_1 + \cdots + c_n X_n.$$

The condition that U be unbiased implies that

$$E(U) = \sum c_i E(X_i)$$
$$= \sum c_i [\alpha + \beta(t_i - \bar{t})] = \alpha + \beta(t - \bar{t}),$$

or that

$$\sum c_i = 1 \quad \text{and} \quad \sum c_i(t_i - \bar{t}) = t - \bar{t}.$$

The variance of U is

$$\text{var } U = \text{var} \left\{ \sum c_i X_i \right\} = \sigma^2 \sum c_i^2.$$

The U with minimum variance is given by that choice of $c = (c_1, \ldots, c_n)$

that minimizes $\sum c_i^2/2$ subject to the two restrictions that $\sum c_i = 1$ and $\sum c_i(t_i - \bar{t}) = t - \bar{t}$. Using the method of Lagrange multipliers, one minimizes (see Example 5–8):

$$\sum c_i^2/2 - \lambda(\sum c_i - 1) - \mu[\sum c_i(t_i - \bar{t}) - (t - \bar{t})]$$

as a function of the $n + 2$ variables $c_1, \ldots, c_n$, λ, and μ. Setting derivatives of this with respect to these variables equal to zero yields

$$\begin{cases} c_j - \lambda - \mu(t_j - \bar{t}) = 0, & j = 1, \ldots, n, \\ \sum c_j = 1, \\ \sum c_j(t_j - \bar{t}) = t - \bar{t}. \end{cases}$$

Elimination of λ and μ then gives the desired coefficients:

$$c_j = \frac{1}{n} + \frac{(t - \bar{t})(t_j - \bar{t})}{ns_t^2},$$

so that the minimum variance estimate is

$$\sum c_j X_j = \bar{X} + \frac{s_{tx}(t - \bar{t})}{s_t^2} = \hat{\alpha} + \hat{\beta}(t - \bar{t}).$$

This is precisely the maximum likelihood estimate of $E(X_t)$.

This phenomenon is a special case of the Gauss–Markov theorem, which will be stated in more general form in discussing the general linear model in Section 9.3.

9.1.3 Testing Linearity

There was nothing in the development of Section 9.1.1 that ruled out the possibility that some of the t's might be alike, and so the results there apply to a situation in which n_1 observations are taken at $t = t_1, \ldots,$ and n_k observations at $t = t_k$. But the notation requires some revision (as it did when going to grouped data in a single sample):

Controlled Variable	Observations	Sample Mean	Population Mean	Sample Size
t_1	$X_{11}, \ldots, X_{1n_1}$	$\bar{X}_1$	$g(t_1)$	n_1
$\vdots$	$\vdots$	$\vdots$	$\vdots$	$\vdots$
t_k	$X_{k1}, \ldots, X_{kn_k}$	$\bar{X}_k$	$g(t_k)$	n_k

If as before n denotes the total number of observations, then $\sum n_i = n$. The mean of the t's is now a weighted average of the distinct t's, with a similar modification for $s_t{}^2$:

$$\bar{t} = \frac{1}{n} \sum n_i t_i, \qquad s_t{}^2 = \frac{1}{n} \sum n_i (t_i - \bar{t})^2.$$

The overall mean of the observations X_{ij} can be expressed in terms of the means at the individual t's:

$$\bar{X} = \frac{1}{n} \sum_{i=1}^{k} \sum_{j=1}^{n_i} X_{ij} = \frac{1}{n} \sum_{i=1}^{k} n_i \bar{X}_i, \qquad \bar{X}_i = \frac{1}{n_i} \sum_{j=1}^{n_i} X_{ij}.$$

The revised formulas for $\hat{\alpha}$, $\hat{\beta}$, and $\hat{\sigma}^2$ are then

$$\hat{\alpha} = \bar{X}, \qquad \hat{\beta} = \frac{1}{n s_t{}^2} \sum n_i \bar{X}_i (t_i - \bar{t}),$$

and

$$\hat{\sigma}^2 = \frac{1}{n} \sum \sum [X_{ij} - \hat{\alpha} - \hat{\beta}(t_i - \bar{t})]^2.$$

Single sums on j extend from 1 to n_i; single sums on i, from 1 to k; and double sums from $j = 1$ to $j = n_i$ and from $i = 1$ to k.

With the assumption that $g(t) = \alpha + \beta(t - \bar{t})$, tests and estimates for α, β, and σ^2 are available as in Section 9.1.1 but with the computation formulas modified as shown here. But it is now possible to test for linearity of the regression function, with the aid of a further breakup of $\hat{\sigma}^2$. Let the empirical regression function $\hat{\alpha} + \hat{\beta}(t_i - \bar{t})$ be denoted by $\tilde{X}_i$, and write

$$X_{ij} - \tilde{X}_i = (X_{ij} - \bar{X}_i) + (\bar{X}_i - \tilde{X}_i).$$

Squaring and summing this over i and j gives

$$\sum \sum (X_{ij} - \tilde{X}_i)^2 = \sum \sum (X_{ij} - \bar{X}_i)^2 + \sum n_i (\bar{X}_i - \tilde{X}_i)^2,$$

the cross-product term again disappearing upon summation. The first term is a contribution to variability of the observations about the empirical regression line caused by variability of the observations about the means at the individual t values; the second term is a contribution caused by variation of these means about the empirical regression line.

Since there are k linear relations among the n quantities $(X_{ij} - \bar{X}_i)$, the sum of squares of these quantities has rank at most $n - k$. (The k linear relations are these: $\sum (X_{ij} - \bar{X}_i) = 0$ for $i = 1, \ldots, k$). There are two linear relations among the k quantities $(\bar{X}_i - \tilde{X}_i)$, namely, the normal equations; the rank of the sum of their squares is then at most $k - 2$. With this further breakup, then, the application of Cochran's theorem in Section 9.1.1 would show that $\sum \sum (X_{ij} - \bar{X}_i)^2 / \sigma^2$ and $\sum n_i (\bar{X}_i - \tilde{X}_i)^2 / \sigma^2$ are independent chi-square variables with $n - k$ and $k - 2$ degrees of freedom, respectively, if the regression function is linear. Under this assumption, therefore, the ratio

$$\frac{\sum n_i(\bar{X}_i - \tilde{X}_i)^2/(k - 2)}{\sum \sum (X_{ij} - \bar{X}_i)^2/(n - k)}$$

has the F distribution $(k - 2, n - k)$. The numerator and denominator are each unbiased estimates of σ^2 if the regression function is linear. The denominator is so, even if the regression function is *not* linear, being a weighted average of independent variance estimates at the individual t values; the latter have $n_1 - 1, \ldots, n_k - 1$ degrees of freedom, the sum of these being $n - k$.

The test that rejects linearity of the regression function for excessively large values of the above ratio is exactly the likelihood ratio test of H_0: $g(t_i) = \alpha + \beta(t_i - \bar{t})$, with unknown α and β, against H_1: $g(t_i)$ are not collinear. The level desired determines the critical value of the ratio as a percentile of the F distribution.

EXAMPLE 9–2.   Consider the following artificial data, made up to look more quadratic than linear:

t_i	X_{ij}	$\bar{X}_i$	n_i	$\sum(X_{ij} - \bar{X}_i)^2$
1	3, 4, 5	4	3	2
2	1, 3	2	2	2
3	3, 4, 5	4	3	2

It is apparent that $\hat{\beta} = 0$, so the empirical regression line is horizontal. Then $\tilde{X}_i = \hat{\alpha} = \bar{X} = 7/2$, and

$$\sum \sum \left(X_{ij} - \frac{7}{2}\right)^2 = 12 = \sum \sum (X_{ij} - \bar{X}_i)^2 + \sum n_i(\bar{X}_i - \tilde{X}_i)^2$$

$$= \quad 6 \quad + \quad 6.$$

Now $n - k = 8 - 3 = 5$ and $k - 2 = 3 - 2 = 1$, and the test ratio is

$$\frac{6/1}{6/5} = 5.$$

For a 5 per cent significance level, the rejection limit is $F_{.95}(1, 5) = 6.61 > 5$. At this level, linearity is accepted, although at the 10 per cent level, the rejection limit is 4.06 and linearity would be rejected.

9–7. Given the data tabulated, and assuming normal, independent observations with constant variance σ^2:

t_i	X_{ij}
1	2, 5, 5
2	4, 6, 5
3	6, 4, 8

(a) Test for linearity of the regression function.
(b) Assuming linearity, give estimates of α, β, and σ^2.
(c) Assuming linearity, determine a 95 per cent confidence region for (α, β).

9–8. With the usual assumptions of independence, normality, and constant variance σ^2, and assuming $E(X_t) = ct^2$, determine maximum likelihood estimates of c and σ^2 based on several observations at each of k values of t. Construct a test for this quadratic type of regression function. Determine an estimate of σ^2 that will apply even if the regression function is not of the quadratic form given, and state how it can be improved if the regression function is ct^2.

9–9. Set up the likelihood ratio test for linearity and show that it turns out as claimed just before Example 9–2. (The denominator of Λ is the maximum of the likelihood function over the $k + 1$ parameters $g(t_1), \ldots, g(t_k)$, and σ^2.)

9–10. Show that $E(\overline{X}_i - \tilde{X}_i) = 0$ if the regression function is linear.

9.1.4 Prediction

Suppose that the purpose in gathering data at various values of the controlled variable t is the prediction of the value $X_0 = X_{t_0}$ at some new value t_0. If success in prediction is measured by mean square error, the best prediction is the expected value at t_0:

$$E(X_0) = \alpha + \beta(t_0 - \bar{t}),$$

but, of course, α and β are not usually known. The problem is then to estimate this linear combination of parameters. The maximum likelihood estimate is $\hat{\alpha} + \hat{\beta}(t_0 - \bar{t})$, which was seen in Section 9.1.2 to be also the minimum variance linear unbiased estimate. Denote this estimate by $\tilde{X}_0$.

The deviation $d = \tilde{X}_0 - X_0$ is normally distributed with mean zero and variance

$$\sigma_d^2 = \sigma^2 + \frac{\sigma^2}{n} + \frac{\sigma^2(t_0 - \bar{t})^2}{ns_t^2},$$

the first term being present even if the regression function were known exactly, and the other terms arising because of errors in the estimates of the regression coefficients. It is evident that the closer t_0 is to $\bar{t}$, the better the prediction (from the point of view of mean square error).

A kind of "confidence interval," better described as a prediction interval, can be constructed by using the variance estimate

$$s^2 = \frac{1}{n-2} \sum \sum (X_{ij} - \bar{X}_i)^2.$$

Since $d^2/\sigma_d{}^2$ is chi-square with one degree of freedom, and since it is independent of $(n-2)s^2/\sigma^2$ (which is chi-square with $n-2$ degrees of freedom), the ratio

$$F = \frac{d^2/\sigma_d{}^2}{s^2/\sigma^2}$$

has the F distribution with $(1, n-2)$ degrees of freedom. Hence,

$$P\left\{\frac{[X_0 - \hat{\alpha} - \hat{\beta}(t_0 - \bar{t})]^2}{s^2[1 + 1/n + (t_0 - \bar{t})^2/(ns_t{}^2)]} < F_n(1, n-2)\right\} = \eta.$$

The inequality can be written also as follows, with $t' = \sqrt{F_n(1, n-2)}$:

$$P\left\{\tilde{X}_0 - t's\left[1 + \frac{1}{n} + \frac{(t_0 - \bar{t})^2}{ns_t{}^2}\right]^{1/2} < X_0 < \tilde{X}_0\right.$$

$$\left. + t's\left[1 + \frac{1}{n} + \frac{(t_0 - \bar{t})^2}{ns_t{}^2}\right]^{1/2}\right\} = \eta.$$

The interval within which X_0 falls with probability η is called a *prediction interval*; this interval and X_0 are both random.

Another type of prediction sometimes desired is the determination of the value t_0 of the controlled variable at which a given set of observations $X_1', \ldots, X_m'$ is obtained, given the usual data for the regression problem. The maximum likelihood estimate of t_0 turns out to be

$$\hat{t}_0 = \frac{\bar{X}' - \hat{\alpha}}{\hat{\beta}} + \bar{t}.$$

Since $\bar{X}' - \hat{\alpha} - \hat{\beta}(t_0 - \bar{t})$ is normal with mean zero and variance

$$\sigma^2\left[\frac{1}{m} + \frac{1}{n} + \frac{(t_0 - \bar{t})^2}{ns_t{}^2}\right],$$

a confidence interval for t_0 is readily constructed.

EXAMPLE 9–3.   Using the data of Example 9–2, a prediction interval for X_0 at $t_0 = 6$ is set up as follows: The pooled variance s^2 is

$$\frac{1}{8-2} \sum \sum \left(X_{ij} - \frac{7}{2}\right)^2 = 2,$$

and $ns_t^2 = \sum n_i(t_i - \bar{t})^2 = 6$. Using $\eta = .90$, and therefore $t' = 1.94$ (since $n - 2 = 6$), the prediction interval has the limits $\bar{X}_0 \pm 1.94\sqrt{91/12} = 3.5 \pm 5.35$.

A confidence interval for determination of the value of t corresponding to some new data cannot be constructed because $\hat{\beta} = 0$, and the empirical regression line is horizontal.

9.1.5   Optimum Allocation of Observations

It was seen earlier that the estimate $\hat{\beta}$ is the unbiased linear combination of observations with the smallest variance and that this smallest variance is $\sigma^2/(ns_t^2)$. Given that n observations are permitted, it is of interest to know how best to distribute these on the axis of the controlled variable. If by "best" is meant that the variance of the slope estimate $\hat{\beta}$ is to be as small as possible, what is wanted is a distribution of observations which maximizes ns_t^2. This is accomplished by putting observations at the smallest and largest t's possible (say, t_1 and t_k), since for any other distribution the quantity ns_t^2 could be increased by moving observations farther toward t_1 or t_k (whichever is closer in each case). But if a proportion p are put at t_1 and q at t_2, with $p + q = 1$, then

$$ns_t^2 = pt_1^2 + qt_2^2 - (pt_1 + qt_2)^2 = pq(t_1 - t_2)^2.$$

This is maximized for $p = q = \frac{1}{2}$, and so the best distribution is achieved by putting half of the observations at each of the values t_1 and t_2.

The problem of allocation has been considered more generally by Elfving and others.[3] Elfving showed[4] by interchanging the minimizing operations (with respect to constants in the linear combination of observations and with respect to distributions of observations) that for estimation of any single linear function of parameters, exactly two t values should be used; he also gave a scheme for determining the proportions at those values.

Of course, for testing linearity, it was found desirable to have k large (the number of distinct t values) in order to make a large number of degrees of freedom in the relevant term. Different aims call for different optimum allocations.

Problems

9–11.   Using the data in Problem 9–7, construct a 90 per cent prediction interval for X_t at $t = 6$, assuming a linear regression function.

9–12.   Construct a 70 per cent confidence interval for t_0, the value of t at which the data 3, 7, 5 are obtained, assuming a linear regression function and the data of Problem 9–7.

[3] See Kiefer, J., and Wolfowitz, J., "Optimum designs in regression problems," *Ann. Math. Stat.* **30**, 271 (1959), and references given there.
[4] Elfving, G., "Optimum allocation in linear regression theory," *Ann. Math. Stat.* **23**, 255 (1952).

9–13.   Show that for a *given* linear unbiased estimator $T = \sum n_i c_i \bar{X}_i$,   where var $\bar{X}_i = \sigma^2/n_i$, the allocation of n observations with n_i at t_i which minimizes the variance of T is given by

$$\frac{n_i}{n} = \frac{|c_i|}{\sum |c_i|}.$$

(Minimize var T by selecting $n_1, \ldots, n_k$ subject to $\sum n_i = n$, using the Lagrange multiplier technique.)

9.2   Analysis of Variance

Although the name "analysis of variance" does not suggest it, the topic deals with tests for equality of means, the various means of a random quantity corresponding to different "treatments," or in the case considered first, corresponding to different "levels" of a single factor that may be affecting the results of a chance experiment.

Most of the work done in the field of analysis of variance assumes normal distributions (as in regression problems), and the discussion here is restricted by this assumption.[5]

It is assumed here that the variances of the observations are all equal. A likelihood ratio test for equality of variances of several normal populations is readily constructed (Problem 9–14).

The technique of analysis of variance is briefly as follows: Taking all the observations in samples from several populations (corresponding to several treatments), one breaks the variability about the over-all mean into components, one associated with the actual population variability and the others associated with variations in the sample means caused by the various factors involved. If the technique sounds familiar, it is because the treatment of regression problems in Section 9.1 employed it.

In regression problems, too, one is concerned with testing hypotheses about the means of several populations; the several populations in the regression case correspond to the chosen values of the controlled variable. That is, the populations are indexed according to the value of the controlled variable, and the concern is not only with equality of population means but (if the means are not equal) also with the functional relationship between the population mean and the indexing parameter. In the problems of "analysis of variance" the populations are not indexed by a single controlled variable, and it does not make sense to consider a regression function. In this respect, the problem

---

[5] See Kruskal, W. H., and Wallis, W. A., "Use of ranks in one-criterion variance analysis," *Jour. Amer. Stat. Assn.* **47**, 583–621 (1952), for discussions of nonparametric analysis of variance.

is simpler. However, the real value of analysis of variance methods lies in its providing a means of studying one factor in the presence of other factors. The case of a single factor will be treated first.

9.2.1   A Single Classification Problem

Consider k independent, normally distributed populations $X_1, \ldots, X_k$ with var $X_i = \sigma^2$, and assume that data are given as follows:

Population	Sample Size	Observations	Sample Means	Population Mean
X_1	n_1	$X_{11}, \ldots, X_{1n_1}$	$\bar{X}_1$	μ_1
$\vdots$	$\vdots$	$\vdots$	$\vdots$	$\vdots$
X_k	n_k	$X_{k1}, \ldots, X_{kn_k}$	$\bar{X}_k$	μ_k

The maximum likelihood estimates of $\mu_1, \ldots, \mu_k$ and σ^2 are

$$\hat{\mu}_1 = \bar{X}_1, \ldots, \qquad \hat{\mu}_k = \bar{X}_k, \qquad \hat{\sigma}^2 = \frac{1}{n} \sum \sum (X_{ij} - \bar{X}_i)^2,$$

where $n = \sum n_i$, the total number of observations.

Now define

$$\mu = \frac{1}{n} \sum n_i \mu_i \qquad \text{and} \qquad \theta_i = \mu_i - \mu.$$

The MLE of μ is $\bar{X}$; of θ_i, $\bar{X}_i - \bar{X}$, where $\bar{X} = \sum n_i \bar{X}_i / n$. If the population means *are* identical, they are equal to μ, and then $\theta_i = 0$ for all i. And if such be the case, the n observations in all the samples make up a sample of size n from a common normal population with mean μ and variance σ^2. An estimate of variance could then be obtained from the sum of squares about $\bar{X}$: $\sum \sum (X_{ij} - \bar{X})^2$. Consider the following partition of this sum:

$$\sum \sum (X_{ij} - \bar{X})^2 = \sum \sum [(X_{ij} - \bar{X}_i) + (\bar{X}_i - \bar{X})]^2$$

$$= \sum \sum (X_{ij} - \bar{X}_i) + \sum n_i (\bar{X}_i - \bar{X})^2.$$

(The cross-product term vanishes because $\sum (X_{ij} - \bar{X}_i) = 0$.) The first term on the right is $n\hat{\sigma}^2$, and is based on "within samples" variation; it will be about the same no matter what the μ_i, and its distribution is independent of the means. The second term on the right, on the other hand, will tend to be large if the means μ_i are not identical, since then the sample means $\bar{X}_i$ will tend to be more widely dispersed about $\bar{X}$ than if all population means are alike.

The distributions of these sums in the partition come from an application of Cochran's theorem. Consider the following sum of squares:

$$\sum\sum\frac{(X_{ij} - \mu)^2}{\sigma^2} = \sum\sum\frac{(X_{ij} - \bar{X}_i)^2}{\sigma^2} + \sum\frac{n_i(\bar{X}_i - \bar{X})^2}{\sigma^2} + \frac{n(\bar{X} - \mu)^2}{\sigma^2}.$$

Under the null hypothesis that $\theta_i = 0$ for all i, the sum on the left has the chi-square distribution with n degrees of freedom. On the right the ranks do not exceed $n - k, k - 1$, and 1, in that order. Consequently the terms on the right are independent chi-square variables with $n - k, k - 1$, and 1 degree of freedom, respectively—under the null hypothesis. Therefore, the ratio

$$F = \frac{\dfrac{1}{k-1}\sum n_i(\bar{X}_i - \bar{X})^2}{\dfrac{1}{n-k}\sum\sum(X_{ij} - \bar{X}_i)^2}$$

has the F distribution $(k - 1, n - k)$ under the null hypothesis, and this distribution is used to set the constant K in the test $F > K$ corresponding to a given size of type I error.

EXAMPLE 9–4.   Consider the following data:

n_i	X_{ij}	$\bar{X}_i$	$\sum_j (X_{ij} - \bar{X}_i)^2$
4	11, 9, 13, 11	11	8
6	25, 28, 31, 27, 30, 33	29	42
5	19, 23, 19, 21, 20	20.4	11.2
$n = 15$			$61.2 = 918/15$.

The pooled variance (unbiased variance estimate based on within samples variation) is

$$s^2 = \frac{1}{15 - 3}(61.2) = 5.1.$$

The mean $\bar{X}$ of all the data is $64/3$, and the total sum of squares about $\bar{X}$ divides as follows:

$$\frac{12,680}{15} = \frac{918}{15} + \frac{11,762}{15}.$$

The second term divided by $k - 1 = 2$ is much too large, in comparison with s^2 (the latter being an unbiased estimate of σ^2 even if the population means are not equal). The ratio is

$$F = \frac{\dfrac{1}{3-1}\cdot\dfrac{11,762}{15}}{\dfrac{1}{15-3}\cdot\dfrac{918}{15}} \doteq 77.$$

The ninety-fifth percentile of the F distribution with parameters $(2, 12)$ is 3.89, and hence the null hypothesis of no difference in population means is rejected at the 5 per cent level.

Operating characteristics have been worked out in terms of the noncentral F distribution for various analysis of variance tests, but these will not be presented here.[6]

Problems

9–14. Construct the likelihood ratio test for equality of variances.

9–15. Construct the likelihood ratio test for $\theta_i = 0$, $i = 1, \ldots, k$ against the alternative that at least one θ_i is not zero.

9–16. Verify that the cross-product terms in the partition of $\sum \sum (X_{ij} - \mu)^2$ vanish, and also verify the ranks given.

9–17. Apply the test for equality of means to the data in Problem 9–7. Does your conclusion agree with that based on regression theory (that is, with the result of testing $\beta = 0$)?

9.2.2   Two Factors—One Observation per Cell

A simple extension of the model discussed in the preceding section is one in which two "factors" are provided for, say, factor A and factor B. Each combination of a level of factor A and a level of factor B is referred to as a *treatment*; and corresponding to each treatment there may be several observations. Before considering this general situation in Section 9.2.3, consider first the case in which just one observation per treatment is available.

Denote by X_{ij} the single observation corresponding to the ith level of factor A and the jth level of factor B. These observations are assumed to be independently and normally distributed with common variance σ^2. Let $\mu_{ij} = E(X_{ij})$, and define

$$\mu_{i\cdot} = \frac{1}{n} \sum_j \mu_{ij}, \qquad \mu_{\cdot j} = \frac{1}{m} \sum_i \mu_{ij}, \qquad \mu = \frac{1}{mn} \sum_j \sum_i \mu_{ij},$$

where sums on i extend from 1 to m, the number of levels of factor A, and sums on j extend from 1 to n, the number of levels of factor B. It is assumed that μ_{ij} can be expressed in the form

$$\mu_{ij} = \mu + \theta_i + \phi_j, \qquad \text{where} \qquad \sum_i \theta_i = \sum_j \phi_j = 0,$$

which implies that

$$\theta_i = \mu_{i\cdot} - \mu, \qquad \phi_j = \mu_{\cdot j} - \mu.$$

---

[6] See Eisenhart, C., Hastay, H. W., and Wallis, W. A. (eds.), *Techniques of Statistical Analysis,* New York: McGraw-Hill, 1947.

This assumption about μ_{ij} is not necessarily fulfilled; the effects of factor A and factor B may not contribute additively to the mean of X_{ij}. In general an "interaction" term would have to be included to incorporate into the model what frequently happens—the effect of factor A, say, is different, when factor B is present than when it is not. This more general model can be treated when there are several observations per cell, as in Section 9.2.3. For the present, there is assumed to be *no interaction*.

The assumed model involves $m + n + 2$ parameters: $\mu, \theta_1, \ldots, \theta_m$, $\phi_1, \ldots, \phi_n$, and σ^2. Their maximum likelihood estimates are

$$\hat{\mu} = \bar{X}, \qquad \hat{\theta}_i = \bar{X}_i. - \bar{X}, \qquad \hat{\phi}_j = \bar{X}_{.j} - \bar{X}$$

and

$$\hat{\sigma}^2 = \frac{1}{mn} \sum \sum [X_{ij} - (\bar{X}_i. - \bar{X}) - (\bar{X}_{.j} - \bar{X}) - \bar{X}]^2,$$

where

$$\bar{X}_i. = \frac{1}{n} \sum_j X_{ij}, \qquad \bar{X}_{.j} = \frac{1}{m} \sum_i X_{ij},$$

and

$$\bar{X} = \frac{1}{mn} \sum \sum X_{ij} = \frac{1}{m} \sum_i \bar{X}_i. = \frac{1}{n} \sum_j \bar{X}_{.j}.$$

These estimates suggest the following partition:

$$\sum \sum (X_{ij} - \mu_{ij})^2 = mn\hat{\sigma}^2 + mn(\bar{X} - \mu)^2 + n \sum (\bar{X}_i. - \bar{X} - \theta_i)^2$$
$$+ m \sum (\bar{X}_{.j} - \bar{X} - \phi_j)^2.$$

(Again all cross-product terms drop out when summed.) The ranks of the quadratic forms on the right are, respectively: $mn - m - n + 1, 1, m - 1$, and $n - 1$, which add up to the rank mn on the left. [The rank of $\hat{\sigma}^2$ is the number of terms, mn, less the number of linear relations; the sum of $(X_{ij} - \mu_{ij})$ from 1 to m on i yields zero for each j, and the sum from 1 to n on j yields zero for each i, but these $m + n$ relations are not completely independent. One is implied by the other $m + n - 1$, so the rank is $mn - (m + n - 1)$.] Cochran's theorem then asserts that, when divided by σ^2, the terms on the right in the partition have independent chi-square distributions with $(m - 1)(n - 1), 1, (m - 1)$, and $(n - 1)$ degrees of freedom, respectively.

Likelihood ratio tests for $\theta_i = 0$ and for $\phi_j = 0$ have the critical regions $F_\theta >$ constant and $F_\phi >$ constant, respectively, where

$$F_\theta = \frac{\frac{n}{m-1} \sum (\bar{X}_i. - \bar{X})^2}{\frac{1}{(m-1)(n-1)} \sum \sum (X_{ij} - \bar{X}_i. - \bar{X}_{.j} + \bar{X})^2}$$

and

$$F_\phi = \frac{\dfrac{m}{n-1} \sum (\overline{X}_{\cdot j} - \overline{X})^2}{\dfrac{1}{(m-1)(n-1)} \sum \sum (X_{ij} - \overline{X}_{i\cdot} - \overline{X}_{\cdot j} + \overline{X})^2} .$$

The ratio F_θ has a noncentral F distribution with $(m - 1, mn - m - n + 1)$ degrees of freedom, and under the null hypothesis that $\theta_i = 0$ for all i, it has a central F distribution. Thus the significance level α of the test $F_\theta >$ constant determines the constant used as a rejection limit through the F distribution, and the power function comes from the noncentral F distribution. Similar statements apply to the ratio F_ϕ and the null hypothesis that $\phi_j = 0$ for all j.

Although the test ratios are not independent, the distribution of F_θ does not depend on the ϕ's, and the distribution of F_ϕ does not depend on the θ's. Therefore, even if factor A is not the same at all levels, a test for factor B can be carried out, and vice versa.

EXAMPLE 9–5. Consider two factors with three levels each, and assume that one observation per cell is obtained, with the results as shown in the following array:

		Factor B			$\overline{X}_{i\cdot}$	$(\overline{X}_{i\cdot} - \overline{X})$
		Level 1	Level 2	Level 3		
Factor A	level 1	3	5	4	4	−7
	level 2	11	10	12	11	0
	level 3	16	21	17	18	7
	$\overline{X}_{\cdot j}$	10	12	11	$\overline{X} = 11$	
	$(\overline{X}_{\cdot j} - \overline{X})$	−1	1	0		

The sum of squared deviations about $\overline{X}$ is 312, which is decomposed as follows:

$$312 = 12 + 294 + 6.$$

The first term, 12, divided by $(3 - 1)(3 - 1) = 4$ gives an unbiased estimate of σ^2 whether or not θ_i and ϕ_j are zero. The second term, 294, divided by $(3 - 1)$, related to factor A, exceeds 3 by a considerable amount. The ratio is

$$\frac{294(3 - 1)}{12/4} = 49.$$

Since this exceeds 6.94, the ninety-fifth percentile of the F distribution with $(2, 4)$ degrees of freedom, the hypothesis that $\theta_i = 0$ for all i is rejected at the 5 per cent level. On the other hand, the ratio related to factor B is

$$\frac{6/(3 - 1)}{12/4} = 1,$$

so the hypothesis that $\phi_j = 0$ for all j is accepted at any level.

9.2.3 Two Factors with Interaction

Consider again factors A and B with m and n levels, respectively, but assume now that in the "cell" corresponding to the ith level of A and the jth level of B there are several observations:

$$X_{ij1}, X_{ij2}, \ldots, X_{ijp},$$

the same number p in each cell, for simplicity. The notation is otherwise as it was in Section 9.2.2 except that

$$\mu_{ij} = \mu + \theta_i + \phi_j + \psi_{ij},$$

and there is now an additional subscript to keep track of:

$$\bar{X} = \frac{1}{mnp} \sum\sum\sum X_{ijk}, \qquad \bar{X}_{i..} = \frac{1}{np} \sum\sum X_{ijk}, \qquad \bar{X}_{ij.} = \frac{1}{p} \sum X_{ijk},$$

and so on. It is assumed that

$$\sum \theta_i = \sum \phi_j = \sum_i \psi_{ij} = \sum_j \psi_{ij} = 0.$$

Maximum likelihood estimates (assuming the usual normal populations with common variance σ^2) are as follows:

$$\hat{\theta}_i = \bar{X}_{i..} - \bar{X}, \qquad \hat{\phi}_j = \bar{X}_{.j.} - \bar{X}, \qquad \hat{\mu} = \bar{X},$$

$$\hat{\psi}_{ij} = \bar{X}_{ij.} - (\bar{X}_{i..} - \bar{X}) - (\bar{X}_{.j.} - \bar{X}) - \bar{X},$$

$$\hat{\sigma}^2 = \frac{1}{mnp} \sum\sum\sum (X_{ijk} - \bar{X}_{ij.})^2.$$

The following partition is used:

$$\sum\sum\sum (X_{ijk} - \mu_{ij})^2 = \sum\sum\sum (X_{ijk} - \bar{X}_{ij.})^2$$

$$+ p \sum\sum (\bar{X}_{ij.} + \bar{X} - \bar{X}_{i..} - \bar{X}_{.j.} - \psi_{ij})^2$$

$$+ mnp(\bar{X} - \mu)^2 + np \sum (\bar{X}_{i..} - \bar{X} - \theta_i)^2$$

$$+ mp \sum (\bar{X}_{.j.} - \bar{X} - \phi_j)^2.$$

(Once more cross-product terms drop out when summed.) Upon division by σ^2, the terms of the partition are seen to have independent chi-square distributions; the rank relationship, which also then gives the degrees of freedom in each case, is as follows:

$$mnp = mn(p - 1) + (m - 1)(n - 1) + 1 + (m - 1) + (n - 1).$$

Under the hypothesis $\psi_{ij} = 0$, the ratio

$$F_\psi = \frac{\dfrac{p}{(m-1)(n-1)} \sum \sum (\bar{X}_{ij.} - \bar{X}_{i..} - \bar{X}_{.j.} + \bar{X})^2}{\dfrac{1}{mn(p-1)} \sum \sum \sum (X_{ijk} - \bar{X}_{ij.})^2}$$

has the F distribution with parameters $[(m - 1)(n - 1), mn(p - 1)]$, independent of any assumption about θ_i or ϕ_j. The denominator has a distribution depending only on σ^2 and can therefore be used as a measuring stick to determine whether the numerator is too large, indicating a presence of interaction. The test $\psi_{ij} = 0$, for all i and j, is then to reject this hypothesis if $F_\psi >$ constant.

The denominator of F is based only on the variation of the observations in the cells about the corresponding cell means and has in it no component of cell-to-cell variation. If $\psi_{ij} = 0$, on the other hand, a more precise estimate of σ^2 can be obtained by pooling the estimates in numerator and denominator of F_ψ, to obtain

$$\frac{1}{mnp - m - n + 1} \sum \sum \sum (X_{ijk} - \bar{X}_{i..} - \bar{X}_{.j.} + \bar{X})^2.$$

This then could be used in place of the less precise estimate based on $\hat{\sigma}^2$ as a denominator for an F_θ or an F_ϕ to test $\theta_i = 0$ or $\phi_j = 0$. These latter tests can be carried out even in the *presence* of interaction using the same denominator as in F_ψ, which is an important feature of the technique.

9.2.4   A Model with Randomly Drawn Levels

In the models considered so far, conclusions are of the form that factor A, say, has no effect when introduced at levels $1, 2, \ldots, m$. One has no right to infer, however, that if a different level of factor A be used, there is still no effect. For example, if factor A is the operator of a machine, and the tests used persons a, b, and c, then no conclusion can be drawn about the operator effect when using persons d and e.

It is sometimes desirable to think of the particular operators used as a sample from a population of possible operators, in order to conclude that the operator has no effect, rather than just that the particular operators used have no effect. For a single factor, with observations $X_{i1}, \ldots, X_{in_i}$ at level i, consider the model in which it is assumed that

$$X_{ij} = \mu + Y_i + Z_{ij},$$

where $Y_1, \ldots, Y_k, Z_{11}, \ldots, Z_{kn_k}$ are independent normal variables with zero means. The quantity Z_{ij} denotes the random variation present with each observation at each level, and Y_i denotes the *random* contribution to X_{ij} associated with the factor at level i. Another instance in which this model might be appropriate is in the experimental determination of a chemical or physical property of a product that comes in batches or sheets, in which there is randomness from batch to batch or sheet to sheet and also randomness in determination of the property of a single batch or sheet, the latter caused either by the measuring process itself or by variations from point to point in the batch or sheet.

It is assumed that var $Y_i = \omega^2$ and var $Z_{ij} = \sigma^2$, so that var $X_{ij} = \omega^2 + \sigma^2$. The observations are not independent in this model, since, for instance,

$$E[(X_{11} - \mu)(X_{12} - \mu)] = E[(Y_1 + Z_{11})(Y_1 + Z_{12})] = E(Y_1^2) = \omega^2.$$

This is not zero unless it happens that $\omega^2 = 0$, which would imply that Y_i is really a constant for all observations and all levels. That is, $\omega^2 = 0$ is the hypothesis that the factor being tested has "no effect" (that is, a constant effect).

We use the following notation:

$$\bar{X}_i = \frac{1}{n_i} \sum_j X_{ij}, \qquad \bar{Z}_i = \frac{1}{n_i} \sum_j Z_{ij} = \bar{X}_i - (\mu + Y_i),$$

$$n = \sum n_i, \qquad \bar{Y} = \frac{1}{n} \sum_i n_i Y_i, \qquad \bar{X} = \frac{1}{n} \sum_i n_i \bar{X}_i,$$

and

$$\bar{Z} = \frac{1}{n} \sum_i n_i \bar{Z}_i = \bar{X} - (\mu + \bar{Y}).$$

As in the linear model for the single classification problem, we have the identity:

$$\sum \sum (X_{ij} - \mu)^2 = \sum \sum (X_{ij} - \bar{X}_i)^2 + \sum n_i(\bar{X}_i - \bar{X})^2 + n(\bar{X} - \mu)^2.$$

However, since the X_{ij} are not independent, the quantity on the left is not in general a chi-square variable when divided by var X_{ij}. But if $\omega^2 = 0$, the X_{ij} are uncorrelated and (because they are normal) independent, with variance σ^2; division of the equation by σ^2 results in a chi-square variable on the left, with n degrees of freedom, and by Cochran's theorem, independent chi-square distributions on the right, with $n - k$, $k - 1$, and 1 degree of freedom in that order. So, under the null hypothesis of *no* effect introduced by the factor, the ratio

$$F = \frac{\dfrac{1}{k-1} \sum n_i (\bar{X}_i - \bar{X})^2}{\dfrac{1}{n-k} \sum \sum (X_{ij} - \bar{X}_i)^2}$$

has the F distribution with parameters $(k - 1, n - k)$.

Now, since $X_{ij} - \bar{X}_i = Z_{ij} - \bar{Z}_i$, and since for each i the sum on j, $\sum (Z_{ij} - \bar{Z}_i)^2 / \sigma^2$, has the chi-square distribution with $n_i - 1$ degrees of freedom (being of the form $n s_z^2 / \sigma^2$ for a sample of size n_i from a normal population), it then follows that the quantity

$$\sum \sum \frac{(X_{ij} - \bar{X}_i)^2}{\sigma^2} = \sum \sum \frac{(Z_{ij} - \bar{Z}_i)^2}{\sigma^2}$$

is the sum of k independent chi-square variables and is therefore also chi square, with $(n_1 - 1) + \cdots + (n_k - 1) = n - k$ degrees of freedom, even if $\omega^2 \neq 0$. The denominator of F is then an estimate of σ^2 independent of the null hypothesis. The numerator, on the other hand, depends on the assumption about the variance of Y_i. Its expected value is

$$\sigma^2 + \frac{n\omega^2 [1 - \sum (n_i/n)^2]}{k - 1},$$

which is smallest when $\omega^2 = 0$. So, if the ratio F is too large as determined by a given significance level and the F table, the hypothesis of no effect from the factor is rejected.

It is interesting that the test statistic used and the critical region $F >$ constant for testing $\omega^2 = 0$ are identical with those used in the linear hypothesis model of Section 9.2.1. The model is different, however, and the conclusion here has to do with the population of possible operators or batches (etc.) rather than with just the particular operators or batches used in the test.

A similar model can be used in a two-factor problem. Given the observation X_{ij} corresponding to the ith level of factor A and the jth level of factor B, it would be assumed that X_{ij} can be represented in the form

$$X_{ij} = \mu + Y_i + Z_i + W_{ij},$$

where W_{ij}, Y_i, Z_j (for $i = 1, \ldots, m$ and $j = 1, \ldots, n$) are independent normal random variables with zero means. An analysis similar to that of the one-factor problem just given shows that again the F ratios used in the linear hypothesis model are appropriate. But again there is a difference in how the phrase "no effect" is interpreted. Details are omitted.

Problems

9–18. Using the data in the accompanying table, test the effects of the two factors.

		Level of Factor A				
		1	2	3	4	5
	1	53	56	45	52	49
Level of	2	47	50	47	47	53
Factor B	3	57	63	54	57	58
	4	45	52	42	41	48

9–19. Using the three observations per cell given, test for no interaction between factors. Test also the hypotheses that the factors have no effect.

		Machine			
		A	B	C	D
	1	59	61	48	47
		43	49	47	40
		63	52	58	51
	2	60	49	40	38
Operator		51	52	48	50
		48	55	56	41
	3	63	58	46	48
		60	48	53	40
		57	56	51	50

9–20. Verify the expression given in the text for the expected value of $\sum n_i(\bar{X}_i - \bar{X})^2/(k - 1)$. [Write $\bar{X}_i - \bar{X} = U_i - \bar{U}$, where $U_i = Y_i + \bar{Z}_i$, and note that $\sum n_i(U_i - \bar{U})^2 = \sum n_i U_i^2 - n\bar{U}^2$, where $\bar{U} = \sum n_i U_i/n$.]

9.2.5 Other Designs

More than two factors can be considered. Indeed, additional factors must be considered if there is any chance that they are confounding the results. For the case of three factors, at m, n, and p levels, with q observations per treatment, a linear model would be of the form

$$E(X_{ijk}) = \mu + \alpha_i + \beta_j + \gamma_k + \zeta_{ij} + \xi_{jk} + \eta_{ki} + \delta_{ijk},$$

with the usual normalizing conditions that sums of these quantities (except μ) with respect to any one of the pertinent subscripts are zero. The α_i, β_j, and γ_k are factor effects, the ζ_{ij}, ξ_{ki}, and η_{jk} are second-order interactions, and

δ_{ijk} is a third-order interaction—a contribution present, when all three factors are involved, which would not be present for any pair of factors. Maximum likelihood estimates are

$$\hat{\mu} = \bar{X}, \qquad \hat{\alpha}_i = \bar{X}_i\ldots - \bar{X}, \ldots,$$

$$\hat{\zeta}_{ij} = \bar{X}_{ij}.. - \bar{X}_i\ldots - \bar{X}._j.. + \bar{X}, \ldots,$$

$$\hat{\delta}_{ijk} = \bar{X}_{ijk}. - \bar{X}_{ij}.. - \bar{X}_{i\cdot k}. - \bar{X}._{jk}. + \bar{X}._j.. + \bar{X}_i\ldots + \bar{X}.._k. - \bar{X}.$$

To carry out a test for the various factors and interactions, it would be necessary to have *mnpq* observations. This could be more observations than are easily obtainable, and it is both interesting and useful that it is possible to test for one of the three factors in the presence of the other two with even fewer than the *mnp* observations that would be needed for one observation per cell. (With fewer observations the sensitivity of the test is reduced, but the point is that there *is* a test.)

Suppose that the three factors are machines, operators, and time periods, and that there are four levels of each. Instead of obtaining a performance figure for each of the 64 combinations of machine, operator, and time period, one obtains the 16 observations as indicated in the accompanying table, each operator working once in each time period and once on each machine. The letter in the array indicates the machine to be used. An array (Latin) of the letters *A, B, C, D* such as is shown, with the property that no letter appears more than once in any column or in any row, is called a *Latin square*; these have been extensively studied, computed, and tabulated. (Cf. References [5] and [11].)

		Time Period			
		1	2	3	4
	1	*A*	*B*	*C*	*D*
	2	*B*	*C*	*D*	*A*
Operator	3	*C*	*D*	*A*	*B*
	4	*D*	*A*	*B*	*C*

The observations in a linear model are assumed to be of the form

$$X_{ij(k)} = \mu + \alpha_i + \beta_j + \gamma_k + Y_{ijk}$$

(no interactions), where the level (k) of the third factor is determined by i, j, and the particular Latin square used. The breakup used is indicated in the accompanying table.

	Sum of Squares	Degrees of Freedom
Rows	$m \sum (\bar{X}_{i\cdot} - \bar{X} - \alpha_i)^2$	$m - 1$
Columns	$m \sum (\bar{X}_{\cdot j} - \bar{X} - \beta_j)^2$	$m - 1$
"Letters"	$m \sum (\bar{X}_{(k)} - \bar{X} - \gamma_k)^2$	$m - 1$
Mean	$m^2 (\bar{X} - \mu)^2$	1
Residual	$\sum \sum (X_{ij(k)} - \bar{X}_{i\cdot} - \bar{X}_{\cdot j} - \bar{X}_{(k)} + 2\bar{X})^2$	$(m - 2)(m - 1)$
Total	$\sum \sum (X_{ij(k)} - \mu_{ij})^2$	m^2

The numbers in the rightmost column denote the number of degrees of freedom of the corresponding chi-square distribution (when the term in question is divided by σ^2). The mean $\bar{X}_{(k)}$ denotes the average of all entries in the table that are taken at the kth level of the third factor (letters).

Four factors can be considered simultaneously using a "Latin-Greco square," in which the levels of factor III are entered as Latin letters and the levels of factor IV are entered as Greek letters. Each level of each factor appears once with each level of each other factor. A three-by-three square of this type (corresponding to three levels of each of four factors) is shown at the right

		\	Factor 2	
		1	2	3
	1	$A\alpha$	$B\beta$	$C\gamma$
Factor 1	2	$B\gamma$	$C\alpha$	$A\beta$
	3	$C\beta$	$A\gamma$	$B\alpha$

The study of designs of experiments to handle many factors while permitting testing one of them has been very extensive but will not be developed further here. These methods are characteristically different from methods in which a factor is studied by keeping all other factors at fixed levels. In the statistical approach, these other factors are allowed to vary, and the results can be exploited to make inferences concerning these other factors as well as the one of interest.

9.3   A General Linear Model

It is possible to subsume the regression, analysis of variance, and analysis of covariance problems under a rather general linear model. The estimation, testing, and distribution problems can be studied in this general model and the general results then made specific for the various applications. (Such a program is carried out in the excellent book of Scheffé [19].) It is our purpose here simply to introduce the model as a hint of what might then be done.

Consider the n observations $Y_1, Y_2, \ldots, Y_n$ and suppose that a given observation is made up as follows:

$$Y_i = x_{1i}\beta_1 + \cdots + x_{pi}\beta_p + \epsilon_i, \qquad i = 1, \ldots, n, \quad p < n.$$

Introducing the matrix notation:

$$Y = \begin{pmatrix} Y_1 \\ \vdots \\ Y_n \end{pmatrix}, \qquad X = \begin{pmatrix} x_{11} & \cdots & x_{1n} \\ \vdots & & \vdots \\ x_{p1} & \cdots & x_{pn} \end{pmatrix}, \qquad \epsilon = \begin{pmatrix} \epsilon_1 \\ \vdots \\ \epsilon_n \end{pmatrix}, \qquad \beta = \begin{pmatrix} \beta_1 \\ \vdots \\ \beta_p \end{pmatrix},$$

the makeup of Y can be exhibited in this way:

$$Y = X'\beta + \epsilon.$$

It is assumed that ϵ is multivariate with zero mean vector and covariance matrix $\sigma^2 I$, where I is the n-by-n identity matrix. Then Y is multivariate normal with the same covariance matrix and mean vector $\mu = EY = X'\beta$. The density function of Y is

$$f_Y(y) = (2\pi\sigma^2)^{-n/2} \exp\left[\frac{-(y - \mu)'(y - \mu)}{2\sigma^2} \right].$$

Most problems in regression and analysis of variance and covariance can be put into the above framework. In regression problems the quantities x_{ij} are functions of selected values of the controlled variable. In analysis of variance problems, they are either 1 or 0 (usually), corresponding to the presence or absence of a factor in the observation. In analysis of covariance problems there are x's of both kinds.

EXAMPLE 9–6. Consider a problem of quadratic regression, in which it is assumed that $E(Y_i) = a + bt_i + ct_i^2$. (Take the simple case of one observation at each t_i.) The following identification is then made:

$$x_{1i} = 1, \qquad x_{2i} = t_i, \qquad x_{3i} = t_i^2, \qquad a = \beta_1, \qquad b = \beta_2, \qquad c = \beta_3.$$

This reduces the general model to this particular regression problem.

EXAMPLE 9–7. Consider a single classification analysis of variance problem with n_i observations at the ith level of the single factor. Here the observations, given earlier in a double array, are strung out:

$$Y' = (Y_{11}, Y_{12}, \ldots, Y_{1n_1}, Y_{21}, \ldots, Y_{kn_k}),$$

$$\epsilon = (\epsilon_{11}, \epsilon_{12}, \ldots, \epsilon_{1n_i}, \ldots, \epsilon_{kn_k}).$$

The x's are either 0 or 1. For the single classification problem it is assumed that observations are made up as follows:

$$Y_{ij} = \mu + \theta_i + \epsilon_{ij}, \qquad i = 1, \ldots, k, \qquad j = 1, \ldots, n_i.$$

The identification

$$\beta_1 = \theta_1, \ldots, \qquad \beta_k = \theta_k, \qquad \beta_{k+1} = \mu,$$

$$x_{1ij} = \begin{cases} 1, & \text{for } i = 1, \quad j = 1, \ldots, n_1 \\ 0, & \text{for } i \neq 1, \end{cases}$$

$$\vdots \qquad\qquad \vdots$$

$$x_{kij} = \begin{cases} 1, & \text{for } i = k, \quad j = 1, \ldots, n_k \\ 0, & \text{for } i \neq k, \end{cases}$$

$$x_{(k+1)ij} = 1$$

reduces the general model to the single classification problem. Sums from $i = 1$ to n in the general model correspond here to double sums, from $i = 1$ to k and from $j = 1$ to n_i.

Consider now the possible estimates b_i for β_i, and form $X'b$ as an estimate of $X'\beta$. The vector

$$e = Y - X'b$$

can be thought of as an estimate of the error vector ϵ, with squared "norm" given by

$$\sum_{i=1}^{n} e_i^2 = e'e = (Y - X'b)'(Y - X'b)$$

$$= \sum_{i=1}^{n} \left\{ Y_i - \sum_{j=1}^{p} x_{ji}b_j \right\}^2.$$

A *least squares estimate* of β is a value $b = \hat{\beta}$ which minimizes this norm. For such a value it must be that

$$\left. \frac{\partial(e'e)}{\partial b_v} \right|_{b=\beta} = -2 \sum_{i=1}^{n} \left\{ Y_i - \sum_{j=1}^{p} x_{ji}\beta_j \right\} x_{vi} = 0$$

for $v = 1, \ldots, p$. This condition can be written in matrix form:

$$XX'\hat{\beta} = XY.$$

The equations represented here are called the *normal equations* of the least squares problem.

The minimum value of $e'e$ is achieved by putting $b = \hat{\beta}$, and is therefore

$$(Y - X'\hat{\beta})'(Y - X'\hat{\beta}) = Y'Y - \hat{\beta}'XY - Y'X'\hat{\beta} + \hat{\beta}'XX'\hat{\beta}$$

$$= Y'Y - \hat{\beta}'XY + [\hat{\beta}'(XX'\hat{\beta} - XY)]'$$

$$= \sum_{i=1}^{n} Y_i^2 - \sum_{v=1}^{k} \hat{\beta}_v \sum_{i=1}^{n} x_{vi} Y_i.$$

This is the *error sum of squares*.

If the rank of X is p, called the case of *full rank*, the matrix XX' is non-singular (as well as square and symmetric) and can be inverted. The solution of the normal equations is then unique:

$$\hat{\beta} = (XX')^{-1}XY.$$

The covariance matrix of this least squares solution is readily computed in terms of $S = XX'$:

$$M_{\hat{\beta}} = (S^{-1}X)M_Y(S^{-1}X)' = \sigma^2 S^{-1}XX'S^{-1} = \sigma^2 S^{-1}.$$

EXAMPLE 9–8.   Consider the linear regression problem with one observation at each of $x_1, \ldots, x_n$. In this problem the identification with the general model is as follows:

$$X = \begin{pmatrix} 1 & 1 & \cdots & 1 \\ x_1 & x_2 & \cdots & x_n \end{pmatrix}, \qquad \beta = \begin{pmatrix} \alpha \\ \beta \end{pmatrix}, \qquad X' = \begin{pmatrix} 1 & x_1 \\ \vdots & \vdots \\ 1 & x_n \end{pmatrix},$$

and

$$XX' = \begin{pmatrix} n & \sum x_i \\ \sum x_i & \sum x_i^2 \end{pmatrix}, \qquad XY = \begin{pmatrix} \sum Y_i \\ \sum x_i Y_i \end{pmatrix}.$$

The normal equations become

$$\begin{pmatrix} na + b \sum x_i \\ a \sum x_i + b \sum x_i^2 \end{pmatrix} = \begin{pmatrix} \sum Y_i \\ \sum x_i Y_i \end{pmatrix}.$$

The solution $a = \hat{\alpha}$ and $b = \hat{\beta}$ is then unique (X is of full rank and XX' can be inverted) if the x_i's are not all the same:

$$(XX')^{-1} = \frac{1}{n^2 s_x^2} \begin{pmatrix} \sum x_i^2 & -\sum x_i \\ -\sum x_i & n \end{pmatrix}.$$

With this one finds

$$\hat{\beta} = \frac{1}{n s_x^2} \begin{pmatrix} \bar{Y} \sum x_i^2 - \bar{x} \sum x_i Y_i \\ \sum x_i Y_i - n \bar{x} \bar{Y} \end{pmatrix},$$

giving again the estimates obtained in Section 9.1. Their variances and covariances are found as the elements of the matrix $\sigma^2 S^{-1}$:

$$\operatorname{var} \hat{\alpha} = \frac{\sigma^2 \sum x_i^2}{n^2 s_x^2}, \qquad \operatorname{var} \hat{\beta} = \frac{\sigma^2}{n s_x^2},$$

and

$$\operatorname{cov}(\hat{\alpha}, \hat{\beta}) = -\frac{\sigma^2 \sum x_i}{n^2 s_x^2}.$$

(Notice that if $\bar{x} = 0$, $\hat{\alpha}$ and $\hat{\beta}$ are uncorrelated.)

It is to be noted (in the full rank case, still) that the least squares estimate $\hat{\beta}$ is a linear transformation of Y. That is, each component of $\hat{\beta}$ is a *linear* function of the observations:

$$\hat{\beta} = (S^{-1}X)Y.$$

Further, it is an *unbiased* estimate (so that each component $\hat{\beta}_i$ is unbiased):

$$E(\hat{\beta}) = (S^{-1}X)E(Y) = S^{-1}XX'\beta = \beta.$$

The Gauss–Markov theorem states that the least squares estimate, in the class of unbiased, linear estimates, has a minimum variance property: the variances of its components are (simultaneously) smallest. This may be seen as follows.

Consider an arbitrary linear estimate of β of the form $\beta^* = AY$, and define B by

$$\beta^* - \hat{\beta} = (A - S^{-1}X)Y \equiv BY.$$

The requirement that β^* be *unbiased*:

$$E(\beta^*) = E[(B + S^{-1}X)Y] = BX'\beta + S^{-1}XX'\beta = BX'\beta + \beta = \beta,$$

implies that BX' must be 0. The second moment matrix is then

$$M_{\beta^*} = \sigma^2(B + S^{-1}X)(B + S^{-1}X)' = \sigma^2(BB' + S^{-1}).$$

Since S^{-1} is constant and the diagonal elements of BB' are

$$(BB')_{ii} = b_{i1}^2 + \cdots + b_{in}^2,$$

the smallest variances of the β_i^* are clearly achieved for $B = 0$ (which satisfies $BX' = 0$), or $\beta^* = \hat{\beta}$.

It is also true (see Problem 9–22) that there is a unique unbiased, minimum variance, linear estimate of any linear function $c'\beta$ which has an unbiased linear estimate, and that this minimum variance estimate is $c'\hat{\beta}$, where $\hat{\beta}$ is the least squares estimate of β.

Obtaining the maximum likelihood estimate of β requires use of the distribution of the observations Y which has not been used in the above discussion of least squares, unbiasedness, and minimum variance. It was assumed at the outset that the observations were normal—that Y is multivariate normal, and the likelihood function has the logarithm

$$\log L(\beta, \sigma^2) = -\frac{n}{2}(\log 2\pi + \log \sigma^2) - \frac{1}{2\sigma^2}(Y - X'\beta)'(Y - X'\beta).$$

It is clear from the form of this expression that minimization with respect to

(β, σ^2) produces maximum likelihood estimates ($\hat{\beta}$, $\hat{\sigma}^2$) of which $\hat{\beta}$ is precisely the least squares estimate, and $\hat{\sigma}^2$ is the error sum of squares divided by n:

$$\hat{\sigma}^2 = \frac{1}{n}(Y - X'\beta)'(Y - X'\beta) = \frac{1}{n}\min(e'e).$$

Thus, least squares estimates are maximum likelihood estimates in the normal case.

We have touched briefly on some of the aspects of estimation in the general linear model. Tests of hypotheses of the kind usually encountered can be phrased in terms of linear subspaces of the parameter space. Distribution problems can be handled quite generally to include the various results obtained earlier by Cochran's theorem. (See Scheffé [19] for such developments.)

Problems

9–21. Verify the "degrees of freedom" results shown in the table for the Latin square problem, Section 9.2.5.

9–22. Using the derivation of the Gauss–Markov theorem as a guide, verify the claim made concerning the minimum variance, unbiased estimate of $c'\beta$, where c' is a given vector of constants.

REFERENCES

[1] Anderson, T. W., *An Introduction to Multivariate Statistical Analysis*. New York: Wiley, 1958.

[2] Blackwell, D., and Girshick, M., *Theory of Games and Statistical Decisions*. New York: Wiley, 1954.

[3] Chernoff, H., and Moses, L., *Elementary Decision Theory*. New York: Wiley, 1959.

[4] Cramér, H., *Mathematical Methods of Statistics*. Princeton, New Jersey: Princeton Univ. Press, 1946.

[5] Cochran, W., and Cox, G., *Experimental Designs*, 2nd ed. New York: Wiley, 1957.

[6] Feller, W., *An Introduction to Probability Theory and Its Applications*, Vol. I, 2nd ed. New York: Wiley, 1957.

[7] Fraser, D. A. S., *Nonparametric Methods in Statistics*. New York: Wiley, 1957.

[8] Gnedenko, B. V., *The Theory of Probability*. New York: Chelsea, 1962.

[9] Hanson, M., Hurwitz, W., and Madow, W., *Sample Survey Methods and Theory*, Vol. I and Vol. II. New York: Wiley, 1953.

[10] Hogg, R., and Craig, A., *Introduction to Mathematical Statistics*, 2nd ed. New York: Macmillan, 1965.

[11] Kempthorne, O., *The Design and Analysis of Experiments*. New York: Wiley, 1952.

[12] Kendall, M. G., and Stuart, A., *The Advanced Theory of Statistics*, Vol. I (2nd ed.), 1963; Vol. II, 1961; Vol. III, 1966. New York: Hafner.

[13] Lehmann, E., *Testing Statistical Hypotheses*. New York: Wiley, 1952.

[14] Lindley, D. V., *Introduction to Probability and Statistics*, Parts I and II. Cambridge, England: Cambridge Univ. Press, 1965.

[15] Loève, M., *Probability Theory*, 3rd ed. New York: Van Nostrand, 1963.

[16] Owen, D. B., *Handbook of Statistical Tables*. Reading, Massachusetts: Addison–Wesley, 1962.

[17] Parzen, E., *Modern Probability Theory and Its Applications*. New York: Wiley, 1960.

[18] Rao, C. R., *Linear Statistical Inference and Its Applications*. New York: Wiley, 1965.

[19] Scheffé, H., *The Analysis of Variance*. New York: Wiley, 1959.

[20] Wald, A., *Sequential Analysis*. New York: Wiley, 1947.

[21] Wald, A., *Statistical Decision Functions*. New York: Wiley, 1950.

[22] Wilks, S. S., *Mathematical Statistics*. New York: Wiley, 1962.

APPENDIX—TABLES

Table I. Values of the Standard Normal Distribution Function

$$\Phi(z) = \int_{-\infty}^{z} (1/\sqrt{2\pi}) \, exp \, (-u^2/2) \, du = P(Z \le z)$$

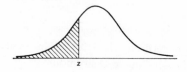

z	0	1	2	3	4	5	6	7	8	9
−3.	.0013	.0010	.0007	.0005	.0003	.0002	.0002	.0001	.0001	.0000
−2.9	.0019	.0018	.0017	.0017	.0016	.0016	.0015	.0015	.0014	.0014
−2.8	.0026	.0025	.0024	.0023	.0023	.0022	.0021	.0021	.0020	.0019
−2.7	.0035	.0034	.0033	.0032	.0031	.0030	.0029	.0028	.0027	.0026
−2.6	.0047	.0045	.0044	.0043	.0041	.0040	.0039	.0038	.0037	.0036
−2.5	.0062	.0060	.0059	.0057	.0055	.0054	.0052	.0051	.0049	.0048
−2.4	.0082	.0080	.0078	.0075	.0073	.0071	.0069	.0068	.0066	.0064
−2.3	.0107	.0104	.0102	.0099	.0096	.0094	.0091	.0089	.0087	.0084
−2.2	.0139	.0136	.0132	.0129	.0126	.0122	.0119	.0116	.0113	.0110
−2.1	.0179	.0174	.0170	.0166	.0162	.0158	.0154	.0150	.0146	.0143
−2.0	.0228	.0222	.0217	.0212	.0207	.0202	.0197	.0192	.0188	.0183
−1.9	.0287	.0281	.0274	.0268	.0262	.0256	.0250	.0244	.0238	.0233
−1.8	.0359	.0352	.0344	.0336	.0329	.0322	.0314	.0307	.0300	.0294
−1.7	.0446	.0436	.0427	.0418	.0409	.0401	.0392	.0384	.0375	.0367
−1.6	.0548	.0537	.0526	.0516	.0505	.0495	.0485	.0475	.0465	.0455
−1.5	.0668	.0655	.0643	.0630	.0618	.0606	.0594	.0582	.0570	.0559
−1.4	.0808	.0793	.0778	.0764	.0749	.0735	.0722	.0708	.0694	.0681
−1.3	.0968	.0951	.0934	.0918	.0901	.0885	.0869	.0853	.0838	.0823
−1.2	.1151	.1131	.1112	.1093	.1075	.1056	.1038	.1020	.1003	.0985
−1.1	.1357	.1335	.1314	.1292	.1271	.1251	.1230	.1210	.1190	.1170
−1.0	.1587	.1562	.1539	.1515	.1492	.1469	.1446	.1423	.1401	.1379
−.9	.1841	.1814	.1788	.1762	.1736	.1711	.1685	.1660	.1635	.1611
−.8	.2119	.2090	.2061	.2033	.2005	.1977	.1949	.1922	.1894	.1867
−.7	.2420	.2389	.2358	.2327	.2297	.2266	.2236	.2206	.2177	.2148
−.6	.2743	.2709	.2676	.2643	.2611	.2578	.2546	.2514	.2483	.2451
−.5	.3085	.3050	.3015	.2981	.2946	.2912	.2877	.2843	.2810	.2776
−.4	.3446	.3409	.3372	.3336	.3300	.3264	.3228	.3192	.3156	.3121
−.3	.3821	.3783	.3745	.3707	.3669	.3632	.3594	.3557	.3520	.3483
−.2	.4207	.4168	.4129	.4090	.4052	.4013	.3974	.3936	.3897	.3859
−.1	.4602	.4562	.4522	.4483	.4443	.4404	.4364	.4325	.4286	.4247
−0	.5000	.4960	.4920	.4880	.4840	.4801	.4761	.4721	.4681	.4641

(Continued)

z	0	1	2	3	4	5	6	7	8	9
.0	.5000	.5040	.5080	.5120	.5160	.5199	.5239	.5279	.5319	.5359
.1	.5398	.5438	.5478	.5517	.5557	.5596	.5636	.5675	.5714	.5753
.2	.5793	.5832	.5871	.5910	.5948	.5987	.6026	.6064	.6103	.6141
.3	.6179	.6217	.6255	.6293	.6331	.6368	.6406	.6443	.6480	.6517
.4	.6554	.6591	.6628	.6664	.6700	.6736	.6772	.6808	.6844	.6879
.5	.6915	.6950	.6985	.7019	.7054	.7088	.7123	.7157	.7190	.7224
.6	.7257	.7291	.7324	.7357	.7389	.7422	.7454	.7486	.7517	.7549
.7	.7580	.7611	.7642	.7673	.7703	.7734	.7764	.7794	.7823	.7852
.8	.7881	.7910	.7939	.7967	.7995	.8023	.8051	.8078	.8106	.8133
.9	.8159	.8186	.8212	.8238	.8264	.8289	.8315	.8340	.8365	.8389
1.0	.8413	.8438	.8461	.8485	.8508	.8531	.8554	.8577	.8599	.8621
1.1	.8643	.8665	.8686	.8708	.8729	.8749	.8770	.8790	.8810	.8830
1.2	.8849	.8869	.8888	.8907	.8925	.8944	.8962	.8980	.8997	.9015
1.3	.9032	.9049	.9066	.9082	.9099	.9115	.9131	.9147	.9162	.9177
1.4	.9192	.9207	.9222	.9236	.9251	.9265	.9278	.9292	.9306	.9319
1.5	.9332	.9345	.9357	.9370	.9382	.9394	.9406	.9418	.9430	.9441
1.6	.9452	.9463	.9474	.9484	.9495	.9505	.9515	.9525	.9535	.9545
1.7	.9554	.9564	.9573	.9582	.9591	.9599	.9608	.9616	.9625	.9633
1.8	.9641	.9648	.9656	.9664	.9671	.9678	.9686	.9693	.9700	.9706
1.9	.9713	.9719	.9726	.9732	.9738	.9744	.9750	.9756	.9762	.9767
2.0	.9772	.9778	.9783	.9788	.9793	.9798	.9803	.9808	.9812	.9817
2.1	.9821	.9826	.9830	.9834	.9838	.9842	.9846	.9850	.9854	.9857
2.2	.9861	.9864	.9868	.9871	.9874	.9878	.9881	.9884	.9887	.9890
2.3	.9893	.9896	.9898	.9901	.9904	.9906	.9909	.9911	.9913	.9916
2.4	.9918	.9920	.9922	.9925	.9927	.9929	.9931	.9932	.9934	.9936
2.5	.9938	.9940	.9941	.9943	.9945	.9946	.9948	.9949	.9951	.9952
2.6	.9953	.9955	.9956	.9957	.9959	.9960	.9961	.9962	.9963	.9964
2.7	.9965	.9966	.9967	.9968	.9969	.9970	.9971	.9972	.9973	.9974
2.8	.9974	.9975	.9976	.9977	.9977	.9978	.9979	.9979	.9980	.9981
2.9	.9981	.9982	.9982	.9983	.9984	.9984	.9985	.9985	.9986	.9986
3.	.9987	.9990	.9993	.9995	.9997	.9998	.9998	.9999	.9999	1.0000

Note 1: If a normal variable X is not "standard," its values must be "standardized": $Z = (X - \mu)/\sigma$, that is, $P(X \leq x) = \Phi[(x - \mu)/\sigma]$.

Note 2: For "two-tail" probabilities, see Table Ic.

Note 3: For $z \geq 4$, $\Phi(z) = 1$ to four decimal places; for $z \leq -4$, $\Phi(z) = 0$ to four decimal places.

Note 4: Entries opposite 3 and -3 are for 3.0, 3.1, 3.2, etc., and -3.0, -3.1, etc., respectively.

Table Ib. Percentiles of
the Standard Normal
Distribution

Table Ic. Two-Tail
Probabilities for the
Standard Normal
Distribution

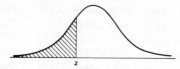

$P(Z \leq z)$	z
.001	−3.09
.005	−2.58
.01	−2.33
.02	−2.05
.03	−1.88
.04	−1.75
.05	−1.645
.10	−1.28
.15	−1.04
.20	− .84
.30	− .52
.40	− .25
.50	0
.60	.25
.70	.52
.80	.84
.85	1.04
.90	1.28
.95	1.645
.96	1.75
.97	1.88
.98	2.05
.99	2.33
.995	2.58
.999	3.09

K	$P(|Z| > K)$
1.04	.30
1.15	.25
1.28	.20
1.44	.15
1.645	.10
1.70	.09
1.75	.08
1.81	.07
1.88	.06
1.96	.05
2.05	.04
2.17	.03
2.33	.02
2.58	.01
2.81	.005
3.09	.002
3.29	.001

Table II. Percentiles of the Chi-Square Distribution

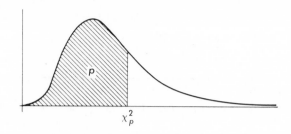

$$\chi^2_p$$

Degrees of freedom	$\chi^2_{.005}$	$\chi^2_{.01}$	$\chi^2_{.025}$	$\chi^2_{.05}$	$\chi^2_{.10}$	$\chi^2_{.20}$	$\chi^2_{.30}$	$\chi^2_{.50}$	$\chi^2_{.70}$	$\chi^2_{.80}$	$\chi^2_{.90}$	$\chi^2_{.95}$	$\chi^2_{.975}$	$\chi^2_{.99}$	$\chi^2_{.995}$
1	.000	.000	.001	.004	.016	.064	.148	.455	1.07	1.64	2.71	3.84	5.02	6.63	7.88
2	.010	.020	.051	.103	.211	.446	.713	1.39	2.41	3.22	4.61	5.99	7.38	9.21	10.6
3	.072	.115	.216	.352	.584	1.00	1.42	2.37	3.66	4.64	6.25	7.81	9.35.	11.3	12.8
4	.207	.297	.484	.711	1.06	1.65	2.20	3.36	4.88	5.99	7.78	9.49	11.1	13.3	14.9
5	.412	.554	.831	1.15	1.61	2.34	3.00	4.35	6.06	7.29	9.24	11.1	12.8	15.1	16.7
6	.676	.872	1.24	1.64	2.20	3.07	3.83	5.35	7.23	8.56	10.6	12.6	14.4	16.8	18.5
7	.989	1.24	1.69	2.17	2.83	3.82	4.67	6.35	8.38	9.80	12.0	14.1	16.0	18.5	20.3
8	1.34	1.65	2.18	2.73	3.49	4.59	5.53	7.34	9.52	11.0	13.4	15.5	17.5	20.1	22.0
9	1.73	2.09	2.70	3.33	4.17	5.38	6.39	8.34	10.7	12.2	14.7	16.9	19.0	21.7	23.6
10	2.16	2.56	3.25	3.94	4.87	6.18	7.27	9.34	11.8	13.4	16.0	18.3	20.5	23.2	25.2
11	2.60	3.05	3.82	4.57	5.58	6.99	8.15	10.3	12.9	14.6	17.3	19.7	21.9	24.7	26.8
12	3.07	3.57	4.40	5.23	6.30	7.81	9.03	11.3	14.0	15.8	18.5	21.0	23.3	26.2	28.3
13	3.57	4.11	5.01	5.89	7.04	8.63	9.93	12.3	15.1	17.0	19.8	22.4	24.7	27.7	29.8
14	4.07	4.66	5.63	6.57	7.79	9.47	10.8	13.3	16.2	18.2	21.1	23.7	26.1	29.1	31.3
15	4.60	5.23	6.26	7.26	8.55	10.3	11.7	14.3	17.3	19.3	22.3	25.0	27.5	30.6	32.8
16	5.14	5.81	6.91	7.96	9.31	11.2	12.6	15.3	18.4	20.5	23.5	26.3	28.8	32.0	34.3
17	5.70	6.41	7.56	8.67	10.1	12.0	13.5	16.3	19.5	21.6	24.8	27.6	30.2	33.4	35.7
18	6.26	7.01	8.23	9.39	10.9	12.9	14.4	17.3	20.6	22.8	26.0	28.9	31.5	34.8	37.2
19	6.83	7.63	8.91	10.1	11.7	13.7	15.4	18.3	21.7	23.9	27.2	30.1	32.9	36.2	38.6
20	7.43	8.26	9.59	10.9	12.4	14.6	16.3	19.3	22.8	25.0	28.4	31.4	34.2	37.6	40.0
21	8.03	8.90	10.3	11.6	13.2	15.4	17.2	20.3	23.9	26.2	29.6	32.7	35.5	38.9	41.4
22	8.64	9.54	11.0	12.3	14.0	16.3	18.1	21.3	24.9	27.3	30.8	33.9	36.8	40.3	42.8
23	9.26	10.2	11.7	13.1	14.8	17.2	19.0	22.3	26.0	28.4	32.0	35.2	38.1	41.6	44.2
24	9.89	10.9	12.4	13.8	15.7	18.1	19.9	23.3	27.1	29.6	33.2	36.4	39.4	43.0	45.6
25	10.5	11.5	13.1	14.6	16.5	18.9	20.9	24.3	28.2	30.7	34.4	37.7	40.6	44.3	46.9
26	11.2	12.2	13.8	15.4	17.3	19.8	21.8	25.3	29.2	31.8	35.6	38.9	41.9	45.6	48.3
27	11.8	12.9	14.6	16.2	18.1	20.7	22.7	26.3	30.3	32.9	36.7	40.1	43.2	47.0	49.6
28	12.5	13.6	15.3	16.9	18.9	21.6	23.6	27.3	31.4	34.0	37.9	41.3	44.5	48.3	51.0
29	13.1	14.3	16.0	17.7	19.8	22.5	24.6	28.3	32.5	35.1	39.1	42.6	45.7	49.6	52.3
30	13.8	15.0	16.8	18.5	20.6	23.4	25.5	29.3	33.5	36.2	40.3	43.8	47.0	50.9	53.7
40	20.7	22.1	24.4	26.5	29.0	32.3	34.9	39.3	44.2	47.3	51.8	55.8	59.3	63.7	66.8
50	28.0	29.7	32.3	34.8	37.7	41.3	44.3	49.3	54.7	58.2	63.2	67.5	71.4	76.2	79.5
60	35.5	37.5	40.5	43.2	46.5	50.6	53.8	59.3	65.2	69.0	74.4	79.1	83.3	88.4	92.0

Note: For degrees of freedom $k > 30$, use $\chi_p{}^2 = \frac{1}{2}(z_p + \sqrt{2k-1})^2$, where z_p is the corresponding percentile of the standard normal distribution.

This table is adapted from Table VIII of *Biometrika Tables for Statisticians*, Vol. 1, 1954, by E. S. Pearson and H. O. Hartley, originally prepared by Catherine M. Thompson, with the kind permission of the editor of *Biometrika*.

Table III. Percentiles of the t Distribution

Degrees of Freedom	$t_{.55}$	$t_{.60}$	$t_{.65}$	$t_{.70}$	$t_{.75}$	$t_{.80}$	$t_{.85}$	$t_{.90}$	$t_{.95}$	$t_{.975}$	$t_{.99}$	$t_{.995}$	$t_{.9995}$
1	.158	.325	.510	.727	1.00	1.38	1.96	3.08	6.31	12.7	31.8	63.7	637
2	.142	.289	.445	.617	.816	1.06	1.39	1.89	2.92	4.30	6.96	9.92	31.6
3	.137	.277	.424	.584	.765	.978	1.25	1.64	2.35	3.18	4.54	5.84	12.9
4	.134	.271	.414	.569	.741	.941	1.19	1.53	2.13	2.78	3.75	4.60	8.61
5	.132	.267	.408	.559	.727	.920	1.16	1.48	2.01	2.57	3.36	4.03	6.86
6	.131	.265	.404	.553	.718	.906	1.13	1.44	1.94	2.45	3.14	3.71	5.96
7	.130	.263	.402	.549	.711	.896	1.12	1.42	1.90	2.36	3.00	3.50	5.40
8	.130	.262	.399	.546	.706	.889	1.11	1.40	1.86	2.31	2.90	3.36	5.04
9	.129	.261	.398	.543	.703	.883	1.10	1.38	1.83	2.26	2.82	3.25	4.78
10	.129	.260	.397	.542	.700	.879	1.09	1.37	1.81	2.23	2.76	3.17	4.59
11	.129	.260	.396	.540	.697	.876	1.09	1.36	1.80	2.20	2.72	3.11	4.44
12	.128	.259	.395	.539	.695	.873	1.08	1.36	1.78	2.18	2.68	3.06	4.32
13	.128	.259	.394	.538	.694	.870	1.08	1.35	1.77	2.16	2.65	3.01	4.22
14	.128	.258	.393	.537	.692	.868	1.08	1.34	1.76	2.14	2.62	2.98	4.14
15	.128	.258	.393	.536	.691	.866	1.07	1.34	1.75	2.13	2.60	2.95	4.07
16	.128	.258	.392	.535	.690	.865	1.07	1.34	1.75	2.12	2.58	2.92	4.02
17	.128	.257	.392	.534	.689	.863	1.07	1.33	1.74	2.11	2.57	2.90	3.96
18	.127	.257	.392	.534	.688	.862	1.07	1.33	1.73	2.10	2.55	2.88	3.92
19	.127	.257	.391	.533	.688	.861	1.07	1.33	1.73	2.09	2.54	2.86	3.88
20	.127	.257	.391	.533	.687	.860	1.06	1.32	1.72	2.09	2.53	2.84	3.85
21	.127	.257	.391	.532	.686	.859	1.06	1.32	1.72	2.08	2.52	2.83	3.82
22	.127	.256	.390	.532	.686	.858	1.06	1.32	1.72	2.07	2.51	2.82	3.79
23	.127	.256	.390	.532	.685	.858	1.06	1.32	1.71	2.07	2.50	2.81	3.77
24	.127	.256	.390	.531	.685	.857	1.06	1.32	1.71	2.06	2.49	2.80	3.74
25	.127	.256	.390	.531	.684	.856	1.06	1.32	1.71	2.06	2.48	2.79	3.72
26	.127	.256	.390	.531	.684	.856	1.06	1.32	1.70	2.06	2.48	2.78	3.71
27	.127	.256	.389	.531	.684	.855	1.06	1.31	1.70	2.05	2.47	2.77	3.69
28	.127	.256	.389	.530	.683	.855	1.06	1.31	1.70	2.05	2.47	2.76	3.67
29	.127	.256	.389	.530	.683	.854	1.05	1.31	1.70	2.04	2.46	2.76	3.66
30	.127	.256	.389	.530	.683	.854	1.05	1.31	1.70	2.04	2.46	2.75	3.65
∞	.126	.253	.385	.524	.674	.842	1.04	1.28	1.64	1.96	2.33	2.58	3.29

Note: For the lower percentiles, use the relation $t_\alpha = -t_{1-\alpha}$. In particular, $t_{.50} = -t_{.50}$ = 0. For example, for 6 degrees of freedom, $t_{.35} = -t_{.65} = -.404$.

This table is abridged from Table II of Fisher and Yates, *Statistical Tables for Biological, Agricultural, and Medical Research* (5th ed.)/Fisher, *Statistical Methods for Research Workers*, published by Oliver and Boyd, Ltd., Edinburgh, by permission of the authors and publishers.

482

Table IVa. *F*.95, *Ninety-Fifth Percentiles of the F Distribution*

					Numerator Degrees of Freedom								
	1	2	3	4	5	6	8	10	12	15	20	24	30
1	161	200	216	225	230	234	239	242	244	246	248	249	250
2	18.5	19.0	19.2	19.2	19.3	19.3	19.4	19.4	19.4	19.4	19.4	19.5	19.5
3	10.1	9.55	9.28	9.12	9.01	8.94	8.85	8.79	8.74	8.70	8.66	8.64	8.62
4	7.71	6.94	6.59	6.39	6.26	6.16	6.04	5.96	5.91	5.86	5.80	5.77	5.75
5	6.61	5.79	5.41	5.19	5.05	4.95	4.82	4.74	4.68	4.62	4.56	4.53	4.50
6	5.99	5.14	4.76	4.53	4.39	4.28	4.15	4.06	4.00	3.94	3.87	3.84	3.81
7	5.59	4.74	4.35	4.12	3.97	3.87	3.73	3.64	3.57	3.51	3.44	3.41	3.38
8	5.32	4.46	4.07	3.84	3.69	3.58	3.44	3.35	3.28	3.22	3.15	3.12	3.08
9	5.12	4.26	3.86	3.63	3.48	3.37	3.23	3.14	3.07	3.01	2.94	2.90	2.86
10	4.96	4.10	3.71	3.48	3.33	3.22	3.07	2.98	2.91	2.85	2.77	2.74	2.70
11	4.84	3.98	3.59	3.36	3.20	3.09	2.95	2.85	2.79	2.72	2.65	2.61	2.57
12	4.75	3.89	3.49	3.26	3.11	3.00	2.85	2.75	2.69	2.62	2.54	2.51	2.47
13	4.67	3.81	3.41	3.18	3.03	2.92	2.77	2.67	2.60	2.53	2.46	2.42	2.38
14	4.60	3.74	3.34	3.11	2.96	2.85	2.70	2.60	2.53	2.46	2.39	2.35	2.31
15	4.54	3.68	3.29	3.06	2.90	2.79	2.64	2.54	2.48	2.40	2.33	2.29	2.25
16	4.49	3.63	3.24	3.01	2.85	2.74	2.59	2.49	2.42	2.35	2.28	2.24	2.19
17	4.45	3.59	3.20	2.96	2.81	2.70	2.55	2.45	2.38	2.31	2.23	2.19	2.15
18	4.41	3.55	3.16	2.93	2.77	2.66	2.51	2.41	2.34	2.27	2.19	2.15	2.11
19	4.38	3.52	3.13	2.90	2.74	2.63	2.48	2.38	2.31	2.23	2.16	2.11	2.07
20	4.35	3.49	3.10	2.87	2.71	2.60	2.45	2.35	2.28	2.20	2.12	2.08	2.04
21	4.32	3.47	3.07	2.84	2.68	2.57	2.42	2.32	2.25	2.18	2.10	2.05	2.01
22	4.30	3.44	3.05	2.82	2.66	2.55	2.40	2.30	2.23	2.15	2.07	2.03	1.98
23	4.28	3.42	3.03	2.80	2.64	2.53	2.37	2.27	2.20	2.13	2.05	2.01	1.96
24	4.26	3.40	3.01	2.78	2.62	2.51	2.36	2.25	2.18	2.11	2.03	1.98	1.94
25	4.24	3.39	2.99	2.76	2.60	2.49	2.34	2.24	2.16	2.09	2.01	1.96	1.92
30	4.17	3.32	2.92	2.69	2.53	2.42	2.27	2.16	2.09	2.01	1.93	1.89	1.84
40	4.08	3.23	2.84	2.61	2.45	2.34	2.18	2.08	2.00	1.92	1.84	1.79	1.74
60	4.00	3.15	2.76	2.53	2.37	2.25	2.10	1.99	1.92	1.84	1.75	1.70	1.65

Denominator Degrees of Freedom (row labels)

This table is adapted from Table XVIII in *Biometrika Tables for Statisticians*, Vol. I, 1954, by E. S. Pearson and H. O. Hartley, originally prepared by M. Merrington and C. M. Thompson, with the kind permission of the editor of *Biometrika*.

Table IVb. $F_{.99}$, Ninety-Ninth Percentiles of the F Distribution

					Numerator Degrees of Freedom								
	1	2	3	4	5	6	8	10	12	15	20	24	30
1	4050	5000	5400	5620	5760	5860	5980	6060	6110	6160	6210	6235	6260
2	98.5	99.0	99.2	99.2	99.3	99.3	99.4	99.4	99.4	99.4	99.4	99.5	99.5
3	34.1	30.8	29.5	28.7	28.2	27.9	27.5	27.3	27.1	26.9	26.7	26.6	26.5
4	21.2	18.0	16.7	16.0	15.5	15.2	14.8	14.5	14.4	14.2	14.0	13.9	13.8
5	16.3	13.3	12 1.	11.4	11.0	10.7	10.3	10.1	9.89	9.72	9.55	9.47	9.38
6	13.7	10.9	9.78	9.15	8.75	8.47	8.10	7.87	7.72	7.56	7.40	7.31	7.23
7	12.2	9.55	8.45	7.85	7.46	7.19	6.84	6.62	6.47	6.31	6.16	6.07	5.99
8	11.3	8.65	7.59	7.01	6.63	6.37	6.03	5.81	5.67	5.52	5.36	5.28	5.20
9	10.6	8.02	6.99	6.42	6.06	5.80	5.47	5.26	5.11	4.96	4.81	4.73	4.65
10	10.0	7.56	6.55	5.99	5.64	5.39	5.06	4.85	4.71	4.56	4.41	4.33	4.25
11	9.65	7.21	6.22	5.67	5.32	5.07	4.74	4.54	4.40	4.25	4.10	4.02	3.94
12	9.33	6.93	5.95	5.41	5.06	4.82	4.50	4.30	4.16	4.01	3.86	3.78	3.70
13	9.07	6.70	5.74	5.21	4.86	4.62	4.30	4.10	3.96	3.82	3.66	3.59	3.51
14	8.86	6.51	5.56	5.04	4.69	4.46	4.14	3.94	3.80	3.66	3.51	3.43	3.35
15	8.68	6.36	5.42	4.89	4.56	4.32	4.00	3.80	3.67	3.52	3.37	3.29	3.21
16	8.53	6.23	5.29	4.77	4.44	4.20	3.89	3.69	3.55	3.41	3.26	3.18	3.10
17	8.40	6.11	5.18	4.67	4.34	4.10	3.79	3.59	3.46	3.31	3.16	3.08	3.00
18	8.29	6.01	5.09	4.58	4.25	4.01	3.71	3.51	3.37	3.23	3.08	3.00	2.92
19	8.18	5.93	5.01	4.50	4.17	3.94	3.63	3.43	3.30	3.15	3.00	2.92	2.84
20	8.10	5.85	4.94	4.43	4.10	3.87	3.56	3.37	3.23	3.09	2.94	2.86	2.78
21	8.02	5.78	4.87	4.37	4.04	3.81	3.51	3.31	3.17	3.03	2.88	2.80	2.72
22	7.95	5.72	4.82	4.31	3.99	3.76	3.45	3.26	3.12	2.98	2.83	2.75	2.67
23	7.88	5.66	4.76	4.26	3.94	3.71	3.41	3.21	3.07	2.93	2.78	2.70	2.62
24	7.82	5.61	4.72	4.22	3.90	3.67	3.36	3.17	3.03	2.89	2.74	2.66	2.58
25	7.77	5.57	4.68	4.18	3.86	3.63	3.32	3.13	2.99	2.85	2.70	2.62	2.54
30	7.56	5.39	4.51	4.02	3.70	3.47	3.17	2.98	2.84	2.70	2.55	2.47	2.39
40	7.31	5.18	4.31	3.83	3.51	3.29	2.99	2.80	2.66	2.52	2.37	2.29	2.20
60	7.08	4.98	4.13	3.65	3.34	3.12	2.82	2.63	2.50	2.35	2.20	2.12	2.03

Denominator Degrees of Freedom

This table is adapted from Table XVIII in *Biometrika Tables for Statisticians*, Vol. I, 1954, by E. S. Pearson and H. O. Hartley, originally prepared by M. Merrington and C. M. Thompson, with the kind permission of the editor of *Biometrika*.

Table V. Distribution of the Standardized Range $W = R/\sigma$
(Assuming a Normal Population)

					Sample Size						
	2	3	4	5	6	7	8	9	10	12	15
$E(W)$	1.128	1.693	2.059	2.326	2.534	2.704	2.847	2.970	3.078	3.258	3.472
σ_W	.853	.888	.880	.864	.848	.833	.820	.808	.797	.778	.755
$W_{.005}$	.01	.13	.34	.55	.75	.92	1.08	1.21	1.33	1.55	1.80
$W_{.01}$	.02	.19	.43	.66	.87	1.05	1.20	1.34	1.47	1.68	1.93
$W_{.025}$	.04	.30	.59	.85	1.06	1.25	1.41	1.55	1.67	1.88	2.14
$W_{.05}$	.09	.43	.76	1.03	1.25	1.44	1.60	1.74	1.86	2.07	2.32
$W_{.1}$	.18	.62	.98	1.26	1.49	1.68	1.83	1.97	2.09	2.30	2.54
$W_{.2}$	.36	.90	1.29	1.57	1.80	1.99	2.14	2.28	2.39	2.59	2.83
$W_{.3}$	.55	1.14	1.53	1.82	2.04	2.22	2.38	2.51	2.62	2.82	3.04
$W_{.4}$	.74	1.36	1.76	2.04	2.26	2.44	2.59	2.71	2.83	3.01	3.23
$W_{.5}$	.95	1.59	1.98	2.26	2.47	2.65	2.79	2.92	3.02	3.21	3.42
$W_{.6}$	1.20	1.83	2.21	2.48	2.69	2.86	3.00	3.12	3.23	3.41	3.62
$W_{.7}$	1.47	2.09	2.47	2.73	2.94	3.10	3.24	3.35	3.46	3.63	3.83
$W_{.8}$	1.81	2.42	2.78	3.04	3.23	3.39	3.52	3.63	3.73	3.90	4.09
$W_{.9}$	2.33	2.90	3.24	3.48	3.66	3.81	3.93	4.04	4.13	4.29	4.47
$W_{.95}$	2.77	3.31	3.63	3.86	4.03	4.17	4.29	4.39	4.47	4.62	4.80
$W_{.975}$	3.17	3.68	3.98	4.20	4.36	4.49	4.61	4.70	4.79	4.92	5.09
$W_{.99}$	3.64	4.12	4.40	4.60	4.76	4.88	4.99	5.08	5.16	5.29	5.45
$W_{.995}$	3.97	4.42	4.69	4.89	5.03	5.15	5.26	5.34	5.42	5.54	5.70

This table is adapted from Tables XX and XXII in *Biometrika Tables for Statisticians*, Vol. I, 1954, by E. S. Pearson and H. O. Hartley, with the kind permission of the editor of *Biometrika*.

Table VI.   Acceptance Limits for the Kolmogorov–Smirnov Test of Goodness of Fit

Sample size (n)	Significance level				
	.20	.15	.10	.05	.01
1	.900	.925	.950	.975	.995
2	.684	.726	.776	.842	.929
3	.565	.597	.642	.708	.829
4	.494	.525	.564	.624	.734
5	.446	.474	.510	.563	.669
6	.410	.436	.470	.521	.618
7	.381	.405	.438	.486	.577
8	.358	.381	.411	.457	.543
9	.339	.360	.388	.432	.514
10	.322	.342	.368	.409	.486
11	.307	.326	.352	.391	.468
12	.295	.313	.338	.375	.450
13	.284	.302	.325	.361	.433
14	.274	.292	.314	.349	.418
15	.266	.283	.304	.338	.404
16	.258	.274	.295	.328	.391
17	.250	.266	.286	.318	.380
18	.244	.259	.278	.309	.370
19	.237	.252	.272	.301	.361
20	.231	.246	.264	.294	.352
25	.21	.22	.24	.264	.32
30	.19	.20	.22	.242	.29
35	.18	.19	.21	.23	.27
40				.21	.25
50				.19	.23
60				.17	.21
70				.16	.19
80				.15	.18
90				.14	
100				.14	
Asymptotic Formula:	$\dfrac{1.07}{\sqrt{n}}$	$\dfrac{1.14}{\sqrt{n}}$	$\dfrac{1.22}{\sqrt{n}}$	$\dfrac{1.36}{\sqrt{n}}$	$\dfrac{1.63}{\sqrt{n}}$

Reject the hypothetical distribution $F(x)$ if $D_n = \max |F_n(x) - F(x)|$ exceeds the tabulated value.

(For $\alpha = .01$ and .05, asymptotic formulas give values which are too high—by 1.5 per cent for $n = 80$.)

This table is taken from Massey, F. J., Jr., "The Kolmogorov–Smirnov test for goodness of fit," *J. Amer. Stat. Assn.*, **46**, 68–78 (1951), except that certain corrections and additional entries are from Birnbaum, Z. W., "Numerical tabulation of the distribution of Kolmogorov's statistic for finite sample size," *J. Amer. Stat. Assn.* **47**, 425–441 (1952), with the kind permission of the authors and the *J. Amer. Stat. Assn.*

Table VII. Acceptance Limits for the Kolmogorov–Smirnov Test of
$H_0 : F_1(x) = F_2(x)$

					Sample Size n_1							
		1	2	3	4	5	6	7	8	9	10	12	15

Sample Size n_2

n_2		1	2	3	4	5	6	7	8	9	10	12	15
1	upper	*	*	*	*	*	*	*	*	*	*		
	lower	*	*	*	*	*	*	*	*	*	*		
2	upper		*	*	*	*	*	*	7/8	16/18	9/10		
	lower		*	*	*	*	*	*	*	*	*		
3	upper			*	*	12/15	5/6	18/21	18/24	7/9		9/12	
	lower			*	*	*	*	*	*	8/9		11/12	
4	upper				3/4	16/20	9/12	21/28	6/8	27/36	14/20	8/12	
	lower				*	*	10/12	24/28	7/8	32/36	16/20	10/12	
5	upper					4/5	20/30	25/35	27/40	31/45	7/10		10/15
	lower					4/5	25/30	30/35	32/40	36/45	8/10		11/15
6	upper						4/6	29/42	16/24	12/18	19/30	7/12	
	lower						5/6	35/42	18/24	14/18	22/30	9/12	
7	upper							5/7	35/56	40/63	43/70		
	lower							5/7	42/56	47/63	53/70		
8	upper								5/8	45/72	23/40	14/24	
	lower								6/8	54/72	28/40	16/24	
9	upper									5/9	52/90	20/36	
	lower									6/9	62/90	24/36	
10	upper										6/10		15/30
	lower										7/10		19/30
12	upper											6/12	30/60
	lower											7/12	35/60
15	upper												7/15
	lower												8/15

Reject H_0 if
$D = \max |F_{n_2}(x) - F_{n_1}(x)|$
exceeds the tabulated value.
The upper value gives a level
at most .05 and the lower
at most .01.

Note 1: Where * appears, do not reject H_0 at the given level.

Note 2: For large values of n_1 and n_2, the following approximate formulas may be used:

$$\alpha = .05: \quad 1.36 \sqrt{\frac{n_1 + n_2}{n_1 n_2}}$$

$$\alpha = .01: \quad 1.63 \sqrt{\frac{n_1 + n_2}{n_1 n_2}}$$

This table is derived from Massey, F. J., Jr., "Distribution table for the deviation between two sample cumulatives," *Ann. Math. Stat*, **23**, 435–441 (1952). Adapted with the kind permission of the author and the *Ann. Math. Stat.* Formulas for large sample sizes were given by Smirnov, N., "Tables for estimating the goodness of fit of empirical distributions," *Ann. Math. Stat.*, **19**, 280–281 (1948).

Table VIII.   Rejection Limits for the Wilcoxon–Mann–Whitney Test

m \ n	3	4	5	6	7	8	9	10
2	*	*	*	*	*	*	*	*
	*	*	*	*	*	*	*	*
	*	*	*	*	*	0 (2.2)	0 (1.8)	0 (1.5)
	*	*	0 (4.7)	0 (3.6)	0 (2.8)	1 (4.4)	1 (3.6)	1 (3.0)
3	*	*	*	*	*	.*	0 (.45)	0 (.35)
	*	*	*	*	0 (.83)	0 (.61)	1 (.91)	1 (.70)
	*	*	0 (1.8)	1 (2.4)	1 (1.7)	2 (2.4)	3 (3.2)	3 (2.5)
	0 (5.0)	0 (2.8)	1 (3.6)	2 (4.8)	2 (3.3)	3 (4.2)	4 (5.0)	4 (3.9)
4		*	*	0 (.48)	0 (.30)	1 (.40)	1 (.28)	2 (.40)
		*	0 (.79)	1 (1.0)	1 (.61)	2 (.81)	3 (.98)	3 (.70)
		0 (1.4)	1 (1.6)	2 (1.9)	3 (2.1)	4 (2.4)	5 (2.5)	5 (1.8)
		1 (2.9)	2 (3.2)	3 (3.3)	4 (3.6)	5 (3.6)	6 (3.8)	7 (3.8)
5			0 (.40)	1 (.43)	1 (.25)	2 (.31)	3 (.35)	4 (.40)
			1 (.79)	2 (.82)	3 (.88)	4 (.93)	5 (.95)	6 (.97)
			2 (1.6)	3 (1.5)	5 (2.4)	6 (2.3)	7 (2.1)	8 (2.0)
			4 (4.8)	5 (4.1)	6 (3.7)	8 (4.7)	9 (4.2)	11 (5.0)
6				2 (.43)	3 (.41)	4 (.40)	5 (.38)	6 (.37)
				3 (.67)	4 (.70)	5 (.63)	7 (.88)	8 (.80)
				5 (2.1)	6 (1.8)	8 (2.1)	10 (2.5)	11 (2.1)
				7 (4.7)	8 (3.7)	10 (4.1)	12 (4.4)	14 (4.7)
7					4 (.35)	5 (.47)	7 (.39)	9 (.48)
					6 (.87)	7 (1.0)	9 (.82)	11 (.93)
					8 (1.9)	10 (2.0)	12 (2.1)	14 (2.2)
					11 (4.9)	13 (4.7)	15 (4.5)	17 (4.4)
8						7 (.35)	9 (.39)	11 (.43)
						9 (.74)	11 (.76)	13 (.78)
						13 (2.5)	15 (2.3)	17 (2.2)
						15 (4.2)	18 (4.6)	20 (4.2)
9							11 (.39)	13 (.38)
							14 (.94)	16 (.86)
							18 (2.5)	20 (2.2)
							21 (4.7)	24 (4.7)
10								16 (.45)
								19 (.93)
								23 (2.2)
								27 (4.5)

Note: See explanations on page 489.

The four entries for each pair of sample sizes are rejection limits when it is desired to have:

a one-sided test at .5 per cent or a two-sided test at 1 per cent;
a one-sided test at 1 per cent or a two-sided test at 2 per cent;
a one-sided test at 2.5 per cent or a two-sided test at 5 per cent;
a one-sided test at 5 per cent or a two-sided test at 10 per cent.

The entries in the table are lower limits; corresponding upper limits are $mn - u$.

An asterisk indicates that the null hypothesis should never be rejected at the level corresponding to that position in the table.

The number in parentheses after a value u is the probability (in per cent) that $U \leq u$. EXAMPLE. If a two-sided test at 5 per cent is desired for $m = 5$ and $n = 8$, use $6 < U < 34$ as the acceptance region. For this test,

$$\alpha = P_{H_0}(U \leq 6 \text{ or } U \geq 34) = 2 \times (.023) = .046,$$

which is less than .05 as desired.

This table is adapted from those given in Mann, H. B., and Whitney, D. R., "On a test of whether one of the two random variables is stochastically larger than the other," *Ann. Math. Stat.*, **18**, 50–60 (1947), with the kind permission of *Ann. Math. Stat.*

Table IX.   *Expected Values of Order Statistics from a Standard Normal Population*

n	$E[X_{(n)}]$	$E[X_{(n-1)}]$	$E[X_{(n-2)}]$	$E[X_{(n-3)}]$	$E[X_{(n-4)}]$	$E[X_{(n-5)}]$	$E[X_{(n-6)}]$	$E[X_{(n-7)}]$	$E[X_{(n-8)}]$	$E[X_{(n-9)}]$
2	.564									
3	.846									
4	1.029	.297								
5	1.163	.495								
6	1.267	.642	.202							
7	1.352	.757	.353							
8	1.424	.852	.473	.153						
9	1.485	.932	.572	.275						
10	1.539	1.001	.656	.376	.123					
11	1.586	1.062	.729	.462	.225					
12	1.629	1.116	.793	.537	.312	.103				
13	1.668	1.164	.850	.603	.388	.190				
14	1.703	1.208	.901	.662	.456	.267	.088			
15	1.736	1.248	.948	.715	.516	.335	.165			
16	1.766	1.285	.990	.763	.570	.396	.234	.077		
17	1.794	1.319	1.030	.807	.619	.451	.295	.146		
18	1.820	1.350	1.066	.848	.665	.502	.351	.208	.069	
19	1.844	1.380	1.099	.886	.707	.548	.402	.264	.131	
20	1.867	1.408	1.131	.921	.745	.590	.448	.315	.187	.062

Adapted from Table XXVIII of *Biometrika Tables for Statisticians*, Vol. I, 1954, by E. S. Pearson and H. O. Hartley, with the kind permission of the editor of *Biometrika*.

$$\text{Table X.} \quad \text{Binomial Coefficients } \binom{n}{k}$$

k \ n	2	3	4	5	6	7	8	9	10
2	1								
3	3	1							
4	6	4	1						
5	10	10	5	1					
6	15	20	15	6	1				
7	21	35	35	21	7	1			
8	28	56	70	56	28	8	1		
9	36	84	126	126	84	36	9	1	
10	45	120	210	252	210	120	45	10	1
11	55	165	330	462	462	330	165	55	11
12	66	220	495	792	924	792	495	220	66
13	78	286	715	1287	1716	1716	1287	715	286
14	91	364	1001	2002	3003	3432	3003	2002	1001
15	105	455	1365	3003	5005	6435	6435	5005	3003
16	120	560	1820	4368	8008	11440	12870	11440	8008
17	136	680	2380	6188	12376	19448	24310	24310	19448
18	153	816	3060	8568	18564	31824	43758	48620	43758
19	171	969	3876	11628	27132	50388	75582	92378	92378
20	190	1140	4845	15504	38760	77520	125970	167960	184756

Table XI. Exponential Functions

x	e^{-x}	e^x	$\log_{10}e^x$
.01	.9900	1.0101	.00434
.02	.9802	1.0202	.00869
.03	.9704	1.0305	.01303
.04	.9608	1.0408	.01737
.05	.9512	1.0513	.02171
.06	.9418	1.0618	.02606
.07	.9324	1.0725	.03040
.08	.9231	1.0833	.03474
.09	.9139	1.0942	.03909
.10	.9048	1.1052	.04343
.20	.8187	1.2214	.08686
.30	.7408	1.3499	.13029
.40	.6703	1.4918	.17372
.50	.6065	1.6487	.21715
.60	.5488	1.8221	.26058
.70	.4966	2.0138	.30401
.80	.4493	2.2255	.34744
.90	.4066	2.4596	.39087
1.00	.3679	2.7183	.43429
2.00	.1353	7.3891	.86859
3.00	.04979	20.0886	1.30288
4.00	.01832	54.598	1.73718
5.00	.00674	148.41	2.17147
6.00	.00248	403.43	2.60577
7.00	.000912	1096.6	3.04006
8.00	.000335	2981.0	3.47536
9.00	.000123	8103.1	3.90865
10.00	.000045	22026.0	4.34294

m (Expected value)

c	.02	.04	.06	.08	.10	.15	.20	.25	.30	.35	.40
0	.980	.961	.942	.923	.905	.861	.819	.779	.741	.705	.670
1	1.000	.999	.998	.997	.995	.990	.982	.974	.963	.951	.938
2		1.000	1.000	1.000	1.000	.999	.999	.998	.996	.994	.992
3						1.000	1.000	1.000	1.000	1.000	.999
4											1.000

c	.45	.50	.55	.60	.65	.70	.75	.80	.85	.90	.95
0	.638	.607	.577	.549	.522	.497	.472	.449	.427	.407	.387
1	.925	.910	.894	.878	.861	.844	.827	.809	.791	.772	.754
2	.989	.986	.982	.977	.972	.966	.959	.953	.945	.937	.929
3	.999	.998	.998	.997	.996	.994	.993	.991	.989	.987	.984
4	1.000	1.000	1.000	1.000	.999	.999	.999	.999	.998	.998	.997
5					1.000	1.000	1.000	1.000	1.000	1.000	1.000

c	1.0	1.1	1.2	1.3	1.4	1.5	1.6	1.7	1.8	1.9	2.0
0	.368	.333	.301	.273	.247	.223	.202	.183	.165	.150	.135
1	.736	.699	.663	.627	.592	.558	.525	.493	.463	.434	.406
2	.920	.900	.879	.857	.833	.809	.783	.757	.731	.704	.677
3	.981	.974	.966	.957	.946	.934	.921	.907	.891	.875	.857
4	.996	.995	.992	.989	.986	.981	.976	.970	.964	.956	.947
5	.999	.999	.998	.998	.997	.996	.994	.992	.990	.987	.983
6	1.000	1.000	1.000	1.000	.999	.999	.999	.998	.997	.997	.995
7					1.000	1.000	1.000	1.000	.999	.999	.999
8									1.000	1.000	1.000

c	2.2	2.4	2.6	2.8	3.0	3.2	3.4	3.6	3.8	4.0	4.2
0	.111	.091	.074	.061	.050	.041	.033	.027	.022	.018	.015
1	.355	.308	.267	.231	.199	.171	.147	.126	.107	.092	.078
2	.623	.570	.518	.469	.423	.380	.340	.303	.269	.238	.210
3	.819	.779	.736	.692	.647	.603	.558	.515	.473	.433	.395
4	.928	.904	.877	.848	.815	.781	.744	.706	.668	.629	.590
5	.975	.964	.951	.935	.916	.895	.871	.844	.816	.785	.753
6	.993	.988	.983	.976	.966	.955	.942	.927	.909	.889	.867
7	.998	.997	.995	.992	.988	.983	.977	.969	.960	.949	.936
8	1.000	.999	.999	.998	.996	.994	.992	.988	.984	.979	.972
9		1.000	1.000	.999	.999	.998	.997	.996	.994	.992	.989
10				1.000	1.000	1.000	.999	.999	.998	.997	.996
11							1.000	1.000	.999	.999	.999
12									1.000	1.000	1.000

(continued)

Table XII. Poisson Distribution Function (continued)

c	4.4	4.6	4.8	5.0	5.2	5.4	5.6	5.8	6.0	6.2	6.4
0	.012	.010	.008	.007	.006	.005	.004	.003	.002	.002	.002
1	.066	.056	.048	.040	.034	.029	.024	.021	.017	.015	.012
2	.185	.163	.143	.125	.109	.095	.082	.072	.062	.054	.046
3	.359	.326	.294	.265	.238	.213	.191	.170	.151	.134	.119
4	.551	.513	.476	.440	.406	.373	.342	.313	.285	.259	.235
5	.720	.686	.651	.616	.581	.546	.512	.478	.446	.414	.384
6	.844	.818	.791	.762	.732	.702	.670	.638	.606	.574	.542
7	.921	.905	.887	.867	.845	.822	.797	.771	.744	.716	.687
8	.964	.955	.944	.932	.918	.903	.886	.867	.847	.826	.803
9	.985	.980	.975	.968	.960	.951	.941	.929	.916	.902	.886
10	.994	.992	.990	.986	.982	.977	.972	.965	.957	.949	.939
11	.998	.997	.996	.995	.993	.990	.988	.984	.980	.975	.969
12	.999	.999	.999	.998	.997	.996	.995	.993	.991	.989	.986
13	1.000	1.000	1.000	.999	.999	.999	.998	.997	.996	.995	.994
14				1.000	1.000	1.000	.999	.999	.999	.998	.997
15							1.000	1.000	.999	.999	.999
16									1.000	1.000	1.000

c	6.6	6.8	7.0	7.2	7.4	7.6	7.8	8.0	8.5	9.0	9.5
0	.001	.001	.001	.001	.001	.001	.000	.000	.000	.000	.000
1	.010	.009	.007	.006	.005	.004	.004	.003	.002	.001	.001
2	.040	.034	.030	.025	.022	.019	.016	.014	.009	.006	.004
3	.105	.093	.082	.072	.063	.055	.048	.042	.030	.021	.015
4	.213	.192	.173	.156	.140	.125	.112	.100	.074	.055	.040
5	.355	.327	.301	.276	.253	.231	.210	.191	.150	.116	.089
6	.511	.480	.450	.420	.392	.365	.338	.313	.256	.207	.165
7	.658	.628	.599	.569	.539	.510	.481	.453	.386	.324	.269
8	.780	.755	.729	.703	.676	.648	.620	.593	.523	.456	.392
9	.869	.850	.830	.810	.788	.765	.741	.717	.653	.587	.522
10	.927	.915	.901	.887	.871	.854	.835	.816	.763	.706	.645
11	.963	.955	.947	.937	.926	.915	.902	.888	.849	.803	.752
12	.982	.978	.973	.967	.961	.954	.945	.936	.909	.876	.836
13	.992	.990	.987	.984	.980	.976	.971	.966	.949	.926	.898
14	.997	.996	.994	.993	.991	.989	.986	.983	.973	.959	.940
15	.999	.998	.998	.997	.996	.995	.993	.992	.986	.978	.967
16	.999	.999	.999	.999	.998	.998	.997	.996	.993	.989	.982
17	1.000	1.000	1.000	.999	.999	.999	.999	.998	.997	.995	.991
18				1.000	1.000	1.000	1.000	.999	.999	.998	.996
19								1.000	.999	.999	.998
20									1.000	1.000	.999
21											1.000

Table XII. Poisson Distribution Function (Continued)

c	10.0	10.5	11.0	11.5	12.0	12.5	13.0	13.5	14.0	14.5	15.0
2	.003	.002	.001	.001	.001	.000					
3	.010	.007	.005	.003	.002	.002	.001	.001	.000		
4	.029	.021	.015	.011	.008	.005	.004	.003	.002	.001	.001
5	.067	.050	.038	.028	.020	.015	.011	.008	.006	.004	.003
6	.130	.102	.079	.060	.046	.035	.026	.019	.014	.010	.008
7	.220	.179	.143	.114	.090	.070	.054	.041	.032	.024	.018
8	.333	.279	.232	.191	.155	.125	.100	.079	.062	.048	.037
9	.458	.397	.341	.289	.242	.201	.166	.135	.109	.088	.070
10	.583	.521	.460	.402	.347	.297	.252	.211	.176	.145	.118
11	.697	.639	.579	.520	.462	.406	.353	.304	.260	.220	.185
12	.792	.742	.689	.633	.576	.519	.463	.409	.358	.311	.268
13	.864	.825	.781	.733	.682	.628	.573	.518	.464	.413	.363
14	.917	.888	.854	.815	.772	.725	.675	.623	.570	.518	.466
15	.951	.932	.907	.878	.844	.806	.764	.718	.669	.619	.568
16	.973	.960	.944	.924	.899	.869	.835	.798	.756	.711	.664
17	.986	.978	.968	.954	.937	.916	.890	.861	.827	.790	.749
18	.993	.988	.982	.974	.963	.948	.930	.908	.883	.853	.819
19	.997	.994	.991	.986	.979	.969	.957	.942	.923	.901	.875
20	.998	.997	.995	.992	.988	.983	.975	.965	.952	.936	.917
21	.999	.999	.998	.996	.994	.991	.986	.980	.971	.960	.947
22	1.000	.999	.999	.998	.997	.995	.992	.989	.983	.976	.967
23		1.000	1.000	.999	.999	.998	.996	.994	.991	.986	.981
24				1.000	.999	.999	.999	.998	.997	.995	.992	.989
25					1.000	.999	.999	.999	.998	.997	.996	.994
26						1.000	1.000	.999	.999	.999	.998	.997
27								1.000	.999	.999	.999	.998
28									1.000	.999	.999	.999
29										1.000	1.000	1.000

Table XIII. Logarithms of Factorials

	0	1	2	3	4	5	6	7	8	9
00	0.0000	0.0000	0.3010	0.7782	1.3802	2.0792	2.8573	3.7024	4.6055	5.5598
10	6.5598	7.6012	8.6803	9.7943	10.9404	12.1165	13.3206	14.5511	15.8063	17.0851
20	18.3861	19.7083	21.0508	22.4125	23.7927	25.1906	26.6056	28.0370	29.4841	30.9465
30	32.4237	33.9150	35.4202	36.9387	38.4702	40.0142	41.5705	43.1387	44.7185	46.3096
40	47.9116	49.5244	51.1477	52.7811	54.4264	56.0778	57.7406	59.4127	61.0939	62.7841
50	64.4831	66.1906	67.9066	69.6309	71.3633	73.1037	74.8519	76.6077	78.3712	80.1420
60	81.9202	83.7055	85.4979	87.2972	89.1034	90.9163	92.7359	94.5619	96.3945	98.2333
70	100.0784	101.9297	103.7870	105.6503	107.5196	109.3946	111.2754	113.1619	115.0540	116.9516
80	118.8547	120.7632	122.6770	124.5961	126.5204	128.4498	130.3843	132.3238	134.2683	136.2177
90	138.1719	140.1310	142.0948	144.0632	146.0364	148.0141	149.9964	151.9831	153.9744	155.9700
100	157.9700	159.9743	161.9829	163.9958	166.0128	168.0340	170.0593	172.0887	174.1221	176.1595
110	178.2009	180.2462	182.2955	184.3485	186.4054	188.4661	190.5306	192.5988	194.6707	196.7462
120	198.8254	200.9082	202.9945	205.0844	207.1779	209.2748	211.3751	213.4790	215.5862	217.6967
130	219.8107	221.9280	224.0485	226.1724	228.2995	230.4298	232.5634	234.7001	236.8400	238.9830
140	241.1291	243.2783	245.4306	247.5860	249.7443	251.9057	254.0700	256.2374	258.4076	260.5808
150	262.7569	264.9359	267.1177	269.3024	271.4899	273.6803	275.8734	278.0693	280.2679	282.4693
160	284.6735	286.8803	289.0898	291.3020	293.5168	295.7343	297.9544	300.1771	302.4024	304.6303
170	306.8608	309.0938	311.3293	313.5674	315.8079	318.0509	320.2965	322.5444	324.7948	327.0477
180	329.3030	331.5606	333.8207	336.0832	338.3480	340.6152	342.8847	345.1565	347.4307	349.7071
190	351.9859	354.2669	356.5502	358.8358	361.1236	363.4136	365.7059	368.0003	370.2970	372.5959

Table XIV. Four-Place Common Logarithms

N	0	1	2	3	4	5	6	7	8	9
10	0000	0043	0086	0128	0170	0212	0253	0294	0334	0374
11	0414	0453	0492	0531	0569	0607	0645	0682	0719	0755
12	0792	0828	0864	0899	0934	0969	1004	1038	1072	1106
13	1139	1173	1206	1239	1271	1303	1335	1367	1399	1430
14	1461	1492	1523	1553	1584	1614	1644	1673	1703	1732
15	1761	1790	1818	1847	1875	1903	1931	1959	1987	2014
16	2041	2068	2095	2122	2148	2175	2201	2227	2253	2279
17	2304	2330	2355	2380	2405	2430	2455	2480	2504	2529
18	2553	2577	2601	2625	2648	2672	2695	2718	2742	2765
19	2788	2810	2833	2856	2878	2900	2923	2945	2967	2989
20	3010	3032	3054	3075	3096	3118	3139	3160	3181	3201
21	3222	3243	3263	3284	3304	3324	3345	3365	3385	3404
22	3424	3444	3464	3483	3502	3522	3541	3560	3579	3598
23	3617	3636	3655	3674	3692	3711	3729	3747	3766	3784
24	3802	3820	3838	3856	3874	3892	3909	3927	3945	3962
25	3979	3997	4014	4031	4048	4065	4082	4099	4116	4133
26	4150	4166	4183	4200	4216	4232	4249	4265	4281	4298
27	4314	4330	4346	4362	4378	4393	4409	4425	4440	4456
28	4472	4487	4502	4518	4533	4548	4564	4579	4594	4609
29	4624	4639	4654	4669	4683	4698	4713	4728	4742	4757
30	4771	4786	4800	4814	4829	4843	4857	4871	4886	4900
31	4914	4928	4942	4955	4969	4983	4997	5011	5024	5038
32	5051	5065	5079	5092	5105	5119	5132	5145	5159	5172
33	5185	5198	5211	5224	5237	5250	5263	5276	5289	5302
34	5315	5328	5340	5353	5366	5378	5391	5403	5416	5428
35	5441	5453	5465	5478	5490	5502	5514	5527	5539	5551
36	5563	5575	5587	5599	5611	5623	5635	5647	5658	5670
37	5682	5694	5705	5717	5729	5740	5752	5763	5775	5786
38	5798	5809	5821	5832	5843	5855	5866	5877	5888	5899
39	5911	5922	5933	5944	5955	5966	5977	5988	5999	6010
40	6021	6031	6042	6053	6064	6075	6085	6096	6107	6117
41	6128	6138	6149	6160	6170	6180	6191	6201	6212	6222
42	6232	6243	6253	6263	6274	6284	6294	6304	6314	6325
43	6335	6345	6355	6365	6375	6385	6395	6405	6415	6425
44	6435	6444	6454	6464	6474	6484	6493	6503	6513	6522
45	6532	6542	6551	6561	6571	6580	6590	6599	6609	6618
46	6628	6637	6646	6656	6665	6675	6684	6693	6702	6712
47	6721	6730	6739	6749	6758	6767	6776	6785	6794	6803
48	6812	6821	6830	6839	6848	6857	6866	6875	6884	6893
49	6902	6911	6920	6928	6937	6946	6955	6964	6972	6981
50	6990	6998	7007	7016	7024	7033	7042	7050	7059	7067
51	7076	7084	7093	7101	7110	7118	7126	7135	7143	7152
52	7160	7168	7177	7185	7193	7202	7210	7218	7226	7235
53	7243	7251	7259	7267	7275	7284	7292	7300	7308	7316
54	7324	7332	7340	7348	7356	7364	7372	7380	7388	7396
N	0	1	2	3	4	5	6	7	8	9

(continued)

Table XIV. Four-Place Common Logarithms (Continued)

N	0	1	2	3	4	5	6	7	8	9
55	7404	7412	7419	7427	7435	7443	7451	7459	7466	7474
56	7482	7490	7497	7505	7513	7520	7528	7536	7543	7551
57	7559	7566	7574	7582	7589	7597	7604	7612	7619	7627
58	7634	7642	7649	7657	7664	7672	7679	7686	7694	7701
59	7709	7716	7723	7731	7738	7745	7752	7760	7767	7774
60	7782	7789	7796	7803	7810	7818	7825	7832	7839	7846
61	7853	7860	7868	7875	7882	7889	7896	7903	7910	7917
62	7924	7931	7938	7945	7952	7959	7966	7973	7980	7987
63	7993	8000	8007	8014	8021	8028	8035	8041	8048	8055
64	8062	8069	8075	8082	8089	8096	8102	8109	8116	8122
65	8129	8136	8142	8149	8156	8162	8169	8176	8182	8189
66	8195	8202	8209	8215	8222	8228	8235	8241	8248	8254
67	8261	8267	8274	8280	8287	8293	8299	8306	8312	8319
68	8325	8331	8338	8344	8351	8357	8363	8370	8376	8382
69	8388	8395	8401	8407	8414	8420	8426	8432	8439	8445
70	8451	8457	8463	8470	8476	8482	8488	8494	8500	8506
71	8513	8519	8525	8531	8537	8543	8549	8555	8561	8567
72	8573	8579	8585	8591	8597	8603	8609	8615	8621	8627
73	8633	8639	8645	8651	8657	8663	8669	8675	8681	8686
74	8692	8698	8704	8710	8716	8722	8727	8733	8739	8745
75	8751	8756	8762	8768	8774	8779	8785	8791	8797	8802
76	8808	8814	8820	8825	8831	8837	8842	8848	8854	8859
77	8865	8871	8876	8882	8887	8893	8899	8904	8910	8915
78	8921	8927	8932	8938	8943	8949	8954	8960	8965	8971
79	8976	8982	8987	8993	8998	9004	9009	9015	9020	9025
80	9031	9036	9042	9047	9053	9058	9063	9069	9074	9079
81	9085	9090	9096	9101	9106	9112	9117	9122	9128	9133
82	9138	9143	9149	9154	9159	9165	9170	9175	9180	9186
83	9191	9196	9201	9206	9212	9217	9222	9227	9232	9238
84	9243	9248	9253	9258	9263	9269	9274	9279	9284	9289
85	9294	9299	9304	9309	9315	9320	9325	9330	9335	9340
86	9345	9350	9355	9360	9365	9370	9375	9380	9385	9390
87	9395	9400	9405	9410	9415	9420	9425	9430	9435	9440
88	9445	9450	9455	9460	9465	9469	9474	9479	9484	9489
89	9494	9499	9504	9509	9513	9518	9523	9528	9533	9538
90	9542	9547	9552	9557	9562	9566	9571	9576	9581	9586
91	9590	9595	9600	9605	9609	9614	9619	9624	9628	9633
92	9638	9643	9647	9652	9657	9661	9666	9671	9675	9680
93	9685	9689	9694	9699	9703	9708	9713	9717	9722	9727
94	9731	9736	9741	9745	9750	9754	9759	9763	9768	9773
95	9777	9782	9786	9791	9795	9800	9805	9809	9814	9818
96	9823	9827	9832	9836	9841	9845	9850	9854	9859	9863
97	9868	9872	9877	9881	9886	9890	9894	9899	9903	9908
98	9912	9917	9921	9926	9930	9934	9939	9943	9948	9952
99	9956	9961	9965	9969	9974	9978	9983	9987	9991	9996
N	0	1	2	3	4	5	6	7	8	9

Table XV. Natural Logarithms

N	0	1	2	3	4	5	6	7	8	9
0.0		5.395	6.088	6.493	6.781	7.004	7.187	7.341	7.474	7.592
0.1	7.697	7.793	7.880	7.960	8.034	8.103	8.167	8.228	8.285	8.339
0.2	8.391	8.439	8.486	8.530	8.573	8.614	8.653	8.691	8.727	8.762
0.3	8.796	8.829	8.861	8.891	8.921	8.950	8.978	9.006	9.032	9.058
0.4	9.084	9.108	9.132	9.156	9.179	9.201	9.223	9.245	9.266	9.287
0.5	9.307	9.327	9.346	9.365	9.384	9.402	9.420	9.438	9.455	9.472
0.6	9.489	9.506	9.522	9.538	9.554	9.569	9.584	9.600	9.614	9.629
0.7	9.643	9.658	9.671	9.685	9.699	9.712	9.726	9.739	9.752	9.764
0.8	9.777	9.789	9.802	9.814	9.826	9.837	9.849	9.861	9.872	9.883
0.9	9.895	9.906	9.917	9.927	9.938	9.949	9.959	9.970	9.980	9.990
1.0	0.00000	0995	1980	2956	3922	4879	5827	6766	7696	8618
1.1	9531	*0436	*1333	*2222	*3103	*3976	*4842	*5700	*6511	*7395
1.2	0.1 8232	9062	9885	*0701	*1511	*2314	*3111	*3902	*4686	*5464
1.3	0.2 6236	7003	7763	8518	9267	*0010	*0748	*1481	*2208	*2930
1.4	0.3 3647	4359	5066	5767	6464	7156	7844	8526	9204	9878
1.5	0.4 0547	1211	1871	2527	3178	3825	4469	5108	5742	6373
1.6	7000	7623	8243	8858	9470	*0078	*0682	*1282	*1879	*2473
1.7	0.5 3063	3649	4232	4812	5389	5962	6531	7098	7661	8222
1.8	8779	9333	9884	*0432	*0977	*1519	*2058	*2594	*3127	*3658
1.9	0.6 4185	4710	5233	5752	6269	6783	7294	7803	8310	8813
2.0	9315	9813	*0310	*0804	*1295	*1784	*2271	*2755	*3237	*3716
2.1	0.7 4194	4669	5142	5612	6081	6547	7011	7473	7932	8390
2.2	8846	9299	9751	*0200	*0648	*1093	*1536	*1978	*2418	*2855
2.3	0.8 3291	3725	4157	4587	5015	5442	5866	6289	6710	7129
2.4	7547	7963	8377	8789	9200	9609	*0016	*0422	*0826	*1228
2.5	0.9 1629	2028	2426	2822	3216	3609	4001	4391	4779	5166
2.6	5551	5935	6317	6698	7078	7456	7833	8208	8582	8954
2.7	9325	9695	*0063	*0430	*0796	*1160	*1523	*1885	*2245	*2604
2.8	1.0 2962	3318	3674	4028	4380	4732	5082	5431	5779	6126
2.9	6471	6815	7158	7500	7841	8181	8519	8856	9192	9527
3.0	9861	*0194	*0526	*0856	*1186	*1514	*1841	*2168	*2493	*2817
3.1	1.1 3140	3462	3783	4103	4422	4740	5057	5373	5688	6002
3.2	6315	6627	6938	7248	7557	7865	8173	8479	8784	9089
3.3	9392	9695	9996	*0297	*0597	*0896	*1194	*1491	*1788	*2083
3.4	1.2 2378	2671	2964	3256	3547	3837	4127	4415	4703	4990
3.5	5276	5562	5846	6130	6413	6695	6976	7257	7536	7815
3.6	8093	8371	8647	8923	9198	9473	9746	*0019	*0291	*0563
3.7	1.3 0833	1103	1372	1641	1909	2176	2442	2708	2972	3237
3.8	3500	3763	4025	4286	4547	4807	5067	5325	5584	5841
3.9	6098	6354	6609	6864	7118	7372	7624	7877	8128	8379
4.0	8629	8879	9128	9377	9624	9872	*0118	*0364	*0610	*0854
N	0	1	2	3	4	5	6	7	8	9

(For rows 0.1–0.9: Take tabular value − 10)

(continued)

Table XV. Natural Logarithms (Continued)

N	0	1	2	3	4	5	6	7	8	9
4.0	8629	8879	9128	9377	9624	9872	*0118	*0364	*0610	*0854
4.1	1.4 1099	1342	1585	1828	2070	2311	2552	2792	3031	3270
4.2	3508	3746	3984	4220	4456	4692	4927	5161	5395	5629
4.3	5862	6094	6326	6557	6787	7018	7247	7476	7705	7933
4.4	8160	8387	8614	8840	9065	9290	9515	9739	9962	*0185
4.5	1.5 0408	0630	0851	1072	1293	1513	1732	1951	2170	2388
4.6	2606	2823	3039	3256	3471	3687	3902	4116	4330	4543
4.7	4756	4969	5181	5393	5604	5814	6025	6235	6444	6653
4.8	6862	7070	7277	7485	7691	7898	8104	8309	8515	8719
4.9	8924	9127	9331	9534	9737	9939	*0141	*0342	*0543	*0744
5.0	1.6 0944	1144	1343	1542	1741	1939	2137	2334	2531	2728
5.1	2924	3120	3315	3511	3705	3900	4094	4287	4481	4673
5.2	4866	5058	5250	5441	5632	5823	6013	6203	6393	6582
5.3	6771	6959	7147	7335	7523	7710	7896	8083	8269	8455
5.4	8640	8825	9010	9194	9378	9562	9745	9928	*0111	*0293
5.5	1.7 0475	0656	0838	1019	1199	1380	1560	1740	1919	2098
5.6	2277	2455	2633	2811	2988	3166	3342	3519	3695	3871
5.7	4047	4222	4397	4572	4746	4920	5094	5267	5440	5613
5.8	5786	5958	6130	6302	6473	6644	6815	6985	7156	7326
5.9	7495	7665	7834	8002	8171	8339	8507	8675	8842	9009
6.0	9176	9342	9509	9675	9840	*0006	*0171	*0336	*0500	*0665
6.1	1.8 0829	0993	1156	1319	1482	1645	1808	1970	2132	2294
6.2	2455	2616	2777	2938	3098	3258	3418	3578	3737	3896
6.3	4055	4214	4372	4530	4688	4845	5003	5160	5317	5473
6.4	5630	5786	5942	6097	6253	6408	6563	6718	6872	7026
6.5	7180	7334	7487	7641	7794	7947	8099	8251	8403	8555
6.6	8707	8858	9010	9160	9311	9462	9612	9762	9912	*0061
6.7	1.9 0211	0360	0509	0658	0806	0954	1102	1250	1398	1545
6.8	1692	1839	1986	2132	2279	2425	2571	2716	2862	3007
6.9	3152	3297	3442	3586	3730	3874	4018	4162	4305	4448
7.0	4591	4734	4876	5019	5161	5303	5445	5586	5727	5869
7.1	6009	6150	6291	6431	6571	6711	6851	6991	7130	7269
7.2	7408	7547	7685	7824	7962	8100	8238	8376	8513	8650
7.3	8787	8924	9061	9198	9334	9470	9606	9742	9877	*0013
7.4	2.0 0148	0283	0418	0553	0687	0821	0956	1089	1223	1357
7.5	1490	1624	1757	1890	2022	2155	2287	2419	2551	2683
7.6	2815	2946	3078	3209	3340	3471	3601	3732	3862	3992
7.7	4122	4252	4381	4511	4640	4769	4898	5027	5156	5284
7.8	5412	5540	5668	5796	5924	6051	6179	6306	6433	6560
7.9	6686	6813	6939	7065	7191	7317	7443	7568	7694	7819
8.0	7944	8069	8194	8318	8443	8567	8691	8815	8939	9063
N	0	1	2	3	4	5	6	7	8	9

(continued)

Table XV. Natural Logarithms (Continued)

N	0	1	2	3	4	5	6	7	8	9
8.0	7944	8069	8194	8318	8443	8567	8691	8815	8939	9063
8.1	9186	9310	9433	9556	9679	9802	9924	*0047	*0169	*0291
8.2	2.1 0413	0535	0657	0779	0900	1021	1142	1263	1384	1505
8.3	1626	1746	1866	1986	2106	2226	2346	2465	2585	2704
8.4	2823	2942	3061	3180	3298	3417	3535	3653	3771	3889
8.5	4007	4124	4242	4359	4476	4593	4710	4827	4943	5060
8.6	5176	5292	5409	5524	5640	5756	5871	5987	6102	6217
8.7	6332	6447	6562	6677	6791	6905	7020	7134	7248	7361
8.8	7475	7589	7702	7816	7929	8042	8155	8267	8380	8493
8.9	8605	8717	8830	8942	9054	9165	9277	9389	9500	9611
9.0	9722	9834	9944	*0055	*0166	*0276	*0387	*0497	*0607	*0717
9.1	2.2 0827	0937	1047	1157	1266	1375	1485	1594	1703	1812
9.2	1920	2029	2138	2246	2354	2462	2570	2678	2786	2894
9.3	3001	3109	3216	3324	3431	3538	3645	3751	3858	3965
9.4	4071	4177	4284	4390	4496	4601	4707	4813	4918	5024
9.5	5129	5234	5339	5444	5549	5654	5759	5863	5968	6072
9.6	6176	6280	6384	6488	6592	6696	6799	6903	7006	7109
9.7	7213	7316	7419	7521	7624	7727	7829	7932	8034	8136
9.8	8238	8340	8442	8544	8646	8747	8849	8950	9051	9152
9.9	9253	9354	9455	9556	9657	9757	9858	9958	*0058	*0158
10.0	2.3 0259	0358	0458	0558	0658	0757	0857	0956	1055	1154
N	0	1	2	3	4	5	6	7	8	9

ANSWERS TO PROBLEMS

Chapter 1

1–1 210.

1–2 (c) 161, 700.

1–3 k^m.

1–4 81.

1–5 1024, 56, 252, 36.

1–6 216, 2^n, 210, 5040.

1–7 52, $\binom{52}{5}$, 26.

1–11 (b) 2^n.

1–12 No. of outcomes: (a) 9 (b) 9 (c) 6 (d) 6 (e) 3.

1–15 (a) 1,098,240 (b) 123,552.

(c) 3,744. (d) 54,912.

(e) 5,148.

1–17 $\varnothing$, $\{a\}$, $\{b\}$, $\{c\}$, $\{a, b\}$, $\{b, c\}$, $\{c, a\}$, $\{a, b, c\}$.

1–20 $\{a, b\}$, $\{c, d\}$, $\varnothing$, Ω.

1–22 $\{a, b\}$, $\{c, d\}$, $\{e\}$.

1–23 Family of parallel, 45° lines.

1–24 Yes; no.

1–25 (a) $\{(x, y, z) \mid x \le y \le z\}$.

(b) Partition set defined by (a, b, c) includes the 6 permutations of a, b, c.

1–26 $\{R, W, Y, V\}$, $\{G, B\}$.

1–27 $\{y \mid 0 \le y < 1\}$.

1–28 $\varnothing, \{c, d\}, \{a, b, e\}, \Omega$.

1–30 1/4, 3/13, 11/26, 4/13, 9/13, 7/13, 8/13.

1–31 1/3, 1/3, 7/12, 2/3, 2/3, 1/3.

1–33 1/6, 5/6, 11/12.

1–34 1/20.

1–35 3/95.

1–36 1/4, 1/4, 1/6, 1/6, 1/12.

1–37 Divide corresponding ans. in **1–15** by $\binom{52}{5}$.

1–38 $e^{-2}, 1 - e^{-1}, e^{-1} - e^{-2}$.

1–39 1/2, 1/8, 3/4, $1 - \pi/16$, 3/8, 3/4, 3/4, 7/8, 0.

1–40 1/6.

1–41 $1 - \sqrt{2}/2$.

1–42 1/3, 1/2.

1–43 (a) P($\{d, e\}$) = 1/2,
P($\{b, c, d, e\}$) = 3/4,
P($\{b, c\}$) = 1/4,
P($\{a, d, e\}$) = 3/4.
(b) 1/2.   (c) 1/2.

1–44 1/33, 1/33, 1/11, 1/3.

1–45 1/26, 11/221, 6/25.

1–46 1/2, 1/2.

1–48 1/46.

1–49 7/19.

1–50 3/25, 2/5, 3/10.

1–54 (a) 1/3, 1/3, no.   (b) Yes.

1–58 (a) $(5/6)^5 (1/6)^3$.   (b) Same.
(c) $(5/6)^2 (1/6)^6$.

1–59 .97, .34.

1–60 .6561.

1–61 .1225, .2450, .4350.

Chapter 2

2–1

Value	0	1	2	3	4
Prob.	1/16	1/4	3/8	1/4	1/16

2–2 1/2, 1/32, 0, 239/288, 1/4.

2–3 1/4, 1/4, 1/64, 3/32.

2–6 .9192, .0099, .3314, .5371, .0228, .0026, .8400, .8426.

2–7 0, 1/4, 1/2, 3/4, 1/4, 3/4.

2–8 $3e^{-2}/4$, 1/4, 1/4.

2–9 $F(\lambda) = 0$ for $\lambda < 0$;
1/3 for $0 \le \lambda < 1$;
5/6 for $1 \le \lambda < 2$;
1 for $\lambda \ge 2$.

2–10 $F_\theta(\lambda) = 1 - \cos \lambda, 0 \le \lambda \le \pi/2$;
$F_\phi(\lambda) = \lambda/(2\pi), 0 \le \lambda \le 2\pi$.

2–11 3.7, .16, .48, .30.

2–12 0, .0142, 2.4, .738.

2–13

x_i	0	1
p_i	4/5	1/5

y_i	0	1	2
p_i	1/3	8/15	2/15

2–14 $p(1) = p(2) = p(3) = 1/5$,
$p(4) = 2/5$.

2–15 $p(0) = 1/3, p(1) = 1/2$,
$p(3) = 1/6$.

2–16 $p(0) = 9/13, \ p(1) = \cdots = $
$p(4) = 1/13$.

2–17 $p(k) = 5^{k-1}/6^k, k = 1, 2, \ldots$

2–18 $P(Y \le 2) = .9, \ P(R > 2) = .7$.

2–19 $P(X = k) = (6 - |k - 7|)/36$,
$k = 2, \ldots, 12$.

2–20 $f_x(x) = 1, 0 < x < 1$;
$f_Y(\theta) = 1/2\pi, 0 < \theta < 2\pi$.

2–21 $f(x) = 2x, 0 < x < 1$.

2–22 $[\pi(1 + x^2)]^{-1}, 1, .5$.

2–23 $F(x) = 0, x < -1$;
$(x + 1)^2/2, \quad -1 \le x \le 0$;
$1 - (x - 1)^2/2, \quad 0 \le x \le 1$;
and 1, $1 < x$. $P(|X| > 1/2)$
$= 1/4$.

2–24 (b) .9544.

2–26 (a) $k = 1/2$.   (b) $k = 6$.
(c) No.   (d) $k = 1/2$.

2-27 (a) No. (b) $k = 1 - p$.

2-29 $[\pi(1 + x)^2]^{-1}$.

2-30 $f(x) = (2A)^{-1}, \; -A \le x \le A$.

2-31 $f_Z(z) = 1, \; 0 < z < 1$.

2-32 $(4y)^{-1/2}, \; 0 < y < 1$.

2-33

y	-2	0	4
$P(Y = y)$	1/3	1/3	1/3

2-34 $F_Y(y) = \begin{cases} 0, & y < 0; \\ y, & 0 \le y \le 1; \\ 1, & y > 1. \end{cases}$

2-35 $f_Y(y) = 1, \; 0 < y < 1$.

2-37 $\pi/4$, 1/2, 1, 7/16.

2-39 (a) $e^{-x-y}, \; (x > 0, \; y > 0)$,
(b) $1 - e^{-1}$,
(c) $1 - 3e^{-2}$, (d) 1/2.

2-40 (a) 5/9,

(b)

	0	1	2
	25/36	10/36	1/36

(same for X as for Y).

2-41 (b) 1/3. (c) 1/2. (d) 5/12.

2-42 (a) 1/2. (b) $[4 - x^2]^{1/2}/2\pi$, $|x| < 2$. (c) 3/4. (d) $z/4$, $0 \le z \le 4$. (e) $z^2/4$, $0 \le z \le 2$.

2-43 (b) $1 - e^{-z} - ze^{-z}, \; z > 0$.

2-44 (a) Uniform on $-1 < x < 1$.
(b) 0, $w < -1$; $(1 + w)^2/4$, $-1 \le w \le 1$; 1, $w \ge 1$.

2-46 (a) 1/2. (b) 1/2. (c) 1/3; 1/3 for $y = 2$, 2/3 for $y = 4$.

2-47 (a) $(2\sqrt{3})^{-1}$, for $x^2 \le 3$.
(b) $2/\sqrt{15}$. (c) $(4 - x^2)^{-1/2}/2$, $x^2 < 4$.

2-48 $f(x \mid y) = 2(1 - x - y)/(1 - y)^2$, $0 < y < 1 - x, \; x > 0$.

2-51 $f(x, y) = 1, \; 0 < x < 1$, $0 < y < 1$.

2-54 (a)

X, Y:	0	1	2
	1/2	1/6	1/3

Z:	0	1
	1/2	1/2

(b) 1/6 for (2, 0), (2, 1), (0, 2), (1, 2); 1/3 for (0, 0).
(c) 1/3 for (0, 0), (2, 0), (1, 2).

2-55 (a) 6. (b) $6(1 - x - y)$, for $x + y < 1, \; x > 0, \; y > 0$.
(c) $3(1 - x)^2$, for $0 < x < 1$,
(d) 8, for $x + y < 1/2$, $x > 0, y > 0$.

2-56 (a) $\exp\{-\Sigma X_i\}$,
(b) $p^{\Sigma x_i}(1 - p)^{n - \Sigma x_i}$.

2-59 4/5.

2-60 14/5.

2-61 1.

2-62 10/13.

2-63 3/2.

2-64 4.5, 3.

2-67 10, 40.

2-68 7.

2-69 3/5, 3/2, 1.

2-70 7/2, 91/6, 2.

2-71 .8, 1.6, .2 + .8/(1 - t).

2-72 0, $g(0)$.

2-74 1/2.

2-75 0.

2-76 0.

2-77 1/2.

2-78 0.

2-79 1.

2-81 $\frac{1}{2}(1 - x)$.

2-82 2.

2-83 1/3.

2-84 1/2.

2-85 1/2.

2-86 1/3.

2-87 ∞.

2–94 1/20.

2–95 (a) 1/3. (b) $(1 + x)/2$.

2–96 32/75.

2–97 1/18

2–98 1/6.

2–99 .96.

2–100 1.

2–103 .02, 1/8.

2–110 0.

2–112 $-1/2$.

2–115 (a) 0. (b) 3/8. (c) 5/4.

2–116 $-30/441$.

2–117 (a) 10. (b) 290/17.

2–118 4.58×10^{-3}.

2–119 1.12 miles.

2–123 $B_0{}^2 \operatorname{var} \alpha + A_0{}^2 \operatorname{var} \beta$.

2–125 e^{tb}; $EX^r = b^r$; $E(X - \mu)^r = 0, r > 1$.

2–126 $(1 - t)^{-1}$.

2–127 $(2 - t)^{-1}, 1, 2$.

2–128 $e^{bt}\psi_X(at)$.

2–129 $(e^t - 1)/t$.

2–132 2.

2–133 $(1 - t)^{-(k+1)}, k + 1, k + 1$.

2–134 $\psi(t) = (1 - t)^{-n}$,
        $f(y) = y^{n-1}e^{-y}/(n - 1)!$,
        $y > 0$.

2–135 (b) $(n + k - 1)_k$

2–136 $\dbinom{r + k - 1}{r - 1}/2^{r+k}$.

2–137 $\exp(t^2/2)$.

2–138 25/216.

2–139 .063.

2–140 $\exp\{itm - |at|\}$.

2–141 $(1 - it/k)^{-1}$.

2–143 $\exp(-t^2/2)$.

2–144 $(1 - it/k)^{-n}, \exp(-nt^2/2)$.

2–145 $1 - \sigma^2 t^2/2 + o(t^2)$.

2–146 $e^{ibt}\phi_X(at)$.

2–147 $\exp\{-\frac{1}{2}(s^2 + t^2)\}$.

2–150 .159.

2–151 .92.

2–152 146.24.

Chapter 3

3–1 20, 16.

3–2 1/16, 7/128, 7/128.

3–3 Bernoulli, $p = 1/4$.

3–4 $1 - (1/12)^4$.

3–5 $(.9)^4$.

3–6 16/2187.

3–7 .59, .92, 5.

3–8 $(n)_r p^r$.

3–9 40.2.

3–10 (a) 6.
       (b) 6, 9/2.

3–11 3 and 4.

3–15 Binomial, $p = F(x)$.

3–16

0	1	2	3	4
3/66	20/66	30/66	12/66	1/66

3–17 .0064, .0081.

3–18 1, 3.

3–19 $\sum_{6}^{10}\dbinom{10}{k}(.45)^k(.55)^{10-k}$.

3–21 $\dbinom{5}{k}\dbinom{15}{5-k}\bigg/\dbinom{20}{5}$.

3–23 $2\dbinom{12}{6}$.

3–24 .46, .08, .94.

3–25 .19.

3–26 $\sum_{0}^{50}\dbinom{100}{k}(.55)^k(.45)^{100-k}$.

3–27 (a) $p(k) = (.3)(.7)^k$,
        $k = 0, 1, 2, \dots$.
       (b) $\left[\dbinom{7}{k}\bigg/\dbinom{10}{k}\right] \times \dfrac{3}{10 - k}$,
        $k = 0, 1, \dots, 7$.

3–30 .57, 30, .035.

3–31 .184.

3–32 .147.

3–33 .0803.

3–34 e^{-4}, $5e^{-4}$.

3–36 $9e^3$.

3–38 $1 - (7e^{-5/2})/2$.

3–39 $(\log 2)/\lambda$.

3–40 .082, .543.

3–41 Neg. exponential, mean 5 hrs.

3–44 .973, .071.

3–45 .1512.

3–46 .049.

3–47 (a) .0736. (b) .265. (c) .0455.

3–48 3/2 hr.

3–49 Same as initial distribution.

3–52 .1336.

3–53 .3830.

3–54 .7257, .2881.

3–56 8.65, 11.35.

3–57 $(-\infty, 6)$ and $(14, \infty)$: 0.0228
(6, 7) and (13,14): 0.0440
(7, 8) and (12, 13): 0.0919
(8, 9) and (11, 12): 0.1498
(9, 10) and (10,11): 0.1915

3–59 $(2/\sigma)f(y/\sigma)$, $y > 0$, where f is std. norm. dens; $(2\sigma^2/\pi)^{1/2}$.

3–61 (a) 6.1%, 2.6%. (b) $3.8k$.

3–63 $(2\sigma^2/\pi)^{-1/2}, 2\sigma^2(1 - 1/\pi)$.

3–64 $\sqrt{\dfrac{2}{u\pi}}\, e^{-u/2}$, $u > 0$; mean $= 1$, variance $= 2$.

3–66 69.03, .16.

3–67 $\dfrac{1}{2^5 4! \sigma^2}(y/\sigma^2)^4 e^{-y/(2\sigma^2)}$, $y > 0$; $10\sigma^2$; $20\sigma^4$.

3–71

x \ y	0	1	2
0	1/36	1/9	1/9
1	1/6	1/3	0
2	1/4	0	0

3–72 $81/1024 = 4(3/8)^4$.

3–73 1000/12597.

3–74 $8!/2^{20}$.

Chapter 4

4–2 $2x + y = 1$.

4–3 (25/8, 25/8).

4–4 (.7, .5, .2).

4–5 All but (e).

4–6 (4/3, 4/3, 4/3), weights 2/9 at (0, 4, 0), 1/3 at (0, 0, 4), 4/9 at (3, 1, 0).

4–7 He should play.

4–8 $m = b + 1$.

4–9

2	0	1
4	3	7
1	4	1
0	5	0

4–10 Same as loss.

4–11 No.

4–12 (a) p (prob. of winning). (b) No. (c) Do not take if $p < 1/9$.

4–13 (a) $p = 1/10$. (b) $1.90.

4–14 a_3, a_1.

4–15 Pure: a_1 (loss), a_2 (regret). Mixed: (1, 0) (loss), (1/3, 2/3) (regret).

4–16 (a) $(0, \alpha, 0, 0, 1 - \alpha)$, where $3/4 \le \alpha \le 1$ (b) Minimax mixed action: (2/3, 1/3, 0, 0, 0).

4–17 a_3, a_4.

4–18 Minimax is at $a = 1/2$.

4–19 a_2 if $w < 2/3$; a_1 if $w > 2/3$ (and either if $w = 2/3$).

4–21 a_1.

4–22 (a) Pass with prob. 1/3, reject with prob. 2/3. (b) Pass.

4–23 $a = 1/2$.

4–26 a_1, a_2, a_5.

4–27 $0, 0, 9, \sqrt{54/5}$.

4-28 ± 2.

4-29 $75, 13; 75, \sqrt{173}$.

4-30 $29, 19, 6$.

4-31 (a) $(b - a)^{-n}$, $a < x_i < b$

$(i = 1, \ldots, n)$.

(b) $(2\pi\sigma^2)^{-n/2} \exp$

$$\left\{ -\frac{1}{2\sigma^2} \Sigma(x_i - \mu)^2 \right\}.$$

(c) $p^{\Sigma x_i}(1 - p)^{n - \Sigma x_i}$, $x_i = 0, 1$.

(d) $e^{-nm} m^{\Sigma x_i} / \Pi x_i!$,

$x_i = 0, 1, 2, \ldots$.

(e) $p^n(1 - p)^{\Sigma x_i}$,

$x_i = 0, 1, 2, \ldots$.

4-32 $f_X(x) = \dfrac{\dbinom{M}{\Sigma x_i} \dbinom{N - M}{n - \Sigma x_i}}{\dbinom{n}{\Sigma x_i} \dbinom{N}{n}}$.

4-35 (a) $f(j, k) = 1/2$ for $j \neq k$, 0 for $j = k$.

(b)

1	2	3
1/2	1/3	1/6

(c)

3/2	2	5/2	3	7/2
1/6	1/6	1/3	1/6	1/6

4-36 $[E(X^{2k}) - (EX^k)^2]/n$.

4-37 (a) 0. (b) 4.004. (c) .0456.

4-38 $(n\lambda)^n x^{n-1} e^{-n\lambda x}/(n - 1)!$, for $x > 0$.

4-39 Normal with mean $= \sigma^2$, variance $=$

$$(1/n) \operatorname{var}(X - \mu)^2.$$

4-41 $[F(\lambda)]^n$.

4-43

	d_1	d_2	d_3	d_4	d_5	d_6	d_7	d_8	d_9
	4	5	2	4	5	4	2	5	2
	4	0	5	0	4	5	4	5	0

4-44 All risk points are convex combinations of points corresponding to (no-data) pure actions—data not of value.

4-45

Decision function	Action, if data are			Risk under	
	$0H$	$1H$	$2H$	$p = \frac{1}{4}$	$p = \frac{3}{4}$
d_1	$\frac{1}{4}$	$\frac{1}{4}$	$\frac{1}{4}$	0	$\frac{1}{4}$
d_2	$\frac{3}{4}$	$\frac{3}{4}$	$\frac{3}{4}$	$\frac{1}{4}$	0
d_3	$\frac{3}{4}$	$\frac{3}{4}$	$\frac{1}{4}$	$\frac{15}{64}$	$\frac{9}{64}$
d_4	$\frac{3}{4}$	$\frac{1}{4}$	$\frac{3}{4}$	$\frac{5}{32}$	$\frac{3}{32}$
d_5	$\frac{1}{4}$	$\frac{3}{4}$	$\frac{3}{4}$	$\frac{7}{64}$	$\frac{1}{64}$
d_6	$\frac{3}{4}$	$\frac{1}{4}$	$\frac{1}{4}$	$\frac{9}{64}$	$\frac{15}{64}$
d_7	$\frac{1}{4}$	$\frac{3}{4}$	$\frac{1}{4}$	$\frac{3}{32}$	$\frac{5}{32}$
d_8	$\frac{1}{4}$	$\frac{1}{4}$	$\frac{3}{4}$	$\frac{1}{64}$	$\frac{7}{64}$

4-46 $1/n$, $\sqrt{2/(n\pi)}$.

4-47 $n/(n + 1)$, $\theta^2/(n + 1)$.

4-48 Announce 1/4 if 0 Heads, 3/4 if 2 Heads, toss coin if 1 Head.

4-49 (a) $p(1 - p)/2$.

(b) $(p^2 - p + 1/2)/8$.

4-50 (a) a_3. (b) Choose a_3 no matter what is observed.

4-51 d_5 or d_8.

4-52 d_9: a_3 if z_1, a_2 if z_2.

4-53 $b = 0$.

4-54 d_3.

4-55 d_5 or d_8.

4-56 d_9: a_3 if $Z = z_1$, a_2 if $Z = z_2$; experiment worth .95.

4-58 No (min. Bayes risk is $-\$1.08$ with test, $-\$1.20$ without).

4-59 $72/73$, $1/73$.

4-62 $1/10$, $9/10$; $9/40$, $1/40$; Bayes action: choose 3/4.

4-66 (a) 1.97. (b) Value of data is .93 (compared with 0).

4-67 Common value is $[6(n + 2)]^{-1}$.

4-68 Take a_3 if $Z = z_1$, a_1 if $Z = z_2$.

4-69 (a) $(2\pi\sigma^2)^{-n/2} \exp$

$$\left\{-\frac{1}{2\sigma^2}\sum(X_i - \mu)^2\right\}.$$

(b) $e^{-nm}m^{\Sigma X_i}/\prod X_i!$

(c) $p^{\Sigma X_i}(1 - p)^{n - \Sigma X_i}$.

4-70 Accept if 0 or 1 def. in sample, reject if 2.

4-71 (a) Same as **4-70**. (b) Accept for any number of def. in sample.

4-72 x.

4-73 (a) 17. (b) Max. of $(x_1, \ldots, x_5)$.

4-74 $\hat{\theta} = 1/\hat{\lambda}$.

4-75 (a) $f(z_3 \mid A) = 1$; $f(z_1 \mid B) = 2/3, f(z_2 \mid B) = 1/3$.
(b) Yes. (c) No.

4-76 U is a reduction of T.

4-78 (b) Each has prob. 1/10.
(c) (iv) {123, 234, 345}, {124, 134, 235, 245}, {125, 135, 145}.

4-79 $1/\binom{n}{k}$; yes.

4-80 (a) No. (b) Yes. (c) No.
(d) a_1 for (0, 0), a_2 for (0, 1) or (1, 0), a_3 for (1, 1).

(e)

M	0	1	2	3	4
Risk	0	2	3/2	2	1

$$d^*: \begin{cases} a_1 \text{ if } X_1 + X_2 = 0 \\ a_2 \text{ if } X_1 + X_2 = 1 \\ a_3 \text{ if } X_1 + X_2 = 2 \end{cases}$$

(f) a_3 if $X_1 + X_2 = 2$, a_1 if $X_1 + X_2 = 0$, toss coin to choose from a_1, a_3 if $X_1 + X_2 = 1$.

4-81 (a) $\sum X_i$. (b) $\sum X_i$. (c) $\sum X_i$.
(d) $X_{(n)}$.

4-82 $\sum X_i$.

4-83 $\sum Z_i^2$.

4-84 $(\sum X_i, \sum X_i^2)$.

4-85 $(f_1, f_2, \ldots, f_k)$, where f_i is the relative frequency of x_i.

4-86 (a) $\sum X_i$. (b) $\sum X_i$. (c) $\sum X_i$.
(d) $\sum X_i^2$. (e) $\sum Z_i^2$. (f) $\sum U_i^2$.

4-87 $\{z_1, z_2\}, \{z_3\}$.

4-88 $\sum X_i$.

4-93 (a) $\sum X_i$. (b) $\sum X_i$. (c) $\sum X_i$.
(d) $\sum(X_i - \mu)^2$.

4-95 Any $t(Z)$ such that $t(z_3) < t(z_1) < t(z_5) < t(z_4) < t(z_2)$.

4-96 Partial ans. $R(\theta_1, d_1) = R(\theta_3, d_1) = .1600$, $R(\theta_2, d_1) = .3174$.
Rules d_1, d_2 are monotone.

Chapter 5

5-2 0.

5-3 $\sum a_i = 1$.

5-5 $[\bar{X}(1 - \bar{X})/n]^{1/2}$.

5-6 $\bar{X}/\sqrt{n}$.

5-10 $1/n, 2/n$.

5-14 $2/n$.

5-15 $2\bar{X}^2/\pi$.

5-16 $(\bar{X}, s_x^2)$.

5-17 $2\bar{X}$.

5-18 $(k + 2)/(n + 4)$.

5-19 (a) $(\sum X_i + 1)/n$.
(b) $(\sum X_i + 1)/(\lambda + n)$.

5-20 $(n + 1)/\sum X_i$.

5-22 $\hat{\theta} = 1/\bar{X}$.

5-23 $\hat{M} = 2$.

5-24 $\hat{b}$ = smallest observation.

5-26 $\bar{X}$.

5-27 $\bar{X}, \frac{1}{n}\sum(X_i - \mu)^2$.

5–28 $\dfrac{1}{m + n}\{\sum(X_i - \bar{X})^2 +$

$\sum(Y_j - \bar{Y})^2\}.$

5–29 664.

5–30 (2.248, 2.352), (2.261, 2.339).

5–31 (2.2902, 2.3098).

5–32 (.39, .71), (.400, .692).

5–33 Limits are $\bar{X}/(1 \pm 2/\sqrt{n}).$

5–34 (1.82, 2.43).

Chapter 6

6–1 *S, C, C, S, C, C, S, C.*

6–2 (b) Type I: 0 for no Whites, 2/5 for 1 White.
Type II: 2/10 for 2 Whites, 1/10 for 3 Whites, 0 for 4 or 5 Whites.

6–3 $\bar{X} > 0.80.$

6–4 $\alpha = .5062, \beta = .4938.$

6–5 (a) 86, .50. (b) 53, .64.

6–6 $\dfrac{d(3\beta)}{d\alpha} = -\dfrac{\Phi'(K - 1)}{3\Phi'(K)}$

6–7 One of the eight tests is to reject H_0 if exactly 1 Heads. Error sizes for this test are $\alpha = 1/2, \beta = 1.$

6–8 $\alpha = .208, \beta = .268.$

6–9 $1 - 3p + 3p^2.$

6–10 104.4, 14,
$\pi(\mu) = \Phi([\mu - 104.4]/2.71).$

6–11 $\left[\dbinom{10 - M}{4} +\right.$

$\left.\dbinom{M}{1}\dbinom{10 - M}{3}\right]/\dbinom{10}{4}.$

6–12 $K = .0351,$

$\pi(\sigma^2) = \Phi\left(\dfrac{.99\sigma^2 - .0351}{.141\sigma^2}\right).$

6–13 $K = .392.$

6–14 $\alpha = .05.$

6–15 $\pi(p) = \Phi\left(\dfrac{5 - 10p}{\sqrt{p(1 - p)}}\right) -$

$\Phi\left(\dfrac{4.9 - 10p}{\sqrt{p(1 - p)}}\right).$

6–16 .0668.

6–17 (a) $\phi(t) = 1$ if $t < 2$, 0 if $t > 2$, $\frac{1}{2}$ if $t = 2$. (b) $\alpha = \displaystyle\sum_{t<2} f_0(t) + \frac{1}{2}f_0(2).$

6–18 Reject H_0 if $\sum X_i > 2$. Accept if $\sum X_i < 2$. Reject with $p = .107$ if $\sum X_i = 2.$

6–19 $\alpha = E_{H_0}[\phi(X)],$
$\beta = 1 - E_{H_1}[\phi(X)].$

6–20 (a) $\sum X_i > K; \alpha = .185,$
$\beta = .285.$ (b) $n = 32, K = 44.7.$

6–21 $\bar{X} > $ const.

6–22 $\displaystyle\sum_1^{73}(X_i - \mu)^2 > 404.$

6–23 $\sum R(X_i) < K$ if
$Q(\theta_0) - Q(\theta_1) > 0.$
$\sum R(X_i) > K$ if
$Q(\theta_0) - Q(\theta_1) < 0.$

6–24 (a) (i) $T < K$, (ii) C: $\varnothing$, $\{z_3\}$, $\{z_3, z_1\}$, $\{z_3, z_1, z_5\}$, $\{z_3, z_1, z_5, z_4\}$, $\Omega.$
(b) Reject H_0 for $Z = z_1$ or z_3; $\beta = .4$ (compared with $\beta = .8$).

6–25 (a) C: $X > 0$ or $X < -1$; $\alpha = .75, \beta = .045.$
(b) C: $7/5 < X < 6$; $\alpha = .16, \beta = .41.$
(c) No, but $\lambda < 1$ is monotone $(C: X > 1).$

6–30 $X_1^2 + \cdots + X_{25}^2 > 36.6.$

6–31 $\sum X_i > 59, \pi(p) =$
$\Phi([100p - 59]/\sqrt{100pq}).$

6–33 $n = 271$, $K = 543$.

6–34 Reject $v = v_0$ if $re^{-r} < K_1$ where $r = \hat{v}/v_0$.

6–36 $\lambda = 1/8$ with probability $1/4$ and $27/32$ with probability $3/4$.

6–37 $s_x^2 > K$; $\pi(\sigma^2) = 1 - F_{\chi^2(n-1)}(nK/\sigma^2)$.

6–38 $(\bar{X} - \mu_0)^2/s_x^2 > K$.

6–39 (a)

C	$\varnothing$	$\{z_3\}$	$\{z_3, z_1\}$	$\{z_3, z_1, z_4\}$	Ω
α	0	.1	.3	.7	1.0

(b) $T(Z) = \theta_1$ if $Z = z_2, z_4$; θ_2 if $Z = z_1$; θ_3 if $Z = z_3$.

6–40 (a) $\chi^2 = 2.26$, acc. $p = 1/2$ at $\alpha = .05$.

6–41 $\chi^2 = .95 < \chi^2_{.95}(3)$, accept at $\alpha = .05$.

6–42 $\chi^2 = 13.5 > \chi^2_{.95}(6)$, reject at $\alpha = .05$.

6–43 $\chi^2 = 5.63 < \chi^2_{.95}(4)$, accept at $\alpha = .05$.

6–44 $\chi^2 = 10.3 > \chi^2_{.95}(2)$, reject at $\alpha = .05$.

6–45 $D_n = .05 < .0957$, accept at 10 per cent level.

6–46 $D_n = .165$, accept H_0.

6–47 .85, compared with approximate lower bound of .4.

6–48 $(F_n(x) \pm d_\alpha)$, where $P(D_n \le d_\alpha) = \alpha$.

6–50 Reject H_0 if $D_n^+ > .20$.

6–51 (c) $D = 24/30 > 15/30$, reject H_0 at $\alpha = .05$.

6–52 Reject $p = 1/2$ if $\sum X_i \le .415n - 3$, accept $p = 1/2$ if $\sum X_i \ge .415n + 2.17$, otherwise continue sampling.

6–53 Continue sampling if $(\theta_0 - \theta_1)\bar{X}$ falls between

$$n(\mu_0 + \mu_1)/2 - \frac{\sigma^2}{\mu_1 - \mu_0}\log_e B$$

and

$$n(\mu_0 + \mu_1)/2 - \frac{\sigma^2}{\mu_1 - \mu_0}\log_e A.$$

6–54 Continue sampling if $(\sum X_i)\log(m_1/m_0)$ falls between $-\log A + n(m_1 - m_0)$ and $-\log B + n(m_1 - m_0)$.

6–56 $\mu = (h + 1)/2$,

$$\pi(\mu) = \frac{99^{2\mu - 1}}{99^{2\mu - 1} + 1}.$$

6–57 $E(N) \doteq \dfrac{2}{2\mu - 1} \dfrac{99^{2\mu - 1}\log_e 99}{99^{2\mu - 1} + 1}$

(with value $(\log 99)^2$ when $\mu = 1/2$).

6–59

θ	0	1	1.44	2	∞
$OC(\theta)$	0	.1	.56	.95	1
$E(N\mid\theta)$	0	7.74	13.5	10.3	3.25

Chapter 7

7–1 (b) $J = J^{-1} = -1$. (c) $u \ge 0$, $u \ge v$. (d) $x = y$, y-axis.

7–2 $f_{X',Y'}(u, v) = f_{X,Y}(u - h, v - k)$.

7–3 $f_{X\mid Y}(v) = [\pi(1 + v^2)]^{-1}$.

7–4 (a) $\begin{pmatrix} 1/5 & -2/5 \\ 1/5 & 3/5 \end{pmatrix}$

(c) $A^{-1}B = \begin{pmatrix} -8/5 \\ 17/5 \end{pmatrix}$.

7–6 $\dfrac{1}{2\pi\sqrt{5}}\exp\{-[9x^2 - 4x(y - 4) + (y - 4)^2]/10\}$.

7-7 $\mu = \begin{pmatrix} 0 \\ 0 \end{pmatrix}$, $M = \begin{pmatrix} 4/7 & 1/7 \\ 1/7 & 2/7 \end{pmatrix}$,

constant $= \sqrt{7}/(2\pi)$.

7-8 Ellipses, center (μ_X, μ_Y); independence implies axes parallel to coordinate axes.

7-9 $\phi_{X,Y}(s, t) =$

$\exp\left[i(\mu_X s + \mu_Y t) - (s\,t)M\begin{pmatrix} s \\ t \end{pmatrix}\right]$.

7-11 $f_X(x) = n!$, if $\sum x_i \le 1$,
$x_i \ge 0$; and 0 elsewhere.

7-13 (b) $\sqrt{10}/5$.

(c) $\begin{pmatrix} 8 \\ 0 \\ 2 \end{pmatrix}$, $\begin{pmatrix} 13 & 9 & 11 \\ 9 & 13 & 11 \\ 11 & 11 & 11 \end{pmatrix}$.

(d) $\phi(t_1, t_2) = \exp[8t_1 i - \frac{1}{2}(13t_1^2 + 18t_1 t_2 + 13t_2^2)]$
$f(y_1, y_2) = (2\pi\sqrt{88})^{-1}$
$\exp\{-[13(y_1 - 8)^2 - 18y_2(y_1 - 8) + 13y_2^2]/176\}$.

7-15 120; $945\sqrt{\pi}/32$; $4/15$;
$15\sqrt{2\pi}/128$; $8/81$; $1/30030$;
$3\pi/512$.

7-16 (a) $Y/18.3 < \sigma^2 < Y/3.94$.
(b) $1 - F_{\chi^2(10)}(40/\sigma^2)$.

7-21 (a) $L_3 = L_1 - L_2$,

(b) $B = \begin{pmatrix} 2 & -1 \\ -1 & 2 \end{pmatrix}$.

7-22 (b) $\chi^2(mn - 1)$, when divided by σ^2.
(c) Ranks are $mn - m, m - 1$; distributions are independent chi-square when divided by σ^2.

7-24 var $F = \dfrac{2n^2(m + n - 2)}{m(n - 2)^2(n - 4)}$.

7-27 $.25$.

7-28 $F_{1-r}(1, n) = [t_{1-r/2}(n)]^2$.

7-30 $(34.9 \times 10^{-8}, 61.2 \times 10^{-8})$.

7-31 $1 - F_{\chi^2(29)}(210/\sigma^2)$.

7-32 $(n + 1)^{-1}$.

7-33 $1, .98, .95, .87$.

7-34 $R > 12.9$, $s_x^2 > 12.1$.

7-35 $4.302 < \mu < 4.332$, $6.11 \times 10^{-4} < \sigma^2 < 23.2 \times 10^{-4}$;
$\begin{cases} 14(\mu - 4.317)^2 < 2.62\sigma^2 \\ 6.11 \times 10^{-4} < \sigma^2 < 23.2 \times 10^{-4}. \end{cases}$

7-36 $1 - \Phi\left(\sqrt{2/\pi}\,\dfrac{K - \mu}{\sigma/\sqrt{n}}\right)$.

7-39 $F = 4/3 < 3.2$, accept at $\alpha = .05$.

7-40 $1 - F_F(2.11\tau^2/\sigma^2) + F_F(.485\tau^2/\sigma^2)$.

7-41 $\tau^2 = 18/7 < 4.75$, accept at $\alpha = .05$.

7-43 -1.44.

Chapter 8

8-1 $a + (b - a)/(n + 1)$,
$b - (b - a)/(n + 1)$,
$(a + b)/2$.

8-2 $[(n + 2)(n + 1)^2]^{-1}$.

8-3 $\dfrac{(b - a)^2}{2(n + 2)(n + 1)}$.

8-4 $12(1 - y_2)^2, 0 < y_1 < y_2 < 1$.

8-5 $2/5$.

8-6 (a) $1 - [1 - R(x)]^n$.
(b) $1 - \prod[1 - R_i(x)]$.

8-7 (a) $[R(x)]^n$. (b) $\prod R_i(x)$.

8-8 $(n - 1)(b - a)/(n + 1)$,
$2(n - 1)(b - a)^2/[(n + 1)^2 (n + 2)]$.

8-10 $k(n + 1 - k)/[(n + 1)^2(n + 2)]$.

8-11 $.0001$.

8-12 $.99$.

8-13 Reject using 2-sided test at $\alpha = .05$.

8-14 $.011, .90$.

8–15 .95.

8–16 Accept equality at any level up to .1635.

8–17 Accept equality at $\alpha = .05$.

8–18 Maximum $\alpha = .127$.

8–21 (a) $r = 19 < 19.9 = r_{.95}$ (accept at 10 per cent level with 2-sided test).
(b) $(s - \mu_s)/\sigma_s = (20 - 59/3)/\sqrt{451/90} = .15$ (accept).

8–22 $d^2/s^2 = 807/671 > 1$, accept H_0 against trend.

8–23 (a) $r = 8 < 8.56 = r_{.05}$.
(b) $s = 13 = s_{.05}$.
(c) $(r - \mu_r)/\sigma_r = -2.06$, where $r = d^2/s^2$.

8–24 $(2n - 2)/(3n - 4)$.

8–25 106, 98, 100, 91, 114, 106, 85, 123, 86, 116, 131, 112, 88, 124.

8–26 5.64, 4.97, 5.15, 3.81, 4.31, 4.97, 4.31, 3.32, 3.81, 3.98, 4.48, 3.32, 3.15, 5.15, 1.66.

8–27 No, $\chi^2 = 4 > 2.71 = \chi^2_{.90}(1)$.

8–28 (a) $\chi^2 \doteq 8 > 3.84$, reject at $\alpha = .05$. (b) Accept at $\alpha = .10$.

8–31 95 per cent: $(-.08, .32)$.

8–33 $-2 \log \Lambda \doteq 4$.

8–34 $C = \{0, 1, 4\}$ has $\alpha = 3/11$.

8–35 (a) $-2 \log \Lambda \doteq \chi^2 \doteq 11.8 > 9.21 = \chi^2_{.99}(2)$.
(b) $\binom{80}{a}\binom{60}{b}\binom{70}{c} / \binom{200}{s}$, for $a + b + c = s$.

8–37 Accept at $\alpha = .05$, because $10 < 11 < 38$ (2-sided test).

8–39 Reject $F_X = F_Y$ at $\alpha = .05$.

8–40 1.

8–41 Accept $F_X = F_Y$ at any level up to 10/35 (either test).

8–42 $c_1/\sigma_{c_1} \doteq 1.71 > 1.64$, reject $F_X = F_Y$.

8–45 Reject $F_X = F_Y$ at $\alpha = .05$.

Chapter 9

9–2 $(.00295, .00473)$.

9–3 $53 + 6x = 34y$.

9–4 (a) $(5.69, 6.93), (.102, .286), (3.31, 7.48)$.
(b) Accept $\beta = 0$ (0 lies within 95 per cent conf. interval).
(c) Ellipse, center $(6.31, .092)$, semi-axes $0.681, 0.213$.

9–6 0.

9–7 (a) Accept linearity at any level $(F = 0)$.
(b) 5, 1, 16/9 (m.l.e.).
(c) Semi-axes of ellipse are $(1.57, 1.93)$.

9–8 $\hat{c} = \sum \sum X_{ij} t_i^2 / \sum n_i t_i^4$.

9–11 $(3.41, 14.59)$.

9–12 $(.47, 3.53)$, using $\hat{\sigma}^2$ from 9–7.

9–14 $\Pi[\sum(X_{ij} - \bar{X}_i)^2/n_i]^{n_i/2} < $ const. $\{\sum \sum (X_{ij} - \bar{X}_i)^2/n\}^{n/2}$.

9–15 LR-test is same as F-test given.

9–17 $F = 9/8$, accept $\theta_i = 0$ at $\alpha = .05$.

9–18 $F_A = 6.5$, $F_B = 23.0$.

9–19 $F_{\text{inter}} = .18$, $F_{\text{mach}} = 5.46$, $F_{\text{oper}} = 1.04$.

9–23 (a)
$$\hat{\beta} = \begin{pmatrix} 4 \\ 2/3 \\ 2/3 \end{pmatrix}.$$
(b) $F = 24 > (1.44)^2$, reject.
(c) 6.

INDEX